21. $\int \sqrt{a^2 + x^2}\, dx = \frac{x}{2}\sqrt{a^2 + x^2} + \frac{a^2}{2}\sinh^{-1}\frac{x}{a} + C$

22. $\int x^2\sqrt{a^2 + x^2}\, dx = \frac{x(a^2 + 2x^2)\sqrt{a^2 + x^2}}{8} - \frac{a^4}{8}\sinh^{-1}\frac{x}{a} + C$

23. $\int \frac{\sqrt{a^2 + x^2}}{x}\, dx = \sqrt{a^2 + x^2} - a\sinh^{-1}\left|\frac{a}{x}\right| + C$

24. $\int \frac{\sqrt{a^2 + x^2}}{x^2}\, dx = \sinh^{-1}\frac{x}{a} - \frac{\sqrt{a^2 + x^2}}{x} + C$

25. $\int \frac{x^2}{\sqrt{a^2 + x^2}}\, dx = -\frac{a^2}{2}\sinh^{-1}\frac{x}{a} + \frac{x\sqrt{a^2 + x^2}}{2} + C$

26. $\int \frac{dx}{x\sqrt{a^2 + x^2}} = -\frac{1}{a}\ln\left|\frac{a + \sqrt{a^2 + x^2}}{x}\right| + C$

27. $\int \frac{dx}{x^2\sqrt{a^2 + x^2}} = -\frac{\sqrt{a^2 + x^2}}{a^2 x} + C$ 28. $\int \frac{dx}{\sqrt{a^2 - x^2}} = \sin^{-1}\frac{x}{a} + C$

29. $\int \sqrt{a^2 - x^2}\, dx = \frac{x}{2}\sqrt{a^2 - x^2} + \frac{a^2}{2}\sin^{-1}\frac{x}{a} + C$

30. $\int x^2\sqrt{a^2 - x^2}\, dx = \frac{a^4}{8}\sin^{-1}\frac{x}{a} - \frac{1}{8}x\sqrt{a^2 - x^2}\,(a^2 - 2x^2) + C$

31. $\int \frac{\sqrt{a^2 - x^2}}{x}\, dx = \sqrt{a^2 - x^2} - a\ln\left|\frac{a + \sqrt{a^2 - x^2}}{x}\right| + C$

32. $\int \frac{\sqrt{a^2 - x^2}}{x^2}\, dx = -\sin^{-1}\frac{x}{a} - \frac{\sqrt{a^2 - x^2}}{x} + C$

33. $\int \frac{x^2}{\sqrt{a^2 - x^2}}\, dx = \frac{a^2}{2}\sin^{-1}\frac{x}{a} - \frac{1}{2}x\sqrt{a^2 - x^2} + C$

34. $\int \frac{dx}{x\sqrt{a^2 - x^2}} = -\frac{1}{a}\ln\left|\frac{a + \sqrt{a^2 - x^2}}{x}\right| + C$ 35. $\int \frac{dx}{x^2\sqrt{a^2 - x^2}} = -\frac{\sqrt{a^2 - x^2}}{a^2 x} + C$

36. $\int \frac{dx}{\sqrt{x^2 - a^2}} = \cosh^{-1}\frac{x}{a} + C = \ln|x + \sqrt{x^2 - a^2}| + C$

37. $\int \sqrt{x^2 - a^2}\, dx = \frac{x}{2}\sqrt{x^2 - a^2} - \frac{a^2}{2}\cosh^{-1}\frac{x}{a} + C$

38. $\int (\sqrt{x^2 - a^2})^n\, dx = \frac{x(\sqrt{x^2 - a^2})^n}{n + 1} - \frac{na^2}{n + 1}\int (\sqrt{x^2 - a^2})^{n-2}\, dx, \quad n \neq -1$

39. $\int \frac{dx}{(\sqrt{x^2 - a^2})^n} = \frac{x(\sqrt{x^2 - a^2})^{2-n}}{(2 - n)a^2} - \frac{n - 3}{(n - 2)a^2}\int \frac{dx}{(\sqrt{x^2 - a^2})^{n-2}}, \quad n \neq 2$

40. $\int x(\sqrt{x^2 - a^2})^n\, dx = \frac{(\sqrt{x^2 - a^2})^{n+2}}{n + 2} + C, \quad n \neq -2$

41. $\int x^2\sqrt{x^2 - a^2}\, dx = \frac{x}{8}(2x^2 - a^2)\sqrt{x^2 - a^2} - \frac{a^4}{8}\cosh^{-1}\frac{x}{a} + C$

42. $\int \frac{\sqrt{x^2 - a^2}}{x}\, dx = \sqrt{x^2 - a^2} - a\sec^{-1}\left|\frac{x}{a}\right| + C$

43. $\int \frac{\sqrt{x^2 - a^2}}{x^2}\, dx = \cosh^{-1}\frac{x}{a} - \frac{\sqrt{x^2 - a^2}}{x} + C$

Continued overleaf.

44. $\displaystyle\int \frac{x^2}{\sqrt{x^2 - a^2}}\, dx = \frac{a^2}{2} \cosh^{-1}\frac{x}{a} + \frac{x}{2}\sqrt{x^2 - a^2} + C$

45. $\displaystyle\int \frac{dx}{x\sqrt{x^2 - a^2}} = \frac{1}{a}\sec^{-1}\left|\frac{x}{a}\right| + C = \frac{1}{a}\cos^{-1}\left|\frac{a}{x}\right| + C$

46. $\displaystyle\int \frac{dx}{x^2\sqrt{x^2 - a^2}} = \frac{\sqrt{x^2 - a^2}}{a^2 x} + C$ \qquad 47. $\displaystyle\int \frac{dx}{\sqrt{2ax - x^2}} = \sin^{-1}\left(\frac{x - a}{a}\right) + C$

48. $\displaystyle\int \sqrt{2ax - x^2}\, dx = \frac{x - a}{2}\sqrt{2ax - x^2} + \frac{a^2}{2}\sin^{-1}\left(\frac{x - a}{a}\right) + C$

49. $\displaystyle\int (\sqrt{2ax - x^2})^n\, dx = \frac{(x - a)(\sqrt{2ax - x^2})^n}{n + 1} + \frac{na^2}{n + 1}\int (\sqrt{2ax - x^2})^{n-2}\, dx,$

50. $\displaystyle\int \frac{dx}{(\sqrt{2ax - x^2})^n} = \frac{(x - a)(\sqrt{2ax - x^2})^{2-n}}{(n - 2)a^2} + \frac{(n - 3)}{(n - 2)a^2}\int \frac{dx}{(\sqrt{2ax - x^2})^{n-2}}$

51. $\displaystyle\int x\sqrt{2ax - x^2}\, dx = \frac{(x + a)(2x - 3a)\sqrt{2ax - x^2}}{6} + \frac{a^3}{2}\sin^{-1}\frac{x - a}{a} + C$

52. $\displaystyle\int \frac{\sqrt{2ax - x^2}}{x}\, dx = \sqrt{2ax - x^2} + a\sin^{-1}\frac{x - a}{a} + C$

53. $\displaystyle\int \frac{\sqrt{2ax - x^2}}{x^2}\, dx = -2\sqrt{\frac{2a - x}{x}} - \sin^{-1}\left(\frac{x - a}{a}\right) + C$

54. $\displaystyle\int \frac{x\, dx}{\sqrt{2ax - x^2}} = a\sin^{-1}\frac{x - a}{a} - \sqrt{2ax - x^2} + C$

55. $\displaystyle\int \frac{dx}{x\sqrt{2ax - x^2}} = -\frac{1}{a}\sqrt{\frac{2a - x}{x}} + C$

56. $\displaystyle\int \sin ax\, dx = -\frac{1}{a}\cos ax + C$ \qquad 57. $\displaystyle\int \cos ax\, dx = \frac{1}{a}\sin ax + C$

58. $\displaystyle\int \sin^2 ax\, dx = \frac{x}{2} - \frac{\sin 2ax}{4a} + C$ \qquad 59. $\displaystyle\int \cos^2 ax\, dx = \frac{x}{2} + \frac{\sin 2ax}{4a} + C$

60. $\displaystyle\int \sin^n ax\, dx = \frac{-\sin^{n-1} ax \cos ax}{na} + \frac{n - 1}{n}\int \sin^{n-2} ax\, dx$

61. $\displaystyle\int \cos^n ax\, dx = \frac{\cos^{n-1} ax \sin ax}{na} + \frac{n - 1}{n}\int \cos^{n-2} ax\, dx$

62. (a) $\displaystyle\int \sin ax \cos bx\, dx = -\frac{\cos (a + b)x}{2(a + b)} - \frac{\cos (a - b)x}{2(a - b)} + C, \qquad a^2 \neq b^2$

(b) $\displaystyle\int \sin ax \sin bx\, dx = \frac{\sin (a - b)x}{2(a - b)} - \frac{\sin (a + b)x}{2(a + b)}, \qquad a^2 \neq b^2$

(c) $\displaystyle\int \cos ax \cos bx\, dx = \frac{\sin (a - b)x}{2(a - b)} + \frac{\sin (a + b)x}{2(a + b)}, \qquad a^2 \neq b^2$

63. $\displaystyle\int \sin ax \cos ax\, dx = -\frac{\cos 2ax}{4a} + C$

64. $\displaystyle\int \sin^n ax \cos ax\, dx = \frac{\sin^{n+1} ax}{(n + 1)a} + C, \qquad n \neq -1$

This table is continued on the endpapers at the back.

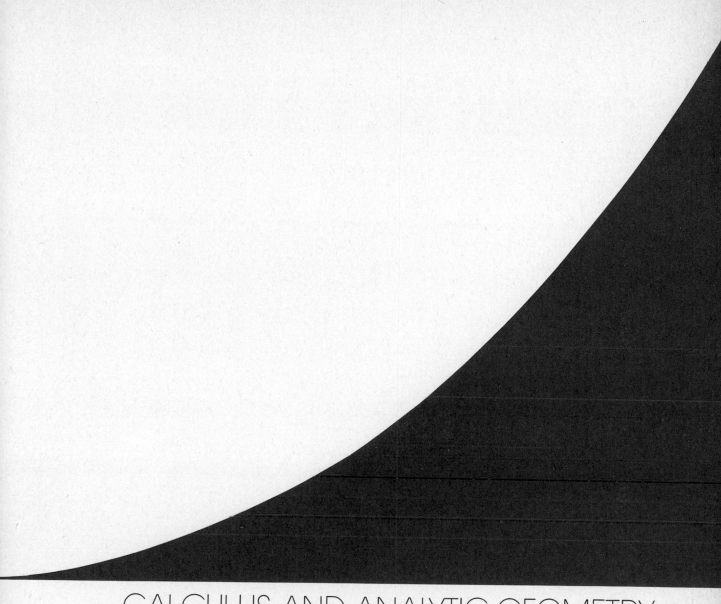

CALCULUS AND ANALYTIC GEOMETRY

GEORGE B. THOMAS, JR.
MASSACHUSETTS INSTITUTE OF TECHNOLOGY

ROSS L. FINNEY
UNIVERSITY OF ILLINOIS AT URBANA-CHAMPAIGN

FIFTH EDITION

CALCULUS

AND

ANALYTIC

GEOMETRY

PART II
VECTORS, FUNCTIONS OF SEVERAL VARIABLES,
INFINITE SERIES, AND DIFFERENTIAL EQUATIONS

ADDISON-WESLEY PUBLISHING COMPANY
READING, MASSACHUSETTS · MENLO PARK, CALIFORNIA · LONDON · AMSTERDAM · DON MILLS, ONTARIO · SYDNEY

Production editor: Mary Cafarella
Designer: Jean King
Illustrator: Richard Morton
Cover design: Marshall Henrichs

ISBN 0-201-07542-3
ABCDEFGHIJK-DO-79

PREFACE

The *Fifth Edition* has been adapted primarily from the *Alternate Edition*, but in addition to some new applications of calculus to engineering and the physical sciences, the present book contains a variety of interesting professional applications of calculus to business, economics, and the life sciences. The chapter on infinite series (Chapter 16) has been completely rewritten, and now contains twice the number of examples and exercises. Sequences are treated first, and separately from series, and more attention is paid to estimation. A chapter on vector analysis (Chapter 15), including line and surface integrals, Green's theorem, Stokes's theorem, and the Divergence Theorem, has been added. A section on Lagrange multipliers is included in Chapter 13 (Partial Differentiation). The presentation of vectors (Chapters 11 and 12) has been reorganized, and now the treatment of vector geometry precedes the treatment of vector functions and their derivatives. The book also incorporates some hand-held calculator exercises. More art has been included, and the art has been captioned throughout.

At the request of many users, we have moved several topics toward the front of the book. Trigonometric functions are introduced briefly in Chapter 1, and the review of trigonometry and the presentation of differentiation of sines and cosines that used to be in Chapter 4 now appear in Chapter 2. L'Hôpital's rule is presented in Chapter 3, and Newton's method has been moved to Chapter 2. Simpson's rule is now included with the trapezoidal rule in Chapter 4.

The level of rigor is about the same as in earlier editions of the Thomas books. For example, we do not prove that a function that is continuous on a closed and bounded interval has a maximum on the interval, but we state that theorem and use it in proving the Mean Value Theorem.

The first three chapters deal with the definition of, formulas for, and applications of derivatives of functions of one variable. Chapters 4 and 5 are on integration, with applications. Among the new applications are: estimating cardiac output, calculating light output from flashbulbs, determining the average daily inventory of a business, and using Delesse's rule to analyze tissue composition.

Chapter 6 deals with the derivatives of the remaining trigonometric functions, and with the logarithmic and exponential functions. If one wished to include some of the material on hyperbolic functions immediately after Chapter 6, then the material on methods of integration in Chapter 7 could be expanded to include the integration formulas XXVII' to XXXII' from Article 9–5. Otherwise, it is possible to skip Chapter 9 if one also omits subsequent problems that involve hyperbolic functions.

Chapter 8 (Plane Analytic Geometry) and Chapter 10 (Polar Coordinates) treat properties of the conic sections, cardioids, and other standard topics, including areas and arc length.

Chapters 11 and 12 introduce coordinates in space, vector algebra, parametric equations, and motion on a space curve. Chapter 12 concludes with a derivation of Kepler's second law of planetary motion in a central force field.

The remaining chapters include partial differentiation, multiple integration, vector analysis, infinite series, complex numbers and functions, differential equations, an appendix on matrices and determinants (useful in its own right and for the formal expansion of a third-order determinant used in Article 11–7), assorted formulas from elementary mathematics, and brief tables of sines, cosines, tangents, exponential functions, and natural logarithms. The endpapers of the book contain a brief table of integrals for convenient reference.

Answers for most of the problems are given and are keyed to the text by page, as well as by problem number, article, and chapter. The answers that are new to this edition were provided by Paul H. Siegel and Daniel W. Litwhiler. We are grateful to them for this valuable help, and we continue to be grateful to our friends and colleagues who contributed solutions and problems to earlier editions.

Many students, colleagues, and friends have given us the benefit of their criticism and suggestions. We would especially like to mention the valuable contributions of Carl W. R. de Boor, Fred A. Franklin, William A. Ferguson, Solomon Garfunkel, Andrew D. Jorgensen, William Ted Martin, Arthur P. Mattuck, Eric Reissner, J. Barkley Rosser, Oliver G. Selfridge, Donald R. Sherbert, Norton Starr, William U. Walton, and Felicia de May Weitzel. But even with the addition of the reviewers mentioned separately, this list is far from complete. To each and every person who has at any time contributed helpful suggestions, comments, or criticisms, whether or not we have been able to incorporate these into the book, we say "Thank you very much."

It is a pleasure to acknowledge the superb assistance in illustration, editing, design, and composition that the staff of Addison-Wesley Publishing Company has given to the preparation of this edition. The senior author also acknowledges with gratitude the special talent and productivity beyond his expectation that his co-author has brought to this new edition.

The text is available in one complete volume, which can be covered in three or four semesters, depending on the pace, or as two separate parts. The first part treats functions of one variable, analytic geometry in two dimensions, and infinite series (Chapters 1 through 10, and Chapter

16). It also contains the appendix on matrices and determinants. The second part begins with Chapter 11 on vectors and parametric equations, and contains all subsequent chapters, including Chapter 16, and the appendix on matrices and determinants. Both parts include answers.

Any errors that may appear are the responsibility of the authors. We will appreciate having these brought to our attention.

October 1978

G. B. T., Jr.
R. L. F.

ACKNOWLEDGMENTS

The authors would like to thank the following reviewers for the quality of their attention and for their many thoughtful suggestions.

Kenneth C. Abernethy	Virginia Military Institute
Fred G. Brauer	University of Wisconsin at Madison
William R. Fuller	Purdue University
Douglas Hall	Michigan State University
Roger B. Hooper	University of Maine
William Perry	Texas A & M University
David Rearick	University of Colorado
Robert D. Stalley	Oregon State University
Virginia Skinner Dwann Veroda	El Camino College

AVAILABLE SUPPLEMENTS

The following supplementary materials are available for use by students:

Pocket Calculator Supplement for Calculus	J. Barkley Rosser and Carl W. R. de Boor (University of Wisconsin at Madison)
Self-Study Manual	Maurice D. Weir (Naval Postgraduate School)
Student Supplement	Gurcharan S. Gill (Brigham Young University)

CONTENTS

ABRIDGED CONTENTS
FOR PART I

VECTORS AND PARAMETRIC EQUATIONS

11–1

VECTOR COMPONENTS AND THE UNIT VECTORS i AND j

Some physical quantities, like length and mass, are completely determined when their magnitudes are given in terms of specific units. Such quantities are called *scalars*. Other quantities, like forces and velocities, in which the direction as well as the magnitude is important, are called *vectors*. It is customary to represent a vector by a directed line segment whose direction represents the direction of the vector and whose length, in terms of some chosen unit, represents its magnitude.

The most satisfactory algebra of vectors is based on a representation of each vector in terms of its components parallel to the axes of a cartesian coordinate system. This is accomplished by using the same unit of length on the two axes, with vectors of unit length along the axes used as basic vectors in terms of which the other vectors in the plane may be expressed. Along the x-axis we choose the vector **i** from $(0, 0)$ to $(1, 0)$.* Along the y-axis we choose the vector **j** from $(0, 0)$ to $(0, 1)$. (See Fig. 11–1.) Then $a\mathbf{i}$, a being a scalar, represents a vector parallel to the x-axis, having magnitude $|a|$ and pointing to the right if a is positive, to the left if a is negative. Similarly, $b\mathbf{j}$ is a vector parallel to the y-axis and having the same direction as **j** if b is positive, or the opposite direction if b is negative.

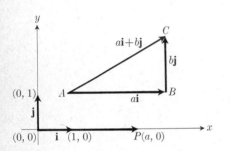

11–1 The vector $\vec{AC}$ expressed as a multiple of **i** plus a multiple of **j**.

We shall ordinarily deal with "free vectors," meaning that a vector is free to move about under parallel displacements. We say that two vectors are *equal* if they have the same direction and the same magnitude. This condition may be expressed algebraically by saying that

$$a\mathbf{i} + b\mathbf{j} = a'\mathbf{i} + b'\mathbf{j} \qquad \text{if and only if} \quad a = a' \quad \text{and} \quad b = b'.$$

That is, two vectors are equal if and only if their corresponding *components* are equal. Thus, in Fig. 11–1, the vector $\vec{AB}$ and the vector $\vec{OP}$ from $(0, 0)$ to $(a, 0)$ are both equal to $a\mathbf{i}$.

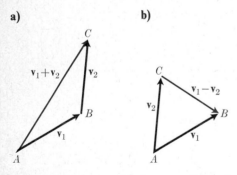

11–2 The sum (a) and difference (b) of two vectors.

Addition

Two vectors, $\mathbf{v}_1$ and $\mathbf{v}_2$ are *added* by drawing a vector $\mathbf{v}_1$, say from A to B in Fig. 11–2(a), and then a vector equal to $\mathbf{v}_2$ starting from the terminal point of $\mathbf{v}_1$; thus $\mathbf{v}_2 = \vec{BC}$ in Fig. 11–2(a). The sum $\mathbf{v}_1 + \mathbf{v}_2$ is then the vector from the starting point A of $\mathbf{v}_1$ to the terminal point C of $\mathbf{v}_2$:

$$\mathbf{v}_1 = \vec{AB}, \qquad \mathbf{v}_2 = \vec{BC},$$
$$\mathbf{v}_1 + \mathbf{v}_2 = \vec{AB} + \vec{BC} = \vec{AC}.$$

If we apply this principle to the vectors $a\mathbf{i}$ and $b\mathbf{j}$ in Fig. 11–1, we see that $a\mathbf{i} + b\mathbf{j}$ is the vector hypotenuse of a right triangle whose vector sides are $a\mathbf{i}$ and $b\mathbf{j}$. If the vectors $\mathbf{v}_1$ and $\mathbf{v}_2$ are given in terms of components

$$\mathbf{v}_1 = a_1\mathbf{i} + b_1\mathbf{j},$$
$$\mathbf{v}_2 = a_2\mathbf{i} + b_2\mathbf{j},$$

---

*   Vectors are indicated by bold-faced Roman letters. In handwritten work it is customary to draw small arrows over letters that represent vectors.

then

$$\mathbf{v_1} + \mathbf{v_2} = (a_1 + a_2)\mathbf{i} + (b_1 + b_2)\mathbf{j} \tag{1}$$

has x- and y-components obtained by adding the x- and y-components of $\mathbf{v_1}$ and $\mathbf{v_2}$.

Subtraction

To *subtract* one vector $\mathbf{v_2}$ from another vector $\mathbf{v_1}$ geometrically, we draw them both from a common initial point and then draw the vector from the tip of $\mathbf{v_2}$ to the tip of $\mathbf{v_1}$. Thus in Fig. 11–2(b), we have

$$\mathbf{v_1} = \overrightarrow{AB}, \qquad \mathbf{v_2} = \overrightarrow{AC},$$

and

$$\mathbf{v_1} - \mathbf{v_2} = -\mathbf{v_2} + \mathbf{v_1} = \overrightarrow{CA} + \overrightarrow{AB} = \overrightarrow{CB}.$$

In terms of components, vector subtraction follows the simple algebraic law

$$\mathbf{v_1} - \mathbf{v_2} = (a_1 - a_2)\mathbf{i} + (b_1 - b_2)\mathbf{j}, \tag{2}$$

which says that corresponding components are subtracted.

Length of a Vector

The length of the vector $\mathbf{v} = a\mathbf{i} + b\mathbf{j}$ is usually denoted by $|\mathbf{v}|$, which may be read "the magnitude of v." Figure 11–1 shows that $\mathbf{v}$ is the hypotenuse of a right triangle whose legs have lengths $|a|$ and $|b|$. Hence we may apply the theorem of Pythagoras to obtain

$$|\mathbf{v}| = |a\mathbf{i} + b\mathbf{j}| = \sqrt{a^2 + b^2}.$$

Multiplication by Scalars

The algebraic operation of multiplying a vector $\mathbf{v} = a\mathbf{i} + b\mathbf{j}$ by a scalar c is also simple, namely

$$c(a\mathbf{i} + b\mathbf{j}) = (ca)\mathbf{i} + (cb)\mathbf{j}.$$

Note how the unit vectors $\mathbf{i}$ and $\mathbf{j}$ allow us to keep the components separated from one another when we operate on vectors algebraically. Geometrically, $c\mathbf{v}$ is a vector whose length is $|c|$ times the length of $\mathbf{v}$:

$$|c\mathbf{v}| = |(ca)\mathbf{i} + (cb)\mathbf{j}| = \sqrt{(ca)^2 + (cb)^2} = |c|\sqrt{a^2 + b^2} = |c||\mathbf{v}|. \tag{3}$$

The direction of $c\mathbf{v}$ agrees with that of $\mathbf{v}$ if c is positive, and is opposite to that of $\mathbf{v}$ is c is negative (Fig. 11–3). If $c = 0$, the vector $c\mathbf{v}$ has no direction.

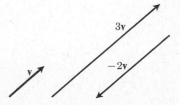

11–3   Scalar multiples of $\mathbf{v}$.

Zero Vector

Any vector whose length is zero is called the *zero vector*, $\mathbf{0}$. The vector

$$a\mathbf{i} + b\mathbf{j} = \mathbf{0}, \qquad \text{if and only if} \quad a = b = 0.$$

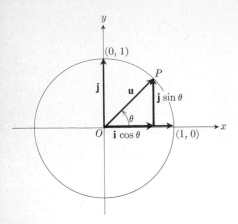

11–4 $\mathbf{u} = \mathbf{i} \cos \theta + \mathbf{j} \sin \theta.$

Unit Vector

Any vector **u** whose length is equal to the unit of length used along the coordinate axes is called a *unit vector*. If **u** is the unit vector obtained by rotating **i** through an angle θ in the positive direction, then (Fig. 11–4) **u** has a horizontal component

$$u_x = \cos \theta$$

and a vertical component

$$u_y = \sin \theta,$$

so that

$$\mathbf{u} = \mathbf{i} \cos \theta + \mathbf{j} \sin \theta. \tag{4}$$

If we allow the angle θ in Eq. (4) to vary from 0 to 2π, then the point P in Fig. 11–4 traces the unit circle $x^2 + y^2 = 1$ once in the counterclockwise direction. Every unit vector in the plane is described by Eq. (4) for some value of θ.

To find a unit vector in the direction of a given nonzero vector v, we divide v by its own length, $|\mathbf{v}|$. This amounts to multiplying v by the scalar $1/|\mathbf{v}|$. The result has length 1 because

$$\left| \frac{\mathbf{v}}{|\mathbf{v}|} \right| = \frac{1}{|\mathbf{v}|} |\mathbf{v}| = 1. \tag{5}$$

Two vectors are said to be *parallel* if the line segments representing them are parallel. Similarly, a vector is parallel to a line if the segments that represent the vector are parallel to the line. When we talk of a vector's being *tangent* or *normal* to a curve at a point, we mean that the vector is parallel to the line that is tangent or normal to the curve at the point. The next example shows how such a vector may be found.

EXAMPLE 1. Find unit vectors tangent and normal to the curve $y = (x^3/2) + \frac{1}{2}$ at the point $(1, 1)$.

Solution. The slope of the line tangent to the curve at the point $(1, 1)$ is

$$y' = \frac{3x^2}{2} \bigg|_{x=1} = \frac{3}{2}.$$

We find a unit vector with this slope. The vector $\mathbf{v} = 2\mathbf{i} + 3\mathbf{j}$ has slope $\frac{3}{2}$ (Fig. 11–5), as does every nonzero multiple of **v**. To find a multiple of **v** that is a unit vector, we divide **v** by its length,

$$|\mathbf{v}| = \sqrt{2^2 + 3^2} = \sqrt{13}.$$

This produces the unit vector

$$\mathbf{u} = \frac{\mathbf{v}}{|\mathbf{v}|} = \frac{2}{\sqrt{13}} \mathbf{i} + \frac{3}{\sqrt{13}} \mathbf{j}.$$

The vector **u** is tangent to the curve at $(1, 1)$ because it has the same direction as **v**. Of course, the vector

$$-\mathbf{u} = -\frac{2}{\sqrt{13}} \mathbf{i} - \frac{3}{\sqrt{13}} \mathbf{j},$$

11–5 If $a \neq 0$, the vector $a\mathbf{i} + b\mathbf{j}$ has slope b/a.

which points in the direction opposite to **u**, is also tangent to the curve at (1, 1). Without some additional requirement, there is no reason to prefer one of these vectors to the other.

To find unit vectors normal to the curve at (1, 1), we look for unit vectors whose slopes are the negative reciprocal of the slope of **u**. This is quickly done by interchanging the components of **u** and changing the sign of one of them. We obtain

$$\mathbf{n} = \frac{3}{\sqrt{13}}\mathbf{i} - \frac{2}{\sqrt{13}}\mathbf{j}, \quad \text{and} \quad -\mathbf{n} = -\frac{3}{\sqrt{13}}\mathbf{i} + \frac{2}{\sqrt{13}}\mathbf{j}.$$

Again, either one will do.

PROBLEMS

In Problems 1–10 express each of the vectors in the form $a\mathbf{i} + b\mathbf{j}$. Indicate all quantities graphically.

1. $\overrightarrow{P_1P_2}$ if P_1 is the point $(1, 3)$ and P_2 is the point $(2, -1)$.

2. $\overrightarrow{OP_3}$ if O is the origin and P_3 is the midpoint of the vector $\overrightarrow{P_1P_2}$ joining $P_1(2, -1)$ and $P_2(-4, 3)$.

3. The vector from the point $A(2, 3)$ to the origin.

4. The sum of the vectors $\overrightarrow{AB}$ and $\overrightarrow{CD}$, given the four points $A(1, -1)$, $B(2, 0)$, $C(-1, 3)$, and $D(-2, 2)$.

5. A unit vector making an angle of 30° with the positive x-axis.

6. The unit vector obtained by rotating $\mathbf{j}$ through 120° in the clockwise direction.

7. A unit vector having the same direction as the vector $3\mathbf{i} - 4\mathbf{j}$.

8. A unit vector tangent to the curve $y = x^2$ at the point $(2, 4)$.

9. A unit vector normal to the curve $y = x^2$ at the point $P(2, 4)$ and pointing from P toward the concave side of the curve (that is, an "inner" normal).

10. A unit vector tangent to the unit circle. [*Hint*. See Eq. (4).]

Find the lengths of each of the following vectors and the angle that each makes with the positive x-axis.

11. $\mathbf{i} + \mathbf{j}$ **12.** $2\mathbf{i} - 3\mathbf{j}$ **13.** $\sqrt{3}\,\mathbf{i} + \mathbf{j}$

14. $-2\mathbf{i} + 3\mathbf{j}$ **15.** $5\mathbf{i} + 12\mathbf{j}$ **16.** $-5\mathbf{i} - 12\mathbf{j}$

17. Let A, B, C, D be the vertices, in order, of a quadrilateral. Let A', B', C', D' be the midpoints of the sides AB, BC, CD, and DA, in order. Prove that $A'B'C'D'$ is a parallelogram. [*Hint*. First show that $\overrightarrow{A'B'} = \overrightarrow{D'C'} = \frac{1}{2}\overrightarrow{AC}$.]

18. Using vectors, show that the diagonals of a parallelogram bisect each other. [*Method*. Let A be one vertex and let M and N be the midpoints of the diagonals. Then show that $\overrightarrow{AM} = \overrightarrow{AN}$.]

In newtonian mechanics, the motion of a particle in a plane is usually described by a pair of differential equations

$$F_x = \frac{d(mv_x)}{dt}, \quad F_y = \frac{d(mv_y)}{dt} \tag{1}$$

that express Newton's second law of motion

$$\mathbf{F} = \frac{d(m\mathbf{v})}{dt} \tag{2}$$

in parametric form. Here, **F** is a vector that represents a force acting on a particle of mass m at time t. The vector **v** is the velocity vector of the particle

11–2

PARAMETRIC EQUATIONS IN KINEMATICS

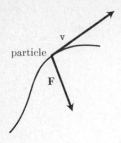

The force and velocity vectors of the motion of a particle in a plane might look like this at a particular time t.

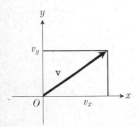

The components v_x and v_y of $\mathbf{v}$

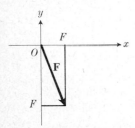

The components F_x and F_y of $\mathbf{F}$

11–6 Motion of a particle in a plane.

at time t (Fig. 11–6). The quantities F_x and F_y are the x- and y-components of $\mathbf{F}$, while v_x and v_y are the components of $\mathbf{v}$.

If we know the position and velocity of the particle at some given instant, then the position of the particle at all later instants can usually be found by integrating Eqs. (1) with respect to time. The constants of integration are determined from given initial conditions. The result is another pair of parametric equations

$$x = f(t), \qquad y = g(t) \tag{3}$$

that give the coordinates x and y of the particle as functions of t.

The equations in (3) contain more information about the motion of the particle than the cartesian equation

$$y = F(x) \tag{4}$$

that we get from (3) by eliminating t. The parametric equations tell where the particle goes and *when* it gets to any given place, whereas the cartesian equation only tells the curve along which the particle travels. (Sometimes, too, a parametric representation of a curve is all that is possible; that is, a parameter cannot always be eliminated in practice.)

EXAMPLE 1. A projectile is fired with an initial velocity v_0 ft/sec at an angle of elevation α. Assuming that gravity is the only force acting on the projectile, find its motion.

Solution. We introduce coordinate axes with the origin at the point where the projectile begins its motion (Fig. 11–7). The distance traveled by the projectile over the ground is measured along the x-axis, and the height of the projectile above the ground is measured along the y-axis. At any time t, the projectile's position is given by a coordinate pair $x(t)$, $y(t)$, that we assume to be differentiable functions of t. If we measure distance in feet and time in seconds, with $t = 0$ at the instant the projectile is fired, then the initial conditions for the projectile's motion are

$$t = 0 \text{ sec}, \qquad x = 0 \text{ ft}, \qquad y = 0 \text{ ft},$$

$$\tag{5}$$

$$v_x(0) = \frac{dx}{dt}(0) = v_0 \cos \alpha \quad \text{ft/sec}, \qquad v_y(0) = \frac{dy}{dt}(0) = v_0 \sin \alpha \quad \text{ft/sec}.$$

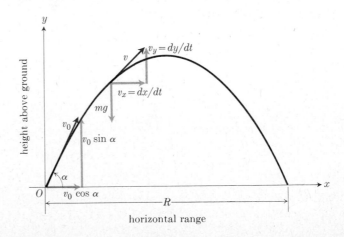

11–7 Ideal projectiles move along parabolas.

If the projectile is to travel only a few miles, and not go very high, it will cause no serious error to model the force of gravity with a constant vector **F** that points straight down. Its x- and y-components are

$$F_x = 0 \text{ lb}, \qquad F_y = -mg \text{ lb},$$

where m is the mass of the projectile and g is the acceleration of gravity. With these values for F_x and F_y, the equations in (1) become

$$0 = m\frac{d^2x}{dt^2}, \qquad -mg = m\frac{d^2y}{dt^2}. \tag{6}$$

To solve these equations for x and y, we integrate each one twice. This introduces four constants of integration, which may be evaluated by using the initial conditions (5). From the first equation in (6), we get

$$\frac{d^2x}{dt^2} = 0 \text{ ft/sec}^2, \qquad \frac{dx}{dt} = c_1 \text{ ft/sec}, \qquad x = c_1 t + c_2 \text{ ft}, \tag{7a}$$

and from the second equation in (6),

$$\frac{d^2y}{dt^2} = -g \text{ ft/sec}^2, \qquad \frac{dy}{dt} = -gt + c_3 \text{ ft/sec}, \qquad y = -\tfrac{1}{2}gt^2 + c_3 t + c_4 \text{ ft}. \tag{7b}$$

From the initial conditions, we find

$$c_1 = v_0 \cos \alpha \text{ ft/sec}, \qquad c_2 = 0 \text{ ft}, \qquad c_3 = v_0 \sin \alpha \text{ ft/sec}, \qquad c_4 = 0 \text{ ft}. \tag{7c}$$

The position of the projectile t seconds after firing is

$$x = (v_0 \cos \alpha) t \text{ ft}, \qquad y = -\tfrac{1}{2}gt^2 + (v_0 \sin \alpha)t \text{ ft}. \tag{8}$$

For a given angle of elevation α and a given muzzle velocity v_0, the position of the projectile at any time may be determined from the parametric equations in (8). The equations may be used to answer such questions as:

1. How high does the projectile rise?
2. How far away does the projectile land, and how does the horizontal range R vary with the angle of elevation?
3. What angle of elevation gives the maximum range?

First, the projectile will reach its highest point when its y-(vertical) velocity component is zero, that is, when

$$\frac{dy}{dt} = -gt + v_0 \sin \alpha = 0 \text{ ft/sec}$$

or

$$t = t_m = \frac{v_0 \sin \alpha}{g} \text{ sec}.$$

For this value of t, the value of y is

$$y_{\max} = -\frac{1}{2} g(t_m)^2 + (v_0 \sin \alpha)t_m = \frac{(v_0 \sin \alpha)^2}{2g} \text{ ft}.$$

Second, to find R we first find the time when the projectile strikes the ground. That is, we find the value of t for which $y = 0$. We then find the value of x for this value of t:

$$y = t(-\tfrac{1}{2}gt + v_0 \sin \alpha) = 0 \text{ ft}$$

when

$$t = 0 \quad \text{or} \quad t = \frac{2v_0 \sin \alpha}{g} = 2t_m \text{ sec.}$$

Since $t = 0$ is the instant when the projectile is fired, $t = 2t_m$ is the time when the projectile hits the ground. The corresponding value of x is

$$R = (v_0 \cos \alpha)(2t_m) = v_0 \cos \alpha \frac{2v_0 \sin \alpha}{g} = \frac{v_0^2}{g} \sin 2\alpha \text{ ft.}$$

Finally, the formula just given for R shows that the maximum range for a given muzzle velocity is obtained when $\sin 2\alpha = 1$, or $\alpha = 45°$.

The cartesian equation of the path of the projectile is readily obtained from (8). We need only substitute

$$t = \frac{x}{v_0 \cos \alpha}$$

from the first into the second equation of (8) to eliminate t and obtain

$$y = -\left(\frac{g}{2v_0^2 \cos^2 \alpha}\right)x^2 + (\tan \alpha)x. \tag{9}$$

Since this equation is linear in y and quadratic in x, it represents a *parabola*. Thus the path of a projectile (neglecting air resistance) is a parabola.

Differential equations that take air resistance into account are usually too complicated for straightforward integration. The M.I.T. differential analyzers were used to solve such equations during War II to build up "range tables." In following moving targets, keeping track of *time* is of great importance, so that equations or tables that give x and y in terms of t are preferred over other forms.

PROBLEMS

In Problems 1–4, the projectile is assumed to obey the laws of motion discussed above, in which air resistance is neglected.

1. Find two values of the angle of elevation that will enable a projectile to reach a target on the same level as the gun and 25,000 feet distant from it if the initial velocity is 1000 ft/sec. Determine the times of flight corresponding to these two angles.

2. Show that doubling the initial velocity of a projectile multiplies both the maximum height and the range by a factor of four.

3. Show that a projectile attains three-quarters of its maximum height in one-half the time required to reach that maximum.

4. Suppose a target moving at the constant rate of a ft/sec is level with and b ft away from a gun at the instant the gun is fired. If the target moves in a horizontal line directly away from the gun, show that the muzzle velocity v_0 and angle of elevation α must satisfy the equation.

$$v_0^2 \sin 2\alpha - 2av_0 \sin \alpha - bg = 0$$

if the projectile is to strike the target.

In Problems 5–7, find parametric equations and sketch the curve described by the point $P(x, y)$ for $t \geq 0$ if its coordinates satisfy the given differential equations and initial conditions.

5. $\dfrac{dx}{dt} = x, \quad \dfrac{dy}{dt} = -x^2; \quad t = 0, \quad x = 1, \quad y = -4.$

[*Hint*. Solve for x first.]

6. $\dfrac{dx}{dt} = y, \quad \dfrac{dy}{dt} = y^2; \quad t = 0, \quad x = 0, \quad y = 1.$

7. $\dfrac{dx}{dt} = \sqrt{1 - x^2}, \quad \dfrac{dy}{dt} = x^2; \quad t = 0, \quad x = 0, \quad y = 1.$

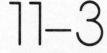

11-3

PARAMETRIC EQUATIONS IN ANALYTIC GEOMETRY

The solutions of differential equations of motion are not the only ways in which parametric equations arise. For example, we have already used the equations

$$x = a \cos \theta, \qquad y = a \sin \theta, \qquad 0 \leq \theta \leq 2\pi, \tag{1}$$

to represent the circle of radius a whose center is at the origin (Fig. 11–8). Similarly, the equations

$$x = a \cos \phi, \qquad y = b \sin \phi, \qquad 0 \leq \theta \leq 2\pi, \tag{2}$$

are parametric equations for the ellipse whose cartesian equation is

$$\frac{x^2}{a^2} + \frac{y^2}{b^2} = 1.$$

EXAMPLE 1.　Find parametric equations for the parabola

$$y^2 = 4px. \tag{3}$$

Solution.　The parabola can be parametrized in several ways. One way is to use the slope

$$t = \frac{dy}{dx}$$

of the tangent to the curve at (x, y) as a parameter (Fig. 11–9(a)). Since

$$2y \frac{dy}{dx} = 4p \qquad \text{or} \qquad \frac{dy}{dx} = \frac{2p}{y},$$

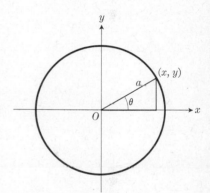

11–8　$x = a \cos \theta, \ y = a \sin \theta.$

a)

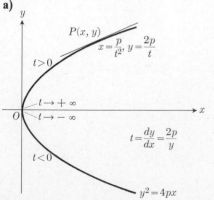

b)

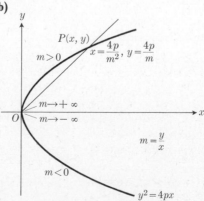

11–9　Parametrizations of the parabola $y^2 = 4px.$

parameter t: slope of the tangent at P　　　　parameter m: slope of OP

the parametric equations in this case are

$$y = \frac{2p}{t}, \qquad x = \frac{p}{t^2}. \tag{4}$$

If we use the parameter

$$m = \frac{y}{x},$$

(Fig. 11–9(b)), which is the slope of the line joining the origin to the point $P(x, y)$ on the parabola, we have

$$y^2 = m^2 x^2 \qquad \text{and} \qquad y^2 = 4px,$$

which lead to

$$x = \frac{4p}{m^2}, \qquad y = \frac{4p}{m} \tag{5}$$

as the parametric equations.

Sometimes the parametric equations of a curve and the cartesian equation are not coextensive.

EXAMPLE 2. Suppose the parametric equations of a curve are

$$x = \cosh \theta, \qquad y = \sinh \theta. \tag{6}$$

Then the hyperbolic identity

$$\cosh^2 \theta - \sinh^2 \theta = 1$$

enables us to eliminate θ and write

$$x^2 - y^2 = 1 \tag{7}$$

as a cartesian equation of the curve. Closer scrutiny, however, shows that Eq. (7) *includes too much*, for $x = \cosh \theta$ is always positive, so the parametric equations represent a curve lying wholly to the right of the y-axis, whereas the cartesian equation (7) represents both the right- and lefthand branches of the hyperbola (Fig. 11–10). The lefthand branch could be excluded by taking only positive values of x. That is,

$$x = \sqrt{1 + y^2} \tag{8}$$

does represent the curve given by (6).

EXAMPLE 3. The curve whose parametric equations are

$$x = \cos 2\theta, \qquad y = \cos \theta, \tag{9}$$

lies within the square $-1 \le x \le 1$, $-1 \le y \le 1$. We may eliminate θ as follows:

$$x = \cos 2\theta = 2 \cos^2 \theta - 1 = 2y^2 - 1.$$

Thus every point on the graph of (9) also lies on the curve

$$x = 2y^2 - 1. \tag{10}$$

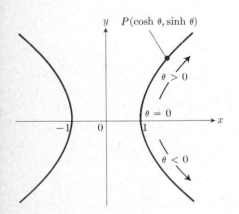

11–10 The parametric equations $x = \cosh \theta$, $y = \sinh \theta$, $-\infty < \theta < \infty$, give only the right branch of the hyperbola $x^2 - y^2 = 1$, because $\cosh \theta \ge 1$.

If we omit the restrictions

$$|x| \le 1, \qquad |y| \le 1,$$

then Eq. (10) represents the complete parabola

$$y^2 = \tfrac{1}{2}(x + 1)$$

shown in Fig. 11–11. The parametric equations, however, represent only the arc ABC. From (9), we see that the point starts at $A(1, 1)$ when $\theta = 0$, moves along AB to $B(-1, 0)$ as θ varies from 0 to $\pi/2$, and continues to $C(1, -1)$ as θ increases to π. As θ varies from π to 2π, the point traverses the arc CBA back to A. Since both x and y are periodic, x of period π and y of period 2π, further variations in θ result in retracing the same portion of the parabola.

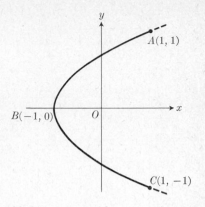

11–11 $x = \cos 2\theta,\ y = \cos \theta.$

EXAMPLE 4. A wheel of radius a rolls along a horizontal straight line without slipping. Find the curve traced by a point P on a spoke of the wheel b units from its center. Such a curve is called a *trochoid* (one Greek word for wheel is *trochos*). When $b = a$, P is on the circumference and the curve is called a *cycloid*. This is like the path traveled by the head of a nail in a tire.

Solution. In Fig. 11–12 we take the x-axis to be the line the wheel rolls along, with the y-axis through a low point of the trochoid. It is customary to use the angle ϕ through which CP has rotated as the parameter. Since the circle rolls without slipping, the distance OM that the wheel has moved horizontally is just equal to the circular arc $MN = a\phi$. (Roll the wheel back. Then N will fall at the origin O.) The xy-coordinates of C are therefore

$$h = a\phi, \qquad k = a. \tag{11}$$

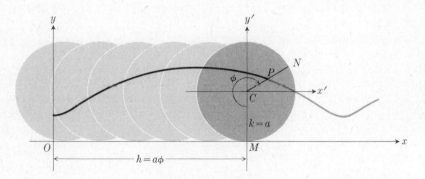

11–12 Trochoid: $x = a\phi - b \sin \phi,\ y = a - b \cos \phi.$

We now introduce $x'y'$-axes parallel to the xy-axes and having their origin at C (Fig. 11–13). The xy- and $x'y'$-coordinates of P are related by the equations

$$x = h + x', \qquad y = k + y'. \tag{12}$$

From Fig. 11–13 we may immediately read

$$x' = b \cos \theta, \qquad y' = b \sin \theta,$$

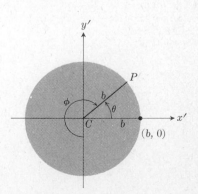

11–13 The $x'y'$-coordinates of P are $x' = b \cos \theta,\ y = b \sin \theta.$

or, since

$$\theta = \frac{3\pi}{2} - \phi,$$

$$x' = -b \sin \phi, \qquad y' = -b \cos \phi. \tag{13}$$

We substitute these results and Eqs. (12) into (11) and obtain

$$x = a\phi - b \sin \phi,$$
$$y = a - b \cos \phi \tag{14}$$

as parametric equations of the trochoid.

The cycloid (Fig. 11–14(a)),

$$x = a(\phi - \sin \phi), \qquad y = a(1 - \cos \phi), \tag{15}$$

obtained from (14) by taking $b = a$, is the most important special case.

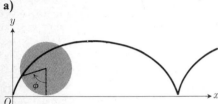
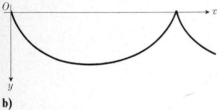

a)

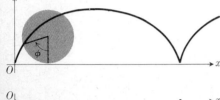

b)

11–14   Cycloid: $x = a(\phi - \sin \phi)$, $y = a(1 - \cos \phi)$.

Brachistochrones and Tautochrones

If we reflect both the cycloid and the y-axis across the x-axis, Eqs. (15) still apply, and the resulting curve (Fig. 11–14(b)) has several interesting properties, one of which we shall now discuss without proof. The proofs belong to a branch of mathematics known as the calculus of variations. Much of the fundamental theory of this subject is attributed to the Bernoulli brothers, John and James, who were friendly rivals and stimulated each other with mathematical problems in the form of challenges. One of these, the brachistochrone problem, was: Among all smooth curves joining two given points, to find that one along which a bead, subject only to the force of gravity, might slide *in the shortest time.*

The two points, labeled P_0 and P_1 in Fig. 11–15, may be taken to lie in a vertical plane at the origin and at (x_1, y_1), respectively. We can formulate the problem in mathematical terms as follows. The kinetic energy of the bead at the start is zero, since its velocity is zero. The work done by gravity in moving the particle from $(0, 0)$ to any point (x, y) is mgy and this must be equal to the change in kinetic energy; that is,

$$mgy = \tfrac{1}{2}mv^2 - \tfrac{1}{2}m(0)^2.$$

Thus the velocity

$$v = ds/dt$$

that the particle has when it reaches $P(x, y)$ is

$$v = \sqrt{2gy}.$$

That is,

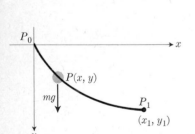

11–15   A bead sliding down a cycloid.

$$\frac{ds}{dt} = \sqrt{2gy} \qquad \text{or} \qquad dt = \frac{ds}{\sqrt{2gy}} = \frac{\sqrt{1 + \left(\dfrac{dy}{dx}\right)^2}\, dx}{\sqrt{2gy}}.$$

The time t_1 required for the bead to slide from P_0 to P_1 depends upon the particular curve $y = f(x)$ along which it moves and is given by

$$t_1 = \int_0^{x_1} \sqrt{\frac{1 + (f'(x))^2}{2gf(x)}}\, dx. \tag{16}$$

The problem is *to find the curve* $y = f(x)$ that passes through the points $P_0(0, 0)$ and $P_1(x_1, y_1)$ and minimizes the value of the integral in Eq. (16). (*Brachistochrone* is derived from two Greek words that together mean "shortest time.")

At first sight, one might guess that the straight line joining P_0 and P_1 would also yield the shortest time, but a moment's reflection will cast some doubt on this conjecture, for there may be some gain in time by having the particle start to fall vertically at first, thereby building up its velocity more quickly than if it were to slide along an inclined path. With this increased velocity, one may be able to afford to travel over a longer path and still reach P_1 in a shorter time. The solution of the problem is beyond the present book, but the brachistochrone curve is actually an arc of a cycloid through P_0 and P_1, having a cusp at the origin.

If we write Eq. (16) in the equivalent form

$$t_1 = \int \sqrt{\frac{dx^2 + dy^2}{2gy}}$$

and then substitute Eqs. (15) into this, we obtain

$$t_1 = \int_{\phi=0}^{\phi_1} \sqrt{\frac{a^2(2 - 2\cos\phi)}{2ga(1 - \cos\phi)}}\, d\phi = \phi_1 \sqrt{\frac{a}{g}}$$

as the time required for the particle to slide from P_0 to P_1. The time required to reach the bottom of the arc is obtained by taking $\phi_1 = \pi$. Now it is a remarkable fact, which we shall soon demonstrate, that the time required to slide along the cycloid from $(0, 0)$ to the lowest point $(a\pi, 2a)$ is the same as the time required for the particle, starting from rest, to slide from *any intermediate point* of the arc, say (x_0, y_0), to $(a\pi, 2a)$. For the latter case, one has

$$v = \sqrt{2g(y - y_0)}$$

as the velocity at $P(x, y)$, and the time required is

$$T = \int_{\phi_0}^{\pi} \sqrt{\frac{a^2(2 - 2\cos\phi)}{2ag(\cos\phi_0 - \cos\phi)}}\, d\phi = \sqrt{\frac{a}{g}} \int_{\phi_0}^{\pi} \sqrt{\frac{1 - \cos\phi}{\cos\phi_0 - \cos\phi}}\, d\phi$$

$$= \sqrt{\frac{a}{g}} \int_{\phi_0}^{\pi} \sqrt{\frac{2\sin^2(\phi/2)}{[2\cos^2(\phi_0/2) - 1] - [2\cos^2(\phi/2) - 1]}}\, d\phi$$

$$= 2\sqrt{\frac{a}{g}} \left[-\sin^{-1}\frac{\cos(\phi/2)}{\cos(\phi_0/2)} \right]_{\phi_0}^{\pi} = 2\sqrt{\frac{a}{g}}(-\sin^{-1}0 + \sin^{-1}1) = \pi\sqrt{\frac{a}{g}}.$$

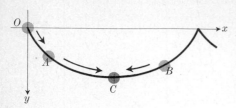

Since this answer is independent of the value of ϕ_0, it follows that the same length of time is required to reach the lowest point on the cycloid no matter where on the arc the particle is released from rest. Thus, in Fig. 11–16, three particles which start at the same time from O, A, and B will reach C simultaneously. In this sense, the cycloid is also a *tautochrone* (meaning "the same time") as well as being a brachistochrone.

11–16 Beads released on the cycloid at O, A, and B will take the same amount of time to reach C.

Pendulum Clocks

One trouble with pendulum clocks is that the rate at which the pendulum swings changes with the size of the swing. The wider the swing, the longer it takes the pendulum to return. This would create no problem if clocks never ran down, but they do. As the spring unwinds, the force exerted on the pendulum decreases, the pendulum swings through increasingly shorter arcs, and the clock speeds up. The ticks come faster as the clock winds down. Christiaan Huygens, a seventeenth-century Dutch mathematician, physicist and astronomer, needed an accurate clock to make careful astronomical measurements. In 1673 he published the first description of an ideal pendulum clock whose bob swings in a cycloid. The period of the swing of Huygens' clock did not depend on the amplitude, and would not change as the clock wound down.

How does one make a pendulum bob swing in a cycloid? Hang it from a fine wire constrained by "cheeks" (Fig. 11–17), which cause the bob to draw up as it swings to the side. And what is the shape of the cheeks? They are cycloids.

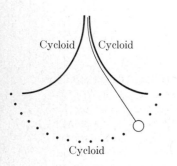

11–17 A flexible pendulum constrained by cycloids swings in a cycloid.

PROBLEMS

In each of Problems 1–10, sketch the graph of the curve described by the point $P(x, y)$ as the parameter t varies over the domain given. Also find a cartesian equation of the curve in each case.

1. $x = \cos t$, $y = \sin t$, $0 \leq t \leq 2\pi$
2. $x = \cos 2t$, $y = \sin t$, $0 \leq t \leq 2\pi$
3. $x = \sec t$, $y = \tan t$, $-\pi/2 < t < \pi/2$
4. $x = 2 + 4 \sin t$, $y = 3 - 2 \cos t$, $0 \leq t \leq 2\pi$
5. $x = 2t + 3$, $y = 4t^2 - 9$, $-\infty < t < \infty$
6. $x = \cosh t$, $y = 2 \sinh t$, $0 \leq t < \infty$
7. $x = 2 + 1/t$, $y = 2 - t$, $0 < t < \infty$
8. $x = t + 1$, $y = t^2 + 4$, $0 \leq t < \infty$
9. $x = t^2 + t$, $y = t^2 - t$, $-\infty < t < \infty$
10. $x = 3 + 2 \operatorname{sech} t$, $y = 4 - 3 \tanh t$, $-\infty < t < \infty$
11. Find parametric equations of the semicircle

$$x^2 + y^2 = a^2, \qquad y > 0,$$

using as parameter the slope $t = dy/dx$ of the tangent to the curve at (x, y).

12. Find parametric equations of the semicircle

$$x^2 + y^2 = a^2, \qquad y > 0,$$

using as parameter the variable θ defined by the equation $x = a \tanh \theta$.

13. Find parametric equations of the circle

$$x^2 + y^2 = a^2,$$

using as parameter the arc length s measured counterclockwise from the point $(a, 0)$ to the point (x, y).

14. Find parametric equations of the catenary $y = a \cosh x/a$, using as parameter the length of arc s from the point $(0, a)$ to the point (x, y), with the sign of s taken to be the same as the sign of x.

15. If a string wound around a fixed circle is unwound while held taut in the plane of the circle, its end traces an *involute* of the circle (Fig. 11–18). Let the fixed circle be located with its center at the origin O and have radius a. Let the initial position of the tracing point P be $A(a, 0)$ and let the unwound portion of the string PT be tangent to the

circle at *T*. Derive parametric equations of the involute, using the angle *AOT* as the parameter *t*.

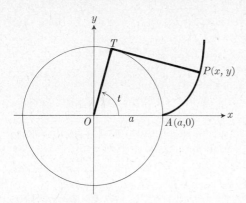

11–18   Involute of a circle.

16. When a circle rolls externally on the circumference of a second, fixed circle, any point *P* on the circumference of the rolling circle describes an *epicycloid* (Fig. 11–19). Let the fixed circle have its center at the origin *O* and have radius *a*. Let the radius of the rolling circle be *b* and let the initial position of the tracing point *P* be *A*(*a*, 0). Determine parametric equations of the epicycloid, using as parameter the angle θ from the positive *x*-axis to the line of centers.

18. Find the length of one arch of the cycloid

$$x = a(\phi - \sin \phi),$$
$$y = a(1 - \cos \phi).$$

19. Show that the slope of the cycloid

$$x = a(\phi - \sin \phi),$$
$$y = a(1 - \cos \phi)$$

is $dy/dx = \cot \phi/2$. In particular, the tangent to the cycloid is vertical when ϕ is 0 or 2π.

20. Show that the slope of the trochoid

$$x = a\phi - b \sin \phi, \qquad y = a - b \cos \phi$$

is always finite if $b < a$.

21. The *witch of Maria Agnesi* is a bell-shaped curve that may be constructed as follows: Let *C* be a circle of radius *a* having its center at (0, *a*) on the *y*-axis (Fig. 11–21). The variable line *OA* through the origin *O* intersects the line *y* = 2*a* in the point *A* and intersects the circle in the point *B*. A point *P* on the witch is now located by taking the intersection of lines through *A* and *B* parallel to the *y*- and *x*-axes, respectively. (a) Find parametric equations of the witch, using as parameter the angle θ from the *x*-axis to

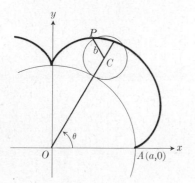

11–19   Epicycloid, with *b* = *a*/4.

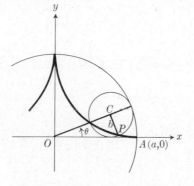

11–20   Hypocycloid, with *b* = *a*/4.

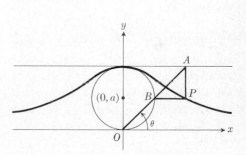

11–21   The witch of Maria Agnesi.

17. When a circle rolls on the inside of a fixed circle any point *P* on the circumference of the rolling circle describes a *hypocycloid*. Let the fixed circle be $x^2 + y^2 = a^2$, let the radius of the rolling circle be *b*, and let the initial position of the tracing point *P* be *A*(*a*, 0). Use the angle θ from the positive *x*-axis to the line of centers as parameter and determine parametric equations of the hypocycloid. In particular, if *b* = *a*/4, as in Fig. 11–20, show that

$$x = a \cos^3 \theta, \qquad y = a \sin^3 \theta.$$

the line *OA*.
(b) Also find the cartesian equation for the witch.

22. (*Calculator*) An automobile tire of radius 1 ft has a pebble stuck in the tread. Estimate to the nearest foot how far the pebble travels when the car goes one mile. Start by finding the ratio of the length of one arch of a cycloid to its base length.

SPACE COORDINATES

A. Cartesian Coordinates

Figure 11–22 shows a system of mutually orthogonal coordinate axes, Ox, Oy, and Oz. The system is called *righthanded* because a right-threaded screw pointing along Oz will advance when turned from Ox to Oy through an angle, say, of 90°. The cartesian coordinates of a point $P(x, y, z)$ in space may be read from the coordinate axes by passing planes through P perpendicular to each axis. The points on the x-axis have their y- and z-coordinates both zero. That is, they have coordinates of the form $(x, 0, 0)$. Points in a plane perpendicular to the z-axis, say, all have the same z-coordinate. Thus the points in the plane perpendicular to the z-axis and 5 units above the xy-plane all have coordinates of the form $(x, y, 5)$. We can write $z = 5$ as an equation for this plane. The three planes

$$x = 2, \qquad y = 3, \qquad z = 5$$

intersect in the point $P(2, 3, 5)$. The points of the yz-plane are obtained by setting $x = 0$. The three coordinate planes $x = 0$, $y = 0$, $z = 0$ divide the space into eight cells, called octants. The octant in which all three coordinates are positive is called the *first octant*, but there is no conventional numbering of the remaining seven octants.

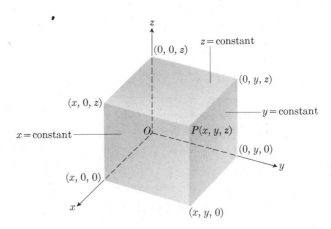

11–22   Righthanded coordinate system.

B. Cylindrical Coordinates

It is frequently convenient to use cylindrical coordinates (r, θ, z) to locate a point in space. These are just the polar coordinates (r, θ) used instead of (x, y) in the plane $z = 0$, coupled with the z-coordinate. Cylindrical and cartesian coordinates are related by the familiar equations (Fig. 11–23)

$$x = r \cos \theta, \qquad r^2 = x^2 + y^2,$$

$$y = r \sin \theta, \qquad \tan \theta = y/x, \tag{1}$$

$$z = z.$$

11–23   Cylindrical coordinates.

The equation $r =$ constant describes a right circular cylinder of radius r whose axis is the z-axis, $r = 0$ being an equation for the z-axis itself. The equation $\theta =$ constant describes a plane containing the z-axis and making an angle θ with the xz-plane (Fig. 11–24). (Some authors require the values of r in cylindrical coordinates to be nonnegative. In this case, the equation $\theta =$ constant describes a half-plane fanning out from the z-axis.)

Cylindrical coordinates are convenient when there is an axis of symmetry in a physical problem.

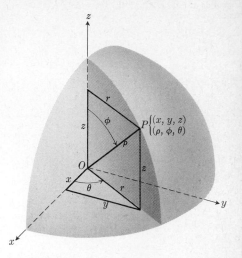

11–25 Spherical coordinates.

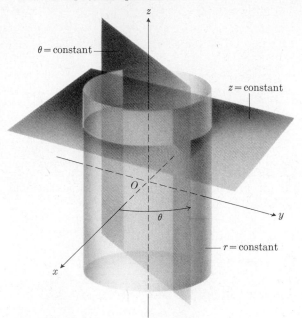

11–24 Some planes and cylinders have simple equations in cylindrical coordinates.

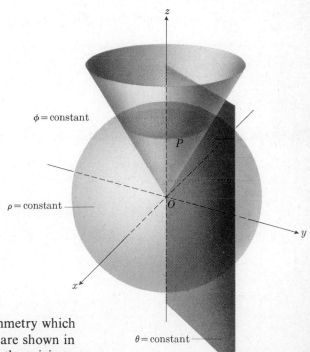

11–26 Spheres and cones whose centers are at the origin have simple equations in spherical coordinates.

C. Spherical Coordinates

Spherical coordinates are useful when there is a center of symmetry which we can take as the origin. The *spherical coordinates* (ρ, ϕ, θ) are shown in Fig. 11–25. The first coordinate $\rho = |OP|$ is the distance from the origin to the point P. It is never negative. The equation $\rho =$ constant describes the surface of a sphere of radius ρ with center at O (Fig. 11–26). The second spherical coordinate, ϕ, is the angle measured down from the z-axis to the line OP. The equation $\phi =$ constant describes a cone with vertex at O, axis Oz, and generating angle ϕ, provided we broaden our interpretation of the word "cone" to include the xy-plane for which $\phi = \pi/2$ and cones with generating angles greater than $\pi/2$. The third spherical coordinate θ is the same as the angle θ in cylindrical coordinates, namely, the angle from the xz-plane to the plane through P and the z-axis. But, in contrast with cylindrical coordinates, the equation $\theta = $ constant in spherical coordinates defines a half-plane (Fig. 11–26).

From Fig. 11–25 we may read the following relationships between the cartesian, cylindrical, and spherical coordinate systems:

$$r = \rho \sin \phi, \qquad x = r \cos \theta, \qquad x = \rho \sin \phi \cos \theta,$$
$$z = \rho \cos \phi, \qquad y = r \sin \theta, \qquad y = \rho \sin \phi \sin \theta,$$
$$\theta = \theta, \qquad z = z, \qquad z = \rho \cos \phi. \qquad (2)$$

Every point in space can be given spherical coordinates restricted to the ranges

$$\rho \geq 0, \qquad 0 \leq \phi \leq \pi, \qquad 0 \leq \theta < 2\pi. \qquad (3)$$

Because of the analogy between the surface of a sphere and the earth's surface, the z-axis is sometimes called the *polar axis*, while ϕ is referred to as *co-latitude* and θ as *longitude*. One also speaks of *meridians*, *parallels*, and the *northern* and *southern hemispheres*.

PROBLEMS

In Problems 1–4, describe the set of points $P(x, y, z)$ whose cartesian coordinates satisfy the given pairs of simultaneous equations. Sketch.

1. $x = $ constant, $\quad y = $ constant

2. $y = x, \quad z = 5$

3. $x^2 + y^2 = 4, \quad z = -2$ **4.** $x = 0, \quad \dfrac{y^2}{a^2} + \dfrac{z^2}{b^2} = 1$

In Problems 5–8, describe the set of points $P(r, \theta, z)$ whose cylindrical coordinates satisfy the given pairs of simultaneous equations. Sketch.

5. $r = 2, \quad z = 3$ **6.** $\theta = \pi/6, \quad z = r$

7. $r = 3, \quad z = 2\theta$ **8.** $r = 2\theta, \quad z = 3\theta$

In Problems 9–12, describe the set of points $P(\rho, \phi, \theta)$ whose spherical coordinates satisfy the given pairs of simultaneous equations. Sketch.

9. $\rho = 5, \quad \theta = \pi/4$ **10.** $\rho = 5, \quad \phi = \pi/4$

11. $\theta = \pi/4, \quad \phi = \pi/4$ **12.** $\theta = \pi/2, \quad \rho = 4 \cos \phi$

Translate the following equations from the given coordinate system (cartesian, cylindrical, or spherical) into forms that are appropriate to the other two systems.

13. $x^2 + y^2 + z^2 = 4$ **14.** $x^2 + y^2 + z^2 = 4z$

15. $z^2 = r^2$ **16.** $\rho = 6 \cos \phi$

Describe the following sets.

17. $x \geq 0$ **18.** $3 \leq \rho \leq 5$

19. $r \geq 2, \quad \rho \leq 5$

20. $0 \leq \theta \leq \pi/4, \quad 0 \leq \phi \leq \pi/4, \quad \rho \geq 0$

21. $4x^2 + 9y^2 \leq 36$

11–5
VECTORS IN SPACE

Vectors in space are the three-dimensional analog of vectors in the plane, and are subject to the same rules of addition, subtraction, and scalar multiplication that govern vectors in the plane. The vectors from the origin to the points whose cartesian coordinates are $(1, 0, 0)$, $(0, 1, 0)$, and $(0, 0, 1)$ are the basic unit vectors. We denote them by $\mathbf{i}$, $\mathbf{j}$, and $\mathbf{k}$, and write the vector from the origin O to the point $P(x, y, z)$ as

$$\mathbf{R} = \overrightarrow{OP} = \mathbf{i}x + \mathbf{j}y + \mathbf{k}z. \qquad (1)$$

If $P_1(x_1, y_1, z_1)$ and $P_2(x_2, y_2, z_2)$ are two points in space (Fig. 11–27), then the vector from P_1 to P_2 is the vector sum

$$\overrightarrow{P_1 P_2} = \overrightarrow{P_1 O} + \overrightarrow{OP_2}.$$

Since

$$\overrightarrow{P_1 O} = -\overrightarrow{OP_1},$$

this is the same as

$$\overrightarrow{P_1 P_2} = \overrightarrow{OP_2} - \overrightarrow{OP_1}$$

or

$$\overrightarrow{P_1 P_2} = \mathbf{i}(x_2 - x_1) + \mathbf{j}(y_2 - y_1) + \mathbf{k}(z_2 - z_1). \qquad (2)$$

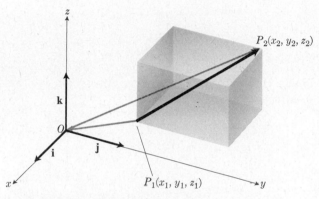

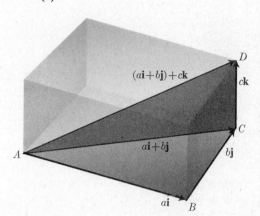

11–27 $\overrightarrow{P_1 P_2} = \overrightarrow{P_1 O} + \overrightarrow{OP_2}.$

11–28 $|\overrightarrow{AD}|$ can be determined from the right triangles ABC and ACD.

The length of any vector

$$\mathbf{A} = a\mathbf{i} + b\mathbf{j} + c\mathbf{k}$$

is readily determined by applying the theorem of Pythagoras twice. In the right triangle ABC (Fig. 11–28),

$$|\overrightarrow{AC}| = |a\mathbf{i} + b\mathbf{j}| = \sqrt{a^2 + b^2},$$

and in the right triangle ACD,

$$|\overrightarrow{AD}| = \sqrt{|\overrightarrow{AC}|^2 + |\overrightarrow{CD}|^2} = \sqrt{(a^2 + b^2) + c^2}.$$

That is,

$$|a\mathbf{i} + b\mathbf{j} + c\mathbf{k}| = \sqrt{a^2 + b^2 + c^2}. \qquad (3)$$

If we apply this result to the vector $\overrightarrow{P_1 P_2}$ of Eq. (2), we obtain a formula for the distance between two points:

$$|\overrightarrow{P_1 P_2}| = \sqrt{(x_2 - x_1)^2 + (y_2 - y_1)^2 + (z_2 - z_1)^2}. \qquad (4)$$

Equation (4) may be used to determine an equation for the sphere of radius a with center at $P_0(x_0, y_0, z_0)$ (Fig. 11–29). The point P is on the sphere if and only if

$$|\overrightarrow{P_0 P}| = a,$$

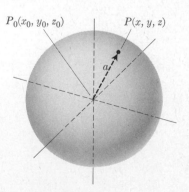

11–29 The sphere $(x - x_0)^2 + (y - y_0)^2 + (z - z_0)^2 = a^2$.

or

$$(x - x_0)^2 + (y - y_0)^2 + (z - z_0)^2 = a^2. \tag{5}$$

EXAMPLE 1.   Find the center and radius of the sphere

$$x^2 + y^2 + z^2 + 2x - 4y = 0.$$

Solution.   Complete the squares in the given equation to obtain

$$x^2 + 2x + 1 + y^2 - 4y + 4 + z^2 = 0 + 1 + 4$$

$$(x + 1)^2 + (y - 2)^2 + z^2 = 5.$$

Comparison with Eq. (5) shows that $x_0 = -1$, $y_0 = 2$, $z_0 = 0$, and $a = \sqrt{5}$. The center is $(-1, 2, 0)$ and the radius is $\sqrt{5}$.

Direction

For any nonzero vector **A**, we obtain a unit vector called *the direction of* **A** by dividing **A** by its own length:*

$$\text{Direction of } \mathbf{A} = \frac{\mathbf{A}}{|\mathbf{A}|}. \tag{6}$$

EXAMPLE 2.   If

$$\mathbf{A} = 2\mathbf{i} - 3\mathbf{j} + 7\mathbf{k},$$

then its length is $\sqrt{4 + 9 + 49} = \sqrt{62}$, and

$$\text{Direction of } (2\mathbf{i} - 3\mathbf{j} + 7\mathbf{k}) = \frac{2\mathbf{i} - 3\mathbf{j} + 7\mathbf{k}}{\sqrt{62}}.$$

---

*   The authors credit Professor Arthur P. Mattuck with this definition.

PROBLEMS

Find the centers and radii of the spheres in Problems 1–4.

1. $x^2 + y^2 + z^2 + 4x - 4z = 0$

2. $2x^2 + 2y^2 + 2z^2 + x + y + z = 9$

3. $x^2 + y^2 + z^2 - 2az = 0$

4. $3x^2 + 3y^2 + 3z^2 + 2y - 2z = 9$

5. Find the distance between the point $P(x, y, z)$ and (a) the x-axis, (b) the y-axis, (c) the z-axis, (d) the xy-plane.

6. The distance from $P(x, y, z)$ to the origin is d_1 and the distance from P to $A(0, 0, 3)$ is d_2. Write an equation for the coordinates of P if

a) $d_1 = 2d_2$,   **b)** $d_1 + d_2 = 6$,   **c)** $|d_1 - d_2| = 2$.

Find the lengths of the following vectors.

7. $2\mathbf{i} + \mathbf{j} - 2\mathbf{k}$ **8.** $3\mathbf{i} - 6\mathbf{j} + 2\mathbf{k}$

9. $\mathbf{i} + 4\mathbf{j} - 8\mathbf{k}$ **10.** $9\mathbf{i} - 2\mathbf{j} + 6\mathbf{k}$

11. Find the direction of $4\mathbf{i} + 3\mathbf{j} + 12\mathbf{k}$.

12. Find the vector from the origin O to the point of intersection of the medians of the triangle whose vertices are the three points

$$A(1, -1, 2), \qquad B(2, 1, 3), \qquad C(-1, 2, -1).$$

13. A bug is crawling straight up the side of a rotating right circular cylinder of radius 2 ft. At time $t = 0$, it is at the point $(2, 0, 0)$ relative to a fixed set of xyz-axes. The axis of the cylinder lies along the z-axis. Assume that the bug travels on the cylinder along a line parallel to the z-axis at the rate of c ft/sec, and that the cylinder rotates (counterclockwise as viewed from above) at the rate of b radians/sec. If $P(x, y, z)$ is the bug's position at the end of t seconds, show that

$$\overrightarrow{OP} = \mathbf{i}(2 \cos bt) + \mathbf{j}(2 \sin bt) + \mathbf{k}(ct).$$

The *scalar product* of two vectors **A** and **B** is a scalar defined by the equation

$$\mathbf{A} \cdot \mathbf{B} = |\mathbf{A}| \, |\mathbf{B}| \cos \theta, \tag{1}$$

11-6

THE SCALAR PRODUCT OF TWO VECTORS

where θ measures the smallest angle determined by **A** and **B** when their initial points coincide, as in Fig. 11–30. This product is also called the *dot product*, because of the dot used to denote it. The definition of the dot product given here is "coordinate-free," in the sense that it is independent of whatever reference frame we might use to describe the vectors in terms of coordinates.

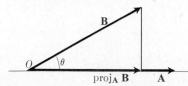
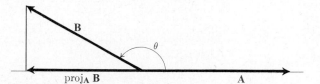

11–30 Vector projections of **B** onto **A**. In (a), the component of **B** in the direction of **A** is the length of the vector projection. In (b), it is *minus* the length of the vector projection.

It is clear from Eq. (1) that interchanging the two factors **A** and **B** does not change the dot product. That is,

$$\mathbf{A} \cdot \mathbf{B} = \mathbf{B} \cdot \mathbf{A}. \tag{2}$$

The operation of scalar multiplication is commutative.

The vector that we get by projecting **B** onto the line through **A** is called the *vector projection of* **B** *onto* **A**. We denote it by proj$_\mathbf{A}$ **B** (Fig. 11–30).

The *component of* **B** *in the direction of* **A** is a number that is plus or minus the length of the vector projection of **B** onto **A**. The sign is plus if proj$_\mathbf{A}$ **B** has the same direction as $+\mathbf{A}$, and is minus if it has the same direction as $-\mathbf{A}$. In either case, the component of **B** in the direction of **A** is equal to $|\mathbf{B}| \cos \theta$ (see Fig. 11–30 again).

The dot product gives a convenient way to calculate the component of **B** in the direction of **A**. We solve Eq. (1) for $|\mathbf{B}| \cos \theta$ to get

$$\text{B-component in A-direction} = |\mathbf{B}| \cos \theta = \frac{\mathbf{A} \cdot \mathbf{B}}{|\mathbf{A}|}. \tag{3}$$

Multiplying both sides of Eq. (3) by $|\mathbf{A}|$ leads to a geometric interpretation of $\mathbf{A} \cdot \mathbf{B}$:

$$\mathbf{A} \cdot \mathbf{B} = |\mathbf{A}|(|\mathbf{B}| \cos \theta)$$

$$= (\text{length of } \mathbf{A}) \text{ times } (\mathbf{B}\text{-component in A-direction}).$$

Of course we may interchange the roles of $|\mathbf{A}|$ and $|\mathbf{B}|$ and write the dot product in the alternative form of

$$\mathbf{A} \cdot \mathbf{B} = |\mathbf{B}|(|\mathbf{A}| \cos \theta)$$

$$= (\text{length of } \mathbf{B}) \text{ times } (\mathbf{A}\text{-component in B-direction}).$$

To calculate $\mathbf{A} \cdot \mathbf{B}$ from the components of $\mathbf{A}$ and $\mathbf{B}$, we let

$$\mathbf{A} = a_1\mathbf{i} + a_2\mathbf{j} + a_3\mathbf{k},$$
$$\mathbf{B} = b_1\mathbf{i} + b_2\mathbf{j} + b_3\mathbf{k}, \tag{4}$$

and

$$\mathbf{C} = \mathbf{B} - \mathbf{A}$$
$$= (b_1 - a_1)\mathbf{i} + (b_2 - a_2)\mathbf{j} + (b_3 - a_3)\mathbf{k}.$$

Then we apply the law of cosines to a triangle whose sides represent the vectors $\mathbf{A}$, $\mathbf{B}$, and $\mathbf{C}$ (Fig. 11–31) and obtain

$$|\mathbf{C}|^2 = |\mathbf{A}|^2 + |\mathbf{B}|^2 - 2|\mathbf{A}||\mathbf{B}|\cos\theta,$$
$$|\mathbf{A}||\mathbf{B}|\cos\theta = \frac{|\mathbf{A}|^2 + |\mathbf{B}|^2 - |\mathbf{C}|^2}{2}. \tag{5}$$

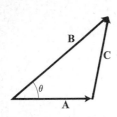

11–31 Equation (6) is obtained by applying the law of cosines to a triangle whose sides represent $\mathbf{A}$, $\mathbf{B}$, and $\mathbf{C} = \mathbf{B} - \mathbf{A}$.

The left side of this equation is $\mathbf{A} \cdot \mathbf{B}$, and we may calculate all terms on the right side of (5) by applying Eq. (3) of Article 11–5 to find the lengths of $\mathbf{A}$, $\mathbf{B}$, and $\mathbf{C}$. The result of this algebra is the formula

$$\mathbf{A} \cdot \mathbf{B} = a_1 b_1 + a_2 b_2 + a_3 b_3. \tag{6}$$

Thus, to find the scalar product of two given vectors we multiply their *corresponding* components together and add the results.

EXAMPLE 1.   Find the angle θ between $\mathbf{A} = \mathbf{i} - 2\mathbf{j} - 2\mathbf{k}$ and $\mathbf{B} = 6\mathbf{i} + 3\mathbf{j} + 2\mathbf{k}$. Also, find the component of $\mathbf{B}$ in the direction of $\mathbf{A}$.

Solution

$$\mathbf{A} \cdot \mathbf{B} = 6 - 6 - 4 = -4$$

from Eq. (6), while

$$\mathbf{A} \cdot \mathbf{B} = |\mathbf{A}||\mathbf{B}|\cos\theta$$

from Eq. (1). Since $|\mathbf{A}| = \sqrt{1 + 4 + 4} = 3$ and $|\mathbf{B}| = \sqrt{36 + 9 + 4} = 7$, we have

$$\cos\theta = \frac{\mathbf{A} \cdot \mathbf{B}}{|\mathbf{A}||\mathbf{B}|} = \frac{-4}{21},$$

$$\theta = \cos^{-1}\frac{-4}{21} \approx 101°.$$

The component of $\mathbf{B}$ in the direction of $\mathbf{A}$ is

$$\frac{\mathbf{A} \cdot \mathbf{B}}{|\mathbf{A}|} = -\frac{4}{3}.$$

This is the negative of the length of the vector projection of $\mathbf{B}$ onto $\mathbf{A}$.

From Eq. (6), it is readily seen that if

$$\mathbf{C} = c_1\mathbf{i} + c_2\mathbf{j} + c_3\mathbf{k}$$

is any third vector, then

$$A \cdot (B + C) = a_1(b_1 + c_1) + a_2(b_2 + c_2) + a_3(b_3 + c_3)$$

$$= (a_1 b_1 + a_2 b_2 + a_3 b_3) + (a_1 c_1 + a_2 c_2 + a_3 c_3)$$

$$= A \cdot B + A \cdot C.$$

Hence scalar multiplication obeys the *distributive* law:

$$A \cdot (B + C) = A \cdot B + A \cdot C. \tag{7}$$

If we combine this with the commutative law, Eq. (2), it is also evident that

$$(A + B) \cdot C = A \cdot C + B \cdot C. \tag{8}$$

Equations (7) and (8) together permit us to multiply sums of vectors by the familiar laws of algebra. For example,

$$(A + B) \cdot (C + D) = A \cdot C + A \cdot D + B \cdot C + B \cdot D. \tag{9}$$

Orthogonal Vectors

It is clear from Eq. (1) that the dot product of two vectors is zero when the vectors are perpendicular, since $\cos 90° = 0$. Conversely, if $A \cdot B = 0$ then one of the vectors is zero or else the vectors are perpendicular. The zero vector has no specified direction, and we can adopt the convention that it is perpendicular to any vector. Then we can say that $A \cdot B = 0$ if and only if the vectors A and B are perpendicular. Perpendicular vectors are also said to be *orthogonal*.

If the scalar product is negative, then $\cos \theta$ is negative and the angle between the vectors is greater than 90°.

If $B = A$, then $\theta = 0$ and $\cos \theta = 1$, so that $A \cdot A = |A|^2$.

EXAMPLE 2. Write the vector B as the sum of a vector B_1 parallel to A and a vector B_2 perpendicular to A (Fig. 11–32).

Solution. Let

$$B = B_1 + B_2,$$

with $B_1 = cA$ and $B_2 \cdot A = 0$. Then, substituting cA for B_1, we have

$$B = cA + B_2$$

and

$$0 = B_2 \cdot A = (B - cA) \cdot A = B \cdot A - c(A \cdot A)$$

or

$$c = \frac{B \cdot A}{A \cdot A}.$$

Then

$$B_2 = B - B_1 = B - cA = B - \frac{B \cdot A}{A \cdot A} A$$

is perpendicular to A because c was chosen to make $B_2 \cdot A = 0$.

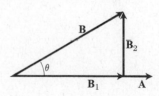

11–32 The vector B as the sum of vectors parallel and perpendicular to A.

For example, if

$$\mathbf{B} = 2\mathbf{i} + \mathbf{j} - 3\mathbf{k} \qquad \text{and} \qquad \mathbf{A} = 3\mathbf{i} - \mathbf{j},$$

then

$$c = \frac{\mathbf{B} \cdot \mathbf{A}}{\mathbf{A} \cdot \mathbf{A}} = \frac{6-1}{9+1} = \frac{1}{2},$$

and

$$\mathbf{B}_1 = \tfrac{1}{2}\mathbf{A} = \tfrac{3}{2}\mathbf{i} - \tfrac{1}{2}\mathbf{j}$$

is parallel to **A**, while

$$\mathbf{B}_2 = \mathbf{B} - \mathbf{B}_1 = \tfrac{1}{2}\mathbf{i} + \tfrac{3}{2}\mathbf{j} - 3\mathbf{k}$$

is perpendicular to **A**.

EXAMPLE 3. Show that the vector $\mathbf{N} = a\mathbf{i} + b\mathbf{j}$ is perpendicular to the line $ax + by = c$ in the xy-plane (Fig. 11–33).

Solution. Let $P_1(x_1, y_1)$ and $P_2(x_2, y_2)$ be any two points on the line; that is,

$$ax_1 + by_1 = c, \qquad ax_2 + by_2 = c.$$

By subtraction, we eliminate c and obtain

$$a(x_2 - x_1) + b(y_2 - y_1) = 0,$$

or

$$(a\mathbf{i} + b\mathbf{j}) \cdot [(x_2 - x_1)\mathbf{i} + (y_2 - y_1)\mathbf{j}] = \mathbf{0}. \qquad \textbf{(10)}$$

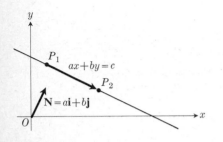

11–33 The vector $\mathbf{N} = a\mathbf{i} + b\mathbf{j}$ is normal to the line $ax + by = c$. Example 3 explains why.

Now $(x_2 - x_1)\mathbf{i} + (y_2 - y_1)\mathbf{j} = \overrightarrow{P_1 P_2}$ is a vector joining two points on the line, while $\mathbf{N} = a\mathbf{i} + b\mathbf{j}$ is the given vector. Equation (10) says that either $\mathbf{N} = \mathbf{0}$, or $\overrightarrow{P_1 P_2} = \mathbf{0}$, or else $\mathbf{N} \perp \overrightarrow{P_1 P_2}$. But $ax + by = c$ is assumed to be an honest equation of a straight line, so that a and b are not both zero and $\mathbf{N} \neq \mathbf{0}$. Furthermore, we may surely choose P_2 different from P_1 on the line to make $\overrightarrow{P_1 P_2} \neq \mathbf{0}$. Hence $\mathbf{N} \perp \overrightarrow{P_1 P_2}$.

For example, $\mathbf{N} = 2\mathbf{i} - 3\mathbf{j}$ is normal to the line $2x - 3y = 5$.

EXAMPLE 4. Using vector methods, find the distance d between the point $P(4, 3)$ and the line L: $x + 3y = 6$ (Fig. 11–34).

Solution. The line cuts the y-axis at $B(0, 2)$. At B, draw the vector

$$\mathbf{N} = \mathbf{i} + 3\mathbf{j}$$

normal to L (see Example 3). Then the distance between P and L is the component of $\overrightarrow{BP}$ in the direction of **N**. Since

$$\overrightarrow{BP} = (4 - 0)\mathbf{i} + (3 - 2)\mathbf{j} = 4\mathbf{i} + \mathbf{j},$$

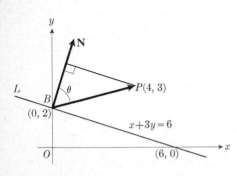

11–34 The distance from P to line L is the length of the vector projection of $\overrightarrow{BP}$ onto **N**.

we have

$$d = \text{proj}_{\mathbf{N}} \overrightarrow{BP} = \frac{\mathbf{N} \cdot \overrightarrow{BP}}{|\mathbf{N}|} = \frac{4 + 3}{\sqrt{10}} = \frac{7\sqrt{10}}{10}.$$

The dot product is useful in mechanics, where it is used in calculating the work done by a force **F** when the point of application of **F** undergoes a displacement $\overrightarrow{AB}$. If the force remains constant in direction and magnitude, this work is given by (Fig. 11–35)

$$\text{Work} = (|\mathbf{F}| \cos \theta)|\overrightarrow{AB}|$$
$$= \mathbf{F} \cdot \overrightarrow{AB}.$$

The concept of work also enters into the study of electricity and magnetism and the scalar product again plays a basic role. (See Sears, Zemansky, Young, *University Physics* (1976), Chapter 26.)

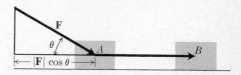

11–35 The work done by **F** during a displacement $\overrightarrow{AB}$ is $\mathbf{F} \cdot \mathbf{AB} = (|F| \cos \theta)|\overrightarrow{AB}|$.

PROBLEMS

1. Suppose it is known that $\mathbf{A} \cdot \mathbf{B}_1 = \mathbf{A} \cdot \mathbf{B}_2$, and **A** is not zero, but nothing more is known about the vectors $\mathbf{B}_1$ and $\mathbf{B}_2$. Is it permissible to cancel **A** from both sides of the equation? Give a reason for your answer.

2. (a) Express the vector projection of **B** onto **A** in a vector form that is convenient for calculation. (b) Find the vector projection of $\mathbf{B} = \mathbf{i} + 3\mathbf{j} + 4\mathbf{k}$ onto the vector $\mathbf{A} = 10\mathbf{i} + 11\mathbf{j} - 2\mathbf{k}$.

3. Find the interior angles of the triangle ABC whose vertices are the points $A(-1, 0, 2)$, $B(2, 1, -1)$, and $C(1, -2, 2)$.

4. Find the point $A(a, a, 0)$ on the line $y = x$ in the xy-plane such that the vector $\overrightarrow{AB}$ is perpendicular to the line OA. Here O is the origin and B is the point $(2, 4, -3)$.

5. Find the scalar projection of the vector $\mathbf{A} = 2\mathbf{i} + 2\mathbf{j} + \mathbf{k}$ onto the vector $\mathbf{B} = 2\mathbf{i} + 10\mathbf{j} - 11\mathbf{k}$.

6. Find the angle between the diagonal of a cube and one of its edges.

7. Find the angle between the diagonal of a cube and a diagonal of one of its faces.

8. Find the angle between vectors **A** and **B** of Problem 5.

9. How many lines through the origin make angles of $60°$ with both the y- and z-axes? What angles do they make with the positive x-axis?

10. If $a = |\mathbf{A}|$ and $b = |\mathbf{B}|$, show that the vector

$$\mathbf{C} = \frac{a\mathbf{B} + b\mathbf{A}}{a + b}$$

bisects the angle between **A** and **B**.

11. With the same notation as in Problem 10, show that the vectors $a\mathbf{B} + b\mathbf{A}$ and $\mathbf{A}b - \mathbf{B}a$ are perpendicular.

12. If **R** is the vector from the origin O to $P(x, y, z)$ and **k** is the unit vector along the z-axis, show geometrically that the equation

$$\frac{\mathbf{R} \cdot \mathbf{k}}{|\mathbf{R}|} = \cos 45°$$

represents a cone with vertex at the origin and generating angle of $45°$. Express the equation in cartesian form.

13. Find the work done by a force $\mathbf{F} = -w\mathbf{k}$ as its point of application moves from the point $P_1(x_1, y_1, z_1)$ to a second point $P_2(x_2, y_2, z_2)$ along the straight line $P_1 P_2$.

14. Using vector methods, show that the distance d between the point (x_1, y_1) and the line $ax + by + c = 0$ is

$$d = \frac{|ax_1 + by_1 + c|}{\sqrt{a^2 + b^2}}.$$

15. *Direction cosines.* If the vector $\mathbf{A} = a\mathbf{i} + b\mathbf{j} + c\mathbf{k}$ makes angles α, β, and γ, respectively, with the positive x-, y-, and z-axes, then $\cos \alpha$, $\cos \beta$, $\cos \gamma$ are called its *direction cosines*. Show that

a) $\cos \alpha = \dfrac{a}{\sqrt{a^2 + b^2 + c^2}}$,

$\cos \beta = \dfrac{b}{\sqrt{a^2 + b^2 + c^2}}$,

$\cos \gamma = \dfrac{c}{\sqrt{a^2 + b^2 + c^2}}$;

b) $\cos^2 \alpha + \cos^2 \beta + \cos^2 \gamma = 1$;

c) $\mathbf{u} = \mathbf{i} \cos \alpha + \mathbf{j} \cos \beta + \mathbf{k} \cos \gamma$ is a unit vector having the same direction as **A**.

16. Show that scalar multiplication is *positive definite*; that is, $\mathbf{A} \cdot \mathbf{A} \geq 0$ for every vector **A**, and $\mathbf{A} \cdot \mathbf{A} = 0$ if and only if **A** is the zero vector.

17. Show that if r is a scalar, then $(r\mathbf{A}) \cdot \mathbf{B} = r(\mathbf{A} \cdot \mathbf{B})$.

18. In Fig. 11–2 it looks as if $\mathbf{v}_1 + \mathbf{v}_2$ and $\mathbf{v}_1 - \mathbf{v}_2$ are orthogonal. Is this mere coincidence, or are there circumstances under which we may expect the sum of two vectors to be perpendicular to the difference of the same two vectors? Find out by expanding the left side of the equation

$$(\mathbf{v}_1 + \mathbf{v}_2) \cdot (\mathbf{v}_1 - \mathbf{v}_2) = 0.$$

11-7

THE VECTOR PRODUCT OF
TWO VECTORS IN SPACE

Two nonzero vectors **A** and **B** in space may be subjected to parallel displacements, if necessary, to bring their initial points into coincidence. Suppose that this has been done and let θ be the angle from **A** to **B**, with $0 \leq \theta \leq \pi$. Then, unless **A** and **B** are parallel, they now determine a plane. Let **n** be a unit vector perpendicular to this plane and pointing in the direction a right-threaded screw advances when its head is rotated from **A** to **B** through the angle θ. The *vector product*, or *cross product*, of **A** and **B**, in that order, is then defined by the equation (Fig. 11-36(a))

$$\mathbf{A} \times \mathbf{B} = \mathbf{n}\,|\mathbf{A}|\,|\mathbf{B}|\,\sin\theta. \qquad (1)$$

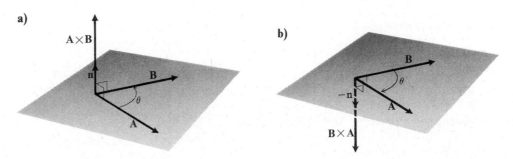

11-36   **A** × **B** and **B** × **A** have the same magnitude but point in opposite directions from the plane of **A** and **B**.

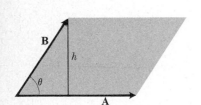

11-37   The area of the parallelogram is $|\mathbf{A} \times \mathbf{B}|$.

Like the definition of the scalar product of two vectors, given in Article 11-6, the definition of the vector product given here is coordinate-free. We emphasize, however, that the vector product **A** × **B** is a *vector*, while the scalar product **A** · **B** is a *scalar*. (Applications of the cross product to electricity and magnetism are discussed in Sears, Zemansky, Young, *University Physics* (1976), Chapters 26 and 30.)

If **A** and **B** are parallel, then $\theta = 0$ or $180°$ and $\sin\theta = 0$, so that **A** × **B** = 0. In this case, the direction of **n** is not determined, but this is immaterial, since the zero vector has no specific direction. In all other cases, however, **n** is determined and the cross product is a vector having the same direction as **n** and having magnitude equal to the area, $|\mathbf{A}|\,|\mathbf{B}|\,\sin\theta$, of the parallelogram determined by the vectors **A** and **B** (Fig. 11-37).

If the order of the factors **A** and **B** is reversed in the construction of the cross product, the direction of the unit vector perpendicular to their plane is reversed (Fig. 11-36(b)). This is because the righthanded screw that turns through θ from **B** to **A** points the other way. The original unit vector **n** is now replaced by $-\mathbf{n}$, with the result that

$$\mathbf{B} \times \mathbf{A} = -\mathbf{A} \times \mathbf{B}. \qquad (2)$$

Thus, cross product multiplication is not commutative. Reversing the order of the factors changes the product.

When the definition is applied to the unit vectors **i**, **j**, and **k**, one readily finds that

$$i \times j = -j \times i = k,$$
$$j \times k = -k \times j = i, \tag{3}$$
$$k \times i = -i \times k = j,$$

while

$$i \times i = j \times j = k \times k = 0.$$

Our next objective is to express $A \times B$ in terms of the components of A and B. First we note that the associative law

$$(rA) \times (sB) = (rs)A \times B, \tag{4}$$

follows from the geometric meaning of the cross product. Secondly, we adopt a geometric argument to establish the distributive law

$$A \times (B + C) = A \times B + A \times C. \tag{5}$$

Proof. To see that Eq. (5) is valid, we interpret the cross product $A \times B$ in a slightly different way. The vectors A and B are drawn from the common point O and a plane M is constructed perpendicular to A at O (Fig. 11–38). Vector B is now projected orthogonally onto M, yielding a vector B' whose length is $|B| \sin \theta$. The vector B' is then rotated 90° about A in the positive sense to produce a vector B''. Finally, B'' is multiplied by the length of A. The resulting vector $|A|B''$ is equal to $A \times B$ since B'' has the same direction as n by its construction (Fig. 11–38) and

$$|A||B''| = |A||B'| = |A||B| \sin \theta = |A \times B|.$$

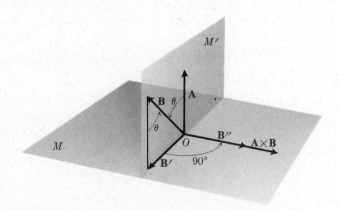

11–38 For reasons explained above, $A \times B = |A|B''$.

Now each of these three operations, namely,

 1. projection onto M,
 2. rotation about A through 90°,
 3. multiplication by the scalar $|A|$,

when applied to a triangle, will produce another triangle. If we start with the triangle whose sides are **B**, **C**, and **B** + **C** (Fig. 11–39) and apply these three steps, we successively obtain:

1. a triangle whose sides are **B′**, **C′**, and (**B** + **C**)′ satisfying the vector equation

$$\mathbf{B}' + \mathbf{C}' = (\mathbf{B} + \mathbf{C})';$$

2. a triangle whose sides are **B″**, **C″**, and (**B** + **C**)″ satisfying the vector equation

$$\mathbf{B}'' + \mathbf{C}'' = (\mathbf{B} + \mathbf{C})'';$$

(the double-prime on each vector has the same meaning as in Fig. 11–38); and finally,

3. a triangle whose sides are $|\mathbf{A}|\mathbf{B}''$, $|\mathbf{A}|\mathbf{C}''$, and $|\mathbf{A}|(\mathbf{B}+\mathbf{C})''$ satisfying the vector equation

$$|\mathbf{A}|\mathbf{B}'' + |\mathbf{A}|\mathbf{C}'' = |\mathbf{A}|(\mathbf{B}+\mathbf{C})''. \tag{6}$$

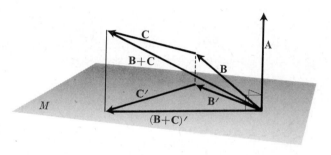

11–39 The vectors of Eq. (7) projected onto a plane perpendicular to **A**.

When we use the equations $|\mathbf{A}|\mathbf{B}'' = \mathbf{A} \times \mathbf{B}$, $|\mathbf{A}|\mathbf{C}'' = \mathbf{A} \times \mathbf{C}$ and $|\mathbf{A}|(\mathbf{B}+\mathbf{C})'' = \mathbf{A} \times (\mathbf{B}+\mathbf{C})$, which result from our discussion above, Eq. (6) becomes

$$\mathbf{A} \times \mathbf{B} + \mathbf{A} \times \mathbf{C} = \mathbf{A} \times (\mathbf{B}+\mathbf{C}),$$

which is the distributive law, (5), that we wanted to establish.

The companion law

$$(\mathbf{B} + \mathbf{C}) \times \mathbf{A} = \mathbf{B} \times \mathbf{A} + \mathbf{C} \times \mathbf{A} \tag{7}$$

now follows at once from Eq. (5) if we multiply both sides of Eq. (5) by minus one and take account of the fact that interchanging the two factors in a cross product changes the sign of the result.

From Eqs. (4), (5), and (7), we may conclude that cross-product multiplication of vectors follows the ordinary laws of algebra, *except that the order of the factors is not reversible.* If we apply these results to calculate **A** × **B** with

$$\mathbf{A} = a_1\mathbf{i} + a_2\mathbf{j} + a_3\mathbf{k},$$

$$\mathbf{B} = b_1\mathbf{i} + b_2\mathbf{j} + b_3\mathbf{k},$$

we obtain

$$\mathbf{A} \times \mathbf{B} = (a_1\mathbf{i} + a_2\mathbf{j} + a_3\mathbf{k}) \times (b_1\mathbf{i} + b_2\mathbf{j} + b_3\mathbf{k})$$

$$= a_1 b_1 \mathbf{i} \times \mathbf{i} + a_1 b_2 \mathbf{i} \times \mathbf{j} + a_1 b_3 \mathbf{i} \times \mathbf{k} + a_2 b_1 \mathbf{j} \times \mathbf{i}$$

$$+ a_2 b_2 \mathbf{j} \times \mathbf{j} + a_2 b_3 \mathbf{j} \times \mathbf{k} + a_3 b_1 \mathbf{k} \times \mathbf{i}$$

$$+ a_3 b_2 \mathbf{k} \times \mathbf{j} + a_3 b_3 \mathbf{k} \times \mathbf{k}$$

$$= \mathbf{i}(a_2 b_3 - a_3 b_2) + \mathbf{j}(a_3 b_1 - a_1 b_3) + \mathbf{k}(a_1 b_2 - a_2 b_1), \qquad \textbf{(8)}$$

where Eqs. (3) have been used to evaluate the products $\mathbf{i} \times \mathbf{i} = 0$, $\mathbf{i} \times \mathbf{j} = \mathbf{k}$, etc. The terms on the right side of Eq. (8) are the same as the terms in the expansion of the third-order determinant below, so that the cross product may conveniently be calculated from the equation

$$\mathbf{A} \times \mathbf{B} = \begin{vmatrix} \mathbf{i} & \mathbf{j} & \mathbf{k} \\ a_1 & a_2 & a_3 \\ b_1 & b_2 & b_3 \end{vmatrix}. \qquad \textbf{(9)}$$

EXAMPLE 1. Find the area of the triangle whose vertices are $A(1, -1, 0)$, $B(2, 1, -1)$, and $C(-1, 1, 2)$ (Fig. 11–40).

Solution. Two sides of the given triangle are represented by the vectors

$$\mathbf{a} = \overrightarrow{AB} = (2 - 1)\mathbf{i} + (1 + 1)\mathbf{j} + (-1 - 0)\mathbf{k} = \mathbf{i} + 2\mathbf{j} - \mathbf{k},$$

$$\mathbf{b} = \overrightarrow{AC} = (-1 - 1)\mathbf{i} + (1 + 1)\mathbf{j} + (2 - 0)\mathbf{k} = -2\mathbf{i} + 2\mathbf{j} + 2\mathbf{k}.$$

The area of the triangle is one-half the area of the parallelogram represented by these vectors. The area of the parallelogram is the magnitude of the vector

$$\mathbf{c} = \mathbf{a} \times \mathbf{b} = \begin{vmatrix} \mathbf{i} & \mathbf{j} & \mathbf{k} \\ 1 & 2 & -1 \\ -2 & 2 & 2 \end{vmatrix}$$

$$= \mathbf{i} \begin{vmatrix} 2 & -1 \\ 2 & 2 \end{vmatrix} - \mathbf{j} \begin{vmatrix} 1 & -1 \\ -2 & 2 \end{vmatrix} + \mathbf{k} \begin{vmatrix} 1 & 2 \\ -2 & 2 \end{vmatrix} = 6\mathbf{i} + 6\mathbf{k},$$

which is $|\mathbf{c}| = \sqrt{6^2 + 6^2} = 6\sqrt{2}$. Therefore, the area of the triangle is $\frac{1}{2}|\mathbf{a} \times \mathbf{b}| = 3\sqrt{2}$.

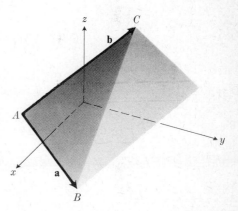

11–40 The area of $\triangle ABC$ is half of $|\mathbf{a} \times \mathbf{b}|$.

EXAMPLE 2. Find a unit vector perpendicular to both $\mathbf{A} = 2\mathbf{i} + \mathbf{j} - \mathbf{k}$ and $\mathbf{B} = \mathbf{i} - \mathbf{j} + 2\mathbf{k}$.

Solution. The vector $\mathbf{N} = \mathbf{A} \times \mathbf{B}$ is perpendicular to both $\mathbf{A}$ and $\mathbf{B}$. We divide $\mathbf{N}$ by $|\mathbf{N}|$ to obtain a unit vector $\mathbf{u}$ that has the same direction as $\mathbf{N}$:

$$\mathbf{u} = \frac{\mathbf{N}}{|\mathbf{N}|} = \frac{\mathbf{A} \times \mathbf{B}}{|\mathbf{A} \times \mathbf{B}|} = \frac{\mathbf{i} - 5\mathbf{j} - 3\mathbf{k}}{\sqrt{1^2 + (-5)^2 + (-3)^2}} = \frac{\mathbf{i} - 5\mathbf{j} - 3\mathbf{k}}{\sqrt{35}}.$$

Either $\mathbf{u}$ or its negative will do.

PROBLEMS

1. Find $\mathbf{A} \times \mathbf{B}$ if $\mathbf{A} = 2\mathbf{i} - 2\mathbf{j} - \mathbf{k}$, $\mathbf{B} = \mathbf{i} + \mathbf{j} + \mathbf{k}$.

2. Find a vector $\mathbf{N}$ perpendicular to the plane determined by the points $A(1, -1, 2)$, $B(2, 0, -1)$, and $C(0, 2, 1)$.

3. Find the area of the triangle ABC of Problem 2.

4. Find the distance between the origin and the plane ABC of Problem 2 by projecting $\overrightarrow{OA}$ onto the normal vector $\mathbf{N}$.

5. Find a vector that is perpendicular to both of the vectors $\mathbf{A} = \mathbf{i} + \mathbf{j} + \mathbf{k}$ and $\mathbf{B} = \mathbf{i} + \mathbf{j}$.

6. Vectors from the origin to the points A, B, C are given by $\mathbf{A} = \mathbf{i} - \mathbf{j} + \mathbf{k}$, $\mathbf{B} = 2\mathbf{i} + 3\mathbf{j} - \mathbf{k}$, $\mathbf{C} = -\mathbf{i} + 2\mathbf{j} + 2\mathbf{k}$. Find all points $P(x, y, z)$ that satisfy the following requirements: $\overrightarrow{OP}$ is a unit vector perpendicular to $\mathbf{C}$ and P lies in the plane determined by $\mathbf{A}$ and $\mathbf{B}$.

7. Using vector methods, find the distance between the line L_1 determined by the two points $A(1, 0, -1)$, $B(-1, 1, 0)$ and the line L_2 determined by the points $C(3, 1, -1)$, $D(4, 5, -2)$. The distance is to be measured along a line perpendicular to both L_1 and L_2.

8. $\mathbf{A} = 3\mathbf{i} + \mathbf{j} - \mathbf{k}$ is normal to a plane M_1 and $\mathbf{B} = 2\mathbf{i} - \mathbf{j} + \mathbf{k}$ is normal to a second plane M_2. (a) Find the angle between the two normals. (b) Do the two planes intersect? Give a reason for your answer. (c) If the two planes do intersect, find a vector parallel to their line of intersection.

9. Let $\mathbf{A}$ be a nonzero vector. Show that (a) $\mathbf{A} \times \mathbf{B} = \mathbf{A} \times \mathbf{C}$ does not guarantee $\mathbf{B} = \mathbf{C}$ (see Problem 1, Article 11–6); (b) $\mathbf{A} \cdot \mathbf{B} = \mathbf{A} \cdot \mathbf{C}$ and $\mathbf{A} \times \mathbf{B} = \mathbf{A} \times \mathbf{C}$ together imply $\mathbf{B} = \mathbf{C}$.

11-8

EQUATIONS OF LINES AND PLANES

Lines

Suppose L is a line in space that passes through a given point $P_1(x_1, y_1, z_1)$ and is parallel to a given nonzero vector

$$\mathbf{v} = A\mathbf{i} + B\mathbf{j} + C\mathbf{k}.$$

Then L is the set of all points $P(x, y, z)$ for which the vector $\overrightarrow{P_1 P}$ is parallel to the given vector $\mathbf{v}$ (Fig. 11–41).

That is, P is on the line L if and only if there is a scalar t such that

$$\overrightarrow{P_1 P} = t\mathbf{v}. \tag{1}$$

When we separate the components in Eq. (1), we have

$$x - x_1 = tA, \qquad y - y_1 = tB, \qquad z - z_1 = tC. \tag{2}$$

These equations are parametric equations for the line. If we allow t to vary from $-\infty$ to $+\infty$, the point $P(x, y, z)$ given by Eqs. (2) will traverse the line L through P_1.

We may eliminate t from the equations in (2) to obtain the following cartesian equations for the line:

$$\frac{x - x_1}{A} = \frac{y - y_1}{B} = \frac{z - z_1}{C}. \tag{3}$$

If any one of the constants A, B, or C is zero in Eqs. (3), the corresponding numerator is also zero. This follows at once from the parametric form, Eqs. (2), which shows, for example, that

$$x - x_1 = tA \qquad \text{and} \qquad A = 0$$

together imply that

$$x - x_1 = 0.$$

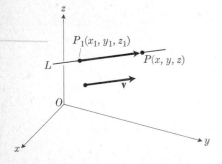

11–41 P is on the line through P_1 parallel to $\mathbf{v}$ if and only if $\overrightarrow{P_1 P}$ is a scalar multiple of $\mathbf{v}$.

Thus, when one of the denominators in Eqs. (3) is zero, we interpret the equations to say that the corresponding numerator is zero. With this interpretation, Eqs. (3) may always be used.

Planes

To obtain an equation for a *plane*, we suppose that a point $P_1(x_1, y_1, z_1)$ on the plane and a nonzero vector

$$\mathbf{N} = A\mathbf{i} + B\mathbf{j} + C\mathbf{k} \qquad (4)$$

perpendicular to the plane are given (Fig. 11-42). Then the point $P(x, y, z)$ will lie in the plane if and only if the vector $\overrightarrow{P_1 P}$ is perpendicular to $\mathbf{N}$; that is, if and only if

$$\mathbf{N} \cdot \overrightarrow{P_1 P} = 0$$

or

$$A(x - x_1) + B(y - y_1) + C(z - z_1) = 0. \qquad (5)$$

This equation may also be put in the form

$$Ax + By + Cz = D, \qquad (6)$$

where D is the constant $Ax_1 + By_1 + Cz_1$. Conversely, if we start from any linear equation such as (6), we may find a point $P_1(x_1, y_1, z_1)$ whose coordinates do satisfy it; that is, such that

$$Ax_1 + By_1 + Cz_1 = D.$$

Then, by subtraction, we may put the given equation (6) into the form of Eq. (5) and factor it into the dot product

$$\mathbf{N} \cdot \overrightarrow{P_1 P} = 0,$$

with $\mathbf{N}$ as in Eq. (4). This says that the constant vector $\mathbf{N}$ is perpendicular to the vector $\overrightarrow{P_1 P}$ for every pair of points P_1 and P whose coordinates satisfy the equation. Hence the set of points $P(x, y, z)$ whose coordinates satisfy such a linear equation is a plane and the vector $A\mathbf{i} + B\mathbf{j} + C\mathbf{k}$, with the same coefficients that x, y, and z have in the given equation, is normal to the plane.

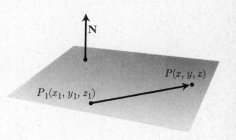

11-42 P lies in the plane through P_1 perpendicular to $\mathbf{N}$ if and only if $\overrightarrow{P_1 P} \cdot \mathbf{N} = 0$.

EXAMPLE 1. Find the distance d between the point $P(2, -3, 4)$ and the plane $x + 2y + 2z = 13$.

Solution 1. Carry out the following steps:

First. Find a line L through P normal to the plane.

Second. Find the coordinates of the point Q in which the line meets the plane.

Third. Compute the distance between P and Q.

The vector $\mathbf{N} = \mathbf{i} + 2\mathbf{j} + 2\mathbf{k}$ is normal to the given plane, and the line

$$L: \quad \frac{x - 2}{1} = \frac{y + 3}{2} = \frac{z - 4}{2}$$

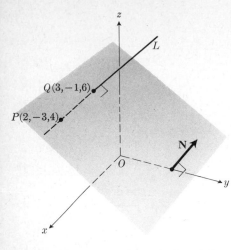

11–43 The distance between P and the plane is the distance between P and Q.

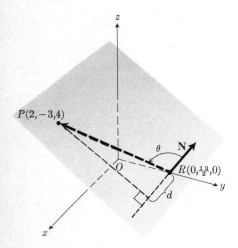

11–44 $d = -\text{proj}_{\mathbf{N}}\ \vec{RP}$.

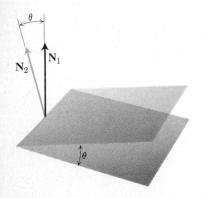

11–45 The angle between two planes can be obtained from their normals.

goes through P and is parallel to $\mathbf{N}$. Hence L is normal to the plane.

If we denote the common ratio in the equations for L by t,

$$\frac{x - 2}{1} = \frac{y + 3}{2} = \frac{z - 4}{2} = t,$$

we have

$$x = t + 2, \qquad y = 2t - 3, \qquad z = 2t + 4$$

as parametric equations of the line in terms of the parameter t. Substituting these into the equation of the plane, we obtain

$$(t + 2) + 2(2t - 3) + 2(2t + 4) = 13,$$

or $t = 1$ at the point of intersection of the plane and the line L. That is, $Q(3, -1, 6)$ is the point of intersection.

The distance between the point and the plane is the distance between $P(2, -3, 4)$ and $Q(3, -1, 6)$ (Fig. 11–43). Hence

$$d = \sqrt{(3 - 2)^2 + (-1 + 3)^2 + (6 - 4)^2} = 3.$$

Solution 2. Let R be any point in the plane, and find the component of $\vec{RP}$ in the direction of $\mathbf{N}$. This will be plus d or minus d, the sign depending on the direction of the vector projection of $\vec{RP}$ onto $\mathbf{N}$. Figure 11–44 shows that the component is negative in this case, but we do not need to know this to find d.

Since R can be any point in the given plane, we might as well choose R to be a point whose coordinates are simple, say the point $R(0, \frac{13}{2}, 0)$ where the plane meets the y-axis. Then,

$$\vec{RP} = (2 - 0)\mathbf{i} + (-3 - \tfrac{13}{2})\mathbf{j} + (4 - 0)\mathbf{k}$$
$$= 2\mathbf{i} - \tfrac{19}{2}\mathbf{j} + 4\mathbf{k}.$$

The component of $\vec{RP}$ in the direction of $\mathbf{N} = \mathbf{i} + 2\mathbf{j} + 2\mathbf{k}$ is

$$\frac{\mathbf{N} \cdot \vec{RP}}{|\mathbf{N}|} = \frac{2 - 19 + 8}{\sqrt{(1)^2 + (2)^2 + (2)^2}} = \frac{-9}{\sqrt{9}} = -3.$$

Therefore, $d = 3$.

EXAMPLE 2. Find the angle between the two planes $3x - 6y - 2z = 7$ and $2x + y - 2z = 5$.

Solution. Clearly the angle between two planes (Fig. 11–45) is the same as the angle between their normals. (Actually there are two angles in each case, namely θ and $180° - \theta$.) From the equations of the planes we may read off their normal vectors:

$$\mathbf{N}_1 = 3\mathbf{i} - 6\mathbf{j} - 2\mathbf{k}, \qquad \mathbf{N}_2 = 2\mathbf{i} + \mathbf{j} - 2\mathbf{k}.$$

Then

$$\cos \theta = \frac{\mathbf{N}_1 \cdot \mathbf{N}_2}{|\mathbf{N}_1|\,|\mathbf{N}_2|} = \frac{4}{21}, \qquad \theta = \cos^{-1}\left(\frac{4}{21}\right) \approx 79°.$$

EXAMPLE 3. Find a vector parallel to the line of intersection of the two planes in Example 2.

Solution. The requirements are met by the vector

$$\mathbf{v} = \mathbf{N}_1 \times \mathbf{N}_2 = \begin{vmatrix} \mathbf{i} & \mathbf{j} & \mathbf{k} \\ 3 & -6 & -2 \\ 2 & 1 & -2 \end{vmatrix} = 14\mathbf{i} + 2\mathbf{j} + 15\mathbf{k}.$$

The vector $\mathbf{v}$ is perpendicular to both of the normals $\mathbf{N}_1$ and $\mathbf{N}_2$, and is therefore parallel to both planes.

The equations of two intersecting planes in space are satisfied simultaneously by the coordinates of all and only those points that lie on the line of intersection of the two planes. Hence, a pair of simultaneous linear equations may be interpreted as equations for a line. For example, recall the Eqs. (3),

$$\frac{x - x_1}{A} = \frac{y - y_1}{B} = \frac{z - z_1}{C},$$

which we found for the line L through the point $P_1(x_1, y_1, z_1)$ and parallel to the vector $\mathbf{v} = A\mathbf{i} + B\mathbf{j} + C\mathbf{k}$. This is equivalent to the three simultaneous equations

$$\begin{aligned} B(x - x_1) &= A(y - y_1), \\ C(x - x_1) &= A(z - z_1), \\ C(y - y_1) &= B(z - z_1). \end{aligned} \tag{7}$$

Each of these equations represents a plane. Any pair of them represents the line of intersection of the corresponding pair of planes. There are three such pairs of planes, namely 1st and 2nd, 1st and 3rd, 2nd and 3rd. But the three lines of intersection so determined are all identical; that is, there is just *one* line of intersection.

To see that this is so, we consider three separate cases.

CASE 1. If any two of the three coefficients A, B, C are zero and the third one is different from zero, then one of the three equations in (7) reduces to $0 = 0$, which imposes no restriction on (x, y, z), while the other two equations represent two planes that intersect in a common line.

CASE 2. If only one of the coefficients is zero, say $A = 0$ and $BC \neq 0$, then the first two of Eqs. (7) say simply that $x = x_1$. These two equations thus represent just one plane and the intersection of this plane with the plane

$$C(y - y_1) = B(z - z_1)$$

is the line L.

CASE 3. If $A \neq 0$, we may multiply the first equation in (7) by C/A and the second by B/A and subtract one from the other to obtain the third equation in (7). Thus we might just as well ignore the third equation, since it contains no new information.

In all cases, we see that the three Eqs. (7) reduce to just two independent equations, and the three planes intersect in one straight line.

The Eqs. (3) for a line are said to be in *standard form*.

EXAMPLE 4. Write a standard form equation for the line determined by the planes of Example 2.

Solution. First find the coordinates of a point common to both planes, say $(9, 1, 7)$. Then obtain the A, B, and C of Eqs. (3') from the coefficients of $\mathbf{v} = \mathbf{N}_1 \times \mathbf{N}_2 = 14\mathbf{i} + 2\mathbf{j} + 15\mathbf{k}$. Finally, substitute all these values in Eqs. (3) to obtain

$$\frac{x-9}{14} = \frac{y-1}{2} = \frac{z-7}{15}.$$

EXAMPLE 5. Find an equation of the plane that passes through the two points $P_1(1, 0, -1)$ and $P_2(-1, 2, 1)$ and is parallel to the line of intersection of the planes $3x + y - 2z = 6$ and $4x - y + 3z = 0$.

Solution. The coordinates of either one of the points P_1 or P_2 will do for the x_1, x_2, and x_3 in Eq. (5). What remains, then, is to find a vector $\mathbf{N}$ normal to the plane in question to furnish the coefficients A, B, and C of Eq. (5) (Fig. 11–46).

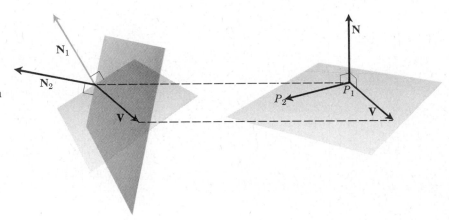

11–46 Constructing a plane through P_1 and P_2 that is parallel to the line of intersection of two other planes.

The line of intersection of the two given planes is parallel to the vector

$$\mathbf{v} = \mathbf{N}_1 \times \mathbf{N}_2 = \begin{vmatrix} \mathbf{i} & \mathbf{j} & \mathbf{k} \\ 3 & 1 & -2 \\ 4 & -1 & 3 \end{vmatrix} = \mathbf{i} - 17\mathbf{j} - 7\mathbf{k},$$

where $\mathbf{N}_1$ and $\mathbf{N}_2$ are normals to the two given planes. The vector

$$\overrightarrow{P_1 P_2} = -2\mathbf{i} + 2\mathbf{j} + 2\mathbf{k}$$

is to lie in the required plane. Now we may slide $\mathbf{v}$ parallel to itself until it also lies in the required plane (since the plane is to be parallel to $\mathbf{v}$). Hence we may take

$$\mathbf{N} = \overrightarrow{P_1 P_2} \times \mathbf{v} = 20\mathbf{i} - 12\mathbf{j} + 32\mathbf{k}$$

as a vector normal to the plane. Actually, $\frac{1}{4}\mathbf{N} = 5\mathbf{i} - 3\mathbf{j} + 8\mathbf{k}$ serves just as well. From this normal vector, we may substitute

$$A = 5, \qquad B = -3, \qquad C = 8$$

in Eq. (5), together with $x_1 = 1$, $y_1 = 0$, $z_1 = -1$, since $P_1(1, 0, -1)$ is to lie in the plane. The required plane is therefore

$$5(x - 1) - 3(y - 0) + 8(z + 1) = 0$$

or

$$5x - 3y + 8z + 3 = 0.$$

PROBLEMS

1. Find the coordinates of the point P in which the line

$$\frac{x - 1}{2} = \frac{y + 1}{-1} = \frac{z}{3}$$

intersects the plane $3x + 2y - z = 5$.

2. Find parametric and cartesian equations of the line joining the points $A(1, 2, -1)$ and $B(-1, 0, 1)$.

3. Show, by vector methods, that the distance from the point $P_1(x_1, y_1, z_1)$ to the plane $Ax + By + Cz - D = 0$ is

$$\frac{|Ax_1 + By_1 + Cz_1 - D|}{\sqrt{A^2 + B^2 + C^2}}.$$

4. (a) What is meant by the angle between a line and a plane? (b) Find the acute angle between the line

$$\frac{x + 1}{2} = \frac{y}{3} = \frac{z - 3}{6}$$

and the plane $10x + 2y - 11z = 3$.

5. Find a plane that passes through the point $(1, -1, 3)$ and is parallel to the plane $3x + y + z = 7$.

6. Show that the planes obtained by substituting different values for the constant D in the equation

$$2x + 3y - 6z = D$$

are parallel. Find the distance between two of these planes, one corresponding, say, to $D = D_1$ and the other to $D = D_2$.

7. Prove that the line

$$\frac{x - 1}{2} = \frac{y + 1}{3} = \frac{z - 2}{4}$$

is parallel to the plane $x - 2y + z = 6$.

8. Find a plane through the points $A(1, 1, -1)$, $B(2, 0, 2)$, and $C(0, -2, 1)$.

9. Let $P_i(x_i, y_i, z_i)$, $i = 1, 2, 3$, be three points. What set is described by the equation

$$\begin{vmatrix} x & y & z & 1 \\ x_1 & y_1 & z_1 & 1 \\ x_2 & y_2 & z_2 & 1 \\ x_3 & y_3 & z_3 & 1 \end{vmatrix} = 0?$$

10. Find a plane through $A(1, -2, 1)$ perpendicular to the vector from the origin to A.

11. Find a plane through $P_0(2, 1, -1)$ perpendicular to the line of intersection of the planes $2x + y - z = 3$, $x + 2y + z = 2$.

12. Find a plane through the points $P_1(1, 2, 3)$ and $P_2(3, 2, 1)$ perpendicular to the plane $4x - y + 2z = 7$.

13. Find the distance between the origin and the line

$$\frac{x - 2}{3} = \frac{y - 1}{4} = \frac{2 - z}{5}.$$

14. (a) Prove that three points A, B, C are collinear if and only if $\overrightarrow{AC} \times \overrightarrow{AB} = 0$. (b) Are the points $A(1, 2, -3)$, $B(3, 1, 0)$, $C(-3, 4, -9)$ collinear?

15. Prove that four points A, B, C, D are coplanar if and only if $\overrightarrow{AD} \cdot (\overrightarrow{AB} \times \overrightarrow{BC}) = 0$.

16. Show that the line of intersection of the planes

$$x + 2y - 2z = 5 \qquad \text{and} \qquad 5x - 2y - z = 0$$

is parallel to the line

$$\frac{x + 3}{2} = \frac{y}{3} = \frac{z - 1}{4}.$$

Find the plane determined by these two lines.

17. Show that the lines

$$\frac{x-2}{1} = \frac{y-2}{3} = \frac{z-3}{1} \quad \text{and} \quad \frac{x-2}{1} = \frac{y-3}{4} = \frac{z-4}{2}$$

intersect. Find the plane determined by these two lines.

18. Find the direction cosines (Article 11–6, Problem 15) of the line $2x + y - z = 5$, $x - 3y + 2z = 2$.

19. The equation $\mathbf{N} \cdot \overrightarrow{P_1 P} = 0$ represents a plane through P_1 perpendicular to $\mathbf{N}$. What set does the inequality $\mathbf{N} \cdot \overrightarrow{P_1 P} > 0$ represent? Give a reason for your answer.

20. The unit vector $\mathbf{u}$ makes angles α, β, γ, respectively, with the positive x-, y-, z-axes. Find the plane normal to $\mathbf{u}$ through $P_0(x_0, y_0, z_0)$.

11–9

PRODUCTS OF THREE VECTORS OR MORE

Products that involve three vectors or more often arise in physical and engineering problems. For example (see Sears, Zemansky, Young, *University Physics* (1976), Chapter 33), the electromotive force $\overrightarrow{dE}$ induced in an element of a conducting wire $\overrightarrow{dl}$ moving with velocity $\mathbf{v}$ through a magnetic field at a point where the flux density is $\mathbf{B}$ is given by $\overrightarrow{dE} = (\mathbf{B} \times \overrightarrow{dl}) \cdot \mathbf{v}$. Here the factor in parentheses is a vector, and the result of forming the scalar product of this vector and $\mathbf{v}$ is a scalar. It is a real economy in thinking to represent the result in the compact vector form which removes the necessity of carrying factors such as the sine of the angle between $\mathbf{B}$ and $\overrightarrow{dl}$ and the cosine of the angle between the normal to their plane and the velocity vector $\mathbf{v}$. All of these are automatically taken account of by the given product of three vectors.

Triple Scalar Product

The product $(\mathbf{A} \times \mathbf{B}) \cdot \mathbf{C}$, called the *triple scalar product*, has the following geometrical significance. The vector $\mathbf{N} = \mathbf{A} \times \mathbf{B}$ is normal to the base of the parallelepiped determined by the vectors $\mathbf{A}$, $\mathbf{B}$, and $\mathbf{C}$ in Fig. 11–47. The magnitude of $\mathbf{N}$ equals the area of the base determined by $\mathbf{A}$ and $\mathbf{B}$. Thus

$$(\mathbf{A} \times \mathbf{B}) \cdot \mathbf{C} = \mathbf{N} \cdot \mathbf{C} = |\mathbf{N}| \, |\mathbf{C}| \cos \theta$$

is, except perhaps for sign, the *volume of a box* of edges $\mathbf{A}$, $\mathbf{B}$, and $\mathbf{C}$, since

$$|\mathbf{N}| = |\mathbf{A} \times \mathbf{B}| = \text{area of base}$$

and

$$|\mathbf{C}| \cos \theta = \pm h = \pm \text{altitude of box.}$$

11–47 Except perhaps for sign, the number $(\mathbf{A} \times \mathbf{B}) \cdot \mathbf{C}$ is the volume of the parallelopiped shown.

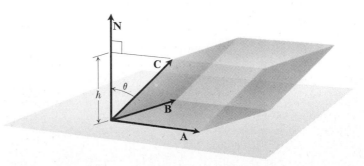

If **C** and **A** × **B** lie on the same side of the plane determined by **A** and **B**, the triple scalar product will be positive. But if the vectors **A**, **B**, and **C** form a lefthanded system, then (**A** × **B**) · **C** is negative. By successively considering the plane of **B** and **C**, then the plane of **C** and **A**, as the base of the parallelepiped, we can readily see that

$$(\mathbf{A} \times \mathbf{B}) \cdot \mathbf{C} = (\mathbf{B} \times \mathbf{C}) \cdot \mathbf{A} = (\mathbf{C} \times \mathbf{A}) \cdot \mathbf{B}. \tag{1}$$

Since the dot product is commutative, we also have

$$(\mathbf{B} \times \mathbf{C}) \cdot \mathbf{A} = \mathbf{A} \cdot (\mathbf{B} \times \mathbf{C}),$$

so that Eq. (1) gives the result

$$(\mathbf{A} \times \mathbf{B}) \cdot \mathbf{C} = \mathbf{A} \cdot (\mathbf{B} \times \mathbf{C}). \tag{2}$$

Equation (2) says that the dot and the cross may be interchanged in the triple scalar product, provided only that the multiplications are performed in a way that "makes sense." Thus (**A** · **B**) × **C** is excluded on the ground that (**A** · **B**) is a scalar and we never "cross" a scalar and a vector.

The triple scalar product in Eq. (2) is conveniently expressed in determinant form as follows:

$$\mathbf{A} \cdot (\mathbf{B} \times \mathbf{C}) = A \cdot \left[\begin{vmatrix} b_2 & b_3 \\ c_2 & c_3 \end{vmatrix} \mathbf{i} - \begin{vmatrix} b_1 & b_3 \\ c_1 & c_3 \end{vmatrix} \mathbf{j} + \begin{vmatrix} b_1 & b_2 \\ c_1 & c_2 \end{vmatrix} \mathbf{k} \right]$$

$$= a_1 \begin{vmatrix} b_2 & b_3 \\ c_2 & c_3 \end{vmatrix} - a_2 \begin{vmatrix} b_1 & b_3 \\ c_2 & c_3 \end{vmatrix} + a_3 \begin{vmatrix} b_1 & b_2 \\ c_1 & c_2 \end{vmatrix} \tag{3}$$

$$= \begin{vmatrix} a_1 & a_2 & a_3 \\ b_1 & b_2 & b_3 \\ c_1 & c_2 & c_3 \end{vmatrix}.$$

A product that involves three vectors but is much simpler than the triple scalar product is (**A** · **B**)**C**. Here the scalar $s = \mathbf{A} \cdot \mathbf{B}$ multiplies the vector **C**.

Triple Vector Product

The triple vector products (**A** × **B**) × **C** and **A** × (**B** × **C**) are usually not equal, but each of them can be evaluated rather simply by formulas which we shall now derive.

We start by showing that the vector product (**A** × **B**) × **C** is given by

$$(\mathbf{A} \times \mathbf{B}) \times \mathbf{C} = (\mathbf{A} \cdot \mathbf{C})\mathbf{B} - (\mathbf{B} \cdot \mathbf{C})\mathbf{A}. \tag{4}$$

CASE 1.   If one of the vectors is the zero vector, Eq. (4) is true because both sides of it are zero.

CASE 2.   If none of the vectors is zero, but if **B** = s**A** for some scalar s, then both sides of Eq. (4) are zero again.

CASE 3.   Suppose that none of the vectors is zero and that **A** and **B** are not parallel. The vector on the left of Eq. (4) is parallel to the plane determined by **A** and **B**, so that it is possible to find scalars m and n such that

$$(\mathbf{A} \times \mathbf{B}) \times \mathbf{C} = m\mathbf{A} + n\mathbf{B}. \tag{5}$$

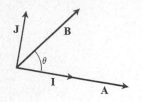

11–48 Orthogonal vectors **I** and **J** in the plane of **A** and **B**.

To calculate m and n, we introduce orthogonal unit vectors **I** and **J** in the plane of **A** and **B** with $\mathbf{I} = \mathbf{A}/|\mathbf{A}|$ (Fig. 11–48). We also introduce a third unit vector $\mathbf{K} = \mathbf{I} \times \mathbf{J}$, and write all our vectors in terms of these unit vectors **I**, **J**, and **K**:

$$\mathbf{A} = a_1\mathbf{I},$$
$$\mathbf{B} = b_1\mathbf{I} + b_2\mathbf{J},$$
$$\mathbf{C} = c_1\mathbf{I} + c_2\mathbf{J} + c_3\mathbf{K}. \tag{6}$$

Then

$$\mathbf{A} \times \mathbf{B} = a_1 b_2 \mathbf{K}$$

and

$$(\mathbf{A} \times \mathbf{B}) \times \mathbf{C} = a_1 b_2 c_1 \mathbf{J} - a_1 b_2 c_2 \mathbf{I}. \tag{7}$$

Comparing this with the right side of Eq. (5), we have

$$m(a_1\mathbf{I}) + n(b_1\mathbf{I} + b_2\mathbf{J}) = a_1 b_2 c_1 \mathbf{J} - a_1 b_2 c_2 \mathbf{I}.$$

This is equivalent to the pair of scalar equations

$$ma_1 + nb_1 = -a_1 b_2 c_2,$$
$$nb_2 = a_1 b_2 c_1.$$

If b_2 were equal to zero, **A** and **B** would be parallel, contrary to hypothesis. Hence b_2 is not zero and we may solve the last equation for n. We find

$$n = a_1 c_1 = \mathbf{A} \cdot \mathbf{C}.$$

Then, by substitution,

$$ma_1 = -nb_1 - a_1 b_2 c_2$$
$$= -a_1 c_1 b_1 - a_1 b_2 c_2,$$

and since $|\mathbf{A}| = a_1 \neq 0$, we may divide by a_1 and have

$$m = -(b_1 c_1 + b_2 c_2) = -(\mathbf{B} \cdot \mathbf{C}).$$

When these values are substituted for m and n in Eq. (5), we obtain the result given in Eq. (4).

The identity

$$(\mathbf{B} \times \mathbf{C}) \times \mathbf{A} = (\mathbf{B} \cdot \mathbf{A})\mathbf{C} - (\mathbf{C} \cdot \mathbf{A})\mathbf{B} \tag{8a}$$

follows from Eq. (4) by a simple interchange of the letters **A**, **B**, and **C**. If we now interchange the factors $\mathbf{B} \times \mathbf{C}$ and **A** we must change the sign on the right side of the equation. This gives the following identity, which is a companion of Eq. (4):

$$\mathbf{A} \times (\mathbf{B} \times \mathbf{C}) = (\mathbf{A} \cdot \mathbf{C})\mathbf{B} - (\mathbf{A} \cdot \mathbf{B})\mathbf{C}. \tag{8b}$$

EXAMPLE 1.   Verify Eq. (4) for the vectors

$$\mathbf{A} = \mathbf{i} - \mathbf{j} + 2\mathbf{k},$$
$$\mathbf{B} = 2\mathbf{i} + \mathbf{j} + \mathbf{k},$$
$$\mathbf{C} = \mathbf{i} + 2\mathbf{j} - \mathbf{k}.$$

Solution.   Since
$$\mathbf{A} \cdot \mathbf{C} = -3, \qquad \mathbf{B} \cdot \mathbf{C} = 3,$$
the right side of Eq. (4) is
$$(\mathbf{A} \cdot \mathbf{C})\mathbf{B} - (\mathbf{B} \cdot \mathbf{C})\mathbf{A} = -3\mathbf{B} - 3\mathbf{A} = -3(3\mathbf{i} + 3\mathbf{k}) = -9\mathbf{i} - 9\mathbf{k}.$$
To calculate the left side of Eq. (4) we have
$$\mathbf{A} \times \mathbf{B} = \begin{vmatrix} \mathbf{i} & \mathbf{j} & \mathbf{k} \\ 1 & -1 & 2 \\ 2 & 1 & 1 \end{vmatrix} = -3\mathbf{i} + 3\mathbf{j} + 3\mathbf{k},$$
so that
$$(\mathbf{A} \times \mathbf{B}) \times \mathbf{C} = \begin{vmatrix} \mathbf{i} & \mathbf{j} & \mathbf{k} \\ -3 & 3 & 3 \\ 1 & 2 & -1 \end{vmatrix} = -9\mathbf{i} - 9\mathbf{k}.$$

EXAMPLE 2.   Use Eqs. (4) and (8b) to express
$$(\mathbf{A} \times \mathbf{B}) \times (\mathbf{C} \times \mathbf{D})$$
in terms of scalar multiplication and cross products involving no more than two factors.

Solution.   Write, for convenience,
$$\mathbf{C} \times \mathbf{D} = \mathbf{V}.$$
Then use Eq. (4) to evaluate
$$(\mathbf{A} \times \mathbf{B}) \times \mathbf{V} = (\mathbf{A} \cdot \mathbf{V})\mathbf{B} - (\mathbf{B} \cdot \mathbf{V})\mathbf{A}$$
or
$$(\mathbf{A} \times \mathbf{B}) \times (\mathbf{C} \times \mathbf{D}) = (\mathbf{A} \cdot \mathbf{C} \times \mathbf{D})\mathbf{B} - (\mathbf{B} \cdot \mathbf{C} \times \mathbf{D})\mathbf{A}.$$

The result, as written, expresses the answer as a scalar times **B** minus a scalar times **A**. One could also represent the answer as a scalar times **C** minus a scalar times **D**. Geometrically, the vector is parallel to the line of intersection of the **A**, **B**-plane and the **C**, **D**-plane.

EXAMPLE 3.   (See Fig. 11–49.) Let
$$\mathbf{A} = \overrightarrow{PQ}, \qquad \mathbf{B} = \overrightarrow{PS}$$
$$\mathbf{A}' = \overrightarrow{P'Q'}, \qquad \mathbf{B}' = \overrightarrow{P'S'}$$
be sides of parallelograms $PQRS$ and $P'Q'R'S'$ that are related in such a way that PP', QQ', and SS' are parallel to one another and to the unit vector **n**. Show that
$$(\mathbf{A} \times \mathbf{B}) \cdot \mathbf{n} = (\mathbf{A}' \times \mathbf{B}') \cdot \mathbf{n} \qquad (9)$$
and discuss the geometrical meaning of this identity.

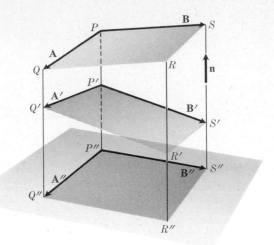

11–49 If $|\mathbf{n}| = 1$, then $(\mathbf{A} \times \mathbf{B}) \cdot \mathbf{n}$ is the area of the projection of the parallelogram determined by $\mathbf{A}$ and $\mathbf{B}$ on a plane perpendicular to $\mathbf{n}$.

Verification of Eq. (9)

From the way the parallelograms are related, it follows that

$$\mathbf{A} = \overrightarrow{PQ} = \overrightarrow{PP'} + \overrightarrow{P'Q'} + \overrightarrow{Q'Q}$$
$$= \overrightarrow{P'Q'} + (\overrightarrow{PP'} - \overrightarrow{QQ'}) = \mathbf{A}' + s\mathbf{n}$$

for some scalar s, since both $\overrightarrow{PP'}$ and $\overrightarrow{QQ'}$ are parallel to $\mathbf{n}$. Similarly,

$$\mathbf{B} = \mathbf{B}' + t\mathbf{n}$$

for some scalar t. Hence

$$\mathbf{A} \times \mathbf{B} = (\mathbf{A}' + s\mathbf{n}) \times (\mathbf{B}' + t\mathbf{n})$$
$$= \mathbf{A}' \times \mathbf{B}' + t(\mathbf{A}' \times \mathbf{n}) + s(\mathbf{n} \times \mathbf{B}') + st(\mathbf{n} \times \mathbf{n}). \tag{10}$$

But $\mathbf{n} \times \mathbf{n} = 0$, while $\mathbf{A}' \times \mathbf{n}$ and $\mathbf{n} \times \mathbf{B}'$ are both perpendicular to $\mathbf{n}$. Therefore when we dot both sides of (10) with $\mathbf{n}$ we get Eq. (9).

Geometrical Meaning of Eq. (9)

The result (9) says that when the parallelograms $PQRS$ and $P'Q'R'S'$ are any two plane sections of a prism with sides parallel to $\mathbf{n}$, then the box determined by $\mathbf{A}$, $\mathbf{B}$, and $\mathbf{n}$ has the same volume as the box determined by $\mathbf{A}'$, $\mathbf{B}'$, and $\mathbf{n}$. Thus, in particular, we may replace the right side of (9) by $(\mathbf{A}'' \times \mathbf{B}'') \cdot \mathbf{n}$, where $\mathbf{A}''$ and $\mathbf{B}''$ are sides of a *right* section $P''Q''R''S''$ as in Fig. 11–49. Then $\mathbf{A}'' \times \mathbf{B}''$ is parallel to $\mathbf{n}$, and

$$\mathbf{A}'' \times \mathbf{B}'' = (\text{Area right section}) \, \mathbf{n}$$

and

$$(\mathbf{A}'' \times \mathbf{B}'') \cdot \mathbf{n} = \text{Area right section}.$$

Therefore, by Eq. (9), we have the following interpretation:

$(A \times B) \cdot n$ is the area of the orthogonal projection of the parallelogram determined by A and B onto a plane whose unit **(11)** normal is n.

This assumes that $A \times B$ and n lie on the same side of the plane $PQRS$. If they are on opposite sides, take the absolute value to get the area. Except possibly for sign, then,

$$(A \times B) \cdot k = \text{Area of projection in the } xy\text{-plane,} \qquad \textbf{(12a)}$$

$$(A \times B) \cdot j = \text{Area of projection in the } xz\text{-plane,} \qquad \textbf{(12b)}$$

$$(A \times B) \cdot i = \text{Area of projection in the } yz\text{-plane.} \qquad \textbf{(12c)}$$

PROBLEMS

In Problems 1–3, take

$$A = 4i - 8j + k,$$

$$B = 2i + j - 2k,$$

$$C = 3i - 4j + 12k.$$

1. Find $(A \cdot B)C$ and $A(B \cdot C)$.

2. Find the volume of the box having A, B, C as three co-terminous edges.

3. (a) Find $A \times B$ and use the result to find $(A \times B) \times C$. (b) Find $(A \times B) \times C$ by another method.

4. Prove that any vector A satisfies the identity

$$A = \tfrac{1}{2}[i \times (A \times i) + j \times (A \times j) + k \times (A \times k)].$$

5. Express the product $R = (A \times B) \times (C \times D)$ in the form $aC + bD$ with scalars a and b.

6. Find the volume of the tetrahedron with vertices at $(0, 0, 0)$, $(1, -1, 1)$, $(2, 1, -2)$, and $(-1, 2, -1)$.

7. Use Eq. (3) to show that

a) $A \cdot (C \times B) = -A \cdot (B \times C)$,   b) $A \cdot (A \times B) = 0$,

c) $(A + D) \cdot (B \times C) = A \cdot (B \times C) + D \cdot (B \times C)$.

Interpret the results geometrically.

8. Explain the statement in the text that $(A \times B) \times C$ is parallel to the plane determined by A and B. Illustrate with a sketch.

9. Explain the statement, at the end of Example 2, that $(A \times B) \times (C \times D)$ is parallel to the line of intersection of the A, B-plane and the C, D-plane. Illustrate with a sketch.

10. Find a line in the plane of $P_0(0, 0, 0)$, $P_1(2, 2, 0)$, $P_2(0, 1, -2)$, and perpendicular to the line

$$\frac{x + 1}{3} = \frac{y - 1}{2} = 2z.$$

11. Let $P(1, 2, -1)$, $Q(3, -1, 4)$, and $R(2, 6, 2)$ be three vertices of a parallelogram $PQRS$.

a) Find the coordinates of S.

b) Find the area of $PQRS$.

c) Find the area of the projection of $PQRS$ in the xy-plane; in the yz-plane; in the xz-plane.

12. Show that the area of a parallelogram in space is the square root of the sum of the squares of the areas of its projections on any three mutually orthogonal planes.

In this article and the next, we shall consider some extensions of analytic geometry to space. We begin with the notion of a surface.

The set of points $P(x, y, z)$ that satisfy an equation

$$F(x, y, z) = 0 \qquad \textbf{(1)}$$

CYLINDERS

may be interpreted in a broad sense as being a surface. The simplest examples of surfaces are planes, which have equations of the form $Ax + By + Cz - D = 0$. Almost as simple as planes are the surfaces called *cylinders*.

In general, a cylinder is a surface that is generated by moving a straight line along a given curve while holding the line parallel to a given fixed line.

EXAMPLE 1. The *parabolic cylinder* of Fig. 11–50 is generated by a line parallel to the z-axis that moves along the curve $y = x^2$ in the xy-plane. If a point $P_0(x, y, 0)$ lies on the parabola, then every point $P(x, y, z)$ with the same x- and y-coordinates lies on the line through P_0 parallel to the z-axis, and hence belongs to the surface. Conversely, if $P(x, y, z)$ lies on the surface, its projection $P_0(x, y, 0)$ on the xy-plane lies on the parabola $y = x^2$, so that its coordinates satisfy the equation $y = x^2$. Regardless of the value of z, the points of the surface are the points whose coordinates satisfy this equation. Thus, the equation $y = x^2$ is an equation for the cylinder as well as for the generating parabola. The cross sections of the cylinder perpendicular to the z-axis are parabolas, too, all of them congruent to the parabola in the xy-plane.

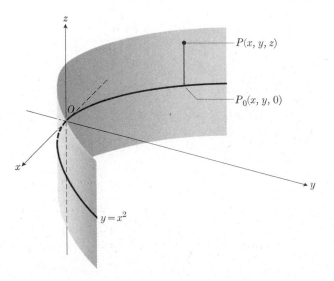

11–50 Parabolic cylinder.

In general, any curve

$$f(x, y) = 0 \qquad (2)$$

in the xy-plane defines a cylinder in space whose equation is also $f(x, y) = 0$, and which is made up of the points of the lines through the curve that are parallel to the z-axis. The lines are sometimes called *elements* of the cylinder.

The discussion above can be carried through for cylinders with elements parallel to the other coordinate axes, and the result is summarized by saying that *an equation in cartesian coordinates, from which one letter is missing, represents a cylinder with elements parallel to the axis associated with the missing letter.*

EXAMPLE 2. The surface

$$y^2 + 4z^2 = 4$$

is an *elliptic cylinder* with elements parallel to the x-axis. It extends indefinitely in both the negative and positive directions along the x-axis, which is the axis of the cylinder, since it passes through the centers of the elliptical cross sections of the cylinder (Fig. 11–51).

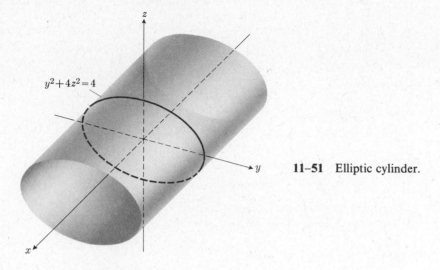

$y^2 + 4z^2 = 4$

11–51   Elliptic cylinder.

EXAMPLE 3.   The surface

$$r^2 = 2a \cos 2\theta$$

in cylindrical coordinates is a cylinder with elements parallel to the z-axis. Each section perpendicular to the z-axis is a lemniscate. The cylinder extends indefinitely in both the positive and negative directions along the z-axis (Fig. 11–52).

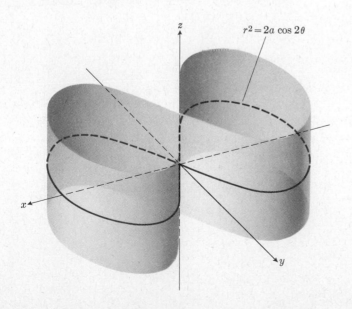

$r^2 = 2a \cos 2\theta$

11–52   A cylinder whose cross sections are lemniscates.

PROBLEMS

Describe and sketch each of the following surfaces [(r, θ, z) are cylindrical coordinates].

1. $x^2 + z^2 = 1$ **2.** $z = x^2$ **3.** $x = -y^2$

4. $4x^2 + y^2 = 4$ **5.** $z = -y$ **6.** $y^2 - x^2 = 1$

7. $x^2 - z^2 = 1$ **8.** $z^2 - y^2 = 1$ **9.** $r = 4$

10. $r = \sin \theta$ **11.** $r = \cos \theta$ **12.** $r = 1 + \cos \theta$

13. $x^2 + y^2 = a^2$ **14.** $y^2 + z^2 - 4z = 0$

15. $x^2 + 4z^2 - 4z = 0$

QUADRIC SURFACES

A surface whose equation is a quadratic in the variables x, y, and z is called a *quadric* surface. We indicate briefly how some of the simpler ones may be recognized from their equations.

The *sphere*

$$(x - h)^2 + (y - k)^2 + (z - m)^2 = a^2 \tag{1}$$

with center at (h, k, m) and radius a has already been mentioned in Article 11–5. Likewise, the various *cylinders*

$$Ax^2 + Bxy + Cy^2 + Dx + Ey + F = 0 \tag{2}$$

with elements parallel to the z-axis, and others with elements parallel to the other coordinate axes, are familiar and will not be further discussed. In the examples that follow, we shall refer the surfaces discussed to coordinate axes that yield simple forms of the equations. For example, we take the origin to be at the center of the ellipsoid in Example 1 below. If the center were at (h, k, m) instead, the equation would simply have $x - h$, $y - k$, and $z - m$, in place of x, y, z, respectively. We take a, b, and c to be positive constants in every case.

EXAMPLE 1. *The ellipsoid*

$$\frac{x^2}{a^2} + \frac{y^2}{b^2} + \frac{z^2}{c^2} = 1 \tag{3}$$

cuts the coordinate axes at $(\pm a, 0, 0)$, $(0, \pm b, 0)$, and $(0, 0, \pm c)$. It lies inside the rectangular box

$$|x| \le a, \qquad |y| \le b, \qquad |z| \le c.$$

Since only even powers of x, y, and z occur in the equation, this surface is symmetric with respect to each of the coordinate planes. The sections cut out by the coordinate planes are ellipses. For example,

$$\frac{x^2}{a^2} + \frac{y^2}{b^2} = 1 \qquad \text{when} \quad z = 0.$$

Each section cut out by a plane

$$z = z_1, \qquad |z_1| < c$$

is an ellipse

$$\frac{x^2}{a^2[1 - (z_1^2/c^2)]} + \frac{y^2}{b^2[1 - (z_1^2/c^2)]} = 1$$

with center on the z-axis and having semiaxes

$$\frac{a}{c}\sqrt{c^2 - z_1^2} \qquad \text{and} \qquad \frac{b}{c}\sqrt{c^2 - z_1^2}.$$

The surface is sketched in Fig. 11–53. When two of the three semiaxes a, b, and c are equal, the surface is an ellipsoid of revolution, and when all three are equal, it is a sphere.

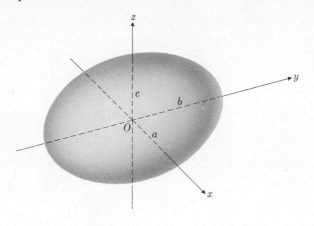

11–53 Ellipsoid.

EXAMPLE 2. *The elliptic paraboloid* (Fig. 11–54)

$$\frac{x^2}{a^2} + \frac{y^2}{b^2} = \frac{z}{c} \tag{4}$$

is symmetric with respect to the planes $x = 0$ and $y = 0$. The only intercept on the axes is at the origin. Since the left side of the equation is nonnegative, the surface is limited to the region $z \geq 0$. That is, away from the origin it lies above the xy-plane. The section cut out from the surface by the yz-plane is

$$x = 0, \qquad y^2 = \frac{b^2}{c} z,$$

which is a parabola with vertex at the origin and opening upward. Similarly, one finds that when $y = 0$,

$$x^2 = \frac{a^2}{c} z,$$

which is also such a parabola. When $z = 0$, the cut reduces to the single point $(0, 0, 0)$. Each plane $z = z_1 > 0$ perpendicular to the z-axis cuts the surface in an ellipse of semiaxes

$$a\sqrt{z_1/c} \qquad \text{and} \qquad b\sqrt{z_1/c}.$$

These semiaxes increase in magnitude as z_1 increases. The paraboloid extends indefinitely upward.

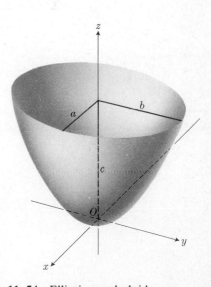

11–54 Elliptic paraboloid.

EXAMPLE 3. *Circular paraboloid, or paraboloid of revolution:*

$$\frac{x^2}{a^2} + \frac{y^2}{a^2} = \frac{z}{c}. \tag{5a}$$

The equation is obtained by taking $b = a$ in Eq. (4) for the elliptic parabo-loid. The cross sections of the surface by planes perpendicular to the z-axis are circles centered on the z-axis. The cross sections by planes containing the z-axis are congruent parabolas with a common focus at the point $(0, 0, a^2/4c)$. In cylindrical coordinates, (5a) becomes

$$\frac{r^2}{a^2} = \frac{z}{c}. \tag{5b}$$

Shapes cut from circular paraboloids are used for antennae in radio tele-scopes, satellite trackers, and microwave radio links (Fig. 11–55).

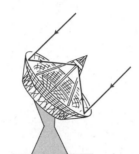

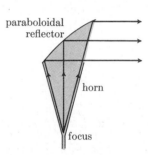

paraboloidal reflector

horn

focus

11–55 Antennas shaped like pieces of paraboloids of revolution. (a) Radio telescopes use the same principles as optical telescopes. (b) A "rectangular-cut" radar reflector. (c) Horn antenna in a microwave radio link.

EXAMPLE 4. *The elliptic cone* (Fig. 11–56)

$$\frac{x^2}{a^2} + \frac{y^2}{b^2} = \frac{z^2}{c^2} \tag{6}$$

is symmetric with respect to all three coordinate planes. The plane $z = 0$ cuts the surface in the single point $(0, 0, 0)$. The plane $x = 0$ cuts it in the two intersecting straight lines

$$x = 0, \qquad \frac{y}{b} = \pm\frac{z}{c} \tag{7}$$

and when

$$y = 0, \qquad \frac{x}{a} = \pm\frac{z}{c}. \tag{8}$$

The section cut out by a plane $z = z_1 > 0$ is an ellipse with center on the z-axis and vertices lying on the straight lines (7) and (8). In fact, the whole surface is generated by a straight line L which passes through the origin and a point Q on the ellipse

$$z = c, \qquad \frac{x^2}{a^2} + \frac{y^2}{b^2} = 1.$$

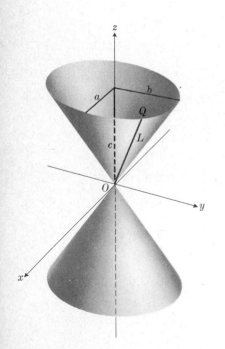

11–56 Elliptic cone.

As the point Q traces out the ellipse, the infinite line L generates the surface, which is a cone with elliptic cross sections. To see why, suppose that $Q(x_1, y_1, z_1)$ is a point on the surface and t is any scalar. Then the vector from O to the point $P(tx_1, ty_1, tz_1)$ is simply t times $\overrightarrow{OQ}$, so that as t varies from $-\infty$ to $+\infty$ the point P traces out the infinite line L. But since Q is assumed to be on the surface, the equation

$$\frac{x_1^2}{a^2} + \frac{y_1^2}{b^2} = \frac{z_1^2}{c^2}$$

is satisfied. Multiplying both sides of this equation by t^2 shows that the point $P(tx_1, ty_1, tz_1)$ is also on the surface. This establishes the validity of the remark that the surface is a cone generated by the line L through O and the point Q on the ellipse.

In case $a = b$, the cone is a right circular cone and its equation in cylindrical coordinates is simply

$$\frac{r}{a} = \frac{z}{c}. \tag{9}$$

EXAMPLE 5. *The hyperboloid of one sheet* (Fig. 11–57)

$$\frac{x^2}{a^2} + \frac{y^2}{b^2} - \frac{z^2}{c^2} = 1 \tag{10}$$

is symmetric with respect to each of the three coordinate planes. The sections cut out by the coordinate planes are:

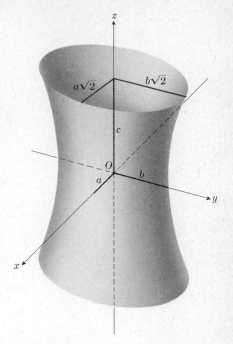

$x = 0$:   the hyperbola $\dfrac{y^2}{b^2} - \dfrac{z^2}{c^2} = 1,$

11–57   Hyperboloid of one sheet.

$y = 0$:   the hyperbola $\dfrac{x^2}{a^2} - \dfrac{z^2}{c^2} = 1,$ **(11)**

$z = 0$:   the ellipse $\dfrac{x^2}{a^2} + \dfrac{y^2}{b^2} = 1.$

The plane $z = z_1$ cuts the surface in an ellipse with center on the z-axis and vertices on the hyperbolas in (11). The surface is connected, meaning that it is possible to travel from any point on it to any other point on it without leaving the surface. For this reason, it is said to have *one* sheet, in contrast to the next example, which consists of *two* sheets. In the special case where $a = b$, the surface is a hyperboloid of revolution with equation given in cylindrical coordinates by

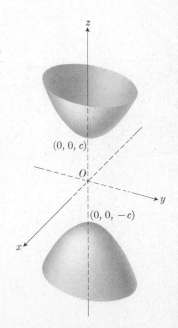

$$\frac{r^2}{a^2} - \frac{z^2}{c^2} = 1. \tag{12}$$

EXAMPLE 6. *The hyperboloid of two sheets* (Fig. 11–58)

$$\frac{z^2}{c^2} - \frac{x^2}{a^2} - \frac{y^2}{b^2} = 1 \tag{13}$$

is symmetric with respect to the three coordinate planes. The plane $z = 0$ **11–58**   Hyperboloid of two sheets. does not intersect the surface; in fact, one must have

$$|z| \geq c$$

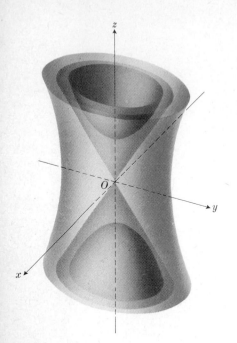

11–59   Cone asymptotic to hyperboloid of one sheet and hyperboloid of two sheets.

for real values of x and y in Eq. (13). The hyperbolic sections

$$x = 0: \quad \frac{z^2}{c^2} - \frac{y^2}{b^2} = 1,$$

$$y = 0: \quad \frac{z^2}{c^2} - \frac{x^2}{a^2} = 1$$

have their vertices and foci on the z-axis. The surface is separated into two portions, one above the plane $z = c$ and the other below the plane $z = -c$. This accounts for its name.

Equations (10) and (13) differ in the number of negative terms that each contains on the left side when the right side is $+1$. The number of negative signs is the same as the number of sheets of the hyperboloid. If we compare with Eq. (6), we see that replacing the unity on the right side of either Eq. (10) or (13) by zero gives the equation of a cone. This cone (Fig. 11–59) is, in fact, asymptotic to both of the hyperboloids (10) and (13) in the same way that the lines

$$\frac{x^2}{a^2} - \frac{y^2}{b^2} = 0$$

are asymptotic to the two hyperbolas

$$\frac{x^2}{a^2} - \frac{y^2}{b^2} = \pm 1$$

in the xy-plane.

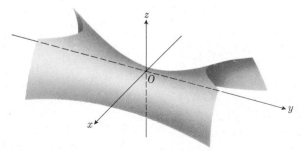

11–60   Hyperbolic paraboloid.

EXAMPLE 7.   *The hyperbolic paraboloid* (Fig. 11–60)

$$\frac{y^2}{b^2} - \frac{x^2}{a^2} = \frac{z}{c} \tag{14}$$

has symmetry with respect to the planes $x = 0$ and $y = 0$. The sections in these planes are

$$x = 0: \quad y^2 = b^2 \frac{z}{c}, \tag{15a}$$

$$y = 0: \quad x^2 = -a^2 \frac{z}{c}, \tag{15b}$$

which are parabolas. In the plane $x = 0$, the parabola opens upward and has vertex at the origin. The parabola in the plane $y = 0$ has the same vertex, but it opens downward. If we cut the surface by a plane $z = z_1 > 0$, the section is a hyperbola,

$$\frac{y^2}{b^2} - \frac{x^2}{a^2} = \frac{z_1}{c}, \tag{16}$$

whose focal axis is parallel to the y-axis and which has its vertices on the parabola in (15a). If, on the other hand, z_1 is negative in Eq. (16), then the focal axis of the hyperbola is parallel to the x-axis, and its vertices lie on the parabola in (15b). Near the origin the surface is shaped like a saddle. To a person traveling along the surface in the yz-plane, the origin looks like a minimum. To a person traveling in the xz-plane, on the other hand, the origin looks like a maximum. Such a point is called a *minimax* or *saddle point* of a surface (Fig. 11–60). We shall discuss maximum and minimum points on surfaces in the next chapter.

If $a = b$ in Eq. (14), the surface is not a surface of revolution, but it is possible to express the equation in the alternative form

$$\frac{2x'y'}{a^2} = \frac{z}{c} \tag{17}$$

if we refer it to $x'y'$-axes obtained by rotating the xy-axes through 45°.

PROBLEMS

Describe and sketch each of the following surfaces [(r, θ, z) are cylindrical coordinates]. Complete the square, when necessary, to put the equation into one of the standard forms shown in the examples.

1. $x^2 + y^2 = z - 1$
2. $x^2 + y^2 + z^2 + 4x - 6y = 3$
3. $x^2 + 4y^2 + z^2 = 4$
4. $x^2 + 4y^2 + z^2 - 8y = 0$
5. $4x^2 + 4y^2 + 4z^2 - 8y = 0$
6. $x^2 - y^2 + z^2 + 4x - 6y = 9$
7. $x^2 - y^2 - z^2 + 4x - 6y = 9$
8. $z^2 = 4x$
9. $z^2 = 4xy$ 10. $z = 4xy$
11. $z = r^2$ 12. $z = r$
13. $z^2 = r$ 14. $z^2 = x^2 + 4y^2$
15. $z^2 = x^2 - 4y^2$ 16. $z^2 = 4y^2 - x^2$
17. $z^2 = x^2 + 4y^2 - 2x + 8y + 4z$
18. $z^2 = x^2 + 4y^2 - 2x + 8y + 4z + 1$
19. $x^2 + 4z^2 = 4$ 20. $x = y^2 + 4z^2 + 1$
21. $z = r \cos \theta$ 22. $z = r \sin \theta$
23. $z = \sin \theta$ $(0 \le \theta \le \pi/2)$ 24. $z = \cosh \theta$ $(0 \le \theta \le \pi/2)$
25. (a) Express the area, $A(z_1)$, of the cross section cut from

the ellipsoid

$$\frac{x^2}{a^2} + \frac{y^2}{b^2} + \frac{z^2}{c^2} = 1$$

by the plane $z = z_1$, as a function of z_1. (The area of an ellipse of semiaxes A and B is πAB.) (b) By integration, find the volume of the ellipsoid of part (a). Consider slices made by planes perpendicular to the z-axis. Does your answer give the correct volume of a sphere in case $a = b = c$?

26. By integration, prove that the volume of the segment of the elliptic paraboloid

$$\frac{x^2}{a^2} + \frac{y^2}{b^2} = \frac{z}{c}$$

cut off by the plane $z = h$ is equal to one-half the area of its base times its altitude.

27. Given the hyperboloid of one sheet of Eq. (10),

  a) By integration, find the volume between the plane $z = 0$ and the plane $z = h$, enclosed by the hyperboloid.

  b) Express your answer to (a) in terms of the altitude h and the areas A_0 and A_h of the plane ends of the segment of the hyperboloid.

  c) Verify that the volume of (a) is also given exactly by the prismoid formula

$$V = h(A_0 + 4A_m + A_h)/6,$$

where A_0 and A_h are the areas of the plane ends of the segment of the hyperboloid and A_m is the area of its midsection cut out by the plane $z = h/2$.

28. If the hyperbolic paraboloid

$$\frac{y^2}{b^2} - \frac{x^2}{a^2} = \frac{z}{c}$$

is cut by the plane $y = y_1$, the resulting curve is a parabola.

Find its vertex and focus.

29. What is the nature, in general, of a surface whose equation in spherical coordinates has the form $\rho = F(\phi)$? Give reasons for your answer.

Describe and sketch the following surfaces, which are special cases of Exercise 29.

30. $\rho = a \cos \phi$ **31.** $\rho = a(1 + \cos \phi)$

REVIEW QUESTIONS AND EXERCISES

1. When are two vectors equal?

2. How are two vectors added? Subtracted?

3. If a vector is multiplied by a scalar, how is the result related to the original vector? In your discussion include all possible values of the scalar: positive, negative, and zero.

4. In a single diagram, show the cartesian, cylindrical, and spherical coordinates of an arbitrary point P, and write the expressions for each set of coordinates in terms of the other two kinds.

5. What set in space is described by:

a) $x = $ constant,   **b)** $r = $ constant,

c) $\theta = $ constant,   **d)** $\rho = $ constant,

e) $\phi = $ constant,   **f)** $ax + by + cz = d$,

g) $ax^2 + by^2 + cz^2 = d$?

6. What is the length of the vector $a\mathbf{i} + b\mathbf{j} + c\mathbf{k}$? On what theorem of plane geometry does this result depend?

7. Define *scalar product* of two vectors. Which algebraic laws (commutative, associative, distributive) are satisfied by the operations of addition and scalar multiplication of vectors? Which of these laws is (are) not satisfied? Explain. When is the scalar product equal to zero?

8. Suppose that $\mathbf{i}, \mathbf{j}, \mathbf{k}$ is one set of mutually orthogonal unit vectors and that $\mathbf{i}', \mathbf{j}', \mathbf{k}'$ is another set of such vectors. Suppose that all the scalar products of a unit vector from one set with a unit vector from the other set are known. Let

$$\mathbf{A} = a\mathbf{i} + b\mathbf{j} + c\mathbf{k} = a'\mathbf{i}' + b'\mathbf{j}' + c'\mathbf{k}'$$

and express a, b, c in terms of a', b', c'; and conversely. (Expressions involve $\mathbf{i} \cdot \mathbf{i}', \mathbf{i} \cdot \mathbf{j}', \mathbf{i} \cdot \mathbf{k}'$, and so forth.)

9. List four applications of the scalar product.

10. Define *vector product* of two vectors. Which algebraic laws (commutative, associative, distributive) are satisfied by the vector product operation (combined with addition), and which are not? Explain. When is the vector product equal to zero?

11. Derive the formula for expressing the vector product of two vectors as a determinant. What is the effect of interchanging the order of the two vectors and the corresponding rows of the determinant?

12. How may vector and scalar products be used to find the equation of a plane through three given points?

13. With the book closed, develop equations for a line

a) through two given points,

b) through one point and parallel to a given line.

14. With the book closed, develop the equation of a plane

a) through a given point and normal to a given vector,

b) through one point and parallel to a given plane,

c) through a point and perpendicular to each of two given planes.

15. What is the geometrical interpretation of

$$\mathbf{A} \cdot (\mathbf{B} \times \mathbf{C})?$$

When is this triple scalar product equal to zero?

16. What is the meaning of

a) $\mathbf{A} \times (\mathbf{B} \times \mathbf{C})$,   **b)** $\mathbf{A} \times (\mathbf{B} \cdot \mathbf{C})$,   **c)** $\mathbf{A} \cdot (\mathbf{B} \cdot \mathbf{C})$?

17. Given a parallelogram $PQRS$ in space, how could you find a vector normal to its plane and with length equal to its area?

18. What set in space is described by an equation of the form

a) $f(x, y) = 0$,   **b)** $f(z, r) = 0$,

c) $z = f(\theta), \quad 0 \le \theta \le 2\pi$?

19. Define *quadric surface*. Name and sketch six different quadric surfaces and indicate their equations.

MISCELLANEOUS PROBLEMS

In Exercises 1 through 10, find parametric equations of the path traced by the point $P(x, y)$ for the data given.

1. $\dfrac{dx}{dt} = x^2, \quad \dfrac{dy}{dt} = x; \quad t = 0, x = 1, y = 1$

which is the vector $\overrightarrow{PQ}$ in Fig. 12–2. The remaining calculations needed to give $d\mathbf{R}/dt$ proceed as follows:

$$\frac{\Delta \mathbf{R}}{\Delta t} = \mathbf{i}\frac{\Delta x}{\Delta t} + \mathbf{j}\frac{\Delta y}{\Delta t},$$

$$\lim_{\Delta t \to 0} \frac{\Delta \mathbf{R}}{\Delta t} = \lim_{\Delta t \to 0} \left(\mathbf{i}\frac{\Delta x}{\Delta t} + \mathbf{j}\frac{\Delta y}{\Delta t} \right)$$

$$= \mathbf{i} \lim_{\Delta t \to 0} \frac{\Delta x}{\Delta t} + \mathbf{j} \lim_{\Delta t \to 0} \frac{\Delta y}{\Delta t},$$

$$\frac{d\mathbf{R}}{dt} = \mathbf{i}\frac{dx}{dt} + \mathbf{j}\frac{dy}{dt}. \tag{6}$$

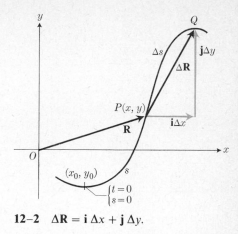

12–2 $\Delta \mathbf{R} = \mathbf{i}\,\Delta x + \mathbf{j}\,\Delta y.$

The result (6) is equivalent to what would be obtained by differentiating both sides of (2a) with respect to t, holding $\mathbf{i}$ and $\mathbf{j}$ constant. The geometric significance of (6) may be learned by calculating the slope and the magnitude of $d\mathbf{R}/dt$:

$$\text{Slope of } \frac{d\mathbf{R}}{dt} = \frac{\text{rise}}{\text{run}} = \frac{dy/dt}{dx/dt} = \frac{dy}{dx},$$

$$\text{Magnitude of } \frac{d\mathbf{R}}{dt} = \left| \frac{d\mathbf{R}}{dt} \right| = \left| \mathbf{i}\frac{dx}{dt} + \mathbf{j}\frac{dy}{dt} \right| \tag{7}$$

$$= \sqrt{\left(\frac{dx}{dt}\right)^2 + \left(\frac{dy^2}{dt}\right)} = \left| \frac{ds}{dt} \right|.$$

Here s represents arc length along the curve measured from some starting point (x_0, y_0).

If we draw a vector equal to $d\mathbf{R}/dt$, placing its initial point at P, the resulting vector will

a) be tangent to the curve at P, since its slope equals dy/dx, which is the same as the slope of the curve at P, and

b) have magnitude = $|ds/dt|$, which gives the instantaneous speed of the particle at P.

Thus, the vector $d\mathbf{R}/dt$, when drawn from P, is a suitable representation of the *velocity vector*, which has the same two properties (a) and (b).

In short, if we differentiate the position vector

$$\mathbf{R} = \mathbf{i}x + \mathbf{j}y$$

with respect to time, we get the *velocity vector*

$$\mathbf{v} = \frac{d\mathbf{R}}{dt} = \mathbf{i}\frac{dx}{dt} + \mathbf{j}\frac{dy}{dt}.$$

It is customary to draw the velocity vector at the point P (Fig. 12–3).

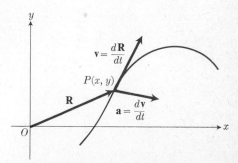

12–3   Typical position ($\mathbf{R}$), velocity ($\mathbf{v}$), and acceleration ($\mathbf{a}$) vectors of a particle moving from left to right on a plane curve.

Acceleration

The acceleration vector **a** is obtained from **v** by a further differentiation:

$$\mathbf{a} = \frac{d\mathbf{v}}{dt} = \mathbf{i}\frac{d^2x}{dt^2} + \mathbf{j}\frac{d^2y}{dt^2}. \tag{8}$$

For a particle of constant mass m moving under the action of an applied force **F**, Newton's second law of motion states that

$$\mathbf{F} = m\mathbf{a}. \tag{9}$$

Since one ordinarily visualizes the force vector as being *applied at P*, it is customary to adopt the same viewpoint about the acceleration vector **a** (Fig. 12–3).

EXAMPLE 1. A particle $P(x, y)$ moves on the hyperbola

$$x = r \cosh \omega t, \qquad y = r \sinh \omega t, \tag{10}$$

where r and ω are positive constants. Then

$$\mathbf{R} = \mathbf{i}(r \cosh \omega t) + \mathbf{j}(r \sinh \omega t),$$

$$\mathbf{v} = \frac{d\mathbf{R}}{dt} = \mathbf{i}(\omega r \sinh \omega t) + \mathbf{j}(\omega r \cosh \omega t)$$

and

$$\mathbf{a} = \mathbf{i}(\omega^2 r \cosh \omega t) + \mathbf{j}(\omega^2 r \sinh \omega t)$$

$$= \omega^2 \mathbf{R}.$$

This means that the force $\mathbf{F} = m\mathbf{a} = m\omega^2\mathbf{R}$ has a magnitude $m\omega^2|\mathbf{R}| = m\omega^2|\overrightarrow{OP}|$ which is directly proportional to the distance OP, and that its direction is the same as the direction of **R**. Thus the force is directed away from O (Fig. 12–4).

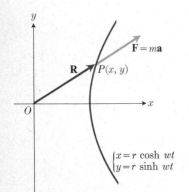

12–4 The force acting on the particle of Example 1 points directly away from O at all times.

The next example illustrates how we obtain the path of motion by integrating Eq. (9) when the force **F** is a given function of time, and the initial position and initial velocity of the particle are given. In general, the force **F** may depend upon the position of P as well as upon the time, and the problem of integrating the differential equations so obtained is usually discussed in textbooks on that subject. [For example, see Martin and Reissner, *Elementary Differential Equations*, Addison-Wesley, 1961.]

EXAMPLE 2. (Fig. 12–5.) The force acting on a particle P of mass m is given as a function of t by

$$\mathbf{F} = \mathbf{i} \cos t + \mathbf{j} \sin t.$$

If the particle starts at the point $(c, 0)$ with initial velocity $v_0\mathbf{j}$, find its path.

Solution. If we denote the position vector by

$$\mathbf{R} = \mathbf{i}x + \mathbf{j}y,$$

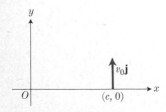

12–5 The particle of Example 2 leaves the x-axis with an initial velocity $v_0\mathbf{j}$.

we may restate the problem as follows. Find $\mathbf{R}$ if

$$\mathbf{F} = m\frac{d^2\mathbf{R}}{dt^2} = \mathbf{i}\cos t + \mathbf{j}\sin t \tag{11}$$

and, at $t = 0$,

$$\mathbf{R} = \mathbf{i}c, \qquad \frac{d\mathbf{R}}{dt} = \mathbf{j}v_0. \tag{12}$$

In (11) we let $\mathbf{v} = d\mathbf{R}/dt$, and separate the variables to obtain

$$m\,d\mathbf{v} = (\mathbf{i}\cos t + \mathbf{j}\sin t)\,dt.$$

Integrating this, we have

$$m\mathbf{v} = m\frac{d\mathbf{R}}{dt} = \mathbf{i}\sin t - \mathbf{j}\cos t + \mathbf{C}_1, \tag{13}$$

where the constant of integration is a *vector* denoted by $\mathbf{C}_1$. The value of $\mathbf{C}_1$ may be found by using the initial velocity, the righthand equation in (12), in Eq. (13), with $t = 0$:

$$m\mathbf{j}v_0 = -\mathbf{j} + \mathbf{C}_1,$$
$$\mathbf{C}_1 = (mv_0 + 1)\mathbf{j}.$$

Substituting this into (13), we have

$$m\frac{d\mathbf{R}}{dt} = \mathbf{i}\sin t + (mv_0 + 1 - \cos t)\mathbf{j}.$$

Another integration gives

$$m\mathbf{R} = -\mathbf{i}\cos t + \mathbf{j}(mv_0 t + t - \sin t) + \mathbf{C}_2.$$

The initial condition $\mathbf{R} = \mathbf{i}c$ (Eq. 12) enables us to evaluate $\mathbf{C}_2$:

$$m\mathbf{c}\mathbf{i} = -\mathbf{i} + \mathbf{C}_2, \qquad \mathbf{C}_2 = \mathbf{i}(mc + 1),$$

so that the position vector $\mathbf{R}$ is given by

$$\mathbf{R} = \frac{1}{m}[\mathbf{i}(mc + 1 - \cos t) + \mathbf{j}(mv_0 t + t - \sin t)].$$

The parametric equations of the curve are found by equating components of this expression for $\mathbf{R}$ with

$$\mathbf{R} = \mathbf{i}x + \mathbf{j}y,$$

which gives

$$x = c + \frac{1 - \cos t}{m}, \qquad y = v_0 t + \frac{t - \sin t}{m}.$$

The foregoing equations for velocity and acceleration in two dimensions would be appropriate for describing the motion of a particle moving on a flat surface, such as a water bug skimming over the surface of a pond, or a hockey puck sliding on ice. But to describe the flight of a bumblebee or a rocket, we need three coordinates. Thus, if

$$\mathbf{R}(t) = \mathbf{i}x + \mathbf{j}y + \mathbf{k}z, \tag{14a}$$

where x, y, z are functions of t that are twice-differentiable, then the velocity of $P(x, y, z)$ is

$$\mathbf{v} = \frac{d\mathbf{R}}{dt} = \mathbf{i}\frac{dx}{dt} + \mathbf{j}\frac{dy}{dt} + \mathbf{k}\frac{dz}{dt}, \tag{14b}$$

and the acceleration is

$$\mathbf{a} = \mathbf{i}\frac{d^2x}{dt^2} + \mathbf{j}\frac{d^2y}{dt^2} + \mathbf{k}\frac{d^2z}{dt^2}. \tag{14c}$$

PROBLEMS

In Problems 1–8, $\mathbf{R} = \mathbf{i}x + \mathbf{j}y$ is the vector from the origin to the moving point $P(x, y)$ at time t. Find the velocity and acceleration vectors for any t. Also find these vectors and the speed at the particular instant given.

1. $\mathbf{R} = (a \cos \omega t)\mathbf{i} + (a \sin \omega t)\mathbf{j}$, a and ω being positive constants; $t = \pi/(3\omega)$.
2. $\mathbf{R} = (2 \cos t)\mathbf{i} + (3 \sin t)\mathbf{j}$, $t = \pi/4$
3. $\mathbf{R} = (t + 1)\mathbf{i} + (t^2 - 1)\mathbf{j}$, $t = 2$
4. $\mathbf{R} = (\cos 2t)\mathbf{i} + (2 \sin t)\mathbf{j}$, $t = 0$
5. $\mathbf{R} = e^t\mathbf{i} + e^{-2t}\mathbf{j}$, $t = \ln 3$
6. $\mathbf{R} = (\sec t)\mathbf{i} + (\tan t)\mathbf{j}$, $t = \pi/6$
7. $\mathbf{R} = (\cosh 3t)\mathbf{i} + (2 \sinh t)\mathbf{j}$, $t = 0$
8. $\mathbf{R} = [\ln (t + 1)]\mathbf{i} + t^2\mathbf{j}$, $t = 1$
9. If the force that acts on a particle P of mass m is

$$\mathbf{F} = -mg\mathbf{j},$$

where m and g are constants, and the particle starts from the origin with velocity

$$\mathbf{v}_0 = (v_0 \cos \alpha)\mathbf{i} + (v_0 \sin \alpha)\mathbf{j}$$

at time $t = 0$, find the vector $\mathbf{R} = \mathbf{i}x + \mathbf{j}y$ from the origin to P at time t.

10. Problem 9 describes the motion of a projectile *in vacuo*. If the projectile encounters a resistance proportional to the velocity, the force is

$$\mathbf{F} = -mg\mathbf{j} - k\frac{d\mathbf{R}}{dt}.$$

Show that one integration of $\mathbf{F} = md^2\mathbf{R}/dt^2$ leads to the differential equation

$$\frac{d\mathbf{R}}{dt} + \frac{k}{m}\mathbf{R} = \mathbf{v}_0 - gt\mathbf{j}.$$

(To solve this equation, one can multiply both sides of the equation by $e^{(k/m)t}$. Then the left side is the derivative of the product $\mathbf{R}e^{(k/m)t}$ and both sides can be integrated.)

Find the velocity $\mathbf{v}$ and the acceleration $\mathbf{a}$ for the motion in Problems 11 through 13. Also, find the angle θ between $\mathbf{v}$ and $\mathbf{a}$ at time $t = 0$.

11. $x = e^t$, $y = e^t \sin t$, $z = e^t \cos t$
12. $x = \tan t$, $y = \sinh 2t$, $z = \text{sech } 3t$
13. $x = \ln (t^2 + 1)$, $y = \tan^{-1} t$, $z = \sqrt{t^2 + 1}$
14. The plane $z = 2x + 3y$ intersects the cylinder $x^2 + y^2 = 9$ in an ellipse.

a) Express the position of a point $P(x, y, z)$ on this ellipse as a vector function $\mathbf{R} = \overrightarrow{OP} = \mathbf{R}(\theta)$, where θ is a measure of the dihedral angle between the xz-plane and the plane containing the z-axis and P.

b) Using the equations of (a), find the velocity and acceleration of P, assuming that $d\theta/dt = \omega$ is constant.

12-3

TANGENTIAL VECTORS

As the point P moves along a given curve in the xy-plane, we may imagine its position as being specified by the length of arc s from some arbitrarily chosen reference point P_0 on the curve. The vector

$$\mathbf{R} = \mathbf{i}x + \mathbf{j}y$$

from O to $P(x, y)$ is therefore a function of s and we shall now investigate the properties of $d\mathbf{R}/ds$. To this end, let P have coordinates (x, y) corresponding to the value s, while $Q(x + \Delta x, y + \Delta y)$ corresponds to $s + \Delta s$. Then

$$\frac{\Delta \mathbf{R}}{\Delta s} = \mathbf{i}\frac{\Delta x}{\Delta s} + \mathbf{j}\frac{\Delta y}{\Delta s} = \frac{\vec{PQ}}{\Delta s} \tag{1}$$

is a *vector* whose magnitude is chord PQ divided by arc PQ, and this approaches unity as $\Delta s \to 0$. Hence

$$\frac{d\mathbf{R}}{ds} = \lim_{\Delta s \to 0} \frac{\Delta \mathbf{R}}{\Delta s} \tag{2}$$

is a *unit* vector. The *direction* of this unit vector is the limiting direction approached by the direction of $\Delta \mathbf{R}/\Delta s$ as $\Delta s \to 0$. Now

$$\frac{\Delta \mathbf{R}}{\Delta s} = \frac{\vec{PQ}}{\Delta s}$$

has the same direction as $\vec{PQ}$ in case (a) when Δs is positive, or else it has the same direction as $\vec{QP}$ in case (b) when Δs is negative. Figures 12–6(a) and (b) illustrate these two cases and show that in *either* case, $\Delta \mathbf{R}/\Delta s$ is directed along the chord through P and Q and points in the direction of increasing s (that is, upward to the right, although $\Delta \mathbf{R}$ points downward and to the left in Fig. 12–6(b)).

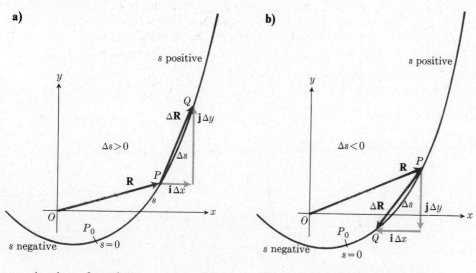

12–6 $\Delta \mathbf{R}/\Delta s$ will point in the direction of increasing s in both (a) and (b). Thus, the direction of $\Delta \mathbf{R}/\Delta s$, and of $\mathbf{T} = d\mathbf{R}/ds$ (part c), is determined by how we decide to measure s, as well as by the geometry of the curve.

As $\Delta s \to 0$ and $Q \to P$, the direction of the chord through P and Q approaches the direction of the *tangent* to the curve at P. Thus the limiting direction of $\Delta \mathbf{R}/\Delta s$, in other words the *direction of $d\mathbf{R}/ds$*, is along the *tangent to the curve at P*, and its sense is that which points in the direction of increasing arc length s. It points away from P_0 when s is positive, and toward P_0 when s is negative.

Whichever way it points, the vector

$$\frac{d\mathbf{R}}{ds} = \mathbf{T} \tag{3}$$

is a *unit vector, tangent to the curve at P* (Fig. 12–6(c)).

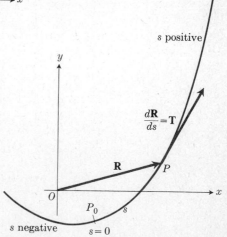

If we let $\Delta s \to 0$ in Eq. (1), we find that

$$\frac{d\mathbf{R}}{ds} = \mathbf{i}\frac{dx}{ds} + \mathbf{j}\frac{dy}{ds}, \qquad (4)$$

and this may be used to find $\mathbf{T}$ at any point of a curve whose equation is given. However, the natural parametrization of a motion in many cases is likely to be time and not arc length. If $\mathbf{R} = x(t)\mathbf{i} + y(t)\mathbf{j}$ and t is not arc length, then the best way to find $\mathbf{T}$ is to normalize $\mathbf{v} = d\mathbf{R}/dt$. That is, first find $\mathbf{v}$ and then divide $\mathbf{v}$ by $|\mathbf{v}|$ to obtain

$$\mathbf{T} = \frac{\mathbf{v}}{|\mathbf{v}|}.$$

This works in all cases, except when $\mathbf{v} = \mathbf{0}$ at a point.

EXAMPLE 1. Find $\mathbf{T}$ for the motion

$$\mathbf{R} = (\cos t + t \sin t)\mathbf{i} + (\sin t - t \cos t)\mathbf{j}, \qquad t \geq 0.$$

Solution

$$\mathbf{v} = \frac{d\mathbf{R}}{dt} = (-\sin t + t \cos t + \sin t)\mathbf{i} + (\cos t + t \sin t - \cos t)\mathbf{j}$$

$$= (t \cos t)\mathbf{i} + (t \sin t)\mathbf{j};$$

$$|\mathbf{v}| = \sqrt{t^2 \cos^2 t + t^2 \sin^2 t} = t;$$

$$\mathbf{T} = \frac{\mathbf{v}}{|\mathbf{v}|} = (\cos t)\mathbf{i} + (\sin t)\mathbf{j}.$$

EXAMPLE 2. For the counterclockwise motion

$$\mathbf{R} = \mathbf{i} \cos \theta + \mathbf{j} \sin \theta$$

around the unit circle, we find that

$$\mathbf{v} = (-\sin \theta)\mathbf{i} + (\cos \theta)\mathbf{j}$$

is already a unit vector, so that $\mathbf{v} = \mathbf{T}$. In fact, $\mathbf{T}$ is $\mathbf{R}$ rotated 90° counterclockwise (Fig. 12–7).

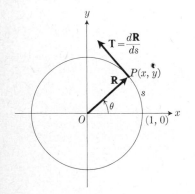

12–7 $\mathbf{R} = \mathbf{i} \cos \theta + \mathbf{j} \sin \theta$.

Space Curves and Arc Length

All that has been done above for two-dimensional motion in a plane can be extended to three-dimensional motion in space. To this end, let $P(x, y, z)$ be a point whose position in space is given by the equations

$$x = f(t), \qquad y = g(t), \qquad z = h(t), \qquad (5)$$

where f, g, and h are differentiable functions of t. As t varies continuously, P traces a curve in space.

EXAMPLE 3. The equations

$$x = a \cos \omega t, \qquad y = a \sin \omega t, \qquad z = bt, \qquad (6)$$

where a, b, and ω are positive constants, represent a circular helix (Fig. 12–8). The projection of the point $P(x, y, z)$ onto the xy-plane moves around the circle $x^2 + y^2 = a^2$, $z = 0$, as t varies, while the distance between P and the xy-plane changes steadily with t.

Let P_0 be any fixed point on the space curve, and adopt a positive direction for measuring the distance along the curve from P_0. To do this we can let P_0 be the position of P when $t = 0$, say, and measure arc length in the direction in which P first moves away from P_0 as t takes on positive values. Then the position of P on the curve becomes a function of the arc length s from P_0 to P.

The vector

$$\mathbf{R} = \mathbf{i}x + \mathbf{j}y + \mathbf{k}z \tag{7}$$

from the origin to P is also a function of s and we propose to discuss the geometrical significance of the derivative,

$$\frac{d\mathbf{R}}{ds} = \mathbf{i}\frac{dx}{ds} + \mathbf{j}\frac{dy}{ds} + \mathbf{k}\frac{dz}{ds}. \tag{8}$$

If we calculate the derivative from the definition

$$\frac{d\mathbf{R}}{ds} = \lim_{\Delta s \to 0} \frac{\Delta \mathbf{R}}{\Delta s},$$

we have (Fig. 12–9)

$$\frac{\Delta \mathbf{R}}{\Delta s} = \text{a vector of magnitude } \frac{\text{chord } PQ}{\text{arc } PQ} \text{ directed along the secant line } PQ.$$

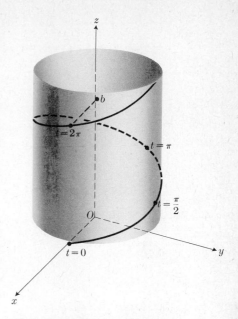

12–8 The helix $x = a \cos \omega t$, $y = a \sin \omega t$, $z = bt$, spirals up from the xy-plane as t increases from zero.

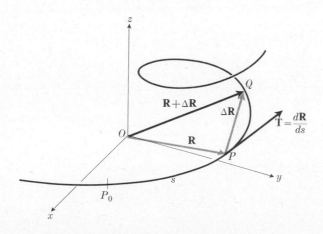

12–9 If $\mathbf{R}$ is differentiable, then $\lim_{\Delta s \to 0} \Delta \mathbf{R}/\Delta s$ is a unit vector tangent to the curve traced out by P.

As $Q \to P$ and $\Delta s \to 0$, the direction of the secant line approaches the direction of the tangent to the curve at P, while the ratio of chord to arc approaches unity (for a "smooth" curve). Therefore the limit of $\Delta \mathbf{R}/\Delta s$ is a unit vector tangent to the curve at P and pointing in the direction in which arc length increases along the curve. In other words, the vector $\mathbf{T}$, which is defined by the equation

$$\frac{d\mathbf{R}}{ds} = \mathbf{T}, \tag{9}$$

is a *unit* vector *tangent* to the space curve described by the endpoint P of the vector $\mathbf{R} = \overrightarrow{OP}$.

To find $\mathbf{T}$ we do not need to express the components of $\mathbf{R}$ in terms of s. As with motion in the plane, the fact that $\mathbf{T}$ is a unit vector lets us compute $\mathbf{T}$ from the velocity vector $\mathbf{v} = d\mathbf{R}/dt$ by the formula

$$\mathbf{T} = \frac{d\mathbf{v}}{|\mathbf{v}|}. \tag{10}$$

EXAMPLE 4. Find $\mathbf{T}$ for the helix of Example 3.

Solution. The velocity vector is

$$\mathbf{v} = \mathbf{i}(-a\omega \sin \omega t) + \mathbf{j}(a\omega \cos \omega t) + \mathbf{k}(b),$$

whose length is

$$|\mathbf{v}| = \sqrt{a^2\omega^2 \sin^2 \omega t + a^2\omega^2 \cos^2 \omega t + b^2} = \sqrt{a^2\omega^2 + b^2}.$$

Therefore,

$$\mathbf{T} = \frac{\mathbf{v}}{|\mathbf{v}|} = \frac{a\omega(-\mathbf{i} \sin \omega t + \mathbf{j} \cos \omega t) + b\mathbf{k}}{\sqrt{a^2\omega^2 + b^2}}$$

If we combine the results of Eqs. (8) and (9), we have

$$\mathbf{T} = \mathbf{i}\frac{dx}{ds} + \mathbf{j}\frac{dy}{ds} + \mathbf{k}\frac{dz}{ds}, \tag{11}$$

and since

$$\mathbf{T} \cdot \mathbf{T} = 1,$$

this means that

$$ds = \pm\sqrt{dx^2 + dy^2 + dz^2}. \tag{12}$$

The length of an arc of a curve may be calculated by computing ds from (12) and integrating between appropriate limits.

EXAMPLE 5. For the helix in Examples 3 and 4,

$$ds = \sqrt{a^2\omega^2 + b^2} \, dt$$

and

$$s = \sqrt{a^2\omega^2 + b^2} \int dt,$$

where appropriate limits of integration are to be supplied. Thus the length of one full turn of the helix

$$x = \cos t, \qquad y = \sin t, \qquad z = t,$$

for which $a = b = \omega = 1$, is

$$\sqrt{2} \int_0^{2\pi} dt = 2\pi\sqrt{2}.$$

This is $\sqrt{2}$ times the length of the unit circle in the xy-plane over which the helix stands.

PROBLEMS

In each of the following problems (1 through 8), $\mathbf{R} = \mathbf{i}x + \mathbf{j}y$ is the vector from the origin O to $P(x, y)$. For each of these motions, find the unit tangent vector $\mathbf{T} = d\mathbf{R}/ds$.

1. $\mathbf{R} = 2\mathbf{i} \cos t + 2\mathbf{j} \sin t$
2. $\mathbf{R} = e^t\mathbf{i} + t^2\mathbf{j}$
3. $\mathbf{R} = (\cos^3 t)\mathbf{i} + (\sin^3 t)\mathbf{j}$
4. $\mathbf{R} = \mathbf{i}x + \mathbf{j}x^2$
5. $\mathbf{R} = (\cos 2t)\mathbf{i} + (2 \cos t)\mathbf{j}$
6. $\mathbf{R} = \dfrac{t^3}{3}\mathbf{i} + \dfrac{t^2}{2}\mathbf{j}$
7. $\mathbf{R} = (e^t \cos t)\mathbf{i} + (e^t \sin t)\mathbf{j}$
8. $\mathbf{R} = \cosh t\,\mathbf{i} + t\mathbf{j}$

In Problems 9 through 12, $\mathbf{R} = \mathbf{i}x + \mathbf{j}y + \mathbf{k}z$. Find the unit tangent vector $\mathbf{T}$ for each space curve.

9. $x = 6 \sin 2t, \quad y = 6 \cos 2t, \quad z = 5t$
10. $x = e^t \cos t, \quad y = e^t \sin t, \quad z = e^t$
11. $x = 3 \cosh 2t, \quad y = 3 \sinh 2t, \quad z = 6t$
12. $x = 3t \cos t, \quad y = 3t \sin t, \quad z = 4t$

For the curves in Problems 13–16, find the length of the curve between $t = 0$ and $t = \pi$.

13. The curve of Problem 9
14. The curve of Problem 10
15. The curve of Problem 11
16. The curve of Problem 12

Our next step is to consider the rate of change of the unit tangent vector $\mathbf{T}$ as P moves along the curve. Of course, the length of $\mathbf{T}$ is constant, always being equal to one. But the direction of $\mathbf{T}$ changes, since it is tangent to the curve and the tangent changes direction from point to point except where the curve is straight.

12-4

CURVATURE AND NORMAL VECTORS

Motion in a Plane

If P moves along a curve in the xy-plane, we measure the direction of $\mathbf{T}$ by the angle ϕ from the positively directed x-axis to $\mathbf{T}$ (Fig. 12–10). We may then measure the rate at which $\mathbf{T}$ turns to one side or the other as we move along the curve by keeping track of the change in ϕ. The absolute value of the derivative $d\phi/ds$ of ϕ with respect to arc length (measured in radians per unit of length) is called the *curvature function* of the curve, and its value at any given point is called the curvature at that point. The usual notation for curvature is the Greek letter κ (kappa):

$$\kappa = \left| \frac{d\phi}{ds} \right|, \tag{1}$$

where

$$\tan \phi = \frac{dy}{dx}$$

and

$$ds = \pm\sqrt{dx^2 + dy^2}.$$

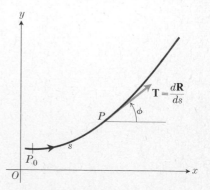

12–10 The value of $|d\phi/ds|$ at P is called the curvature of the curve at P.

One may derive a formula for κ from the equations above in a straightforward manner. Namely,

$$\phi = \tan^{-1}\frac{dy}{dx},$$

$$\frac{d\phi}{dx} = \frac{d^2y/dx^2}{1 + (dy/dx)^2},$$

and

$$\frac{ds}{dx} = \pm\sqrt{1 + (dy/dx)^2},$$

so that

$$\kappa = \left|\frac{d\phi}{ds}\right| = \left|\frac{d\phi/dx}{ds/dx}\right| = \frac{|d^2y/dx^2|}{[1 + (dy/dx)^2]^{3/2}}. \qquad \textbf{(2a)}$$

We may arrive at a formula for κ in terms of dx/dy and d^2x/dy^2 if we use

$$\phi = \cot^{-1}\frac{dx}{dy}$$

and

$$\kappa = \left|\frac{d\phi}{ds}\right| = \left|\frac{d\phi/dy}{ds/dy}\right|$$

The result, which corresponds to (2a), is

$$\kappa = \frac{|d^2x/dy^2|}{[1 + (dx/dy)^2]^{3/2}}. \qquad \textbf{(2b)}$$

If the equation of the curve is given in parametric form,

$$x = f(t), \qquad y = g(t),$$

then

$$\phi = \tan^{-1}\left(\frac{dy/dt}{dx/dt}\right),$$

and if we use

$$\kappa = \left|\frac{d\phi/dt}{ds/dt}\right|,$$

the calculations are as follows:

$$\frac{d\phi}{dt} = \frac{1}{1 + \left(\dfrac{dy/dt}{dx/dt}\right)^2}\,\frac{\dfrac{dx}{dt}\dfrac{d^2y}{dt^2} - \dfrac{dy}{dt}\dfrac{d^2x}{dt^2}}{\left(\dfrac{dx}{dt}\right)^2} = \frac{\dot{x}\ddot{y} - \dot{y}\ddot{x}}{\dot{x}^2 + \dot{y}^2} \qquad \left[\dot{x} = \frac{dx}{dt},\ \ddot{x} = \frac{d^2x}{dt^2}\right]$$

and

$$\frac{ds}{dt} = \pm\sqrt{\dot{x}^2 + \dot{y}^2},$$

so that

$$\kappa = \frac{|\dot{x}\ddot{y} - \dot{y}\ddot{x}|}{[\dot{x}^2 + \dot{y}^2]^{3/2}}. \tag{2c}$$

EXAMPLE 1. *The curvature of a straight line is 0.*
On a straight line, ϕ is constant. Therefore $d\phi/ds$ in Eq. (2a) is zero.

EXAMPLE 2. *The curvature of a circle of radius a is $1/a$.*
We place the center of the circle at the origin to make its equation simple (Fig. 12–11).

METHOD 1.   Parametrize the circle with the equations

$$x = a \cos \theta, \qquad y = a \sin \theta.$$

Then,

$$\dot{x} = -a \sin \theta, \qquad \dot{y} = a \cos \theta,$$

$$\ddot{x} = -a \cos \theta, \qquad \ddot{y} = -a \sin \theta.$$

From Eq. (2c) we have

$$\kappa = \frac{|(-a \sin \theta)(-a \sin \theta) - (a \cos \theta)(-a \cos \theta)|}{[a^2 \sin^2 \theta + a^2 \cos^2 \theta]^{3/2}}$$

$$= \frac{a^2}{a^3} = \frac{1}{a}.$$

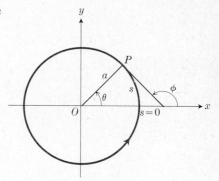

12–11 P: $x = a \cos \theta$, $y = a \sin \theta$.

METHOD 2.   (Special to the circle) The geometry of Fig. 12–11 allows s and ϕ to be expressed in terms of θ as follows:

$$s = a\theta, \qquad \phi = \theta + \frac{\pi}{2}. \tag{3}$$

Equation (1) then gives

$$\kappa = \left| \frac{d\phi}{ds} \right| = \left| \frac{d\theta}{a\,d\theta} \right| = \frac{1}{a}.$$

The curvature of a circle is equal to the reciprocal of its radius. The smaller the circle, the greater its curvature. To "turn on a dime" indicates a more rapid change of direction per unit of arc length than does to turn on a silver dollar!

Circle and Radius of Curvature

The circle that is tangent to a plane curve at P, whose center lies on the concave side of the curve and that has the same curvature as the curve has at P, is called the *circle of curvature*. Its radius is $1/\kappa$, from Example 2. We define the *radius of curvature* ρ at P to be

$$\rho = \frac{1}{\kappa} = \frac{[1 + (dy/dx)^2]^{3/2}}{|d^2y/dx^2|}. \tag{4}$$

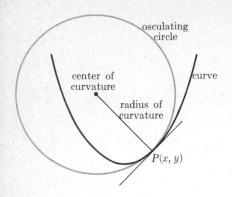

12–12 The osculating circle or circle of curvature at $P(x, y)$.

The center of the circle of curvature is called the center of curvature. The circle of curvature has its first and second derivatives equal, respectively, to the first and second derivatives of the curve itself at this point. For this reason it has a higher degree of contact with the curve at P than has any other circle, so it is also called the *osculating* circle! (See Fig. 12–12.) Since velocity and acceleration involve only the first and second time derivatives of the coordinates of P, it is natural to anticipate that the instantaneous velocity and acceleration of a particle moving on any curve may be expressed in terms of instantaneous velocity and acceleration of an associated particle moving on the osculating circle. This will be investigated in the next article.

Unit Normal Vector

We return once more to the question of the rate of change of the unit vector $\mathbf{T}$ as P moves along the curve. In terms of the slope angle ϕ (Fig. 12–13), we may write

$$\mathbf{T} = \mathbf{i} \cos \phi + \mathbf{j} \sin \phi, \tag{5}$$

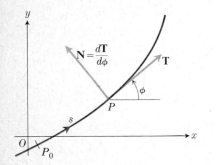

and then the derivative

$$\frac{d\mathbf{T}}{d\phi} = -\mathbf{i} \sin \phi + \mathbf{j} \cos \phi \tag{6}$$

has magnitude

$$\left| \frac{d\mathbf{T}}{d\phi} \right| = \sqrt{\sin^2 \phi + \cos^2 \phi} = 1.$$

From Eqs. (5) and (6) we see that

$$\mathbf{T} \cdot \frac{d\mathbf{T}}{d\phi} = 0.$$

Therefore $d\mathbf{T}/d\phi$ is perpendicular to $\mathbf{T}$. In fact, we see from Eq. (6) that

$$\frac{d\mathbf{T}}{d\phi} = \mathbf{N}, \tag{7}$$

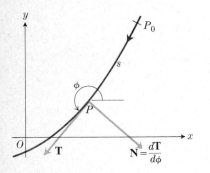

12–13 Turn $\mathbf{T}$ counterclockwise 90° to get $\mathbf{N}$.

where

$$\mathbf{N} = \mathbf{i} \cos (\phi + 90°) + \mathbf{j} \sin (\phi + 90°) = -\mathbf{i} \sin \phi + \mathbf{j} \cos \phi$$

is the *unit normal* vector obtained by rotating the unit tangent vector $\mathbf{T}$ clockwise through 90° (Fig. 12–13).

A comparison of Eqs. (5) and (6) shows that $\mathbf{N}$ can be found from $\mathbf{T}$ by interchanging components and changing the sign of the new first component.

EXAMPLE 3. Find $\mathbf{N}$ for the curve traced by

$$\mathbf{R} = (2t + 3)\mathbf{i} + (t^2 - 1)\mathbf{j}.$$

Solution. We first find **T**:

$$\mathbf{v} = 2\mathbf{i} + 2t\mathbf{j},$$

$$|\mathbf{v}| = \sqrt{4 + 4t^2} = 2\sqrt{1 + t^2},$$

$$\mathbf{T} = \frac{\mathbf{v}}{|\mathbf{v}|} = \frac{1}{\sqrt{1 + t^2}}\mathbf{i} + \frac{t}{\sqrt{1 + t^2}}\mathbf{j}.$$

We then interchange the components of **T** and change the sign of the new first component, to get

$$\mathbf{N} = -\frac{t}{\sqrt{1 + t^2}}\mathbf{i} + \frac{1}{\sqrt{1 + t^2}}\mathbf{j}.$$

For a curve in 3-space, the direction of the unit tangent vector **T** is not determined by a single angle such as ϕ. Instead, we shall use arc length, s, as the parameter for the theoretical study of **T**. In Article 12–5, we shall see that **T** and $d\mathbf{T}/ds$ are orthogonal vectors. If $d\mathbf{T}/ds$ is not the zero vector, we then use its direction to specify the *principal normal* to the curve. In the two-dimensional case, we have (from the chain rule)

$$\frac{d\mathbf{T}}{ds} = \frac{d\mathbf{T}}{d\phi}\frac{d\phi}{ds} = \mathbf{N}(\pm\kappa).$$

If we direct the curve so that ϕ is an *increasing function* of s, then

$$\frac{d\phi}{ds} = \kappa,$$

and

$$\frac{d\mathbf{T}}{ds} = \frac{d\mathbf{T}}{d\phi}\frac{d\phi}{ds} = \mathbf{N}\kappa. \tag{8}$$

To combine both the two-dimensional and three-dimensional curves in one equation, we drop the middle part of Eq. (8) and obtain the simple equation

$$\frac{d\mathbf{T}}{ds} = \mathbf{N}\kappa. \tag{9}$$

In Eq. (9), κ is the magnitude of $d\mathbf{T}/ds$:

$$\kappa = \left|\frac{d\mathbf{T}}{ds}\right|. \tag{10}$$

This number is called the *curvature* of the space curve. Such a definition is consistent with Eq. (1) for a plane curve, and extends the concept of curvature to curves in space. Equations (9) and (10) together define the unit principal normal vector **N**, whenever $d\mathbf{T}/ds \neq \mathbf{0}$:

$$\mathbf{N} = \frac{d\mathbf{T}/ds}{|d\mathbf{T}/ds|}. \tag{11}$$

EXAMPLE 4. Find the curvature and principal normal of the helix of Examples 3 and 4 of Article 12–3.

Solution. In Example 4, Article 12–3, we found

$$\mathbf{T} = \frac{a\omega(-\mathbf{i}\sin\omega t + \mathbf{j}\cos\omega t) + b\mathbf{k}}{\sqrt{a^2\omega^2 + b^2}} \tag{12}$$

and

$$\frac{ds}{dt} = \sqrt{a^2\omega^2 + b^2}.$$

Hence

$$\frac{d\mathbf{T}}{ds} = \frac{d\mathbf{T}/dt}{ds/dt}$$

$$= \frac{-a\omega^2}{a^2\omega^2 + b^2}(\mathbf{i}\cos\omega t + \mathbf{j}\sin\omega t),$$

and

$$\kappa = \left| \frac{d\mathbf{T}}{ds} \right| = \frac{a\omega^2}{a^2\omega^2 + b^2}. \tag{13}$$

Two limiting cases of Eq. (13) are worth checking. First, if $b = 0$, then $z = 0$, and the helix reduces to a circle of radius a in the xy-plane, while Eq. (13) reduces to $\kappa = 1/a$ as it should. Second, if $a = 0$, then $x = y = 0$ and $z = bt$. This tells us that the point moves along the z-axis. Again Eq. (13) gives the correct curvature, namely $\kappa = 0$. In the general case, the curvature of a circular helix is constant and less than the curvature of the circle that is the cross section of the cylinder around which the helix winds (Fig. 12–8).

The principal normal of the helix is the vector

$$\mathbf{N} = \frac{d\mathbf{T}/ds}{|d\mathbf{T}/ds|} = -(\mathbf{i}\cos\omega t + \mathbf{j}\sin\omega t)$$

$$= -\frac{\mathbf{i}x + \mathbf{j}y}{a}, \tag{14}$$

which is parallel to the vector from the point $(0, 0, z)$ on the z-axis to the point $P(x, y, z)$ on the helix.

Once the unit vectors $\mathbf{T}$ and $\mathbf{N}$ have been determined, it is a simple matter to define a third unit vector, perpendicular to both $\mathbf{T}$ and $\mathbf{N}$, by the equation

$$\mathbf{B} = \mathbf{T} \times \mathbf{N}. \tag{15}$$

The vector $\mathbf{B}$ so defined may be thought of as lying in the plane normal to $\mathbf{T}$ at P (Fig. 12–14) and is called the *binormal* at P. The three unit vectors, $\mathbf{T}$, $\mathbf{N}$, and $\mathbf{B}$, form a righthanded system of mutually orthogonal unit vectors which are useful in more thorough investigations of space curves. (Struik, *Differential Geometry*, Chapter 1; Addison-Wesley.)

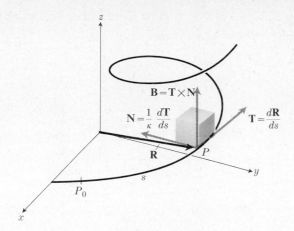

12–14   **T**, **N**, and **B** form a righthanded coordinate frame.

PROBLEMS

Find the curvature of each of the curves in Problems 1–12.

1. $y = a \cosh (x/a)$

2. $y = \ln (\cos x)$

3. $y = e^{2x}$

4. $x = a \cos^3 t, \quad y = a \sin^3 t$

5. $x = a(\cos \theta + \theta \sin \theta),$
$y = a(\sin \theta - \theta \cos \theta)$

6. $x = a(\theta - \sin \theta),$
$y = a(1 - \cos \theta)$

7. $x = \ln \sec y$

8. $x = \frac{1}{3}(y^2 + 2)^{3/2}$

9. $x = \dfrac{y^4}{4} + \dfrac{1}{8y^2}$

10. $x = 2t + 3, \quad y = 5 - t^2$

11. $x = \dfrac{t^3}{3}, \quad y = \dfrac{t^2}{2}$

12. $x = e^t \cos t, \quad y = e^t \sin t$

13. Find the equation of the osculating circle associated with the curve $y = e^x$ at the point $(0, 1)$. By calculating dy/dx and d^2y/dx^2 at the point $(0, 1)$ from the equation of this circle, verify that these derivatives have the same values there as do the corresponding derivatives for the curve $y = e^x$. Sketch the curve and the osculating circle.

14. Show that when x and y are considered as functions of arc length s, the unit vectors **T** and **N** may be expressed as follows:

$$\mathbf{T} = \mathbf{i}\frac{dx}{ds} + \mathbf{j}\frac{dy}{ds}, \qquad \mathbf{N} = -\mathbf{i}\frac{dy}{ds} + \mathbf{j}\frac{dx}{ds},$$

where $dx/ds = \cos \phi,\, dy/ds = \sin \phi$, and ϕ is the angle from the positive x-axis to the tangent line.

In Problems 15–17, find the principal normal vector **N**, the curvature κ, and the unit binormal vector **B**.

15. The curve of Problem 9, Article 12–3

16. The curve of Problem 10, Article 12–3

17. The curve of Problem 11, Article 12–3

18. Let $\mathbf{R} = \overrightarrow{OP}$ be the vector from the origin to a moving point P. Let **T** and **N** be the unit tangent and principal normal vectors, respectively, for the curve described by P. Express the velocity and acceleration vectors $d\mathbf{R}/dt$ and $d^2\mathbf{R}/dt^2$ in terms of their **T**- and **N**-components.

If the components of a vector are differentiable functions of a scalar variable t, then we know that the vector is a differentiable function of t, and its derivative is obtained by differentiating the components (Article 12–1, Eq. 8).

It is also convenient to develop formulas for the derivative of the dot and cross products of two vectors that are differentiable functions of t. Suppose, for example, that

$$\mathbf{U} = \mathbf{i}f_1(t) + \mathbf{j}f_2(t) + \mathbf{k}f_3(t),$$
$$\mathbf{V} = \mathbf{i}g_1(t) + \mathbf{j}g_2(t) + \mathbf{k}g_3(t),$$

(1)

12–5

DIFFERENTIATION OF PRODUCTS OF VECTORS

where the f's and g's are differentiable functions of t. Then, by the ordinary formulas for differentiating products of scalar functions, it is easy to verify that

$$\frac{d}{dt}(\mathbf{U} \cdot \mathbf{V}) = \frac{d\mathbf{U}}{dt} \cdot \mathbf{V} + \mathbf{U} \cdot \frac{d\mathbf{V}}{dt}, \tag{2}$$

$$\frac{d}{dt}(\mathbf{U} \times \mathbf{V}) = \frac{d\mathbf{U}}{dt} \times \mathbf{V} + \mathbf{U} \times \frac{d\mathbf{V}}{dt}. \tag{3}$$

However, instead of appealing to the component-wise verification of the identities in Eqs. (2) and (3), it is instructive to establish these equations by the Δ-process. For example, let

$$\mathbf{W} = \mathbf{U} \times \mathbf{V},$$

where t has some specific value. Then give t an increment Δt and denote the new values of the vectors by $\mathbf{U} + \Delta\mathbf{U}$, etc., so that

$$\mathbf{W} + \Delta\mathbf{W} = (\mathbf{U} + \Delta\mathbf{U}) \times (\mathbf{V} + \Delta\mathbf{V})$$

$$= \mathbf{U} \times \mathbf{V} + \mathbf{U} \times \Delta\mathbf{V} + \Delta\mathbf{U} \times \mathbf{V} + \Delta\mathbf{U} \times \Delta\mathbf{V},$$

and

$$\frac{\Delta\mathbf{W}}{\Delta t} = \mathbf{U} \times \frac{\Delta\mathbf{V}}{\Delta t} + \frac{\Delta\mathbf{U}}{\Delta t} \times \mathbf{V} + \frac{\Delta\mathbf{U}}{\Delta t} \times \Delta\mathbf{V}.$$

Now take limits as $\Delta t \to 0$, noting that

$$\lim \frac{\Delta\mathbf{W}}{\Delta t} = \frac{d\mathbf{W}}{dt}, \qquad \lim \frac{\Delta\mathbf{U}}{\Delta t} = \frac{d\mathbf{U}}{dt}, \qquad \lim \Delta\mathbf{V} = \lim \frac{\Delta\mathbf{V}}{\Delta t} \cdot \lim \Delta t = 0,$$

so that

$$\frac{d\mathbf{W}}{dt} = \mathbf{U} \times \frac{d\mathbf{V}}{dt} + \frac{d\mathbf{U}}{dt} \times \mathbf{V},$$

which is equivalent to Eq. (3).

Equations (2) and (3) are both like the equation for the derivative of the product of two scalar functions u and v. Indeed, the proofs by the Δ-process are the same for vectors as for scalars. The only place we need to be careful is in a derivative involving a cross product. The relative order of the factors must be preserved, because reversing the order changes the sign of the product.

EXAMPLE 1. The formula for the derivative of the triple scalar product leads to an interesting identity for the derivative of a determinant of order three. Let

$$\mathbf{U} = u_1\mathbf{i} + u_2\mathbf{j} + u_3\mathbf{k},$$

$$\mathbf{V} = v_1\mathbf{i} + v_2\mathbf{j} + v_3\mathbf{k}, \tag{4}$$

$$\mathbf{W} = w_1\mathbf{i} + w_2\mathbf{j} + w_3\mathbf{k},$$

where the components are differentiable functions of a scalar t. Then the identity

$$\frac{d}{dt}(\mathbf{U} \cdot \mathbf{V} \times \mathbf{W}) = \frac{d\mathbf{U}}{dt} \cdot \mathbf{V} \times \mathbf{W} + \mathbf{U} \cdot \frac{d\mathbf{V}}{dt} \times \mathbf{W} + \mathbf{U} \cdot \mathbf{V} \times \frac{d\mathbf{W}}{dt} \quad (5)$$

is equivalent to

$$\frac{d}{dt}\begin{vmatrix} u_1 & u_2 & u_3 \\ v_1 & v_2 & v_3 \\ w_1 & w_2 & w_3 \end{vmatrix} = \begin{vmatrix} \dfrac{du_1}{dt} & \dfrac{du_2}{dt} & \dfrac{du_3}{dt} \\ v_1 & v_2 & v_3 \\ w_1 & w_2 & w_3 \end{vmatrix} + \begin{vmatrix} u_1 & u_2 & u_3 \\ \dfrac{dv_1}{dt} & \dfrac{dv_2}{dt} & \dfrac{dv_3}{dt} \\ w_1 & w_2 & w_3 \end{vmatrix} + \begin{vmatrix} u_1 & u_2 & u_3 \\ v_1 & v_2 & v_3 \\ \dfrac{dw_1}{dt} & \dfrac{dw_2}{dt} & \dfrac{dw_3}{dt} \end{vmatrix} \quad (6)$$

This says that the derivative of a determinant of order three is the sum of three determinants obtained from the original determinant by differentiating one row at a time. The result may be extended to determinants of any order n.

Derivatives of Vectors of Constant Length

An interesting geometrical result is obtained by differentiating the identity

$$\mathbf{V} \cdot \mathbf{V} = |\mathbf{V}|^2 \quad \text{(7a)}$$

when $\mathbf{V}$ is a vector of constant magnitude, for then $|\mathbf{V}|^2$ is a constant, so its derivative is zero, and one has

$$\mathbf{V} \cdot \frac{d\mathbf{V}}{dt} + \frac{d\mathbf{V}}{dt} \cdot \mathbf{V} = 0$$

or, since the scalar product is commutative,

$$2\mathbf{V} \cdot \frac{d\mathbf{V}}{dt} = 0. \quad \text{(7b)}$$

This means that either $\mathbf{V}$ is zero, $d\mathbf{V}/dt$ is zero (and hence $\mathbf{V}$ is constant in direction as well as magnitude), or else that $d\mathbf{V}/dt$ is perpendicular to $\mathbf{V}$.

EXAMPLE 2. Suppose that a point P moves about on the surface of a sphere. Then the magnitude of the vector $\mathbf{R}$ from the center to P is a constant equal to the radius of the sphere. Therefore, the velocity vector $d\mathbf{R}/dt$ is always perpendicular to $\mathbf{R}$ (Fig. 12–15).

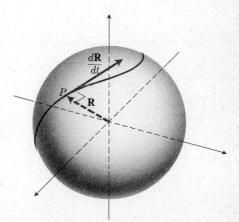

12–15 The velocity vector of a particle P that moves on the surface of a sphere is tangent to the sphere.

We can also use the foregoing results to show that the derivative of the unit tangent vector $\mathbf{T}$ is orthogonal to $\mathbf{T}$. Because $|\mathbf{T}| = 1$, we have

$$\mathbf{T} \cdot \mathbf{T} = 1,$$

so that, by the same kind of reasoning we used in going from Eq. (7a) to (7b), we can deduce that

$$\mathbf{T} \cdot \frac{d\mathbf{T}}{ds} = 0.$$

This validates our earlier statement that $d\mathbf{T}/ds$ is perpendicular to $\mathbf{T}$, so that the definition

$$\frac{d\mathbf{T}}{ds} = \mathbf{N}\kappa, \tag{8}$$

as given in Eq. (9), Article 12–4, with $\kappa = |d\mathbf{T}/ds|$, produces a vector $\mathbf{N}$ orthogonal to $\mathbf{T}$.

Tangential and Normal Components of the Velocity and Acceleration Vectors

In mechanics it is useful to be able to discuss the motion of a particle P in terms of its instantaneous speed ds/dt, acceleration along its path d^2s/dt^2, and the curvature of the path. This is easy if we refer the velocity and acceleration vectors to the unit vectors $\mathbf{T}$ and $\mathbf{N}$.

In Article 12–2 we found the velocity vector to be given by

$$\mathbf{v} = \frac{d\mathbf{R}}{dt}, \tag{9}$$

where $\mathbf{R} = \mathbf{i}x + \mathbf{j}y + \mathbf{k}z$ is the position vector $\overrightarrow{OP}$. We may also write this in the form

$$\mathbf{v} = \frac{d\mathbf{R}}{dt} = \frac{d\mathbf{R}}{ds}\frac{ds}{dt}$$

or

$$\mathbf{v} = \mathbf{T}\frac{ds}{dt} \tag{10}$$

if we use the result of Eq. (9), Article 12–3. This is in keeping with our earlier remark that the velocity vector is tangent to the curve and has magnitude $|\mathbf{v}| = |ds/dt|$. (See Fig. 12–16.)

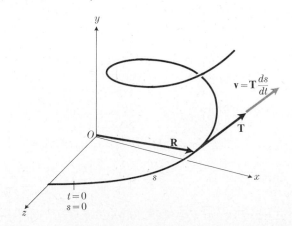

12–16   Divide $\mathbf{v}$ by ds/dt to get $\mathbf{T}$.

To obtain the acceleration vector, we differentiate Eq. (10) with respect to t:

$$\mathbf{a} = \frac{d\mathbf{v}}{dt} = \mathbf{T}\frac{d^2s}{dt^2} + \frac{d\mathbf{T}}{dt}\frac{ds}{dt}.$$

By Eq. (8),

$$\frac{d\mathbf{T}}{dt} = \frac{d\mathbf{T}}{ds}\frac{ds}{dt} = \mathbf{N}\kappa\frac{ds}{dt},$$

so that

$$\mathbf{a} = \mathbf{T}\frac{d^2s}{dt^2} + \mathbf{N}\kappa\left(\frac{ds}{dt}\right)^2. \tag{11}$$

Equation (11) expresses the acceleration vector in terms of its tangential and normal components. The *tangential component*, $a_\mathrm{T} = d^2s/dt^2$, is simply the derivative of the speed ds/dt of the particle in its path. The *normal component* $a_\mathrm{N} = \kappa(ds/dt)^2$ is directed toward the concave side of the curve and has magnitude

$$a_\mathrm{N} = \kappa\left(\frac{ds}{dt}\right)^2 = \frac{(ds/dt)^2}{\rho} = \frac{v^2}{\rho},$$

where v is the instantaneous speed of the particle and ρ is the radius of curvature of the path at the point in question. This explains why a large normal force, which must be supplied by friction between the tires and the roadway, is required to hold an automobile on a level road if it makes a sharp turn (small ρ) or a moderate turn at high speed (large v^2). (See Sears, Zemansky, Young, *University Physics* (1976), Chapter 6, for a discussion of the banking of curves.)

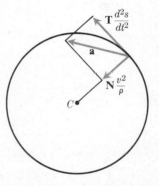

If the particle is moving in a circle with *constant* speed $v = ds/dt$, then d^2s/dt^2 is zero, and the only acceleration is the normal acceleration v^2/ρ toward the center of the circle. If the speed is not constant, the acceleration vector $\mathbf{a}$ is the resultant of the tangential and normal components, as in Fig. 12–17.

12–17 Tangential and normal components of an acceleration vector.

The following example illustrates how the tangential and normal components of velocity and acceleration may be computed when the equations of motion are known. In particular, it should be noted that the equation

$$|\mathbf{a}|^2 = a_x^2 + a_y^2 = a_\mathrm{T}^2 + a_\mathrm{N}^2 \tag{12}$$

is used to determine the normal component of acceleration

$$a_\mathrm{N} = \sqrt{|\mathbf{a}|^2 - a_\mathrm{T}^2}. \tag{13}$$

Note that Eq. (13) gives a way to find a_N without having to find κ first.

EXAMPLE 3. The coordinates of a moving particle at time t are given by

$$x = \cos t + t \sin t, \qquad y = \sin t - t \cos t.$$

Find the velocity and acceleration vectors, the speed ds/dt, and the normal and tangential components of acceleration.

Solution

$$\mathbf{v} = \mathbf{i}\frac{dx}{dt} + \mathbf{j}\frac{dy}{dt} = \mathbf{i}[-\sin t + t \cos t + \sin t] + \mathbf{j}[\cos t + t \sin t - \cos t]$$

$$= \mathbf{i}t \cos t + \mathbf{j}t \sin t$$

and

$$\mathbf{a} = \frac{d\mathbf{v}}{dt} = \mathbf{i}[-t \sin t + \cos t] + \mathbf{j}[t \cos t + \sin t].$$

Now the tangential component of velocity is

$$\frac{ds}{dt} = |\mathbf{v}| = \sqrt{(t \cos t)^2 + (t \sin t)^2} = t$$

and the tangential component of acceleration is

$$a_\mathrm{T} = \frac{d^2s}{dt^2} = \frac{d}{dt}\left(\frac{ds}{dt}\right) = \frac{d}{dt}(t) = 1.$$

We use Eq. (13) to determine the normal component of acceleration:

$$a_\mathrm{N} = \sqrt{|\mathbf{a}|^2 - a_\mathrm{T}^2} = \sqrt{(-t \sin t + \cos t)^2 + (t \cos t + \sin t)^2 - 1} = t.$$

Here the tangential acceleration has constant magnitude and the normal acceleration starts with zero magnitude at $t = 0$ and increases with time. The equations of motion are the same as the parametric equations for the *involute* of a circle of unit radius. This is the path of the endpoint P of a string that is held taut as it is unwound from the circle. To get the parametrization, the origin is taken as the center of the circle (Fig. 12–18), with $(1, 0)$ being the position where P starts. The angle t is measured from the positively directed x-axis counterclockwise to the ray from O to the point of tangency Q.

We can find the radius of curvature from the equation $a_\mathrm{N} = v^2/\rho$, since $v^2 = |\mathbf{v}|^2 = t^2$ and $a_\mathrm{N} = t$ and hence

$$\rho = \frac{v^2}{a_\mathrm{N}} = \frac{t^2}{t} = t.$$

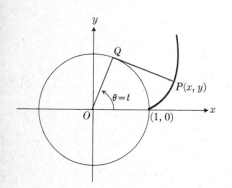

12–18   Involute of a circle.

Equations (10) and (11) can be used to find a formula for the curvature κ in terms of the velocity and acceleration. First, we compute the cross product of the velocity and acceleration vectors. We obtain

$$\mathbf{v} \times \mathbf{a} = \mathbf{T}\frac{ds}{dt} \times \left[\mathbf{T}\frac{d^2s}{dt^2} + \mathbf{N}\kappa\left(\frac{ds}{dt}\right)^2\right]$$

$$= \mathbf{T} \times \mathbf{N}\kappa\left(\frac{ds}{dt}\right)^3 \tag{14}$$

because we can apply the distributive law for the cross product, and $\mathbf{T} \times \mathbf{T} = \mathbf{0}$. Moreover, $\mathbf{T} \times \mathbf{N}$ is the unit binormal vector $\mathbf{B}$, as given by Eq. (15), Article 12–4. Therefore

$$\mathbf{v} \times \mathbf{a} = \mathbf{B}\kappa\left(\frac{ds}{dt}\right)^3. \tag{15}$$

Since **B** is a *unit* vector, the magnitude of $\mathbf{v} \times \mathbf{a}$ is

$$|\mathbf{v} \times \mathbf{a}| = \kappa \left| \frac{ds}{dt} \right|^3 = \kappa |\mathbf{v}|^3.$$

Finally, if $|\mathbf{v}| \neq 0$, we get (by division)

$$\kappa = \frac{|\mathbf{v} \times \mathbf{a}|}{|\mathbf{v}|^3}. \tag{16}$$

How do we use this equation? Given the motion in the form $\mathbf{R} = \mathbf{i}x + \mathbf{j}y + \mathbf{k}z$, we differentiate with respect to time to get $\mathbf{v}$, then differentiate again to get $\mathbf{a}$, and compute $\mathbf{v} \times \mathbf{a}$ using a determinant of order 3 in the usual way for cross products. We then divide the length of this vector by the cube of the length of $\mathbf{v}$.

EXAMPLE 4. Use Eq. (16) to find the curvature of the curve of the preceding example.

Solution. In that example, we found the velocity

$$\mathbf{v} = \mathbf{i}t \cos t + \mathbf{j}t \sin t,$$

and acceleration

$$\mathbf{a} = \mathbf{i}(-t \sin t + \cos t) + \mathbf{j}(t \cos t + \sin t).$$

Therefore

$$\mathbf{v} \times \mathbf{a} = \begin{vmatrix} \mathbf{i} & \mathbf{j} & \mathbf{k} \\ t \cos t & t \sin t & 0 \\ (-t \sin t + \cos t) & (t \cos t + \sin t) & 0 \end{vmatrix};$$

this leads to

$$\mathbf{v} \times \mathbf{a} = \mathbf{k}(t^2 \cos^2 t + t \cos t \sin t + t^2 \sin^2 t - t \sin t \cos t)$$
$$= \mathbf{k}t^2,$$

and

$$\kappa = \frac{|\mathbf{v} \times \mathbf{a}|}{|\mathbf{v}|^3} = \frac{t^2}{t^3} = \frac{1}{t}.$$

This result is valid for $t > 0$. If the curve and the motion also exist for $t < 0$, we should replace t by $|t|$ for $t < 0$.

PROBLEMS

1. Derive Eq. (2) by the Δ-process.

2. Apply Eqs. (2) and (3) to $\mathbf{U} \cdot \mathbf{V}_1$ with $\mathbf{V}_1 = \mathbf{V} \times \mathbf{W}$ and thereby derive Eq. (5) for

$$\frac{d}{dt}[\mathbf{U} \cdot (\mathbf{V} \times \mathbf{W})].$$

3. If $\mathbf{F}(t) = \mathbf{i}f(t) + \mathbf{j}g(t) + \mathbf{k}h(t)$, where f, g, and h are functions of t that have derivatives of orders one, two, and three, show that

$$\frac{d}{dt}\left[\mathbf{F} \cdot \left(\frac{d\mathbf{F}}{dt} \times \frac{d^2\mathbf{F}}{dt^2} \right) \right] = \mathbf{F} \cdot \left(\frac{d\mathbf{F}}{dt} \times \frac{d^3\mathbf{F}}{dt^3} \right).$$

Explain why the answer contains just this one term rather than the three terms that one might expect.

4. With the book closed, derive vector expressions for the velocity and acceleration in terms of tangential and normal components. Check your derivations with those given in the text.

In Problems 5 through 9, find the velocity and acceleration vectors, and then find the speed ds/dt and the tangential and normal components of acceleration.

5. $\mathbf{R} = \mathbf{i} \cosh 2t + \mathbf{j} \sinh 2t$

6. $\mathbf{R} = (2t + 3)\mathbf{i} + (t^2 - 1)\mathbf{j}$

7. $\mathbf{R} = (a \cos \omega t)\mathbf{i} + (a \sin \omega t)\mathbf{j}$, a and ω positive constants

8. $\mathbf{R} = \mathbf{i} \ln (t^2 + 1) + \mathbf{j}(t - 2 \tan^{-1} t)$

9. $\mathbf{R} = \mathbf{i}e^t \cos t + \mathbf{j}e^t \sin t$

10. Deduce from Eq. (11) that a particle will move in a straight line if the normal component of acceleration is identically zero.

11. Show that the radius of curvature of a plane curve is given by

$$\rho = \frac{(\dot{x}^2 + \dot{y}^2)}{\sqrt{\dot{x}^2 + \dot{y}^2 - \ddot{s}^2}},$$

where

$$\dot{x} = \frac{dx}{dt}, \qquad \ddot{x} = \frac{d^2x}{dt^2}, \qquad \ldots$$

and

$$\ddot{s} = \frac{d}{dt} \left(\sqrt{\dot{x}^2 + \dot{y}^2} \right).$$

12. If a particle moves in a curve with constant speed, show that the force is always directed along the normal.

13. If the force acting on a particle is at all times perpendicular to the direction of motion, show that the speed remains constant.

14. Use Eq. (16) to find the curvature of the helix $x = \cos t$, $y = \sin t$, $z = t$.

12–6

POLAR COORDINATES

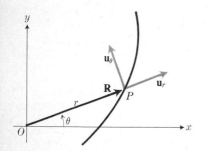

12–19 The unit vectors $\mathbf{u}_r$ and $\mathbf{u}_\theta$.

When a particle P moves on a curve whose equation is given in polar coordinates, it is convenient to express the velocity and acceleration vectors in terms of the unit vectors

$$\mathbf{u}_r = \mathbf{i} \cos \theta + \mathbf{j} \sin \theta, \qquad \mathbf{u}_\theta = -\mathbf{i} \sin \theta + \mathbf{j} \cos \theta. \tag{1}$$

The vector $\mathbf{u}_r$ points along the radius vector $\overrightarrow{OP}$, and $\mathbf{u}_\theta$ points at right angles to $\overrightarrow{OP}$ and in the direction of increasing θ, as shown in Fig. 12–19. From (1), we find that

$$\frac{d\mathbf{u}_r}{d\theta} = -\mathbf{i} \sin \theta + \mathbf{j} \cos \theta = \mathbf{u}_\theta,$$

$$\frac{d\mathbf{u}_\theta}{d\theta} = -\mathbf{i} \cos \theta - \mathbf{j} \sin \theta = -\mathbf{u}_r. \tag{2}$$

This says that differentiating either $\mathbf{u}_r$ or $\mathbf{u}_\theta$ with respect to θ is equivalent to rotating that vector $90°$ counterclockwise.

Since the vectors $\mathbf{R} = \overrightarrow{OP}$ and $r\mathbf{u}_r$ have the same direction, and the length of $\mathbf{R}$ is the absolute value of the polar coordinate r of $P(r, \theta)$, we have

$$\mathbf{R} = r\mathbf{u}_r. \tag{3}$$

We differentiate this equation with respect to t to obtain the velocity, remembering that both r and $\mathbf{u}_r$ may be variables. From (2) and the chain rule we get

$$\frac{d\mathbf{u}_r}{dt} = \frac{d\mathbf{u}_r}{d\theta} \frac{d\theta}{dt} = \mathbf{u}_\theta \frac{d\theta}{dt}, \qquad \frac{d\mathbf{u}_\theta}{dt} = \frac{d\mathbf{u}_\theta}{d\theta} \frac{d\theta}{dt} = -\mathbf{u}_r \frac{d\theta}{dt}. \tag{4}$$

Hence,

$$\mathbf{v} = \frac{d\mathbf{R}}{dt} = \mathbf{u}_r \frac{dr}{dt} + r \frac{d\mathbf{u}_r}{dt}$$

becomes

$$\mathbf{v} = \mathbf{u}_r \frac{dr}{dt} + \mathbf{u}_\theta r \frac{d\theta}{dt}. \tag{5}$$

Of course this velocity vector is tangent to the curve at P and has magnitude

$$|\mathbf{v}| = \sqrt{(dr/dt)^2 + r^2(d\theta/dt)^2} = |ds/dt|.$$

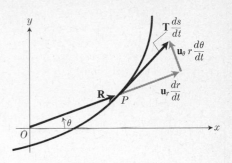

12–20 $\mathbf{u}_r \dfrac{dr}{dt} + \mathbf{u}_\theta r \dfrac{d\theta}{dt}$ is the velocity vector.

In fact, if the three sides of the "differential triangle" of sides dr, $r\,d\theta$, and ds are all divided by dt (Fig. 12–20), the result will be a similar triangle having sides dr/dt, $r\,d\theta/dt$, and ds/dt, which illustrates the vector equation

$$\mathbf{v} = \mathbf{T}\frac{ds}{dt} = \mathbf{u}_r \frac{dr}{dt} + \mathbf{u}_\theta r \frac{d\theta}{dt}.$$

The acceleration vector is found by differentiating the velocity vector in (5) as follows:

$$\mathbf{a} = \frac{d\mathbf{v}}{dt} = \left(\mathbf{u}_r \frac{d^2 r}{dt^2} + \frac{d\mathbf{u}_r}{dt}\frac{dr}{dt}\right) + \left(\mathbf{u}_\theta r \frac{d^2\theta}{dt^2} + \mathbf{u}_\theta \frac{dr}{dt}\frac{d\theta}{dt} + \frac{d\mathbf{u}_\theta}{dt} r \frac{d\theta}{dt}\right).$$

When Eqs. (4) are used to evaluate the derivatives of $\mathbf{u}_r$ and $\mathbf{u}_\theta$ and the components are separated, the result becomes

$$\mathbf{a} = \mathbf{u}_r \left[\frac{d^2 r}{dt^2} - r\left(\frac{d\theta}{dt}\right)^2\right] + \mathbf{u}_\theta \left[r \frac{d^2\theta}{dt^2} + 2\frac{dr}{dt}\frac{d\theta}{dt}\right]. \tag{6}$$

The polar form is particularly convenient in discussing the motion of a particle in what is called a "central force field." By this we mean that the force acting on the particle is always directed toward a single point, the center of force, which we choose as origin (Fig. 12–21). Then from $\mathbf{F} = m\mathbf{a}$, we see that the $\mathbf{u}_\theta$ component of acceleration must vanish. That is, in any central force field,

$$r\frac{d^2\theta}{dt^2} + 2\frac{dr}{dt}\frac{d\theta}{dt} = 0, \tag{7}$$

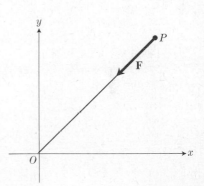

12–21 $\mathbf{F}$ is a central force if it points toward a fixed point (here the origin) no matter how P moves.

where the origin is at the center of force. (For instance, the sun would be chosen as the origin in discussing the gravitational attraction between the sun and a planet.) To integrate (7), let

$$u = \frac{d\theta}{dt}.$$

Then

$$r\frac{du}{dt} + 2u\frac{dr}{dt} = 0,$$

or

$$r\,du = -2u\,dr, \qquad \frac{du}{u} = -2\frac{dr}{r},$$

$$\ln|u| = -2\ln|r| + c_1,$$

$$\ln|ur^2| = c_1, \qquad |ur^2| = e^{c_1} = C,$$

or

$$r^2\frac{d\theta}{dt} = \pm C. \tag{8}$$

The left side of this equation is $2\,dA/dt$, where $dA = \frac{1}{2}r^2\,d\theta$ is the area swept over as the radius vector $\overline{OP}$ rotates through a small angle $d\theta$. Hence, Eq. (8) says that the radius vector *sweeps over area at a constant rate* in a central force field. Kepler's second law of planetary motion is thus a consequence of the fact that the field of gravitational attraction of the sun for the planets is a central force field (Fig. 12–22).

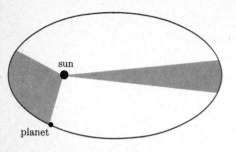

12–22 The line joining a planet and its sun sweeps over equal areas in equal times.

PROBLEMS

1. With the book closed, derive vector expressions for the velocity and acceleration in terms of components along and at right angles to the radius vector. Check your derivations with those given in the text.

In Problems 2–6, find the velocity and acceleration vectors in terms of $\mathbf{u}_r$ and $\mathbf{u}_\theta$.

2. $r = a(1 - \cos\theta)$ and $\dfrac{d\theta}{dt} = 3$

3. $r = a\sin 2\theta$ and $\dfrac{d\theta}{dt} = 2t$

4. $r = e^{a\theta}$ and $\dfrac{d\theta}{dt} = 2$

5. $r = a(1 + \sin t)$ and $\theta = 1 - e^{-t}$

6. $r = 2\cos 4t$ and $\theta = 2t$

7. If a particle moves in an ellipse whose polar equation is $r = c/(1 - e\cos\theta)$ and the force is directed toward the origin, show that the magnitude of the force is proportional to $1/r^2$.

REVIEW QUESTIONS AND EXERCISES

1. Define the derivative of a vector function.

2. Develop formulas for the derivatives, with respect to θ, of the unit vectors $\mathbf{u}_r$ and $\mathbf{u}_\theta$.

3. Develop vector formulas for velocity and acceleration of a particle moving in a plane curve:

a) in terms of cartesian coordinates,
b) in terms of polar coordinates,
c) in terms of distance traveled along the curve and unit vectors tangent and normal to the curve.

4. a) Define curvature of a plane curve.
b) Define radius of curvature.
c) Define center of curvature.
d) Define osculating circle.

5. Develop a formula for the curvature of a curve whose parametric equations are $x = f(t)$, $y = g(t)$.

6. In what way does the curvature of a curve affect the acceleration of a particle moving along the curve? In particular, discuss the case of constant-speed motion along a curve.

7. State and derive Kepler's second law concerning motion in a central force field.

8. If a vector $\mathbf{V}$ is a differentiable function of t and $|\mathbf{V}| =$ constant, what do you know about $d\mathbf{V}/dt$?

9. Define arc length and curvature of a space curve.

10. For a space curve, explain how to find the unit tangent vector, unit principal normal, and unit binormal.

MISCELLANEOUS PROBLEMS

1. A particle moves in the xy-plane according to the time law

$$x = 1/\sqrt{1 + t^2}, \qquad y = t/\sqrt{1 + t^2}.$$

a) Compute the velocity vector and acceleration vector when $t = 1$.
b) At what time is the speed of the particle a maximum?

2. A circular wheel with unit radius rolls along the x-axis uniformly, rotating one half-turn per second. The position of a point P on the circumference is given by the formula

$$\overrightarrow{OP} = \mathbf{R} = \mathbf{i}(\pi t - \sin \pi t) + \mathbf{j}(1 - \cos \pi t).$$

a) Determine the velocity (*vector*) $\mathbf{v}$ and the acceleration (*vector*) $\mathbf{a}$ at time t.
b) Determine the slopes (as functions of t) of the two straight lines PC and PQ joining P to the center C of the wheel and to the point Q that is topmost at the instant.
c) Show that the directions of the vectors $\mathbf{v}$ and $\mathbf{a}$ can be expressed in terms of the straight lines described in (b).

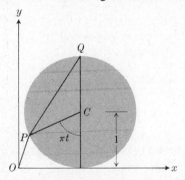

Figure 12–23

3. The motion of a particle in the xy-plane is given by

$$\mathbf{R} = \mathbf{i}at \cos t + \mathbf{j}at \sin t.$$

Find the speed, and the tangential and normal components of the acceleration.

4. A particle moves in the xy-plane in such a manner that the derivative of the position vector is always perpendicular to the position vector. Show that the particle moves on a circle with center at the origin.

5. The position of a point at time t is given by the formulas $x = e^t \cos t$, $y = e^t \sin t$.

a) Show that $\mathbf{a} = 2\mathbf{v} - 2\mathbf{r}$.
b) Show that the angle between the radius vector $\mathbf{r}$ and the acceleration vector $\mathbf{a}$ is constant, and find this angle.

6. Given the instantaneous velocity $\mathbf{v} = a\mathbf{i} + b\mathbf{j}$ and acceleration $\mathbf{a} = c\mathbf{i} + d\mathbf{j}$ of a particle at a point P on its path of motion, determine the curvature of the path at P.

7. Find the parametric equations, in terms of the parameter θ, of the position of the center of curvature of the cycloid

$$x = a(\theta - \sin \theta), \qquad y = a(1 - \cos \theta).$$

8. Find the point on the curve $y = e^x$ for which the radius of curvature is a minimum.

9. Given a closed curve having the property that every line parallel to the x-axis or the y-axis has at most two points in common with the curve. Let

$$x = x(t), \qquad y = y(t), \qquad \alpha \le t \le \beta,$$

be equations of the curve.

a) Prove that if dx/dt and dy/dt are continuous, then the area bounded by the curve is

$$\frac{1}{2} \left| \int_\alpha^\beta \left[x(t) \frac{dy}{dt} - y(t) \frac{dx}{dt} \right] dt \right|.$$

b) Use the result of (a) to find the area inside the ellipse

$$x = a \cos \phi, \qquad y = b \sin \phi, \qquad 0 \le \phi \le 2\pi.$$

What does the answer become when $a = b$?

10. For the curve defined by the equations

$$x = \int_0^\theta \cos \left(\tfrac{1}{2}\pi t^2 \right) dt, \qquad y = \int_0^\theta \sin \left(\tfrac{1}{2}\pi t^2 \right) dt,$$

calculate the curvature κ as a function of the length of arc s, where s is measured from $(0, 0)$.

11. The curve for which the length of the tangent intercepted between the point of contact and the y-axis is always equal to 1 is called the *tractrix*. Find its equation. Show that the radius of curvature at each point of the curve is inversely proportional to the length of the normal intercepted between the point on the curve and the y-axis. Calculate the length of arc of the tractrix, and find the parametric equations in terms of the length of arc.

12. Let $x = x(t)$, $y = y(t)$ be a closed curve. A constant length p is measured off along the normal to the curve. The extremity of this segment describes a curve which is called a *parallel curve* to the original curve. Find the length of arc, the radius of curvature, and the area enclosed by the parallel curve. Assume that the appropriate derivatives exist and are continuous.

13. Given the curve represented by the parametric equations

$$x = 32t, \qquad y = 16t^2 - 4.$$

a) Calculate the radius of curvature of the curve at the point where $t = 3$.
b) Find the length of the curve between the points where $t = 0$ and $t = 1$.

14. Find the velocity, acceleration, and speed of a particle whose position at time t is

$$x = 3 \sin t, \qquad y = 2 \cos t.$$

Also find the tangential and normal components of the acceleration.

15. The position of a particle at time t is given by the equations

$$x = 1 + \cos 2t, \qquad y = \sin 2t.$$

Find:

 a) the normal and tangential components of acceleration at time t;
 b) the radius of curvature of the path;
 c) the equation of the path in polar coordinates, using the x-axis as the line $\theta = 0$ and the y-axis as the line $\theta = \pi/2$.

16. A particle moves so that its position at time t has the polar coordinates $r = t$, $\theta = t$. Find the velocity $\mathbf{v}$, the acceleration $\mathbf{a}$, and the curvature κ at any time t.

17. Find an expression for the curvature of the curve whose equation in polar coordinates is $r = f(\theta)$.

18. a) Find the equation in *polar coordinates* of the curve

$$x = e^{2t} \cos t, \qquad y = e^{2t} \sin t.$$

 b) Find the length of this curve from $t = 0$ to $t = 2\pi$.

19. Express the velocity vector in terms of $\mathbf{u}_r$ and $\mathbf{u}_\theta$ for a point moving in the xy-plane according to the law

$$\mathbf{r} = (t + 1)\mathbf{i} + (t - 1)\mathbf{j}.$$

20. The polar coordinates of a particle at time t are

$$r = e^{\omega t} + e^{-\omega t}, \qquad \theta = t,$$

where ω is a constant. Find the acceleration vector when $t = 0$.

21. A slender rod, passing through the fixed point O, is rotating about O in a plane at the constant rate of 3 rad/min. An insect is crawling along the rod toward O at the constant rate of 1 in/min. Use polar coordinates in the plane, with point O as the origin, and assume that the insect starts at the point $r = 2$, $\theta = 0$.

 a) Find, in polar form, the vector velocity and vector acceleration of the insect when it is halfway to the origin.
 b) What will be the length of the path, in the plane, that the insect has traveled when it reaches the origin?

22. A smooth ball rolls inside a long hollow tube while the tube rotates with constant angular velocity ω about an axis perpendicular to the axis of the tube. Assuming no friction between the ball and the sides of the tube, show that the distance r from the axis of rotation to the ball satisfies the differential equation

$$d^2r/dt^2 - \omega^2 r = 0.$$

If at time $t = 0$ the ball is at rest (relative to the tube) at $r = a > 0$, find r as a function of t.

In Problems 23–26, r, θ, and z are cylindrical coordinates of a moving point P. The vectors $\mathbf{u}_r = \mathbf{i} \cos \theta + \mathbf{j} \sin \theta$ and $\mathbf{u}_\theta = -\mathbf{i} \sin \theta + \mathbf{j} \cos \theta$ are the usual unit vectors used with polar coordinates, as in Article 12–6.

23. Express the vector $\mathbf{R} = \overrightarrow{OP}$ in terms of cylindrical coordinates and the unit vectors $\mathbf{u}_r$, $\mathbf{u}_\theta$, and $\mathbf{k}$.

24. Derive formulas for the velocity $\mathbf{v} = d\mathbf{R}/dt$ and acceleration $\mathbf{a} = d\mathbf{v}/dt$ in terms of cylindrical coordinates and the unit vectors $\mathbf{u}_r$, $\mathbf{u}_\theta$, and $\mathbf{k}$.

25. A particle P slides without friction along a coil spring having the form of a right circular helix. If the positive z-axis is taken downward, the cylindrical coordinates of P at time t are $r = a$, $z = b\theta$, where a and b are positive constants. If the particle starts at $r = a$, $\theta = 0$ with zero velocity and falls under gravity, the law of conservation of energy then tells us that its speed after it has fallen a vertical distance z is $\sqrt{2gz}$.

 a) Find the angular velocity $d\theta/dt$ when $\theta = 2\pi$.
 b) Express θ and z as functions of the time t.
 c) Determine the tangential and normal components of the velocity $d\mathbf{R}/dt$ and acceleration $d^2\mathbf{R}/dt^2$ as functions of t. Is there any component of acceleration in the direction of the binormal $\mathbf{B}$?

26. Suppose the curve in Problem 25 is replaced by the conical helix

$$r = a\theta, \qquad z = b\theta.$$

 a) Express the angular velocity $d\theta/dt$ as a function of θ.
 b) Express the distance that the particle travels along this helix as a function of θ.

27. Hold two of the three spherical coordinates ρ, ϕ, θ of point P in Fig. 11–25 constant while letting the other coordinate increase. Let $\mathbf{u}$, with subscript corresponding to the coordinate that is permitted to vary, denote the unit vector that points in the direction in which P starts to move under these conditions.

 a) Express the three unit vectors $\mathbf{u}_\rho$, $\mathbf{u}_\phi$, $\mathbf{u}_\theta$ which are obtained in this manner, in terms of ρ, ϕ, θ, and the unit vectors $\mathbf{i}$, $\mathbf{j}$, $\mathbf{k}$.
 b) Show that $\mathbf{u}_\rho \cdot \mathbf{u}_\phi = 0$.
 c) Show that $\mathbf{u}_\theta = \mathbf{u}_\rho \times \mathbf{u}_\phi$.
 d) Do the vectors $\mathbf{u}_\rho$, $\mathbf{u}_\phi$, $\mathbf{u}_\theta$ form a system of mutually orthogonal vectors? Is the system, in the order given, a righthanded or a lefthanded system?

28. If the spherical coordinates ρ, ϕ, θ of a moving point P are differentiable functions of the time t, and $\mathbf{R} = \overrightarrow{OP}$ is the vector from the origin to P, express $\mathbf{R}$ and $d\mathbf{R}/dt$ in terms of ρ, ϕ, θ and their derivatives and the unit vectors $\mathbf{u}_\rho$, $\mathbf{u}_\phi$, $\mathbf{u}_\theta$ of Problem 27.

29. Express $ds^2 = dx^2 + dy^2 + dz^2$ in terms of

a) cylindrical coordinates r, θ, z,

b) spherical coordinates ρ, ϕ, θ (see Problem 28).

Interpret your results geometrically in terms of the sides and a diagonal of a rectangular box. Sketch.

30. Using the results of Problem 29, find the lengths of the following curves between $\theta = 0$ and $\theta = \ln 8$.

a) $z = r = ae^\theta$

b) $\phi = \pi/6$, $\quad \rho = 2e^\theta$

31. Determine parametric equations giving x, y, z in terms of the parameter θ for the curve of intersection of the sphere $\rho = a$ and the plane $y + z = 0$, and find its length.

32. In Article 12–6, we found the velocity vector of a particle moving in a plane to be

$$\mathbf{v} = \frac{d\mathbf{R}}{dt} = \mathbf{i}\frac{dx}{dt} + \mathbf{j}\frac{dy}{dt}$$

$$= \mathbf{u}_r\frac{dr}{dt} + \mathbf{u}_\theta\frac{r\,d\theta}{dt}.$$

a) Express dx/dt and dy/dt in terms of dr/dt and $r\,d\theta/dt$ by computing $\mathbf{v} \cdot \mathbf{i}$ and $\mathbf{v} \cdot \mathbf{j}$.

b) Express dr/dt and $r\,d\theta/dt$ in terms of dx/dt and dy/dt by computing $\mathbf{v} \cdot \mathbf{u}_r$ and $\mathbf{v} \cdot \mathbf{u}_\theta$.

33. The line through OA, A being the point $(1, 1, 1)$, is the axis of rotation of a rigid body that is rotating with a constant angular speed of 6 rad/sec. The rotation appears clockwise when we look towards the origin from A. Find the velocity vector of the point of the body that is at the position $(1, 3, 2)$ (see Example 5, Article 2–10).

34. Consider the space curve whose parametric equations are

$$x = t, \qquad y = t, \qquad z = \tfrac{2}{3}t^{3/2}.$$

Compute the equation of the plane that passes through the point $(1, 1, \tfrac{2}{3})$ of this curve, and is perpendicular to the tangent of this curve at the same point.

35. A curve is given by the parametric equations

$$x = e^t \sin 2t, \qquad y = e^t \cos 2t, \qquad z = 2e^t.$$

Let P_0 be the point where $t = 0$. Determine

a) the direction cosines of the tangent, principal normal, and binormal at P_0;

b) the curvature at P_0.

36. The *normal plane* to a space curve at any point P of the curve is defined as the plane through P that is perpendicular to the tangent vector. The *osculating plane* at P is the plane containing the tangent and the principal normal. Given the space curve whose vector equation is

$$\mathbf{r}(t) = t\mathbf{i} + t^2\mathbf{j} + t^3\mathbf{k},$$

find:

a) the equation of the normal plane at $(1, 1, 1)$;

b) the equation of the osculating plane at $(1, 1, 1)$.

37. Given the curve whose vector is

$$\mathbf{r}(t) = (3t - t^3)\,\mathbf{i} + 3t^2\mathbf{j} + (3t + t^3)\mathbf{k},$$

compute the curvature.

38. Show that the length of the arc described by the endpoint of

$$\mathbf{R} = (3\cos t)\mathbf{i} + (3\sin t)\mathbf{j} + t^2\mathbf{k},$$

as t varies from 0 to 2, is $5 + \tfrac{9}{4}\ln 3$.

39. The curve whose vector equation is

$$\mathbf{r}(t) = (2\sqrt{t}\cos t)\mathbf{i} + (3\sqrt{t}\sin t)\mathbf{j} + \sqrt{1-t}\,\mathbf{k}, \qquad 0 \le t \le 1,$$

lies on a quadric surface. Find the equation of this surface and describe it.

40. Find the orbit of a planet relative to the sun, assuming the sun to be fixed at the origin and the force acting on the planet to be directed toward the sun with magnitude $\gamma mM/r^2$, where γ is the universal gravitational constant, M is the mass of the sun, m is the mass of the planet, and r is its distance from the sun. Choose the initial line to pass through the perihelion point of the orbit, and assume the velocity at perihelion is v_0. Show that the path is a circle, ellipse, parabola, or hyperbola according as $v_0^2 r_0/\gamma M$ equals one, lies between one and two, equals two, or is greater than two.

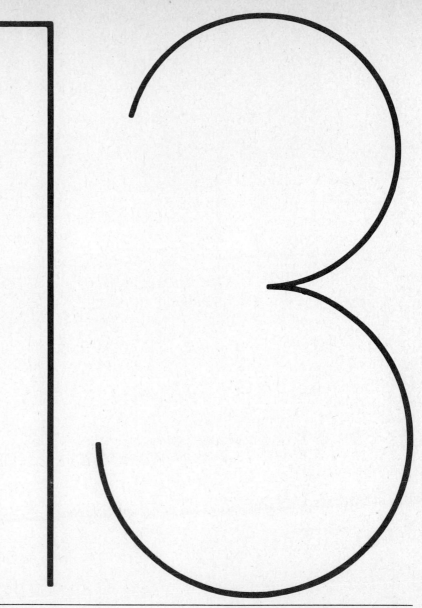

13

PARTIAL DIFFERENTIATION

13–1

FUNCTIONS OF TWO OR MORE VARIABLES

As we saw in Chapter 1, there are many instances in science, engineering, and everyday life where a quantity w is determined by a number of other quantities. For example, the volume of a right circular cone of radius r and altitude h is

$$V = \tfrac{1}{3}\pi r^2 h. \tag{1}$$

The values of r and h in this formula can be assigned independently of each other and, once they have been assigned, the corresponding value of V is determined. We say that V *is a function of* r and h, and we call r and h the *independent* variables of the function. The variable V is the *dependent* variable of the function.

In general, if w is uniquely determined when the values of two independent variables x and y are given, we say that w is a function of x and y, and indicate this fact by writing some such notation as

$$w = f(x, y). \tag{2}$$

The set of pairs (x, y) for which w is defined is called the domain of w, and the set of values that w assumes for the pairs in its domain is called the range of w.

The notation

$$w = f(x, y, z) \tag{3}$$

means, similarly, that the value of w is determined by assigning values to three independent variables x, y, and z. For example, if

$$\rho = \sqrt{x^2 + y^2 + z^2}, \tag{4}$$

as in the relationship between $\rho = |\overrightarrow{OP}|$ and the cartesian coordinates of $P(x, y, z)$, then the assignment of values to the coordinates x, y, and z determines a unique value of ρ.

Continuity

A function $w = f(x, y)$ is *continuous* at a point (x_0, y_0) in its domain if and only if

$$w \to w_0 = f(x_0, y_0)$$

as

$$(x, y) \to (x_0, y_0),$$

or

$$\lim_{\substack{x \to x_0 \\ y \to y_0}} f(x, y) = f(x_0, y_0).$$

In other words, w is continuous at (x_0, y_0) provided $|w - w_0|$ can be made arbitrarily small by making both $|x - x_0|$ and $|y - y_0|$ small. This is like the definition of continuity for functions of one variable, except that there are two independent variables involved instead of one.

EXAMPLE 1. The function $w = xy$ is continuous at any (x_0, y_0) since

$$
\begin{aligned}
|w - w_0| &= |xy - x_0 y_0| \\
&= |xy - xy_0 + xy_0 - x_0 y_0| \\
&= |x(y - y_0) + y_0(x - x_0)|
\end{aligned}
$$

can be made arbitrarily small by making both $|x - x_0|$ and $|y - y_0|$ small.

EXAMPLE 2. The function w defined by

$$
w(x, y) = \begin{cases} \dfrac{xy}{x^2 + y^2} & \text{when} \quad (x, y) \neq (0, 0), \\ 0 & \text{when} \quad (x, y) = (0, 0) \end{cases}
$$

is not continuous at $(0, 0)$. For, if we take

$$
x = r \cos \theta, \qquad y = r \sin \theta, \qquad (r \neq 0),
$$

we have

$$
w = \sin \theta \cos \theta = \tfrac{1}{2} \sin 2\theta,
$$

so that w takes all values between $-\tfrac{1}{2}$ and $+\tfrac{1}{2}$ as the point (x, y), or (r, θ), moves around the origin, no matter how small r may be. We cannot make w stay close to zero simply by keeping (x, y) close to $(0, 0)$.

In most cases, the so-called elementary functions, which include functions given by algebraic combinations of polynomials, trigonometric functions, logarithms, or exponentials, are continuous, except possibly where a denominator is zero or the function is otherwise undefined.

PROBLEMS

1. How close to the point $(0, 0)$ should one take the point (x, y) in order to make $|f(x, y) - f(0, 0)| < \varepsilon$ if:

a) $f(x, y) = x^2 + y^2$ and $\varepsilon = 0.01$?

b) $f(x, y) = \dfrac{y}{x^2 + 1}$ and $\varepsilon = 0.001$?

2. (a) How close to the point $(0, 0, 0)$ should one take the point (x, y, z) in order to make $|f(x, y, z) - f(0, 0, 0)| < \varepsilon$ if $f(x, y, z) = x^2 + y^2 + z^2$ and $\varepsilon = 0.01$? If $f(x, y, z) = xyz$ and $\varepsilon = 0.008$? (b) Is the function $f(x, y, z) = x^2 + y^2 + z^2$ continuous at $(0, 0, 0)$? Give reasons for your answer.

3. Let $f(x, y) = (x + y)/(x^2 + y)$ when $x^2 + y \neq 0$.

a) Is it possible to define $f(1, -1)$ in such a way that $f(x, y) \to f(1, -1)$ as $(x, y) \to (1, -1)$ along the line $x = 1$? Along the line $y = -1$?

b) Is it possible to define $f(1, -1)$ in such a way that f is continuous at $(1, -1)$?

Give the reasons for your answers.

The functions in Problems 4–7 are modifications of the function in Example 2. Express each one in polar coordinates and see whether it has a limit as (x, y) approaches $(0, 0)$. If the limit exists, say what it is; if it does not exist, say why not.

4. $g(x, y) = \dfrac{x^2 y}{x^2 + y^2}$

5. $h(x, y) = \dfrac{x^2}{x^2 + y^2}$

6. $w(x, y) = \dfrac{x^2 - y^2}{x^2 + y^2}$

7. $z(x, y) = \dfrac{xy}{\sqrt{x^2 + y^2}}$

Find the limits in Problems 8 and 9.

8. $\displaystyle \lim_{\substack{x \to 0 \\ y \to 0}} \dfrac{3x^2 - y^2 + 5}{x^2 + y^2 + 1}$

9. $\displaystyle \lim_{\substack{x \to 0 \\ y \to 0}} \dfrac{e^y \sin x}{x}$

Find the largest possible domain in the xy-plane for each of the following functions, if w is to be a real variable.

10. $w = e^{x-y}$

11. $w = \ln (x^2 + y^2)$

12. $w = \dfrac{\sin xy}{xy}$

13. $w = \dfrac{x}{\sqrt{y}}$

13–2

THE DIRECTIONAL DERIVATIVE: SPECIAL CASES

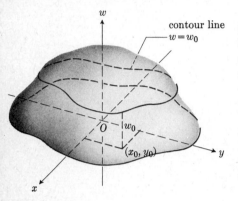

13–1   Contour line.

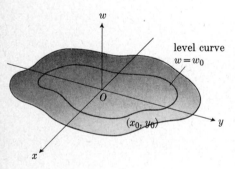

13–2   Level curve.

Let f be a function of two independent variables x and y and denote the dependent variable by w. The equation

$$w = f(x, y) \tag{1}$$

may be interpreted as defining a surface in xyw-space. In particular, we might imagine that the equation represents the elevation of points on a hill above the plane $w = 0$, as in Fig. 13–1.

If we cut the surface with a plane $w = w_0$, a constant, we get a *contour line* on the surface. And if we project this contour line straight down onto the xy-plane, we obtain a *level curve* in the domain of w (Fig. 13–2).* The level curve consists of the points in the domain where f has the value w_0. An equation for the level curve is obtained by setting $f(x, y) = w_0$.

EXAMPLE 1.   The function

$$w = 100 - x^2 - y^2, \qquad w \ge 0. \tag{2}$$

Figure 13–3 shows the plane $w = 75$ cutting the surface (a paraboloid of revolution) defined by the function, in a contour line. The corresponding level curve is

$$100 - x^2 - y^2 = 75,$$

or

$$x^2 + y^2 = 25,$$

a circle in the xy-plane. This is the circle that carries the marker $w = 75$ in Fig. 13–4.

Level curves are particularly useful in engineering applications. For instance, if Eq. (2) gave the celsius temperature at each point in a flat circular plate, then the level curves would be the isotherms of the temperature distribution.

Along with the launching and positioning of satellites has come an increased interest in mapping the variations in the earth's gravitational field. The strength of the field may vary significantly from place to place on the surface of the earth. In fact, changes in the performance of pendulum clocks taken by voyagers from Europe to other continents are said to have provided early supporting evidence for Newton's law of gravitation. If one takes the strength of the field at mean sea level as a standard, then the points in the earth's gravitational field that have the same gravitational potential as the standard value constitute a potato-shaped surface that geophysicists call the *geoid*. The geoid differs from the surface of the earth itself in most places, and it also differs from the ellipsoid that is normally used to approximate the surface of the earth (Fig. 13–5). The height of the geoid above or below the

---

*   There seems to be no firm agreement about the language to use here, for level curves may also be called *contours*.

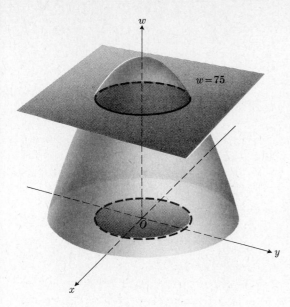

13–3   Contour line $w = 75$ on the surface $w = 100 - x^2 - y^2$, $w \geq 0$.

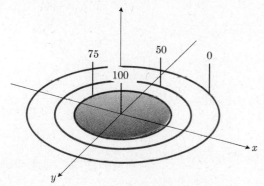

13–4   Level curves in the domain of $w = 100 - x^2 - y^2$, $w \geq 0$.

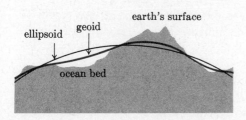

13–5   Surfaces of the earth, geoid, and ellipsoid.

ellipsoid is called the *geoidal height*. Geoidal heights are counted as positive when the geoid rises above the ellipsoid, and negative when it dips below the ellipsoid. Figure 13–6 shows contours of geoidal height on a Mercator map of the earth. These contours are the level curves of the geoidal height function.

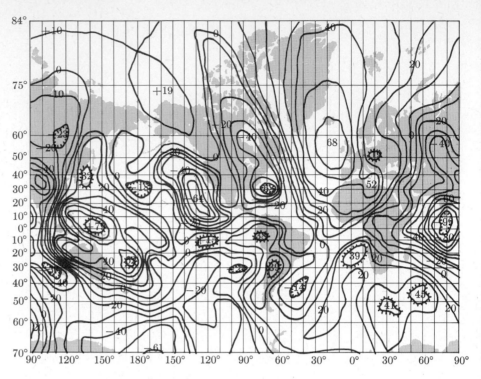

13–6 Contour map of geoidal height (meters).

EXAMPLE 2. *Potential wells.* Newton's law of gravitation says that the magnitude with which an object, say a space vehicle, is attracted to the sun is inversely proportional to the square of the distance r between the object and the sun's center. If we denote the magnitude of the force by k/r^2, then the amount of work required to move the vehicle from a unit distance $r = 1$ from the sun out to a distance $r = b$ from the sun is

$$w = \int_{r=1}^{r=b} \frac{k}{r^2}\,dr = -\frac{k}{r}\bigg]_1^b = k\left(1 - \frac{1}{b}\right). \tag{3}$$

Figure 13–7 shows a graph of w as a function of r in the rw-plane. However, we may also think of $w = k(1 - (1/r))$ as a function of the two polar coordinate variables r and θ, and graph w as a surface over the $r\theta$-plane. When we do so, we obtain the funnel-shaped surface of revolution shown in Fig. 13–8. The amount of work W_a^b required to move a mass against gravity from a position $r = a$ units from the sun to a position $r = b$ units from the sun can then be pictured as a change in elevation on this surface. Specifically, W_a^b is the difference in height between the contour lines that lie above the level curves $r = a$ and $r = b$. To see that this is so, we calculate

$$W_a^b = \int_a^b \frac{k}{r^2}\,dr = \int_1^b \frac{k}{r^2}\,dr - \int_1^a \frac{k}{r^2}\,dr = k\left(1 - \frac{1}{b}\right) - k\left(1 - \frac{1}{a}\right). \tag{4}$$

Therefore, if we think of the surface as a well, then W_a^b is the amount of work

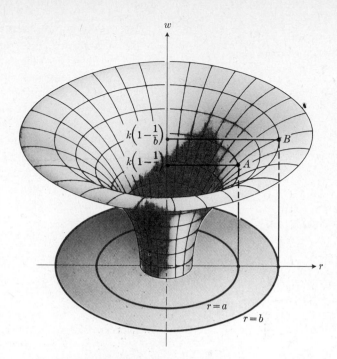

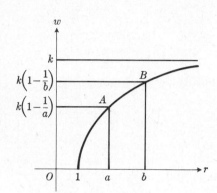

13–7   Graph of $w = k(1 - (1/r))$, $r \geq 1$.

13–8   The potential well $w = k(1 - (1/r))$, $r \geq 1$, is obtained by revolving the curve of Fig. 13–7 about the w-axis.

it would take to move a unit mass up the side of the well from contour A to contour B against a constant downward unit force. Since W_a^b is the difference in the potential energies possessed by a unit mass at distances $r = a$ and $r = b$ from the sun, the surface in Fig. 13–8 is often called a *potential well*, and the contour rings around it *equipotential* curves. The level curves of the potential function $w = k(1 - (1/r))$ are concentric circles around the origin that represents the sun in the polar coordinate plane.

Suppose now that w is a function of x and y, defined for points (x, y) in some domain D in the xy-plane. Let $P_0(x_0, y_0)$ and $P_1(x_1, y_1)$ be any two points of D. Then the increment in w in going from w_0 at P_0 to w_1 at P_1 is

$$\Delta w = w_1 - w_0 = f(x_1, y_1) - f(x_0, y_0) \tag{5}$$

corresponding to

$$\Delta x = x_1 - x_0, \qquad \Delta y = y_1 - y_0.$$

Keeping P_0 fixed, suppose we require P_1 to approach it along some specific smooth curve in the xy-plane. This curve would in general not be one of the level curves referred to above, but would instead cut across these level curves. To be definite, suppose P_1 approaches P_0 along a straight line L, making an angle ϕ with the x-axis (Fig. 13–9). Then, if the limit

$$\frac{dw}{ds} = \lim_{\Delta s \to 0} \frac{\Delta w}{\Delta s} = \lim_{P_1 \to P_0} \frac{f(x_1, y_1) - f(x_0, y_0)}{\sqrt{\Delta x^2 + \Delta y^2}} \tag{6}$$

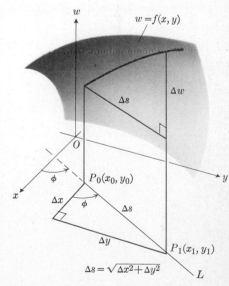

13–9   The derivative of $w = f(x, y)$ at P_0 in the direction of $\overrightarrow{P_0 P_1}$ is the limit of $\Delta w/\Delta s$ as P_1 approaches P_0 along L.

exists, its value is called the *directional derivative* of $w = f(x, y)$ at (x_0, y_0) in the direction of $\overrightarrow{P_0 P_1}$. The adjective *directional* is used because the value of the limit in (6) may depend not only on the function and the point P_0 but also on the direction from which P_1 approaches P_0.

Before investigating the directional derivative, we look at two closely related limits. The first is the limit as P_1 is allowed to approach P_0 from either side on the line $y = y_0$ parallel to the x-axis. The second is the limit as P_1 is allowed to approach P_0 from either side on the line $x = x_0$ parallel to the y-axis. These cases are not as restrictive as they might seem at first, for it turns out that we can calculate all directional derivatives in terms of these two special limits whenever the surface $w = f(x, y)$ is smooth enough to have a unique tangent plane at P_0. (The theorems in Articles 13–4 and 13–5 give the details.)

In the case where P_1 is allowed to approach P_0 from either side on the line $y = y_0$, we write

$$f_x(x_0, y_0) = \lim_{\Delta x \to 0} \frac{f(x_0 + \Delta x, y_0) - f(x_0, y_0)}{\Delta x}, \tag{7}$$

and call the limit, when it exists, the *partial derivative of $w = f(x, y)$ with respect to x at $P_0(x_0, y_0)$*. This is just the usual derivative with respect to x of the function $f(x, y_0)$ obtained from $f(x, y)$ by holding the value of y constant. It measures the instantaneous rate of change in f per unit change in x at P_0. We sometimes write $\partial w/\partial x$ for f_x.

If we delete the subscript 0 in (7), the result is the definition of the partial derivative of f with respect to x at an arbitrary point (x, y):

$$\frac{\partial w}{\partial x} = f_x(x, y) = \lim_{\Delta x \to 0} \frac{f(x + \Delta x, y) - f(x, y)}{\Delta x}. \tag{8}$$

Note. In passing to the limit in Eq. (7) or (8) it is understood that Δx may be either positive or negative. In certain "pathological" cases, a function may have a directional derivative from the right ($\Delta x > 0$) but not from the left ($\Delta x < 0$); or it may have both directional derivatives but the two may fail to have the same magnitude. In either of these cases, the partial derivative f_x would not exist. If, however, f_x does exist, then it gives the directional derivative from the right, while $-f_x$ gives the directional derivative from the left. The change in sign is due to the fact that when Δx is negative, $\Delta x = -\sqrt{\Delta x^2}$, and Eq. (8) gives the negative of what Eq. (6) gives. Thus, if f_x exists at a point, then both the right and left directional derivatives exist at that point, and they have the same magnitude but opposite signs.

To calculate f_x we hold y constant and apply the rules for ordinary differentiation with respect to x.

EXAMPLE 3.   If

$$w = 100 - x^2 - y^2,$$

then

$$\frac{\partial w}{\partial x} = 0 - 2x - 0 = -2x.$$

If w is the celsius temperature of a steel plate at (x, y), where x and y are in centimeters, then the temperature at $(3, 4)$ is $75°C$ and

$$\frac{\partial w}{\partial x} = -6 \,°C/cm.$$

That is, a small positive change in x would decrease the temperature at the rate of $6°C$ per cm change in x, while a negative change in x would increase w at the same rate.

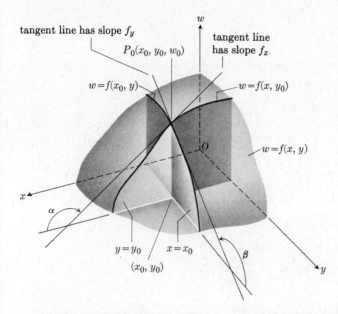

13–10 The plane $y = y_0$ cuts the surface $w = f(x, y)$ in the curve $w = f(x, y_0)$. At each x, the slope of this curve is $f_x(x, y_0)$. Similarly, the plane $x = x_0$ cuts the surface in a curve whose slope is $f_y(x_0, y)$.

The geometric interpretation of Eq. (5), (Fig. 13–10), is that

$$f_x(x_0, y_0) = \left(\frac{\partial w}{\partial x}\right)_{(x_0, y_0)}.$$

gives the slope at (x_0, y_0, w_0) of the curve $w = f(x, y_0)$ in which the plane $y = y_0$ cuts the surface $w = f(x, y)$.

Thus, in Fig. 13–10, if x, y, and w are measured in the same units,

$$\tan \alpha = \left(\frac{\partial w}{\partial x}\right)_{(x_0, y_0)} = f_x(x_0, y_0).$$

Similarly,

$$\tan \beta = \left(\frac{\partial w}{\partial y}\right)_{(x_0, y_0)} = f_y(x_0, y_0).$$

Here the partial derivative of $w = f(x, y)$ with respect to y is denoted either by $\partial w/\partial y$ or by $f_y(x, y)$ and we have the definitions

$$f_y(x_0, y_0) = \lim_{\Delta y \to 0} \frac{f(x_0, y_0 + \Delta y) - f(x_0, y_0)}{\Delta y},$$

$$\frac{\partial w}{\partial y} = f_y(x, y) = \lim_{\Delta y \to 0} \frac{f(x, y + \Delta y) - f(x, y)}{\Delta y}.$$

(9)

There are similar definitions for $\partial w/\partial x$, $\partial w/\partial y$, $\partial w/\partial z$, $\partial w/\partial u$, and $\partial w/\partial v$ in case $w = f(x, y, z, u, v)$. To compute them, we hold all but one of the variables constant while differentiating with respect to that one. The alternative subscript notation has the advantage of permitting us to exhibit the values of the variables where the derivative is to be evaluated. For example, $f_u(x_0, y_0, z_0, u_0, v_0)$ is the partial derivative of $w = f(x, y, z, u, v)$ with respect to u at $(x_0, y_0, z_0, u_0, v_0)$. This can also be denoted by $(\partial w/\partial u)_{(x_0, y_0, z_0, u_0, v_0)}$, or simply by $(\partial w/\partial u)_0$ when no confusion will result.

EXAMPLE 4. Three resistors of resistances R_1, R_2, and R_3 connected in parallel produce a resistance R given by

$$\frac{1}{R} = \frac{1}{R_1} + \frac{1}{R_2} + \frac{1}{R_3}.$$

Find $\partial R/\partial R_2$.

Solution. Treat R_1 and R_3 as constants and differentiate both sides of the equation with respect to R_2. Then

$$-\frac{1}{R^2}\frac{\partial R}{\partial R_2} = -\frac{1}{R_2^2}$$

or

$$\frac{\partial R}{\partial R_2} = \left(\frac{R}{R_2}\right)^2.$$

EXAMPLE 5. If $w = (xy)^z$, find $\partial w/\partial z$.

Solution. Here, we treat x and y, and hence xy, as constant and apply the law

$$\frac{d(a^u)}{dz} = a^u \ln a\, \frac{du}{dz}.$$

Hence

$$\frac{\partial w}{\partial z} = (xy)^z \ln (xy).$$

PROBLEMS

In Problems 1–5, show two ways to represent the function $w = f(x, y)$, (a) by sketching a surface in xyw-space, and (b) by drawing a family of level curves, $f(x, y) =$ constant.

1. $f(x, y) = x$

2. $f(x, y) = y$

3. $f(x, y) = x^2 + y^2$

4. $f(x, y) = x^2 - y^2$

5. $f(x, y) = ye^x$

In each of the following problems (6–10), find $\partial w/\partial x$ and $\partial w/\partial y$:

6. $w = e^x \cos y$

7. $w = e^x \sin y$

8. $w = \tan^{-1} \dfrac{y}{x}$

9. $w = \ln \sqrt{x^2 + y^2}$

10. $w = \cosh (y/x)$

In Problems 11–16, find the partial derivatives of the given function with respect to each variable.

11. $f(x, y, z, w) = x^2 e^{2y+3z} \cos (4w)$

12. $f(x, y, z) = z \sin^{-1} (y/x)$

13. $f(u, v, w) = \dfrac{u^2 - v^2}{v^2 + w^2}$

14. $f(r, \theta, z) = \dfrac{r(2 - \cos 2\theta)}{r^2 + z^2}$

15. $f(x, y, u, v) = \dfrac{x^2 + y^2}{u^2 + v^2}$

16. $f(x, y, r, s) = \sin 2x \cosh 3r + \sinh 3y \cos 4s$

In Problems 17 and 18, A, B, C are the angles of a triangle and a, b, c are the respective opposite sides.

17. Express A (explicitly or implicitly) as a function of a, b, c and calculate $\partial A/\partial a$ and $\partial A/\partial b$.

18. Express a (explicitly or implicitly) as a function of A, b, B and calculate $\partial a/\partial A$ and $\partial a/\partial B$.

In Problems 19–24, express the spherical coordinates ρ, ϕ, θ as functions of the cartesian coordinates x, y, z and calculate:

19. $\partial\rho/\partial x$　　20. $\partial\phi/\partial z$　　21. $\partial\theta/\partial y$

22. $\partial\theta/\partial z$　　23. $\partial\phi/\partial x$　　24. $\partial\theta/\partial x$

In Problems 25–27, let $\mathbf{R} = \mathbf{i}x + \mathbf{j}y + \mathbf{k}z$ be the vector from the origin to (x, y, z). Express x, y, z as functions of the spherical coordinates ρ, ϕ, θ, and calculate:

25. $\partial\mathbf{R}/\partial\rho$　　26. $\partial\mathbf{R}/\partial\phi$　　27. $\partial\mathbf{R}/\partial\theta$

28. Express the answers to Problems 25–27 in terms of the unit vectors $\mathbf{u}_\rho, \mathbf{u}_\phi, \mathbf{u}_\theta$ discussed in Miscellaneous Problem 27, Chapter 12.

29. In Fig. 13–10, let

$$\mathbf{R} = \mathbf{i}x + \mathbf{j}y + \mathbf{k}f(x, y)$$

be the vector from the origin to (x, y, w). What can you say about the direction of the vector (a) $\partial\mathbf{R}/\partial x$, (b) $\partial\mathbf{R}/\partial y$? (c) Calculate the vector product

$$\mathbf{v} = \left(\frac{\partial\mathbf{R}}{\partial x}\right) \times \left(\frac{\partial\mathbf{R}}{\partial y}\right).$$

What can you say about the direction of this vector $\mathbf{v}$ with respect to the surface $w = f(x, y)$?

In Article 13–2 we saw that the partial derivatives

$$f_x(x_0, y_0) = \left(\frac{\partial w}{\partial x}\right)_{(x_0, y_0)} \tag{1a}$$

and

$$f_y(x_0, y_0) = \left(\frac{\partial w}{\partial y}\right)_{(x_0, y_0)} \tag{1b}$$

13-3

TANGENT PLANE AND NORMAL LINE

give the slopes of the lines L_1 and L_2 which are tangent to the curves C_1 and C_2 that are cut from the surface $w = f(x, y)$ by the planes $y = y_0$ and $x = x_0$. The lines L_1 and L_2 determine a plane. If the surface is sufficiently smooth near $P_0(x_0, y_0, w_0)$, this plane will be tangent to the surface at P_0.

Definition. Tangent plane. *Let $w = f(x, y)$ be the equation of a surface S. Let $P_0(x_0, y_0, w_0)$ be a point on the surface. Let T be a plane through P_0. Let $P(x, y, w)$ be any other point on S. If the angle between T and the line $P_0 P$ approaches zero as P approaches P_0 along the surface, we say that T is tangent to S at P_0 (Fig. 13–11).*

The line through P_0 normal to the tangent plane is called the *normal line* to the surface at P_0.

REMARK 1. If a surface has a tangent plane at $P_0(x_0, y_0, w_0)$, the lines L_1 and L_2 that are tangent to the curves C_1 and C_2 must lie in it. Since two intersecting lines determine a plane, the plane determined by L_1 and L_2 is the tangent plane, if there is one.

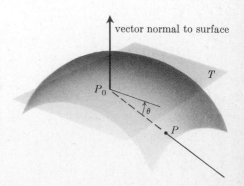

13–11 If θ approaches zero as P approaches P_0 along the surface, then the plane T is tangent to the surface at P_0.

REMARK 2. The curves C_1 and C_2, cut from the surface by the planes $x = x_0$ and $y = y_0$, may be smooth enough to have tangent lines L_1 and L_2 and the surface still not have a tangent plane at P_0. In other words, the plane determined by L_1 and L_2 may fail to be tangent to the surface. This would happen, for example, if the curves cut from the surface by other planes, such as the planes $y - y_0 = \pm(x - x_0)$, either failed to have tangent lines, or had tangent lines L', L'' which did not lie in the plane determined by L_1 and L_2. In the next article, we shall show that this does not happen if the partial derivatives $f_x(x, y)$, $f_y(x, y)$ exist in some rectangle centered at (x_0, y_0) and are continuous at (x_0, y_0).

We shall assume for now that the surface does have a tangent plane and a normal line and see how to find their equations. They may easily be written down once we have found a vector $\mathbf{N}$ perpendicular to the plane of L_1 and L_2. For such a vector $\mathbf{N}$, we may use the cross product of vectors $\mathbf{v}_1$ and $\mathbf{v}_2$ along the lines L_1 and L_2. So we now consider how to find $\mathbf{v}_1$ and $\mathbf{v}_2$.

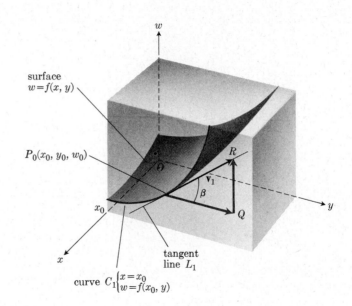

13–12 $\mathbf{v}_1 = \mathbf{j} + f_y(x_0, y_0)\mathbf{k}$ is tangent to C_1 at (x_0, y_0) because its slope is $f_y(x_0, y_0)$.

Figure 13–12 shows part of the curve C_1 cut from the surface by the plane $x = x_0$. Triangle $P_0 QR$ is a right triangle with hypotenuse $P_0 R$ lying along the tangent line L_1. The slope of L_1 is

$$\tan \beta = \frac{QR}{P_0 Q} = f_y(x_0, y_0).$$

Therefore, if we take $P_0 Q = 1$ y-unit, QR will be equal to $f_y(x_0, y_0)$ w-units. In terms of vectors, we may take

$$\overrightarrow{P_0 Q} = 1\mathbf{j}, \qquad \overrightarrow{QR} = f_y(x_0, y_0)\mathbf{k}$$

and

$$\mathbf{v}_1 = \overrightarrow{P_0 Q} + \overrightarrow{QR} = \mathbf{j} + f_y(x_0, y_0)\mathbf{k}, \tag{2a}$$

where $\mathbf{i}$, $\mathbf{j}$, and $\mathbf{k}$ will be used to denote unit vectors along the x-, y-, and w-axes, respectively.

Similarly, by considering the curve C_2 cut from the surface by the plane $y = y_0$, we see that the vector

$$\mathbf{v}_2 = \mathbf{i} + f_x(x_0, y_0)\mathbf{k} \qquad \text{(2b)}$$

is parallel to the line L_2.

For the normal vector $\mathbf{N}$ we may therefore take

$$\mathbf{N} = \mathbf{v}_1 \times \mathbf{v}_2 = \begin{vmatrix} \mathbf{i} & \mathbf{j} & \mathbf{k} \\ 0 & 1 & f_y(x_0, y_0) \\ 1 & 0 & f_x(x_0, y_0) \end{vmatrix} = \mathbf{i}f_x(x_0, y_0) + \mathbf{j}f_y(x_0, y_0) - \mathbf{k}. \quad \text{(3)}$$

The equations of the tangent plane and normal line at $P_0(x_0, y_0, w_0)$ may now be written down with coefficients taken from the normal vector $\mathbf{N}$:

Tangent plane: $A(x - x_0) + B(y - y_0) + C(w - w_0) = 0,$ **(4a)**

Normal line: $\dfrac{x - x_0}{A} = \dfrac{y - y_0}{B} = \dfrac{w - w_0}{C},$ **(4b)**

Coefficients: $A = f_x(x_0, y_0), \quad B = f_y(x_0, y_0), \quad C = -1.$ **(4c)**

PROBLEMS

In Problems 1–5, find the plane that is tangent to the given surface $z = f(x, y)$ at the given point P_0. Also find the line normal to the surface at P_0.

1. $z = x^2 + y^2$; $(3, 4, 25)$

2. $z = \sqrt{9 - x^2 - y^2}$; $(1, -2, 2)$

3. $z = x^2 - xy - y^2$; $(1, 1, -1)$

4. $z = \tan^{-1} \dfrac{y}{x}$; $(1, 1, \pi/4)$

5. $z = x/\sqrt{x^2 + y^2}$; $(3, -4, \tfrac{3}{5})$

6. (a) If the equation of a surface is given in the form $x = f(y, z)$, what takes the place of Eq. (3) for a vector $\mathbf{N}$ normal to the surface at a point $P_0(x_0, y_0, z_0)$? (b) Find the tangent plane and normal line to the surface $x = e^{2y-z}$ at the point $(1, 1, 2)$.

7. Show that there is a line on the cone $z^2 = 2x^2 + 4y^2$ where the tangent plane is parallel to the plane $12x + 14y + 11z = 25$. Find the line and the tangent plane.

8. At each point of the curve of intersection of the paraboloid $z = x^2 + y^2$ and the plane $z = z_0 \ (> 0)$, a line is drawn normal to the paraboloid. Show that these lines generate a cone and find its vertex. Sketch the paraboloid and the associated cone.

9. The intersection of the surface $z = f(x, y)$ and the surface $z = g(x, y)$ is a curve C. Find a vector tangent to C at a point $P_0(x_0, y_0, z_0)$ on it. Express the result in terms of partial derivatives of f and g at P_0.

10. Apply the result of Problem 9 to find a vector of length $\sqrt{3}$ tangent to the curve of intersection of the cone $z^2 = 4x^2 + 9y^2$ and the plane $6x + 3y + 2z = 5$ at the point $P_0(2, 1, -5)$.

We saw in the previous article, Eqs. (4a, c), that if the surface $w = f(x, y)$ has a tangent plane at $P_0(x_0, y_0, w_0)$, then the equation of the tangent plane is

$$w - w_0 = f_x(x_0, y_0)(x - x_0) + f_y(x_0, y_0)(y - y_0). \qquad \text{(1)}$$

13-4

APPROXIMATE VALUE OF Δw

In this equation, (x_0, y_0, w_0) are coordinates of a point on the surface, while

(x, y, w) are coordinates of a point on the *tangent plane*. If we take

$$x = x_0 + \Delta x,$$

$$y = y_0 + \Delta y$$

in Eq. (1), and denote the change, $w - w_0$, by Δw_{tan}, we have

$$\Delta w_{\text{tan}} = f_x(x_0, y_0)\, \Delta x + f_y(x_0, y_0)\, \Delta y. \tag{2}$$

This equation tells how much change is produced in w, corresponding to the changes Δx and Δy, when we move along the *tangent plane*. In this article we shall see that, under suitable restrictions on the function f, (a) the surface does have a tangent plane, and (b) the change in w *on the surface* $w = f(x, y)$ differs from Δw_{tan} by an amount $\epsilon_1\, \Delta x + \epsilon_2\, \Delta y$, where both ϵ_1 and ϵ_2 are small when Δx and Δy are small. We shall discuss the suitable restrictions on f and then prove the theorem below.

Theorem 1. *Let the function $w = f(x, y)$ be continuous and have partial derivatives f_x, f_y throughout a region*

$$R: \; |x - x_0| < h, \qquad |y - y_0| < k$$

of the xy-plane. Let f_x and f_y be continuous at (x_0, y_0). Let

$$\Delta w = f(x_0 + \Delta x, y_0 + \Delta y) - f(x_0, y_0). \tag{3}$$

Then

$$\Delta w = f_x(x_0, y_0)\, \Delta x + f_y(x_0, y_0)\, \Delta y + \epsilon_1\, \Delta x + \epsilon_2\, \Delta y, \tag{4}$$

where

$$\epsilon_1 \text{ and } \epsilon_2 \to 0 \qquad when \quad \Delta x \text{ and } \Delta y \to 0. \tag{5}$$

The region R is a rectangle with center (x_0, y_0) and sides $2h$ by $2k$. We shall restrict Δx and Δy to be so small that the points

$$(x_0, y_0), \quad (x_0 + \Delta x, y_0 + \Delta y), \quad (x_0 + \Delta x, y_0), \quad (x_0, y_0 + \Delta y)$$

all lie inside this rectangle R. The function f is assumed to be continuous and to have partial derivatives f_x and f_y throughout R. In particular, these functions are well behaved at each of the points listed above and along the segments joining them. This is sufficient to make valid the applications of the Mean Value Theorem in the proof below.

Proof. The key to the proof is a double application of the Mean Value Theorem. The increment Δw is the change in f from $A(x_0, y_0)$ to $B(x_0 + \Delta x, y_0 + \Delta y)$ in R. We resolve this into two parts

$$\Delta w_1 = f(x_0 + \Delta x, y_0) - f(x_0, y_0) \tag{6}$$

and

$$\Delta w_2 = f(x_0 + \Delta x, y_0 + \Delta y) - f(x_0 + \Delta x, y_0). \tag{7}$$

The first is the change in w from A to C; the second, from C to B (Fig.

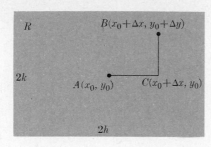

13–13   The region R of Theorem 1.

13–13). Their sum is

$$\Delta w_2 + \Delta w_1 = f(x_0 + \Delta x, y_0 + \Delta y) - f(x_0 + \Delta x, y_0)$$

$$+ f(x_0 + \Delta x, y_0) - f(x_0, y_0) \qquad (8)$$

$$= f(x_0 + \Delta x, y_0 + \Delta y) - f(x_0, y_0) = \Delta w.$$

In Δw_1, we hold $y = y_0$ fixed and have an increment of a function of x that is continuous and differentiable. The Mean Value Theorem is therefore applicable, and yields

$$\Delta w_1 = f(x_0 + \Delta x, y_0) - f(x_0, y_0) = f_x(x_1, y_0)\,\Delta x \qquad (9)$$

for some x_1 between x_0 and $x_0 + \Delta x$.

Similarly, in Δw_2 we hold $x = x_0 + \Delta x$ fixed and have an increment of a function of y that is continuous and differentiable. By the Mean Value Theorem,

$$\Delta w_2 = f(x_0 + \Delta x, y_0 + \Delta y) - f(x_0 + \Delta x, y_0) = f_y(x_0 + \Delta x, y_1)\,\Delta y \qquad (10)$$

for some y_1 between y_0 and $y_0 + \Delta y$. Hence

$$\Delta w = f_x(x_1, y_0)\,\Delta x + f_y(x_0 + \Delta x, y_1)\,\Delta y \qquad (11)$$

for some x_1 between x_0 and $x_0 + \Delta x$, and y_1 between y_0 and $y_0 + \Delta y$.

We now use the hypothesis that f_x and f_y are continuous at $P_0(x_0, y_0)$. This means that

$$f_x(x_1, y_0) \rightarrow f_x(x_0, y_0) \qquad (12a)$$

and

$$f_y(x_0 + \Delta x, y_1) \rightarrow f_y(x_0, y_0) \qquad (12b)$$

as Δx and Δy approach zero. Therefore

$$f_x(x_1, y_0) = f_x(x_0, y_0) + \epsilon_1, \qquad (13a)$$

$$f_y(x_0 + \Delta x, y_1) = f_y(x_0, y_0) + \epsilon_2, \qquad (13b)$$

where ϵ_1 and ϵ_2 both approach zero as Δx and Δy approach zero. Substituting (13a, b) into (11) gives the desired result,

$$\Delta w = [f_x(x_0, y_0) + \epsilon_1]\,\Delta x + [f_y(x_0, y_0) + \epsilon_2]\,\Delta y,$$

while (12a) and (12b) guarantee that ϵ_1 and $\epsilon_2 \rightarrow 0$ when Δx and $\Delta y \rightarrow 0$.

Q.E.D.

13–14 Part of the surface $w = f(x, y)$ near $P_0(x_0, y_0, w_0)$, and part of the plane tangent to the surface at P_0. The points P_0, P', and P'' have the same height $w_0 = f(x_0, y_0)$ above the xy-plane. The change in w on the surface is $\Delta w = P'R$, and the change in w on the tangent plane is $\Delta w_{\text{tan}} = P'S$. The change

$$\Delta w_1 = f(x_0 + \Delta x, y_0) - f(x_0, y_0),$$

shown as $P''Q = P'Q'$, is caused by changing x from x_0 to $x_0 + \Delta x$ while holding y equal to y_0. Then, with x held equal to $x_0 + \Delta x$,

$$\Delta w_2 = f(x_0 + \Delta x, y_0 + \Delta y) \\ - f(x_0 + \Delta x, y_0)$$

is the change in w caused by changing y from y_0 to $y_0 + \Delta y$. This is represented by $Q'R$. The total change in w is the sum of Δw_1 and Δw_2.

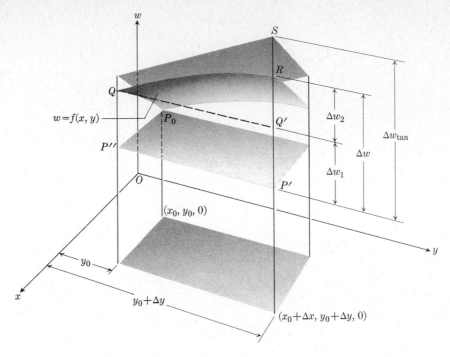

For a pictorial representation of Δw, Δw_{tan}, Δw_1, and Δw_2, see Fig. 13–14.

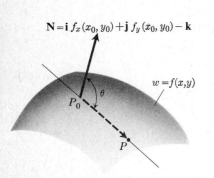

13–15 If f, f_x, and f_y are continuous in a region about (x_0, y_0), then $\theta \to 90°$ as $P \to P_0$.

Theorem 2. Let $w = f(x, y)$ be continuous in a region R: $|x - x_0| < h$, $|y - y_0| < k$. Let f_x and f_y exist in R and be continuous at (x_0, y_0). Let $P_0(x_0, y_0, w_0)$ be a point on the surface $w = f(x, y)$. Then the plane T through P_0 normal to the vector

$$\mathbf{N} = \mathbf{i}f_x(x_0, y_0) + \mathbf{j}f_y(x_0, y_0) - \mathbf{k} \tag{14}$$

is tangent to the surface.

Proof. We show that the plane T satisfies the requirement set forth in the tangent-plane definition in Article 13–3. Namely, we show that if P is any point on the surface other than P_0, then the angle between $\overrightarrow{P_0P}$ and T approaches 0 as $P \to P_0$. This is done by showing that the angle between $\overrightarrow{P_0P}$ and $\mathbf{N}$ approaches 90° as $P \to P_0$ (Fig. 13–15).

The cosine of the angle θ between $\overrightarrow{P_0P}$ and $\mathbf{N}$ is

$$\cos \theta = \frac{\overrightarrow{P_0P} \cdot \mathbf{N}}{|\overrightarrow{P_0P}||\mathbf{N}|}. \tag{15}$$

Now

$$\overrightarrow{P_0P} = \mathbf{i}(x - x_0) + \mathbf{j}(y - y_0) + \mathbf{k}(w - w_0)$$
$$= \mathbf{i}\,\Delta x + \mathbf{j}\,\Delta y + \mathbf{k}\,\Delta w. \tag{16}$$

Therefore

$$\cos \theta = \frac{f_x(x_0, y_0)\, \Delta x + f_y(x_0, y_0)\, \Delta y - \Delta w}{|\overrightarrow{P_0 P}|\,|\mathbf{N}|} \tag{17}$$

$$= \frac{-\epsilon_1 \,\Delta x - \epsilon_2 \,\Delta y}{|\overrightarrow{P_0 P}|\,|\mathbf{N}|}.$$

From (14) we see that $|\mathbf{N}| \ge 1$, and from (16)

$$\frac{|\Delta x|}{|\overrightarrow{P_0 P}|} \le 1, \qquad \frac{|\Delta y|}{|\overrightarrow{P_0 P}|} \le 1.$$

Hence, from (17) and the previous theorem,

$$|\cos \theta| \le |\epsilon_1| + |\epsilon_2| \to 0$$

as $P \to P_0$. Therefore, for any point $P \ne P_0$ on the surface, the angle between the vector $\overrightarrow{P_0 P}$ and the vector $\mathbf{N}$, Eq. (14), approaches 90°. This concludes the proof.

REMARK 1.   The hypotheses of Theorems 1 and 2 are more refined than we usually need. It is usually enough to remember that the conclusions of these two theorems hold when $f, f_x,$ and f_y are all continuous throughout R.

The power of Theorem 1 lies in Eqs. (4) and (5), which say that

$$\Delta w = \Delta w_{\tan} + \epsilon_1 \,\Delta x + \epsilon_2 \,\Delta y$$

consists of a part $\Delta w_{\tan}$, which is *linear* in Δx and Δy, plus error terms $\epsilon_1 \,\Delta x$ and $\epsilon_2 \,\Delta y$ that are *products* of small terms when Δx and Δy are small.

EXAMPLE 1.   If

$$w = x^2 + y^2 = f(x, y),$$

then

$$\Delta w = (x + \Delta x)^2 + (y + \Delta y)^2 - (x^2 + y^2)$$

$$= \underbrace{2x \,\Delta x + 2y \,\Delta y}_{\Delta w_{\tan}} + \underbrace{(\Delta x)^2 + (\Delta y)^2}_{\epsilon_1 \,\Delta x + \epsilon_2 \,\Delta y}.$$

Since $f_x = 2x,\, f_y = 2y,$ the part $2x \,\Delta x + 2y \,\Delta y$ is the same as $\Delta w_{\tan}$. Then $\Delta w - \Delta w_{\tan}$ is $(\Delta x)^2 + (\Delta y)^2$. This agrees with Eq. (4) with $\epsilon_1 = \Delta x$ and $\epsilon_2 = \Delta y$, which approach zero when Δx and Δy do.

Theorem 1 sometimes lets us approximate a complicated function $w = f(x, y)$ by a linear function that we can construct from it. The approximation comes from Eq. (4). If we replace Δw in Eq. (4) by $f(x, y) - f(x_0, y_0)$, and add $f(x_0, y_0)$ to both sides, we see that

$$f(x, y) = f(x_0, y_0) + f_x(x_0, y_0)\, \Delta x + f_y(x_0, y_0)\, \Delta y + \epsilon_1 \,\Delta x + \epsilon_2 \,\Delta y. \tag{18}$$

Theorem 1 then says that

$$f(x, y) \approx f(x_0, y_0) + f_x(x_0, y_0)\, \Delta x + f_y(x_0, y_0)\, \Delta y \tag{19}$$

when Δx and Δy are small. Finally, when we replace Δx and Δy by $x - x_0$ and $y - y_0$, we obtain the following linear approximation to $f(x, y)$ near the point (x_0, y_0):

$$f(x, y) \approx f(x_0, y_0) + f_x(x_0, y_0)(x - x_0) + f_y(x_0, y_0)(y - y_0). \qquad (20)$$

EXAMPLE 2. Show that

$$\frac{1}{1 + x - y} \approx 1 - x + y \qquad (21)$$

when x and y are very small.

Solution. The function $f(x, y) = 1/(1 + x - y)$ is certainly continuous for $|x - y| < 1$, as are the derivatives

$$f_x(x, y) = \frac{-1}{(1 + x - y)^2},$$
$$f_y(x, y) = \frac{1}{(1 + x - y)^2}. \qquad (22)$$

Thus the conclusion of Theorem 1 holds for f when $|x - y| < 1$.

If we take $(x_0, y_0) = (0, 0)$ in (20), the equation becomes

$$f(x, y) \approx f(0, 0) + x f_x(0, 0) + y f_y(0, 0).$$

Evaluating this equation gives

$$\frac{1}{1 + x - y} \approx 1 + x(-1) + y(1) = 1 - x + y,$$

which is the desired result.

To estimate the error in the approximation, we could estimate ϵ_1 and ϵ_2 from Eqs. (13a) and (13b), and calculate

$$\epsilon_1 \Delta x + \epsilon_2 \Delta y = \epsilon_1 x + \epsilon_2 y.$$

The calculation is a long one, however, and we need not go into it in this case because it is easier to find the remainder that results from dividing $1 + x - y$ into 1 directly by long division. When the result of the division is simplified, we find that

$$\frac{1}{1 + x - y} = 1 - x + y + \frac{(x - y)^2}{1 + x - y}.$$

Thus, the error in the approximation (21) is exactly $(x - y)^2/(1 + x - y)$. To estimate this error when $|x - y| < \frac{1}{2}$, for instance, we have

$$0 \le \frac{(x - y)^2}{1 + x - y} \le \frac{(x - y)^2}{1 - \frac{1}{2}} = 2(x - y)^2. \qquad (23)$$

Note that the accuracy of (21) does not depend on x and y being small, but on $|x - y|$ being small (see Problem 3).

Example 2 gives a linear approximation to $f(x, y) = 1/(1 + x - y)$ when the point (x, y) is near the point $(0, 0)$. The next example gives a linear approximation to f that works when the point (x, y) is close to the point $(2, 1)$.

EXAMPLE 3. Find a linear function that approximates $1/(1 + x - y)$ near the point $(2, 1)$.

Solution. We begin by taking $(x_0, y_0) = (2, 1)$ in Eq. (20), which then becomes

$$f(x, y) \approx f(2, 1) + f_x(2, 1)(x - 2) + f_y(2, 1)(y - 1). \qquad (24)$$

We then use the formulas for f and its partial derivatives, Eq. (22), to evaluate both sides of (24), obtaining

$$\frac{1}{1 + x - y} \approx \frac{1}{2} + \left(-\frac{1}{4}\right)(x - 2) + \left(\frac{1}{4}\right)(y - 1) = \frac{3}{4} - \frac{x}{4} + \frac{y}{4}. \qquad (25)$$

REMARK 2.   The surface

$$w = f(x_0, y_0) + f_x(x_0, y_0)(x - x_0) + f_y(x_0, y_0)(y - y_0) \qquad (26)$$

generated by the right side of (20) is the plane that is tangent to the surface $w = f(x, y)$ at the point (x_0, y_0). Thus the plane $w = 1 - x + y$ in Example 2 is tangent to the surface $w = 1/(1 + x - y)$ at the point $(0, 0)$. The plane

$$w = \frac{3}{4} - \frac{x}{4} + \frac{y}{4}$$

in Example 3 is tangent to the surface at the point $(2, 1)$. What we did in making the approximations in Examples 2 and 3 was to substitute heights on the tangent plane for heights on the surface near the point of tangency.

The approximation

$$\Delta w \approx \Delta w_{\tan} = f_x(x_0, y_0)\, \Delta x + f_y(x_0, y_0)\, \Delta y, \qquad (27)$$

which we get from Eq. (4), gives a way to see how *sensitive* $w = f(x, y)$ is to changes in its variables near the point (x_0, y_0). This is illustrated in the next example.

EXAMPLE 4.   For the volume

$$V = \pi r^2 h$$

of a right circular cylinder, Eq. (27) gives

$$\Delta V \approx V_r(r_0, h_0)\, \Delta r + V_h(r_0, h_0)\, \Delta h. \qquad (28)$$

Therefore, near the point $r_0 = 1$, $h_0 = 5$, ΔV is related to Δr and Δh by the approximation

$$\Delta V \approx V_r(1, 5)\, \Delta r + V_h(1, 5)\, \Delta h. \qquad (29)$$

13–16   The volume of cylinder (a) is more sensitive to a small change in r than it is to an equally small change in h. The volume of cylinder (b) is more sensitive to small changes in h than it is to small changes in r.

Since

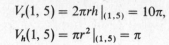

$$V_r(1, 5) = 2\pi rh \big|_{(1,5)} = 10\pi,$$

$$V_h(1, 5) = \pi r^2 \big|_{(1,5)} = \pi$$

at the point $(1, 5)$, Eq. (29) gives

$$\Delta V \approx 10\pi \, \Delta r + \pi \, \Delta h.$$

A one-unit change in r will change V by about 10π units. A one-unit change in h will change V by only about π units. The volume of a cylinder with radius 1 and height 5 is nearly ten times more sensitive to a small change in r than it is to a change of the same size in h (Fig. 13–16).

In contrast, if the given values of r and h are reversed, so that $r = 5$ and $h = 1$, then

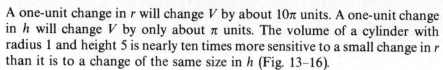

$$V_r = 2\pi rh \big|_{(5,1)} = 10\pi, \qquad V_h = \pi r^2 \big|_{(5,1)} = 25\pi,$$

and Eq. (28) becomes

$$\Delta V \approx 10\pi \, \Delta r + 25\pi \, \Delta h.$$

The volume is more sensitive now to a small change in h than it is to an equally small change in r.

There is a general rule to be learned from Example 4. Namely, a differentiable function is most sensitive to small changes in the variables with respect to which it has the largest partial derivatives.

Functions of More Variables

Analogous results hold for functions of any finite number of independent variables. For a function of three variables

$$w = f(x, y, z),$$

that is continuous and has partial derivatives f_x, f_y, f_z at and in some neighborhood of the point (x_0, y_0, z_0), and whose derivatives are continuous at the point, we have

$$\Delta w = f(x_0 + \Delta x, y_0 + \Delta y, z_0 + \Delta z) - f(x_0, y_0, z_0) \tag{30}$$

$$= f_x \, \Delta x + f_y \, \Delta y + f_z \, \Delta z + \epsilon_1 \, \Delta x + \epsilon_2 \, \Delta y + \epsilon_3 \, \Delta z,$$

where

$$\epsilon_1, \epsilon_2, \epsilon_3 \to 0 \qquad \text{when} \quad \Delta x, \Delta y, \text{ and } \Delta z \to 0.$$

The partial derivatives f_x, f_y, f_z in this formula are to be evaluated at the point (x_0, y_0, z_0).

Note.   The result (30) may be proved by treating Δw as the sum of three increments,

$$\Delta w_1 = f(x_0 + \Delta x, y_0, z_0) - f(x_0, y_0, z_0), \tag{31a}$$

$$\Delta w_2 = f(x_0 + \Delta x, y_0 + \Delta y, z_0) - f(x_0 + \Delta x, y_0, z_0), \tag{31b}$$

$$\Delta w_3 = f(x_0 + \Delta x, y_0 + \Delta y, z_0 + \Delta z) - f(x_0 + \Delta x, y_0 + \Delta y, z_0), \tag{31c}$$

and applying the Mean Value Theorem to each of these separately. Note that two coordinates remain constant and only one varies in each of these partial increments Δw_1, Δw_2, Δw_3. For example, in (31b), only y varies, since x is held equal to $x_0 + \Delta x$ and z is held equal to z_0. Since the function $f(x_0 + \Delta x, y, z_0)$ is a continuous function of y with a derivative f_y, it is subject to the Mean Value Theorem, and we have

$$\Delta w_2 = f_y(x_0 + \Delta x, y_1, z_0)\, \Delta y$$

for some y_1 between y_0 and $y_0 + \Delta y$.

The formula

$$\Delta w_{\tan} = f_x(x_0, y_0, z_0)\, \Delta x + f_y(x_0, y_0, z_0)\, \Delta y + f_z(x_0, y_0, z_0)\, \Delta z$$

$$= \left(\frac{\partial w}{\partial x}\right)_0 \Delta x + \left(\frac{\partial w}{\partial y}\right)_0 \Delta y + \left(\frac{\partial w}{\partial z}\right)_0 \Delta z, \qquad \text{(32)}$$

gives a good approximation to Δw when the increments in the independent variables are small.

EXAMPLE 5. *Deflection of loaded beams.* A rectangular beam that is supported at its two ends (Fig. 13–17) will sag in the middle when subjected to a uniform load. The amount S of sag, called the *deflection* of the beam, may be estimated from the formula

$$S = C\frac{p\ell^4}{wh^3} \quad \text{(m)}, \qquad \text{(33)}$$

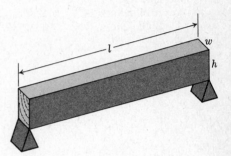

13–17 Beam supported at ends.

where

$p = $ the load (kg/meter of beam length),
$\ell = $ the length between supports (m),
$w = $ the width of the beam (m),
$h = $ the height of the beam (m),
$C = $ a constant that depends on the units of measurement and on the material from which the beam is made.

When

$$\Delta S \approx \Delta S_{\tan} = S_p\, \Delta p + S_\ell\, \Delta\ell + S_w\, \Delta w + S_h\, \Delta h$$

is written out for a particular set of values p_0, ℓ_0, w_0, h_0, and simplified, the resulting approximation is

$$\Delta S \approx S_0\left[\frac{\Delta p}{p_0} + \frac{4\,\Delta\ell}{\ell_0} - \frac{\Delta w}{w_0} - \frac{3\,\Delta h}{h_0}\right], \qquad \text{(34)}$$

where $S_0 = S(p_0, \ell_0, h_0, w_0) = Cp_0\ell_0^4/w_0 h_0^3$.

At $p_0 = 100$ kg/m, $\ell_0 = 4$ m, $w_0 = 0.1$ m, and $h_0 = 0.2$ m,

$$\Delta S \approx S_0\left[\frac{\Delta p}{100} + \Delta\ell - 10\,\Delta w - 15\,\Delta h\right]. \qquad \text{(35)}$$

13–18 The dimensions of the beam in Example 5.

(See Fig. 13–18.)

Conclusions about this beam from Eq. (35). Since Δp and $\Delta \ell$ appear with positive coefficients in Eq. (35), increases in p and in ℓ will increase the sag. But Δw and Δh appear with negative coefficients, so that increases in w and h will *decrease* the sag (make the beam stiffer). The sag is not very sensitive to small changes in load, because the coefficient of Δp is $1/100$. The coefficient of Δh is a negative number of greater magnitude than the coefficient of Δw. Therefore, making the beam $\Delta h = 1$ cm higher will decrease the sag more than making the beam $\Delta w = 1$ cm wider.

PROBLEMS

1. Find $\Delta w_{\tan}$ and Δw if $w = x^2 - xy + y^2$, $(x_0, y_0) = (1, -2)$, $x = 0.01$, $y = -0.02$.

2. Calculate Δw, $\Delta w_{\tan}$, ϵ_1, and ϵ_2 at the general point (x, y) for the function $w = x^2 + xy$.

3. (a) Sketch the region in the xy-plane whose coordinates satisfy the inequality $|x - y| < \frac{1}{2}$. (b) Based on inequality (23) at the end of Example 2, how small should one make $|x - y|$ to be sure that the error in the approximation $1/(1 + x - y) \approx 1 - x + y$ is less than 10^{-3}?

4. (*Calculator*) Evaluate both sides of Eq. (25) for (a) $(x, y) = (2.1, 1.1)$; (b) $(x, y) = (2.1, 0.9)$.

In Problems 5–7, use Eq. (20) to find linear approximations to the given functions near the given points. If you have a *calculator*, check your approximations for an assortment of values of x and y.

5. $f(x, y) = \sqrt{x^2 + y^2}$;
near (a) $(1, 0)$; (b) $(0, 1)$; (c) $(1, 1)$.

6. $f(x, y) = (\sin x)/y$; near (a) $(\pi/2, 1)$; (b) $(0, 1)$.

7. $f(x, y) = e^x \cos y$; near (a) $(0, 0)$; (b) $(0, \pi/2)$.

8. What relationship must hold between the r and h in Example 4 if the volume of the cylinder is to be equally sensitive to small changes in the two variables?

9. The beam of Example 5 is tipped on its side, so that $h = 0.1$ m and $w = 0.2$ m. (a) What is the approximation for ΔS now? (b) Compare the sensitivity of the beam to a small change in height with its sensitivity to a change of the same amount in width.

10. Use $\Delta w_{\tan}$ to calculate how much an error of 2 percent in each of the factors a, b, c may affect the product abc.

11. (*Calculator*) Let $Q = \sqrt{2KM/h}$ be the economic order quantity of Example 24, Article 1–6. (a) Write an approximation for ΔQ, with partial derivatives evaluated at $K_0 = \$2.00$, $M_0 = 20$ radios/week, and $h_0 = \$0.05$. (b) At the values for K_0, M_0, h_0, given in (a), to which variable is Q most sensitive? least sensitive?

12. The dimensions of a rectangular box are measured as 3, 4, and 12 in. If the measurements may be in error by ± 0.01, ± 0.01, and ± 0.03 in., respectively, calculate the length of the diagonal and estimate the possible error in this length.

13. Carry through the details of deriving Eq. (11).

14. A function $w = f(x, y)$ is said to be *differentiable* at $P(a, b)$ if there are constants M and N (possibly depending on f and P) such that

$$\Delta w = M \, \Delta x + N \, \Delta y + \alpha[\,|\Delta x| + |\Delta y|\,]$$

and $\alpha \to 0$ as $|\Delta x| + |\Delta y| \to 0$. Here $\Delta w = f(a + \Delta x, b + \Delta y) - f(a, b)$. Prove that if f is differentiable at (a, b), then $M = f_x(a, b)$ and $N = f_y(a, b)$.

15. If the function $w = f(x, y)$ is differentiable at $P(a, b)$ (see Problem 14), prove it is continuous there.

13-5

THE DIRECTIONAL DERIVATIVE: GENERAL CASE

Let us return once more to Fig. 13–9 and the problem of determining the instantaneous rate of change at $P_0(x_0, y_0)$ of a function $w = f(x, y)$, measured in units of change of w per unit of distance along a ray L with vertex at P_0 and making an angle ϕ with the positive x-axis. Hold $P_0(x_0, y_0)$ fixed, and let $P_1(x_1, y_1)$ be a point on L near P_0. Let

$$\Delta x = x_1 - x_0,$$
$$\Delta y = y_1 - y_0.$$

The ratio

$$\frac{\Delta w}{\Delta s} = \frac{w_1 - w_0}{\sqrt{\Delta x^2 + \Delta y^2}}$$

$$= \frac{f(x_1, y_1) - f(x_0, y_0)}{\sqrt{(x_1 - x_0)^2 + (y_1 - y_0)^2}}$$

is the average rate of change of w along L from P_0 to P_1. If $\Delta w/\Delta s$ has a limit as $P_1 \to P_0$ along L, we denote the limit by dw/ds and call it the *directional derivative of w at P_0 in the direction of $\overrightarrow{P_0 P_1}$*. The next theorem tells how to calculate this derivative from the partial derivatives of f.

Theorem. *Let $w = f(x, y)$ be continuous and possess partial derivatives f_x, f_y throughout some neighborhood of the point $P_0(x_0, y_0)$. Let f_x and f_y be continuous at P_0. Then the directional derivative at P_0 exists for any direction angle ϕ, and is given by*

$$\frac{dw}{ds} = f_x(x_0, y_0) \cos \phi + f_y(x_0, y_0) \sin \phi. \tag{1}$$

Note that the special cases $\phi = 0$, $\pi/2$, π, $3\pi/2$, respectively, lead to

$$\frac{dw}{ds} = \frac{\partial f}{\partial x}, \quad \frac{\partial f}{\partial y}, \quad -\frac{\partial f}{\partial x}, \quad -\frac{\partial f}{\partial y},$$

in harmony with our earlier discussion.

Proof of the theorem.   Equation (4) of the previous article is valid under the hypotheses we have made for the continuity of $f(x, y)$, $\partial f/\partial x$, and $\partial f/\partial y$.
Hence,

$$\frac{\Delta w}{\Delta s} = f_x(x_0, y_0) \frac{\Delta x}{\Delta s} + f_y(x_0, y_0) \frac{\Delta y}{\Delta s} + \epsilon_1 \frac{\Delta x}{\Delta s} + \epsilon_2 \frac{\Delta y}{\Delta s},$$

where

$$\epsilon_1 \text{ and } \epsilon_2 \to 0 \qquad \text{as} \quad \Delta x \text{ and } \Delta y \to 0.$$

Now, if $P_1 \to P_0$ along L, or even along a smooth curve that is tangent to L at P_0, we have

$$\lim \frac{\Delta x}{\Delta s} = \frac{dx}{ds} = \cos \phi,$$

$$\lim \frac{\Delta y}{\Delta s} = \frac{dy}{ds} = \sin \phi$$

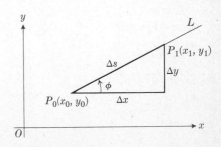

13–19 As $P_1 \to P_0$ on L, $\Delta x/\Delta s = \cos \phi$ and $\Delta y/\Delta s = \sin \phi$.

(Fig. 13–19), and hence

$$\frac{dw}{ds} = \lim \frac{\Delta w}{\Delta s} = f_x(x_0, y_0) \cos \phi + f_y(x_0, y_0) \sin \phi. \qquad \text{Q.E.D.}$$

EXAMPLE 1. Let $w = 100 - x^2 - y^2$. If one starts from the point $P_0(3, 4)$, in which direction should one go to make w increase most rapidly?

Solution. We have

$$f(x, y) = 100 - x^2 - y^2,$$

$$f_x(3, 4) = -6, \qquad f_y(3, 4) = -8,$$

and

$$\left(\frac{dw}{ds}\right)_{(3,4)} = -6 \cos \phi - 8 \sin \phi.$$

To make w increase most rapidly, we seek the angle ϕ for which the function

$$F(\phi) = -6 \cos \phi - 8 \sin \phi$$

has a maximum. Since

$$F'(\phi) = 6 \sin \phi - 8 \cos \phi$$

is zero when

$$\tan \phi = \tfrac{4}{3},$$

$$\sin \phi = \pm \tfrac{4}{5},$$

$$\cos \phi = \pm \tfrac{3}{5},$$

while

$$F''(\phi) = 6 \cos \phi + 8 \sin \phi$$

is negative in case both $\sin \phi$ and $\cos \phi$ are negative, we observe that the maximum value of $F(\phi)$ is attained when

$$\cos \phi = -\tfrac{3}{5},$$

$$\sin \phi = -\tfrac{4}{5}.$$

The geometric meaning of this result is that w increases most rapidly in the direction from $P_0(3, 4)$ toward the origin (Fig. 13–20). The derivative of w in this direction is found to be

$$\left.\frac{dw}{ds}\right|_{(3,4)} = -6(-\tfrac{3}{5}) - 8(-\tfrac{4}{5}) = 10.$$

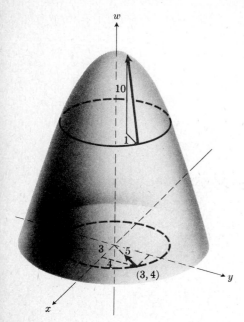

13–20 At $(3, 4)$ the change in $w = 100 - x^2 - y^2$ is greatest in the direction toward the origin. This corresponds to the direction of steepest ascent on the surface.

The notion of the directional derivative can easily be extended from the case of functions of two independent variables to the case of functions of three independent variables. To this end, consider the values of a function

$$w = f(x, y, z)$$

at $P_0(x_0, y_0, z_0)$ and at a nearby point $P_1(x_1, y_1, z_1)$ lying on a ray L emanating from P_0. It will be convenient to specify the direction of L by a unit vector $\mathbf{u}$. To find such a vector, we let

$$x_1 - x_0 = \Delta x, \qquad y_1 - y_0 = \Delta y, \qquad z_1 - z_0 = \Delta z,$$

so that

$$\overrightarrow{P_0 P_1} = \mathbf{i}\,\Delta x + \mathbf{j}\,\Delta y + \mathbf{k}\,\Delta z.$$

Since the length of $\overrightarrow{P_0 P_1}$ is

$$\Delta s = \sqrt{(\Delta x)^2 + (\Delta y)^2 + (\Delta z)^2},$$

the direction of $\overrightarrow{P_0 P_1}$ is given by

$$\frac{\overrightarrow{P_0 P_1}}{\Delta s} = \mathbf{u}.$$

That is,

$$\mathbf{u} = \mathbf{i}\,\frac{\Delta x}{\Delta s} + \mathbf{j}\,\frac{\Delta y}{\Delta s} + \mathbf{k}\,\frac{\Delta z}{\Delta s} = \mathbf{i}\cos\alpha + \mathbf{j}\cos\beta + \mathbf{k}\cos\gamma,$$

or

$$\frac{\Delta x}{\Delta s} = \cos\alpha, \qquad \frac{\Delta y}{\Delta s} = \cos\beta, \qquad \frac{\Delta z}{\Delta s} = \cos\gamma.$$

These direction cosines of $\overrightarrow{P_0 P_1}$ remain constant as P_1 approaches P_0 along L. Hence, in the limit as $\Delta s \to 0$, we also have

$$\frac{dx}{ds} = \cos\alpha, \qquad \frac{dy}{ds} = \cos\beta, \qquad \frac{dz}{ds} = \cos\gamma.$$

With these geometrical considerations out of the way, we now define the directional derivative of w at P_0 in the direction $\mathbf{u}$ to be the limit, as P_1 approaches P_0 along L, of the average rate of change of w with respect to distance:

$$\frac{dw}{ds} = \lim_{\Delta s \to 0} \frac{\Delta w}{\Delta s} = \lim_{P_1 \to P_0} \frac{f(x_1, y_1, z_1) - f(x_0, y_0, z_0)}{\sqrt{(x_1 - x_0)^2 + (y_1 - y_0)^2 + (z_1 - z_0)^2}}.$$

If f, f_x, f_y, and f_z are all continuous functions of x, y, z in some neighborhood of the point $P_0(x_0, y_0, z_0)$, then Eq. (30) of Article 13–4 applies, and we find that the directional derivative of $w = f(x, y, z)$ at P_0 in the direction of $\mathbf{u} = \mathbf{i}\cos\alpha + \mathbf{j}\cos\beta + \mathbf{k}\cos\gamma$ is

$$\frac{dw}{ds} = f_x(x_0, y_0, z_0)\cos\alpha + f_y(x_0, y_0, z_0)\cos\beta + f_z(x_0, y_0, z_0)\cos\gamma. \quad \textbf{(2)}$$

This can be expressed as the dot product of the vector $\mathbf{u}$ above and the vector

$$\mathbf{v} = \mathbf{i}f_x(x_0, y_0, z_0) + \mathbf{j}f_y(x_0, y_0, z_0) + \mathbf{k}f_z(x_0, y_0, z_0). \quad \textbf{(3)}$$

That is,

$$\frac{dw}{ds} = \mathbf{u} \cdot \mathbf{v}. \quad \textbf{(4)}$$

This factorization separates the directional derivative into a part $\mathbf{u}$ which depends only upon the *direction* and a part $\mathbf{v}$ which depends only upon the *function and the point P*. The vector $\mathbf{v}$ is called the *gradient* of f at P_0. It will be considered in detail in the next article. Equation (4) applies also in two dimensions as well as in three and includes Eq. (1) as a special case, with $\gamma = 90°$, $\cos\gamma = 0$.

EXAMPLE 2. Find the directional derivative of

$$f(x, y, z) = x^3 - xy^2 - z$$

at $P_0(1, 1, 0)$ in the direction of the vector $\mathbf{A} = 2\mathbf{i} - 3\mathbf{j} + 6\mathbf{k}$.

Solution. The partial derivatives of f at P_0 are

$$f_x = 3x^2 - y^2 \big|_{(1,1,0)} = 2,$$
$$f_y = -2xy \big|_{(1,1,0)} = -2,$$
$$f_z = -1 \big|_{(1,1,0)} = -1.$$

Therefore, the gradient of f at $(1, 1, 0)$ is

$$\mathbf{v} = 2\mathbf{i} - 2\mathbf{j} - \mathbf{k}.$$

Since

$$|\mathbf{A}| = \sqrt{2^2 + 3^2 + 6^2} = \sqrt{49} = 7,$$

the direction of $\mathbf{A}$ is

$$\mathbf{u} = \frac{\mathbf{A}}{|\mathbf{A}|} = \frac{2}{7}\mathbf{i} - \frac{3}{7}\mathbf{j} + \frac{6}{7}\mathbf{k}.$$

The derivative of f in the direction of $\mathbf{A}$ can now be calculated from Eq. (4) as

$$\mathbf{u} \cdot \mathbf{v} = 2(\tfrac{2}{7}) + 2(\tfrac{3}{7}) - 1(\tfrac{6}{7}) = \tfrac{4}{7}.$$

PROBLEMS

In Problems 1–4, find the directional derivative of the given function, $f = f(x, y, z)$, at the given point, and in the direction of the given vector $\mathbf{A}$.

1. $f = e^x \cos (yz)$, $P_0(0, 0, 0)$, $\mathbf{A} = 2\mathbf{i} + \mathbf{j} - 2\mathbf{k}$.
2. $f = \ln \sqrt{x^2 + y^2 + z^2}$, $P_0(3, 4, 12)$, $\mathbf{A} = 3\mathbf{i} + 6\mathbf{j} - 2\mathbf{k}$.
3. $f = x^2 + 2y^2 + 3z^2$, $P_0(1, 1, 1)$, $\mathbf{A} = \mathbf{i} + \mathbf{j} + \mathbf{k}$.
4. $f = xy + yz + zx$, $P_0(1, -1, 2)$, $\mathbf{A} = 10\mathbf{i} + 11\mathbf{j} - 2\mathbf{k}$.

5. In which direction should one travel, starting from $P_0(1, 1, 0)$, to obtain the most rapid rate of decrease of the function

$$f = (x + y - 2)^2 + (3x - y - 6)^2?$$

6. The directional derivative of a given function $w = f(x, y)$ at $P_0(1, 2)$ in the direction toward $P_1(2, 3)$ is $+2\sqrt{2}$, and in the direction toward $P_2(1, 0)$ it is -3. What is the value of dw/ds at P_0 in the direction toward the origin?

7. Investigate the following graphical method of representing the directional derivative. Let $w = f(x, y)$ be a given function and let $P_0(x_0, y_0)$ be a given point. Through P_0 draw any ray making an angle θ with the positive x-direction, $0 \le \theta \le 2\pi$. On this directed line (or on its backward extension through P_0, if r is negative), mark the point Q such that the polar coordinates of Q relative to P_0 are (r, θ) with $r = (dw/ds)_0$. Show that Q is located on a circle of diameter

$$\sqrt{\left(\frac{\partial w}{\partial x}\right)_0^2 + \left(\frac{\partial w}{\partial y}\right)_0^2}.$$

Show that P_0 and

$$P_1\left(x_0 + \left(\frac{\partial w}{\partial x}\right)_0, \; y_0 + \left(\frac{\partial w}{\partial y}\right)_0\right)$$

are opposite ends of one diameter of the circle. (This gives an easy way to construct the circle: Locate P_0 and P_1, and then draw the circle with diameter $P_0 P_1$. This circle is analogous to the Mohr circle in mechanics.)

8. Find the directional derivative of $f(x, y) = x \tan^{-1} y/x$ at $(1, 1)$ in the direction of $\mathbf{A} = 2\mathbf{i} - \mathbf{j}$.

9. In which direction is the directional derivative of

$$f(x, y) = \frac{x^2 - y^2}{x^2 + y^2}$$

at $(1, 1)$ equal to zero?

In the previous article we found that the directional derivative of a function $w = f(x, y, z)$ could be expressed as the dot product of a unit vector **u** specifying the direction and the vector **v** of Eq. (3). This latter vector depends only upon the values of the partial derivatives of w at P_0 and is called the *gradient* of w. Two symbols are commonly used to denote the gradient, namely, grad w and ∇w, where ∇ is an inverted capital delta and is generally called *del*. The gradient is defined by the equation

$$\text{grad } w = \nabla w = \mathbf{i}\frac{\partial w}{\partial x} + \mathbf{j}\frac{\partial w}{\partial y} + \mathbf{k}\frac{\partial w}{\partial z}. \tag{1}$$

The del operator

$$\nabla = \mathbf{i}\frac{\partial}{\partial x} + \mathbf{j}\frac{\partial}{\partial y} + \mathbf{k}\frac{\partial}{\partial z} \tag{2}$$

is akin to, but somewhat more complex than, the familiar differentiation operator d/dx. When del operates on a differentiable function $w = f(x, y, z)$, it produces a vector, namely the vector grad w or grad f given by Eq. (1).

In courses in advanced calculus and vector analysis, a detailed study is made of the operator ∇, including not only the operation of forming the gradient of a scalar function w but also the additional operations of forming the dot and cross products of the vector operator del with other vectors.

In this article we develop some of the geometric properties of the gradient.

The Connection between the Gradient and the Directional Derivative

Using ∇w to represent the gradient, we may write Eq. (2) of Article 13–5 as

$$\left(\frac{dw}{ds}\right)_0 = (\nabla w)_0 \cdot \mathbf{u}, \tag{3}$$

where the subscript 0 is used to show that both ∇w and dw/ds are to be evaluated at the point $P_0(x_0, y_0, z_0)$.

From Eq. (3) and the geometric significance of the dot product of two vectors, we can say that

$$\left(\frac{dw}{ds}\right)_0 = |(\nabla w)_0|\,|\mathbf{u}|\cos\theta$$

$$= |(\nabla w)_0|\cos\theta, \tag{4}$$

where θ is the angle between the vector $(\nabla w)_0$ and the unit vector **u**. That is, $(dw/ds)_0$ is just the component of grad w at P_0, in the direction **u** (Fig. 13–21a). Since this component is largest when $\cos\theta = 1$ in Eq. (4), that is, when **u** and ∇w have the same direction, we can say:

The function $w = f(x, y, z)$ changes most rapidly in the direction given by the vector grad w. Moreover, the directional derivative in this direction is equal to the magnitude of the gradient.

---

1 3 – 6

THE GRADIENT

a)

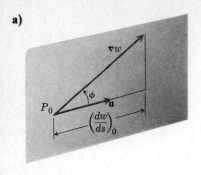

dw/ds is the component of ∇w in the direction of **u**.

b)

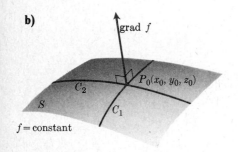

$(\text{grad } f)_0$ is perpendicular to the surface $f(x, y, z) = w_0$ at $P_0(x_0, y_0, z_0)$.

Figure 13–21

We may therefore characterize the gradient of the function $w = f(x, y, z)$ at the point $P_0(x_0, y_0, z_0)$ as a vector

a) whose *direction* is that in which $(dw/ds)_0$ has its maximum value, and

b) whose *magnitude* is equal to that maximum value of $(dw/ds)_0$.

The Connection between $(\nabla w)_0$ and the Surface $f(x, y, z) = w_0$

The points at which the function $w = f(x, y, z)$ has a constant value w_0 will generally constitute a surface in space. The equation of this surface is

$$f(x, y, z) = w_0, \tag{5a}$$

or

$$f(x, y, z) - w_0 = 0. \tag{5b}$$

If w represents temperature, the surface given by Eq. (5) is an isothermal surface. If w represents electrical or gravitational potential, then the surface is an equipotential surface. What we now wish to establish is that the gradient vector is normal to this isothermal or potential surface, as shown in Fig. 13–21(b). To see that this is so, we consider any curve C on the surface S of Eq. (5) and passing through the point $P_0(x_0, y_0, z_0)$ on S. We calculate the directional derivative $(dw/ds)_0$ in the direction of the tangent vector to C at P_0. This derivative is zero because w remains constant on C and hence $(\Delta w)_C = 0$, so that

$$\left(\frac{dw}{ds}\right)_0 = \lim \frac{\Delta w}{\Delta s} = 0.$$

If we compare this result with Eq. (4), we see that at any point P_0 where $(\nabla w)_0$ is not zero, $\cos \theta$ vanishes; that is,

$(\nabla w)_0$ is perpendicular to **u**,

where **u** is a unit vector tangent to C at P_0. Now since C could be any curve on S through P_0, we have the result that

---

The gradient $(\nabla w)_0$ of the function $w = f(x, y, z)$ is normal to the surface

$$f(x, y, z) = w_0$$

at the point $P_0(x_0, y_0, z_0)$.

In the exceptional case where $(\nabla w)_0$ is the zero vector, it has no definite direction. But if we adopt the convention that the zero vector is orthogonal to every direction, then we may say without exception that the gradient of a function $f(x, y, z)$ at a point $P_0(x_0, y_0, z_0)$ is orthogonal to the surface $f(x, y, z) = $ constant passing through that point.

EXAMPLE.   Find the plane which is tangent to the surface $z = x^2 + y^2$ at the point $P_0(1, -2, 5)$.

Solution. Let $w = f(x, y, z) = x^2 + y^2 - z$, so that the equation of the surface has the form

$$f(x, y, z) = \text{constant},$$

where the constant in this case is zero. Then the vector

$$(\text{grad } f)_0 = \left(\mathbf{i} \frac{\partial f}{\partial x} + \mathbf{j} \frac{\partial f}{\partial y} + \mathbf{k} \frac{\partial f}{\partial z} \right)_0$$

$$= (\mathbf{i}2x + \mathbf{j}2y - \mathbf{k})_{(1,-2,5)} = 2\mathbf{i} - 4\mathbf{j} - \mathbf{k}$$

is *normal* to the surface at P_0. But we recall that the equation of the plane through $P_0(x_0, y_0, z_0)$ normal to the vector

$$\mathbf{N} = A\mathbf{i} + B\mathbf{j} + C\mathbf{k}$$

is

$$A(x - x_0) + B(y - y_0) + C(z - z_0) = 0.$$

For the particular case at hand, we therefore have

$$2(x - 1) - 4(y + 2) - (z - 5) = 0,$$

or

$$2x - 4y - z = 5,$$

as the equation of the tangent plane.

Note that the equation of the surface should be put into the form

$$f(x, y, z) = \text{constant}$$

in order to find the normal vector, grad f.

PROBLEMS

In Problems 1–7, find the electric intensity vector $\mathbf{E} = -\text{grad } V$ from the given potential function V, at the given point:

1. $V = x^2 + y^2 - 2z^2$ $(1, 1, 1)$
2. $V = 2z^3 - 3(x^2 + y^2)z$ $(1, 1, 1)$
3. $V = e^{-2y} \cos 2x$ $(\pi/4, 0, 0)$
4. $V = \ln \sqrt{x^2 + y^2}$ $(3, 4, 0)$
5. $V = (x^2 + y^2 + z^2)^{-(1/2)}$ $(1, 2, -2)$
6. $V = e^{3x+4y} \cos 5z$ $(0, 0, \pi/6)$
7. $V = \cos 3x \cos 4y \sinh 5z$ $(0, \pi/4, 0)$
8. Find equations of the line normal to the surface $z^2 = x^2 + y^2$ at $(3, 4, -5)$.
9. Lines are drawn through the origin and normal to the surface $xy + z = 2$. (a) Find equations of all such lines. (b) Find all points of intersection of these lines with the surface.
10. Find the points on the surface

$$(y + z)^2 + (z - x)^2 = 16,$$

where the normal is parallel to the yz-plane.

11. Find the tangent plane and normal to the hyperboloid $x^2 + y^2 - z^2 = 18$ at $(3, 5, -4)$.

12. In which direction should one travel, starting from the point $P_0(2, -1, 2)$, in order to obtain the most rapid rate of increase of the function $f = (x + y)^2 + (y + z)^2 + (z + x)^2$? What is the instantaneous rate of change of f per unit of distance in this direction?

13. Suppose cylindrical coordinates r, θ, z are introduced into a function $w = f(x, y, z)$ to yield $w = F(r, \theta, z)$. Show that the gradient may be expressed in terms of cylindrical coordinates and the unit vectors $\mathbf{u}_r$, $\mathbf{u}_\theta$, $\mathbf{k}$ as follows:

$$\nabla w = \mathbf{u}_r \frac{\partial w}{\partial r} + \frac{1}{r} \mathbf{u}_\theta \frac{\partial w}{\partial \theta} + \mathbf{k} \frac{\partial w}{\partial z}.$$

[*Hint*. The component of ∇w in the direction of $\mathbf{u}_r$ is equal to the directional derivative dw/ds in that direction. But this is precisely $\partial w/\partial r$. Reason similarly for the components of ∇w in the directions of $\mathbf{u}_\theta$ and $\mathbf{k}$.]

14. Express the gradient in terms of spherical coordinates and the appropriate unit vectors $\mathbf{u}_\rho$, $\mathbf{u}_\phi$, $\mathbf{u}_\theta$. Use a geometrical argument to determine the component of ∇w in each of these directions. (See hint for Problem 13.)

15. (a) In the case of a function $w = f(x, y)$ of two independent variables, what is the expression for grad f? (b) Find the direction in which the function $w = x^2 + xy + y^2$ increases most rapidly, at the point $(-1, 1)$. What is the magnitude of dw/ds in this direction?

In Problems 16–23, verify that the function V satisfies Laplace's equation

$$\frac{\partial^2 V}{\partial x^2} + \frac{\partial^2 V}{\partial y^2} + \frac{\partial^2 V}{\partial z^2} = 0,$$

where V is as given:

16. In Problem 1   **17.** In Problem 2
18. In Problem 3   **19.** In Problem 4
20. In Problem 5   **21.** In Problem 6
22. In Problem 7

23. *Method of steepest descent.* Suppose it is desired to find a solution of the equation $f(x, y, z) = 0$. Let $P_0(x_0, y_0, z_0)$ be a first guess, and suppose $f(x_0, y_0, z_0) = f_0$ is not zero. Let $(\nabla f)_0$ be the gradient vector normal to the surface $f(x, y, z) = f_0$ at P_0. If f_0 is positive, we want to decrease the value of f. The gradient points in the direction of most rapid increase, its negative in the direction of "steepest descent." We therefore take as next approximation

$$x_1 = x_0 - hf_x(x_0, y_0, z_0),$$

$$y_1 = y_0 - hf_y(x_0, y_0, z_0),$$

$$z_1 = z_0 - hf_z(x_0, y_0, z_0).$$

What value of h corresponds to making $\Delta f_{\text{tan}} = -f_0$? What change is suggested if f_0 is negative? [The method could be applied to the problem of solving the simultaneous equations

$$x - y + z = 3,$$

$$x^2 + y^2 + z^2 = 20,$$

$$xyz = 8,$$

by writing

$$f(x, y, z) = (x - y + z - 3)^2$$

$$+ (x^2 + y^2 + z^2 - 20)^2 + (xyz - 8)^2.]$$

13-7

THE CHAIN RULE FOR PARTIAL DERIVATIVES

The formula

$$\frac{dy}{dt} = \frac{dy}{dx}\frac{dx}{dt}, \tag{1}$$

developed in Chapter 2, expresses the chain rule for differentiating a function

$$y = f(x) \tag{2}$$

with respect to t, when x is a function of t,

$$x = g(t). \tag{3}$$

Substituting Eq. (3) into Eq. (2) gives y as a function of t:

$$y = f[g(t)] = F(t). \tag{4}$$

Equation (1) in turn tells us that

$$F'(t) = f'(x)g'(t) \tag{5a}$$

or, in subscript notation, that

$$F_t = f_x g_t, \tag{5b}$$

or

$$y_t = y_x x_t. \tag{5c}$$

In this article we extend the chain rule to functions of several variables. We start with a function

$$w = f(x, y, z) \tag{6}$$

that has continuous partial derivatives

$$\frac{\partial w}{\partial x} = f_x, \qquad \frac{\partial w}{\partial y} = f_y, \qquad \frac{\partial w}{\partial z} = f_z \qquad (7)$$

throughout some region R of xyz-space. Suppose we want to study the behavior of the function f along a curve C lying in R and given by parametric equations

$$x = x(t), \qquad y = y(t), \qquad z = z(t). \qquad (8)$$

Such a situation arises, for example, in studying the pressure or density in a moving fluid. Then the equation that takes the place of Eq. (1) or (5) is

$$\frac{dw}{dt} = \frac{\partial w}{\partial x}\frac{dx}{dt} + \frac{\partial w}{\partial y}\frac{dy}{dt} + \frac{\partial w}{\partial z}\frac{dz}{dt}, \qquad (9)$$

as we shall now show. Let t_0 be a value of t that corresponds to a point P_0 in R and let Δt be an increment in t such that the point P that corresponds to $t_0 + \Delta t$ also lies in R. Let $\Delta x, \Delta y, \Delta z, \Delta w$ denote the increments in x, y, z, w. Then, by Eq. (30) of Article 13–4, we may write

$$\frac{\Delta w}{\Delta t} = \left(\frac{\partial w}{\partial x}\right)_0 \frac{\Delta x}{\Delta t} + \left(\frac{\partial w}{\partial y}\right)_0 \frac{\Delta y}{\Delta t} + \left(\frac{\partial w}{\partial z}\right)_0 \frac{\Delta z}{\Delta t} + \epsilon_1 \frac{\Delta x}{\Delta t} + \epsilon_2 \frac{\Delta y}{\Delta t} + \epsilon_3 \frac{\Delta z}{\Delta t},$$
$$(10)$$

where the subscript zero shows that the partial derivatives are to be evaluated at P_0, and where

$$\epsilon_1, \epsilon_2, \epsilon_3 \to 0 \qquad \text{as} \quad \Delta x, \Delta y, \Delta z \to 0.$$

Suppose we now let $\Delta t \to 0$ in Eq. (10) and assume that the curve C given by Eqs. (8) has derivatives $dx/dt, dy/dt, dz/dt$ at t_0. Then

$$\Delta x, \Delta y, \Delta z \to 0 \qquad \text{as} \quad \Delta t \to 0$$

and the three terms in Eq. (10) that involve the epsilons go to zero, while the other terms give

$$\left(\frac{dw}{dt}\right)_0 = \left(\frac{\partial w}{\partial x}\right)_0\left(\frac{dx}{dt}\right)_0 + \left(\frac{\partial w}{\partial y}\right)_0\left(\frac{dy}{dt}\right)_0 + \left(\frac{\partial w}{\partial z}\right)_0\left(\frac{dz}{dt}\right)_0.$$

This is Eq. (9) with all derivatives evaluated for $t = t_0$, $x = x_0$, $y = y_0$, and $z = z_0$.

EXAMPLE 1. Express dw/dt as a function of t if $w = xy + z$ and $x = \cos t, y = \sin t, z = t$. (This derivative shows how w varies along a particular helix in its domain.)

Solution. Starting with Eq. (9) we have

$$\frac{dw}{dt} = \frac{\partial w}{\partial x}\frac{dx}{dt} + \frac{\partial w}{\partial y}\frac{dy}{dt} + \frac{\partial w}{\partial z}\frac{dz}{dt}$$

$$= y(-\sin t) + x(\cos t) + 1(1)$$

$$= -\sin^2 t + \cos^2 t + 1$$

$$= 1 + \cos 2t.$$

No essential complication is introduced by considering the behavior of the function w in Eq. (6) on a *surface S* lying in R. We usually use *two* parameters to give the equations of a surface (for example, *latitude* and *longitude* on the surface of a sphere). Hence, consider the case where x, y, and z are functions of two parameters, say r and s,

$$x = x(r, s), \qquad y = y(r, s), \qquad z = z(r, s), \tag{11}$$

and calculate

$$\frac{\partial w}{\partial r} = \lim_{\Delta r \to 0} \frac{\Delta w}{\Delta r} \tag{12}$$

with s held constant. In this case Eq. (10) is to be replaced by a similar equation with Δr in place of Δt throughout. When $\Delta r \to 0$ (s held constant), we have

$$\lim_{\Delta r \to 0} \frac{\Delta x}{\Delta r} = \frac{\partial x}{\partial r}$$

and two similar expressions with y and z in place of x. Thus when $\Delta r \to 0$, the result is

$$\frac{\partial w}{\partial r} = \frac{\partial w}{\partial x} \frac{\partial x}{\partial r} + \frac{\partial w}{\partial y} \frac{\partial y}{\partial r} + \frac{\partial w}{\partial z} \frac{\partial z}{\partial r}. \tag{13}$$

We could also derive a similar expression, with s in place of r, for $\partial w/\partial s$.

EXAMPLE 2.   Find $\partial w/\partial r$ and $\partial w/\partial s$ as functions of r and s if $w = x + 2y + z^2$, and $x = r/s$, $y = r^2 + e^s$, $z = 2r$.

Solution.   From Eq. (13),

$$\frac{\partial w}{\partial r} = \frac{\partial w}{\partial x} \frac{\partial x}{\partial r} + \frac{\partial w}{\partial y} \frac{\partial y}{\partial r} + \frac{\partial w}{\partial z} \frac{\partial z}{\partial r}$$

$$= 1 \left(\frac{1}{s} \right) + 2(2r) + 2z(2) = \frac{1}{s} + 12r.$$

Similarly,

$$\frac{\partial w}{\partial s} = \frac{\partial w}{\partial x} \frac{\partial x}{\partial s} + \frac{\partial w}{\partial y} \frac{\partial y}{\partial s} + \frac{\partial w}{\partial z} \frac{\partial z}{\partial s}$$

$$= 1 \left(-\frac{r}{s^2} \right) + 2(e^s) + 2z(0) = -\frac{r}{s^2} + 2e^s.$$

EXAMPLE 3.   We may use the chain rule to solve the partial differential equation

$$\frac{\partial w}{\partial x} - a \frac{\partial w}{\partial y} = 0$$

for $w = f(x, y)$, given that a is a constant different from zero. We introduce new independent variables r, s such that

$$y - ax = r, \qquad y + ax = s.$$

Now we think of w as a function of r, s,

$$w = F(r, s),$$

and apply the chain rule in the form

$$\frac{\partial w}{\partial x} = \frac{\partial w}{\partial r}\frac{\partial r}{\partial x} + \frac{\partial w}{\partial s}\frac{\partial s}{\partial x} = -a\frac{\partial w}{\partial r} + a\frac{\partial w}{\partial s},$$

$$\frac{\partial w}{\partial y} = \frac{\partial w}{\partial r}\frac{\partial r}{\partial y} + \frac{\partial w}{\partial s}\frac{\partial s}{\partial y} = \frac{\partial w}{\partial r} + \frac{\partial w}{\partial s}.$$

When we substitute these expressions for $\partial w/\partial x$ and $\partial w/\partial y$ into the partial differential equation

$$\frac{\partial w}{\partial x} - a\frac{\partial w}{\partial y} = 0,$$

we obtain

$$-2a\frac{\partial w}{\partial r} = 0 \qquad \text{or} \qquad \frac{\partial w}{\partial r} = 0.$$

But this equation is *easy* to solve! It simply requires $w = F(r, s)$ to be a constant when s is constant and r is allowed to vary. That is, w must be a function of s alone:

$$w = \phi(s)$$
$$= \phi(y + ax).$$

Here $\phi(s)$ is *any* differentiable function of s whatever; for example,

$$\phi(s) = e^{2s} + \tan^{-1}(s^2) + \sqrt{s^2 + 4}$$

would be a suitable function. For this special case, we have

$$w = \phi(y + ax) = e^{2y + 2ax} + \tan^{-1}(y + ax)^2 + \sqrt{(y + ax)^2 + 4}$$

as a function that satisfies the original partial differential equation.

Functions of Many Variables

More generally, we may consider a function

$$w = f(x, y, z, u, \ldots, v)$$

of any number of variables $x, y, z, u, \ldots, v$ and study the behavior of this function when these variables are related to any number of other variables p, q, r, s, $\ldots$, t by equations

$$x = x(p, q, r, s, \ldots, t),$$
$$y = y(p, q, r, s, \ldots, t),$$
$$\vdots$$
$$v = v(p, q, r, s, \ldots, t).$$

Then, suppose we are required to find $\partial w/\partial p$, $\partial w/\partial q$, $\partial w/\partial r$, ..., $\partial w/\partial t$. By the methods used above, we find

$$\frac{\partial w}{\partial p} = \frac{\partial w}{\partial x}\frac{\partial x}{\partial p} + \frac{\partial w}{\partial y}\frac{\partial y}{\partial p} + \frac{\partial w}{\partial z}\frac{\partial z}{\partial p} + \cdots + \frac{\partial w}{\partial v}\frac{\partial v}{\partial p}, \tag{14}$$

or, in terms of the subscript notation for partial derivatives,

$$w_p = w_x x_p + w_y y_p + w_z z_p + \cdots + w_v v_p.$$

There are analogous equations for $\partial w/\partial q$, ..., $\partial w/\partial t$ obtained by replacing p by q, ..., t, respectively. This "chain rule" may be summarized as follows:

Let w be a differentiable function of the variables $x, y, \ldots, v$ and let these in turn be differentiable functions of a second set of variables $p, q, \ldots, t$:

First set of variables: $x, y, z, \ldots, v$,

Second set of variables: $p, q, r, \ldots, t$.

Then the derivative of w with respect to any one of the variables in the second set, say p, may be obtained by the following procedure:

1. Differentiate w with respect to each one of the variables in the first set; that is, calculate

$$\frac{\partial w}{\partial x}, \quad \frac{\partial w}{\partial y}, \quad \ldots, \quad \frac{\partial w}{\partial v}.$$

2. Differentiate each variable of the first set with respect to the one variable of the second set, in this case p; that is, calculate

$$\frac{\partial x}{\partial p}, \quad \frac{\partial y}{\partial p}, \quad \ldots, \quad \frac{\partial v}{\partial p}.$$

3. Form the products of the corresponding derivatives in 1 and 2, such as $(\partial w/\partial x)(\partial x/\partial p)$, $(\partial w/\partial y)(\partial y/\partial p)$, etc., and add these products together. Their sum gives $\partial w/\partial p$ [Eq. (14)].

PROBLEMS

In each of the following problems (1–3), find dw/dt (a) by expressing w explicitly as a function of t and then differentiating, and (b) by using the chain rule.

1. $w = x^2 + y^2 + z^2$, $x = e^t \cos t$, $y = e^t \sin t$, $z = e^t$

2. $w = \dfrac{xy}{x^2 + y^2}$, $x = \cosh t$, $y = \sinh t$

3. $w = e^{2x+3y} \cos 4z$, $x = \ln t$, $y = \ln(t^2 + 1)$, $z = t$

4. If $w = \sqrt{x^2 + y^2 + z^2}$, $x = e^r \cos s$, $y = e^r \sin s$, $z = e^s$, find $\partial w/\partial r$ and $\partial w/\partial s$ by the chain rule, and check your answer by using a different method.

5. If $w = \ln(x^2 + y^2 + 2z)$, $x = r + s$, $y = r - s$, $z = 2rs$, find $\partial w/\partial r$ and $\partial w/\partial s$ by the chain rule, and check your answer by using a different method.

6. If a and b are constants and

$$w = (ax + by)^3 + \tanh(ax + by) + \cos(ax + by),$$

show that

$$a\frac{\partial w}{\partial y} = b\frac{\partial w}{\partial x}.$$

7. If a and b are constants and $w = f(ax + by)$ is a differentiable function of $u = ax + by$, show that

$$a\frac{\partial w}{\partial y} = b\frac{\partial w}{\partial x}.$$

[*Hint*. Apply the chain rule with u as the only independent variable in the first set of variables.]

8. If $w = f[xy/(x^2 + y^2)]$ is a differentiable function of

$u = xy/(x^2 + y^2)$, show that $x(\partial w/\partial x) + y(\partial w/\partial y) = 0$. (See the hint for Problem 7.)

9. If $w = f(x + y, x - y)$ has continuous partial derivatives with respect to $u = x + y$, $v = x - y$, show that

$$\frac{\partial w}{\partial x}\frac{\partial w}{\partial y} = \left(\frac{\partial f}{\partial u}\right)^2 - \left(\frac{\partial f}{\partial v}\right)^2.$$

10. Verify the result given in Problem 13, Article 13–6, by transforming the given expression on the right side of the equation into **i, j, k** components and replacing the cylindrical coordinates r, θ by cartesian coordinates x, y, and making use of the chain rule for partial derivatives.

11. Verify the answer obtained in Problem 14, Article 13–6, by transforming the expression you obtained in spherical coordinates back into cartesian coordinates. Make use of the chain rule for partial derivatives.

12. If we substitute polar coordinates $x = r \cos \theta$ and $y = r \sin \theta$ in a function $w = f(x, y)$, show that

$$\frac{\partial w}{\partial r} = f_x \cos \theta + f_y \sin \theta,$$

$$\frac{1}{r}\frac{\partial w}{\partial \theta} = -f_x \sin \theta + f_y \cos \theta.$$

13. Using determinants, solve the equations given in Problem 12 for f_x and f_y in terms of $(\partial w/\partial r)$ and $(\partial w/\partial \theta)$.

14. In connection with Problem 12, show that

$$\left(\frac{\partial w}{\partial r}\right)^2 + \frac{1}{r^2}\left(\frac{\partial w}{\partial \theta}\right)^2 = f_x^2 + f_y^2.$$

The differential of a function

$$w = f(x, y, z) \tag{1}$$

is defined to be

$$dw = \frac{\partial w}{\partial x}dx + \frac{\partial w}{\partial y}dy + \frac{\partial w}{\partial z}dz. \tag{2}$$

13–8

THE TOTAL DIFFERENTIAL

The chain rule [Eq. (9), Article 13–7] tells us that we may formally divide both sides of Eq. (2) by dt to calculate dw/dt in case x, y, z are differentiable functions of t. Or, if x, y, z are functions of the independent variables r, s, and we want to calculate $\partial w/\partial r$, we hold s constant in calculating dx, dy, dz and divide both sides of Eq. (2) by dr, but write $\partial w/\partial r$, etc., in place of dw/dr, etc., to show that s has been held constant.

The separate terms

$$\frac{\partial w}{\partial x}dx, \qquad \frac{\partial w}{\partial y}dy, \qquad \frac{\partial w}{\partial z}dz$$

are sometimes called "partial differentials" of w with respect to x, y, z. The sum dw of these partial differentials, Eq. (2), is called the *total differential of w.*

In general, the total differential of a function

$$w = F(x, y, z, u, \ldots, v)$$

is defined to be the sum of all its partial differentials

$$dw = F_x\, dx + F_y\, dy + F_z\, dz + F_u\, du + \cdots + F_v\, dv.$$

If x, y, and z are independent variables in Eq. (1), then dx, dy, and dz are three *new independent variables* in Eq. (2). But in any problem involving increments we shall agree to take

$$dx = \Delta x, \qquad dy = \Delta y, \qquad dz = \Delta z, \tag{3}$$

in order to be able to use the differential dw as a good approximation to Δw [see Eq. (32), Article 13–4]. When x, y, and z are *not* independent variables but are themselves given by equations such as

$$x = x(t), \qquad\qquad x = x(r, s),$$
$$y = y(t), \qquad \text{or} \qquad y = y(r, s),$$
$$z = z(t), \qquad\qquad z = z(r, s),$$

then in the first case we have

$$dx = x'(t)\, dt, \qquad dy = y'(t)\, dt, \qquad dz = z'(t)\, dt,$$

and in the second case,

$$dx = \frac{\partial x}{\partial r}\, dr + \frac{\partial x}{\partial s}\, ds,$$

$$dy = \frac{\partial y}{\partial r}\, dr + \frac{\partial y}{\partial s}\, ds, \qquad\qquad (4)$$

$$dz = \frac{\partial z}{\partial r}\, dr + \frac{\partial z}{\partial s}\, ds,$$

if we are to be consistent.

Suppose we consider the second case in more detail. If we consider

$$w = f[x(r, s),\, y(r, s),\, z(r, s)] = F(r, s)$$

as a function of r and s, then instead of Eq. (2) we should have

$$dw = \frac{\partial w}{\partial r}\, dr + \frac{\partial w}{\partial s}\, ds, \qquad\qquad (5)$$

where

$$\frac{\partial w}{\partial r} = F_r(r, s), \qquad \frac{\partial w}{\partial s} = F_s(r, s).$$

Is the dw given by Eq. (2) the same as the dw given by Eq. (5)? The answer, which is "yes, they are the same," is a consequence of the chain rule for derivatives. For, if we start with the dw given by Eq. (2) and into it substitute dx, dy, dz given by Eq. (4), we obtain

$$dw = \frac{\partial w}{\partial x}\left(\frac{\partial x}{\partial r}\, dr + \frac{\partial x}{\partial s}\, ds\right) + \frac{\partial w}{\partial y}\left(\frac{\partial y}{\partial r}\, dr + \frac{\partial y}{\partial s}\, ds\right) + \frac{\partial w}{\partial z}\left(\frac{\partial z}{\partial r}\, dr + \frac{\partial z}{\partial s}\, ds\right)$$

$$= \left(\frac{\partial w}{\partial x}\frac{\partial x}{\partial r} + \frac{\partial w}{\partial y}\frac{\partial y}{\partial r} + \frac{\partial w}{\partial z}\frac{\partial z}{\partial r}\right) dr + \left(\frac{\partial w}{\partial x}\frac{\partial x}{\partial s} + \frac{\partial w}{\partial y}\frac{\partial y}{\partial s} + \frac{\partial w}{\partial z}\frac{\partial z}{\partial s}\right) ds.$$

The expressions in parentheses which here multiply dr and ds are the same as $\partial w/\partial r$ and $\partial w/\partial s$, respectively, by virtue of the chain rule for derivatives. Thus, starting with the expression for dw given by Eq. (2), we have transformed it into the expression for dw given by Eq. (5), thereby establishing the equivalence of the two.

It should be pointed out that in the case just discussed, where r and s are the *independent* variables, we are to treat dr and ds also as independent variables, but *not* dx, dy, and dz, which indeed are given by Eqs. (4). Thus, in a problem involving increments, we could, for convenience, take

$$dr = \Delta r \qquad \text{and} \qquad ds = \Delta s,$$

but we should *not* take $dx = \Delta x$, $dy = \Delta y$, and $dz = \Delta z$, since we are bound by Eqs. (4). The differentials dx, dy, and dz will, however, usually be reasonably good *approximations* to the increments Δx, Δy, and Δz when Δr and Δs are small (Article 13-4).

EXAMPLE 1. Find the total differential of

$$w = x^2 + y^2 + z^2$$

if

$$x = r \cos s, \qquad y = r \sin s, \qquad z = r.$$

Solution. If we use Eq. (2), we have

$$dw = 2(x \, dx + y \, dy + z \, dz)$$

with

$$dx = \cos s \, dr - r \sin s \, ds,$$
$$dy = \sin s \, dr + r \cos s \, ds,$$
$$dz = dr,$$

and hence

$$dw = 2(x \cos s + y \sin s + z) \, dr + 2(-xr \sin s + yr \cos s) \, ds$$
$$= 2(r \cos^2 s + r \sin^2 s + r) \, dr + 2(-r^2 \cos s \sin s + r^2 \sin s \cos s) \, ds$$
$$= 4r \, dr.$$

On the other hand, if we first express w directly in terms of r and s, we obtain

$$w = r^2 \cos^2 s + r^2 \sin^2 s + r^2 = 2r^2,$$

from which we also obtain

$$dw = 4r \, dr.$$

EXAMPLE 2. Show that the slope at the point (x, y) of the plane curve whose equation is given implicitly by

$$F(x, y) = 0$$

is

$$\frac{dy}{dx} = \frac{-F_x(x, y)}{F_y(x, y)} \qquad \text{if} \quad F_y(x, y) \neq 0.$$

Solution. Let $w = F(x, y)$ and consider the directional derivative of w at the point (x, y) in the direction of the tangent to the curve. If s denotes arc length along the curve, the directional derivative is

$$\frac{dF}{ds} = F_x \frac{dx}{ds} + F_y \frac{dy}{ds}.$$

But along the given curve F is constant, so that

$$\frac{dF}{ds} = \lim_{\Delta s \to 0} \frac{\Delta F}{\Delta s} = 0.$$

Therefore

$$F_x \frac{dx}{ds} + F_y \frac{dy}{ds} = 0,$$

and hence

$$\frac{dy}{dx} = \frac{dy/ds}{dx/ds} = \frac{-F_x}{F_y}.$$

EXAMPLE 3. Let $w = F(x, y, z)$ be *constant* along a curve C passing through $P_0(x_0, y_0, z_0)$. Let dx, dy, dz be such that the vector

$$d\mathbf{R} = \mathbf{i}\, dx + \mathbf{j}\, dy + \mathbf{k}\, dz$$

is tangent to C at P_0. Show that

$$dw = \text{grad } F \cdot d\mathbf{R} = 0.$$

Solution.   By definition,

$$dw = F_x\, dx + F_y\, dy + F_z\, dz$$

$$= (\mathbf{i}F_x + \mathbf{j}F_y + \mathbf{k}F_z) \cdot (\mathbf{i}\, dx + \mathbf{j}\, dy + \mathbf{k}\, dz)$$

$$= \text{grad } F \cdot d\mathbf{R}.$$

Also, the directional derivative of w, at P_0, in the direction of $d\mathbf{R}$ is

$$\frac{dw}{ds} = \text{grad } F \cdot \mathbf{u},$$

where

$$\mathbf{u} = \frac{d\mathbf{R}}{|d\mathbf{R}|}$$

is a unit vector in the direction of $d\mathbf{R}$. Along C, w remains constant and $dw/ds = 0$. Therefore

$$dw = \text{grad } F \cdot d\mathbf{R}$$

$$= \text{grad } F \cdot \mathbf{u}\,|d\mathbf{R}|$$

$$= \frac{dw}{ds}\,|d\mathbf{R}| = 0.$$

PROBLEMS

1. Show that the formulas

a) $d(u + v) = du + dv$,   **b)** $d(uv) = v\, du + u\, dv$,

c) $d\left(\dfrac{u}{v}\right) = \dfrac{v\, du - u\, dv}{v^2}$

are valid for total differentials, in case u and v are independent variables or if they are functions of any number of independent variables, such as $u = u(x, y, \ldots, p)$, $v = v(x, y, \ldots, p)$.

2. Using differentials to approximate increments, find the amount of material in a hollow rectangular box whose inside measurements are 5 ft long, 3 ft wide, 2 ft deep, if the box is made of lumber that is $\frac{1}{2}$ in. thick and the box has no top.

3. The area of a triangle is $A = \frac{1}{2}ab \sin C$, where a and b are two sides of the triangle and C is the included angle. In surveying a particular triangular plot of land, a and b are measured to be 150 ft and 200 ft, respectively, and C is read to be 60°. By how much (approximately) is the computed area in error if a and b are in error by $\frac{1}{2}$ ft each and C is in error by 2°?

4. (a) Given $x = r \cos \theta$, $y = r \sin \theta$, express dx and dy in terms of dr and $d\theta$. (b) Solve the equations of part (a) for dr and $d\theta$ in terms of dx and dy. (c) In the answer to part (b), suppose A and B are the coefficients of dx and dy in the expression for dr, that is,

$$dr = A\, dx + B\, dy.$$

Verify by direct computation that $A = \partial r/\partial x$ and $B = \partial r/\partial y$, where $r^2 = x^2 + y^2$.

5. Given $x = f(u, v)$, $y = g(u, v)$. If these equations are considered as implicitly defining u and v as functions of x and y,

a) Express dx and dy in terms of du and dv;

b) Use determinants to solve the equations of part (a) for du and dv in terms of dx and dy;

c) Show that

$$\frac{\partial u}{\partial x} = \frac{g_v}{f_u g_v - f_v g_u},$$

provided $f_u g_v - f_v g_u \neq 0$.

6. a) Given $x = \rho \sin \phi \cos \theta$,

$$y = \rho \sin \phi \sin \theta,$$

$$z = \rho \cos \phi,$$

express dx, dy, dz in terms of $d\rho$, $d\phi$, $d\theta$.

b) Solve the equations of part (a) for $d\rho$ in terms of dx, dy, dz by the use of determinants.

c) From your answers to part (b), read off $\partial \rho/\partial x$, consider-ing ρ, ϕ, θ as functions of x, y, z that are given implicitly by the equations of part (a).

7. *Newton's method.* It is desired to find values of x and y that satisfy the pair of equations $f(x, y) = 0$ and $g(x, y) = 0$ simultaneously. Suppose that, by trial and error or otherwise, it is found that $u_0 = f(x_0, y_0)$ and $v_0 = g(x_0, y_0)$ are both small in absolute value. It is now desired to find "corrections" dx and dy such that $f(x_0 + dx, y_0 + dy) = g(x_0 + dx, y_0 + dy) = 0$. Using $u_0 + df$ and $v_0 + dg$ to approximate to $f(x_0 + dx, y_0 + dy)$ and $g(x_0 + dx, y_0 + dy)$ respectively, determine approximate values of dx and dy. The procedure may be repeated with (x_0, y_0) replaced by $(x_1, y_1) = (x_0 + dx, y_0 + dy)$.

8. Generalize the method of Problem 7 to the case of three equations in three unknowns: $f(x, y, z) = 0$, $g(x, y, z) = 0$, $h(x, y, z) = 0$, assuming that

$$u_0 = f(x_0, y_0, z_0),$$

$$v_0 = g(x_0, y_0, z_0),$$

$$w_0 = h(x_0, y_0, z)$$

are small in absolute value.

9. Suppose $P_0(x_0, y_0, z_0)$ is a point on the surface $S: F(x, y, z) = 0$. Let dx and dy be arbitrary except that at least one of them should be different from zero. Show that a dz can be found, provided $F_z(x_0, y_0, z_0) \neq 0$, such that the vector $d\mathbf{R} = \mathbf{i}\, dx + \mathbf{j}\, dy + \mathbf{k}\, dz$ is tangent to the surface S at P_0. Find an expression for such a dz. Also show that, for such a vector $d\mathbf{R}$, dF is zero at P_0.

10. In Problem 9, consider the equation $F(x, y, z) = 0$ as determining z implicitly as a function of x and y, say $z = \phi(x, y)$. Show that

$$\phi_x = -\frac{F_x}{F_z}, \qquad \phi_y = -\frac{F_y}{F_z}$$

at any point where $F_z \neq 0$.

11. *Ruled surfaces.* [See "Rulings," by C. S. Ogilvy, *The American Mathematical Monthly*, **59** (1952), pp. 547–549.] The surface $z = f(x, y)$ is said to have *rulings* if through the point $P_0(x_0, y_0, z_0)$ there is a straight line segment all of whose points are on the surface. This happens if through the point $(x_0, y_0, 0)$ in the xy-plane there is a line of points $(x_0 + h, y_0 + k, 0)$ such that along this line dz and Δz are equal. This happens if and only if

$$f(x_0 + h, y_0 + k) - f(x_0, y_0) = \left(\frac{\partial f}{\partial x}\right)_0 h + \left(\frac{\partial f}{\partial y}\right)_0 k$$

when $h = \Delta x = dx$ and $k = \Delta y = dy$. Show that (a) the surface $z = \sqrt{1 + xy}$ has rulings through the point $P_0(2, 4, 3)$, given by the conditions $h = k$ or $4h = k$, (b) the surface $z = x^2 - y^2$ has rulings through any point $P_0(x_0, y_0, z_0)$, given by $h = \pm k$.

13–9

**MAXIMA AND
MINIMA OF FUNCTIONS OF
TWO INDEPENDENT VARIABLES**

In Chapter 3 we learned how to use the differential calculus to solve max-min problems for functions $y = f(x)$ of a single independent variable. In this article we shall extend the method to problems involving more than one independent variable.

We discuss the method in terms of finding high and low points on a smooth surface,

$$z = f(x, y). \tag{1}$$

The function f is assumed to be continuous and to have continuous partial derivatives with respect to x and y in some region R in the xy-plane. If there is a point (a, b) in R such that

$$f(x, y) \geq f(a, b) \tag{2}$$

for all points (x, y) sufficiently near to the point (a, b), then the function f is said to have a *local*, or *relative*, *minimum* at (a, b). If the inequality (2) holds for all points (x, y) in R, then f has an absolute minimum over R at (a, b). If the inequality in (2) is reversed, f then has a maximum (relative or absolute) at (a, b).

Suppose that the maximum (or minimum) value of f, over the region R, occurs at a point (a, b) that is not on the boundary of R; and that both $\partial f/\partial x$ and $\partial f/\partial y$ exist at (a, b). Then the first *necessary condition* that must be satisfied is that

$$\frac{\partial f}{\partial x} = 0 \quad \text{and} \quad \frac{\partial f}{\partial y} = 0 \quad \text{at } (a, b),$$

as we shall now show, for the section of the surface $z = f(x, y)$ lying in the plane $y = b$ is simply the curve

$$z = f(x, b), \qquad y = b,$$

and this curve has a high or low turning point at $x = a$ (Fig. 13–22). Hence

$$\left(\frac{\partial z}{\partial x} \right)_{x=a, y=b} = 0.$$

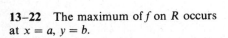

13–22   The maximum of f on R occurs at $x = a$, $y = b$.

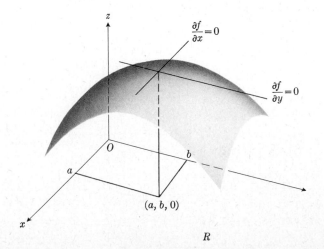

Similarly, the curve

$$z = f(a, y), \qquad x = a,$$

in which the plane $x = a$ intersects the surface, also has a high or low turning point when $y = b$, so that

$$\left(\frac{\partial z}{\partial y}\right)_{x=a, y=b} = 0.$$

We shall not at this time enter into a detailed discussion of second derivative tests for distinguishing between maxima and minima. The fundamental principle used in deriving such a test is that the difference

$$D = f(x, y) - f(a, b)$$

should be nonnegative (that is, positive or zero) for all points (x, y) close to the point (a, b) in case of a minimum at (a, b), or nonpositive in the case of a maximum. One way to test for a maximum or a minimum is to take

$$x = a + h, \qquad y = b + k,$$

and to examine the difference D for small values of h and k, as in the example that follows.

EXAMPLE.   Find the high and low points on the surface

$$z = x^2 - xy + y^2 + 2x + 2y - 4 = f(x, y).$$

Solution.   We apply the first necessary condition for a maximum or minimum of z, namely,

$$\frac{\partial z}{\partial x} = 0 \qquad \text{and} \qquad \frac{\partial z}{\partial y} = 0.$$

This leads to the simultaneous equations

$$2x - y = -2, \qquad -x + 2y = -2,$$

with solution

$$x = y = -2.$$

Thus, $(-2, -2)$ is the point that we have been calling (a, b). The corresponding value of z is

$$f(-2, -2) = -8.$$

To examine the behavior of the difference $D = f(x, y) - f(-2, -2)$, we let

$$x = -2 + h, \qquad y = -2 + k$$

and obtain

$$D = f(-2 + h, -2 + k) - f(-2, -2) = h^2 - hk + k^2$$
$$= \left(h - \frac{k}{2}\right)^2 + \frac{3k^2}{4}$$

This is readily seen to be positive for all values of h, k, except $h = k = 0$. That is,

$$f(x, y) \geq f(-2, -2)$$

for all (x, y) different from $(-2, -2)$. Thus the surface has a *low* point at $(-2, -2, -8)$. The given function has an absolute minimum -8.

REMARK. As with functions of a single independent variable, it is often possible to see that the function $z = f(x, y)$ has exactly one maximum (or minimum), that it occurs at an interior point of the domain of f, and that f everywhere possesses partial derivatives that must be zero at the critical point. No further test is then required. This is true, for instance, in the example above.

PROBLEMS

Examine the following surfaces for high and low points:

1. $z = x^2 + xy + y^2 + 3x - 3y + 4$

2. $z = x^2 + 3xy + 3y^2 - 6x + 3y - 6$

3. $z = 5xy - 7x^2 + 3x - 6y + 2$

4. $z = 2xy - 5x^2 - 2y^2 + 4x + 4y - 4$

5. $z = x^2 + xy + 3x + 2y + 5$

6. $z = y^2 + xy - 2x - 2y + 2$

7. Sketch the surface

$$z = \sqrt{x^2 + y^2}$$

over the region $R: |x| \le 1, |y| \le 1$. Find the high and low points of the surface over R. Discuss the existence, and the values, of $\partial z/\partial x$ and $\partial z/\partial y$ at these points.

13–10

THE METHOD OF LEAST SQUARES

An important application of minimizing a function of two variables is the *method of least squares* for fitting a straight line

$$y = mx + b \tag{1}$$

to a set of experimentally observed points $(x_1, y_1), (x_2, y_2), \ldots, (x_n, y_n)$ (Fig. 13–23). Corresponding to each observed value of x there are two values of y, namely, the observed value y_{obs} and the value predicted by the straight line $mx_{obs} + b$. We call the difference,

$$y_{obs} - (mx_{obs} + b), \tag{2}$$

a *deviation*. Each deviation measures the amount by which the predicted value of y falls short of the observed value. The set of all deviations

$$d_1 = y_1 - (mx_1 + b), \quad \ldots, \quad d_n = y_n - (mx_n + b) \tag{3}$$

gives a picture of how closely the line of Eq. (1) fits the observed data. The line is a perfect fit if and only if all of these deviations are zero. But in general no straight line will give a perfect fit. Then we are confronted with the problem of finding a line that fits *best* in some sense or other. Here is where the method of least squares comes in.

For a straight line that comes *close* to fitting all of the observed points, some of the deviations will probably be positive and some will be negative. But their squares will all be positive, and the expression

$$f(m, b) = (y_1 - mx_1 - b)^2 + (y_2 - mx_2 - b)^2 + \cdots + (y_n - mx_n - b)^2$$

counts a positive deviation d and a negative deviation $-d$ equally. This sum

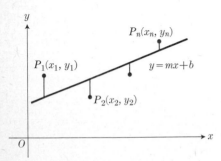

13–23 To fit a line to noncollinear points, we may choose a line that minimizes the sum of the squares of the deviations.

of squares of the deviations depends upon the choice of m and b. It is never negative and it can be zero only if m and b have values that produce a straight line that is a perfect fit.

Whether such a perfectly fitting line can be found or not, the method of least squares says, "*take as the line $y = mx + b$ of best fit that one for which the sum of squares of the deviations*

$$f(m, b) = d_1^2 + d_2^2 + \cdots + d_n^2$$

is a minimum." Thus we try to find the values of m and b where the surface

$$w = f(m, b)$$

in mbw-space has a low point (Fig. 13–24). To do this, we solve the equations

$$\frac{\partial f}{\partial m} = 0 \qquad \text{and} \qquad \frac{\partial f}{\partial b} = 0$$

simultaneously.

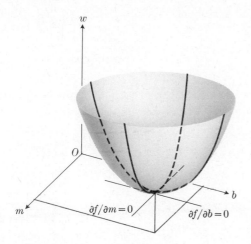

13–24   The sum $f(m, b)$ of the squares of the deviations has a minimum when $\partial f/\partial m$ and $\partial f/\partial b$ are both zero.

EXAMPLE.   Find the straight line that best fits the points $(0, 1)$, $(1, 3)$, $(2, 2)$, $(3, 4)$, $(4, 5)$ according to the method of least squares.

Solution.   The sum of squares of the deviations is

$$f(m, b) = \sum (y_{\text{obs}} - mx_{\text{obs}} - b)^2,$$

where y_{obs} and x_{obs} are the observed (or given) coordinates of the points to be fitted by the line $y = mx + b$.

We list these, together with the deviations and their squares, in Table 13–1.

We differentiate the formula in the last line of Table 13–1, and find

$$\frac{\partial f}{\partial m} = -78 + 20b + 60m,$$

$$\frac{\partial f}{\partial b} = -30 + 10b + 20m.$$

Table 13–1

x_{obs}	y_{obs}	dev = $y_{obs} - mx_{obs} - b$	$(dev)^2$
0	1	$1 - b$	$1 - 2b + b^2$
1	3	$3 - m - b$	$9 - 6b + b^2 - 6m + 2mb + m^2$
2	2	$2 - 2m - b$	$4 - 4b + b^2 - 8m + 4mb + 4m^2$
3	4	$4 - 3m - b$	$16 - 8b + b^2 - 24m + 6mb + 9m^2$
4	5	$5 - 4m - b$	$25 - 10b + b^2 - 40m + 8mb + 16m^2$

$$\sum (dev)^2 = 55 - 30b + 5b^2 - 78m + 20mb + 30m^2 = f(m, b)$$

The values of m and b for which f has a minimum must satisfy the simultaneous equations

$$\frac{\partial f}{\partial m} = 0, \qquad 20b + 60m = 78,$$

$$\frac{\partial f}{\partial b} = 0, \qquad 10b + 20m = 30.$$

The only solution is $m = 0.9$, $b = 1.2$. The "best-fitting" line (in the sense of least sum of squares of deviations) is therefore

$$y = 0.9x + 1.2.$$

(See Fig. 13–25.)

To verify that these values of m and b do in fact correspond to a minimum, we let

$$m = 0.9 + h, \qquad b = 1.2 + k$$

and calculate

$$\Delta = f(0.9 + h, 1.2 + k) - f(0.9, 1.2).$$

Doing this algebraically, we find

$$\Delta f = f(m + h, b + k) - f(m, b)$$
$$= (-30 + 10b + 20m)k + (-78 + 20b + 60m)h + 5k^2 + 20kh + 30h^2.$$

The expressions in parentheses are $\partial f/\partial b$ and $\partial f/\partial m$, respectively, and these are zero if $m = 0.9$ and $b = 1.2$. Hence

$$f(0.9 + h, 1.2 + k) - f(0.9, 1.2) = 5k^2 + 20kh + 30h^2$$
$$= 5(k + 2h)^2 + 10h^2.$$

This is greater than zero for all values of h and k other than $h = k = 0$. That is,

$$f(0.9 + h, 1.2 + k) \geq f(0.9, 1.2),$$

and we have found the values of m and b for which the function $f(m, b)$ is an absolute minimum.

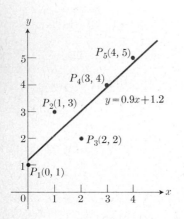

13–25 The least-squares line for the data in Table 13–1.

It is customary to omit the details of testing the answer obtained in solving a problem in least squares. Indeed, it can be shown that, for the case of fitting a straight line, the answer *always* corresponds to a minimum.

The method of least squares may also be applied to equations that are more complicated than the equation of a straight line, and the method has been widely extended. It is even the basis of departure for the modern theory of cybernetics developed originally by Professor Norbert Wiener of M.I.T.

PROBLEMS

1. The observed points (x_i, y_i), $i = 1, 2, \ldots, n$, are to be fitted by a straight line $y = mx + b$ by the method of least squares. The sum of squares of the deviations is

$$f(m, b) = \sum_{i=1}^{n} (mx_i + b - y_i)^2.$$

a) Show that the equations $\partial f/\partial b = 0$ and $\partial f/\partial m = 0$ are equivalent to

$$m(\sum x_i) + nb = \sum y_i,$$

$$m(\sum x_i^2) + b(\sum x_i) = \sum x_i y_i,$$

where all sums run from $i = 1$ to $i = n$. (b) Express the solutions b, m of the equations of part (a) in terms of determinants.

In Problems 2–4, apply the method of least squares to obtain the line $y = mx + b$ that best fits the three given points. [The computations can be systematized by making use of the results of Problem 1.]

2. $(-1, 2)$, $(0, 1)$, $(3, -1)$ **3.** $(-2, 0)$, $(0, 2)$, $(2, 3)$
4. $(0, 0)$, $(1, 2)$, $(2, 3)$

5. (*Calculator*) To determine the intermolecular potential between potassium ions and xenon gas, Budenholzer, Gislason, and Jorgensen (June 1, 1977, *Journal of Chemical Physics*, **66**, No. 11; p. 4832) accelerated a beam of potassium ions toward a cell containing xenon, and measured the current I of ions leaving the cell as a percentage of the current I_0 entering the cell. This fraction, which is a function of xenon gas pressure, was recorded at five different pressures, with the results shown in Table 13–2.

As a step in their determination, the authors used the method of least squares to find the slope m and intercept b

Table 13–2.   Scattering of potassium ions by xenon

x (pressure in millitorr)	0.165	0.399	0.573	0.930	1.281
I/I_0	0.940	0.862	0.810	0.712	0.622

of a line $y = mx + b$, where $y = \ln (I/I_0)$. In particular, they hoped to find that, within the limits of experimental error, b was zero. (a) Write down the value of y for each x in the table and fit a least-squares line to the (x, y) data points. Round m and b to three decimal places. (b) Express I/I_0 as a function of x.

6. (*Calculator*) Write a linear equation for the effect of irrigation on the yield of alfalfa by fitting a least-squares line to the following data from the University of California Experimental Station, *Bulletin* No. 450, p. 8. Plot the data and draw the line.

Table 13–3.   Growth of alfalfa

x (total seasonal depth of water applied (in.))	12	18	24	30	36	42
y (average alfalfa yield (tons/acre))	5.27	5.68	6.25	7.21	8.20	8.71

7. (*Calculator*) *Hubble's law* for the expansion of the universe is the linear equation

Velocity = the Hubble constant · distance

or

$$v = Hx.$$

It says that the velocity with which a galaxy appears to move away from us is proportional to how far away the galaxy lies. The farther away it lies, the faster it recedes. If the velocity is measured in kilometers per second and the distance in millions of light-years, then Hubble's constant is given in kilometers per second per million light-years. H is the rate at which the universe appears to be expanding. For

Table 13–4.   Observed velocities and distances of five receding galaxies

Galaxy	A	B	C	D	E
Observed distance (10^6 1-yr)	500	1,400	2,100	2,900	3,000
Recession velocity (km/s)	9,000	22,000	39,000	51,000	49,000

every extra million light-years of distance, the galaxies we can observe recede faster by H kilometers per second.

The table above lists the observed distances and velocities for five galaxies. Discover Hubble's constant H by fitting a least-squares line to the data (Fig. 13–26). Round your answer to the nearest integer. You will find that the y-intercept of the line is 240 km/s when rounded to the nearest integer, and not zero. A discrepancy in the intercept is to be expected, given the uncertainties in measurement and, here, the small size of the sample. Note that the discrepancy is a small percentage of the observed recession velocities. (For more information, see Jastrow and Thompson's *Astronomy: Fundamentals and Frontiers*, Second Edition, John Wiley and Sons, Inc., 1974, Chapter 11.)

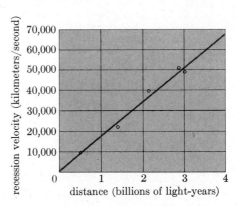

13–26   Velocity vs. distance observed for the galaxies in Table 13–4.

8. *(Calculator) Craters of Mars.* One theory of crater formation suggests that the frequency of large craters should fall off as the square of the diameter (Marcus, *Science*, June 21, 1968, p. 1334). Pictures from Mariner IV show the frequencies listed in Table 13–5.

Table 13–5.   Crater sizes on Mars

Diameter in km, D	32–45	45–64	64–90	90–128
$1/D^2$ (for left value of class interval)	0.001	0.0005	0.00025	0.000125
Frequency, F	53	22	14	3

Fit a line of the form $F = m(1/D^2) + b$ to the data. Plot the data and draw the line.

9. If $y = mx + b$ is the best-fitting straight line, in the sense of least squares, show that the sum of deviations

$$\sum_{i=1}^{n} (y_i - mx_i - b)$$

is zero. (This means that positive and negative deviations cancel.)

10. Show that the point

$$(\bar{x}, \bar{y}) = \left[\frac{1}{n} \left(\sum_{i=1}^{n} x_i \right), \frac{1}{n} \left(\sum_{i=1}^{n} y_i \right) \right]$$

lies on the straight line $y = mx + b$ that is determined by the method of least squares. (This means that the "best-fitting" line passes through the center of gravity of the n points.)

In certain applications, particularly in statistics, it becomes necessary to find maximum or minimum values of a function

$$w = f(x, y, z, u, \ldots, v)$$

of several independent variables. If the given function has an extreme value at an interior point of the domain, say at

$$x = a, \qquad y = b, \qquad z = c, \qquad \ldots, \qquad v = e,$$

then by setting $y = b, z = c, \ldots, v = e$ we obtain a function of x alone,

$$F(x) = f(x, b, c, d, \ldots, e),$$

which has an extreme value at $x = a$. Hence, if f has a partial derivative with respect to x at $x = a, y = b, \ldots, v = e$, that partial derivative must be zero by virtue of the theory for max-min for functions $F(x)$ of a single independent variable. That is,

$$\frac{\partial f}{\partial x} = 0 \quad \text{at } (a, b, c, \ldots, e).$$

By similar reasoning, we arrive at the first necessary condition for extreme values of a function of several independent variables, namely,

$$\frac{\partial f}{\partial x} = 0, \qquad \frac{\partial f}{\partial y} = 0, \qquad \ldots, \qquad \frac{\partial f}{\partial v} = 0 \quad \text{at } (a, b, \ldots, e).$$

The number of simultaneous equations $\partial f/\partial x = 0$, etc., which are thus obtained is precisely equal to the number of *independent variables* $x, y, \ldots, v$. Of course the solutions of this system of equations may correspond to maximum values of f, or to minimum values, or neither, in much the same way as for solutions of the equation $dy/dx = 0$.

Occasionally, the problem arises of finding the extreme value of one function, say

$$w = f(x, y, z, u, \ldots, v),$$

subject to *side conditions* or *constraints* given by equations like

$$g(x, y, z, u, \ldots, v) = 0,$$

$$h(x, y, z, u, \ldots, v) = 0, \ldots$$

(see Fig. 13–27). The theory behind such problems is discussed in most books on advanced calculus. (See Kaplan, *Advanced Calculus*, Second edition (1973, Addison-Wesley), p. 184). Here we shall do no more than point out that the equations representing the side restrictions may be used to express some of the variables $x, y, z, \ldots, v$ in terms of the remaining ones before we take partial derivatives. This is done so that the variables that remain may be *independent*. After the next two problems, which show how this method works, we shall present a second method, that of Lagrange multipliers.

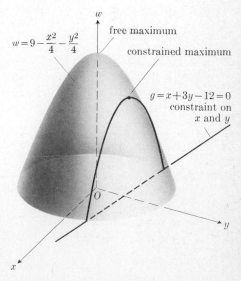

13–27 $f(x, y) = 9 - (x^2/4) - (y^2/4)$, subject to the constraint $g(x, y) = x + 3y - 12 = 0$.

EXAMPLE 1.   Find the minimum distance from the origin to the plane

$$2x + y - z = 5.$$

Solution.   If $P(x, y, z)$ is any point on the plane, then the distance from the origin to P is

$$|\overrightarrow{OP}| = \sqrt{x^2 + y^2 + z^2},$$

and clearly this has a minimum wherever the function

$$f(x, y, z) = |\overrightarrow{OP}|^2 = x^2 + y^2 + z^2$$

does. (The latter is simpler to work with since it does not involve radicals.) But the three variables x, y, z are not all independent, since P is to lie on the plane

$$2x + y - z = 5.$$

If we solve this equation for z, we find

$$z = 2x + y - 5,$$

and we may treat x and y as independent variables and minimize the function

$$g(x, y) = x^2 + y^2 + (2x + y - 5)^2.$$

The necessary conditions

$$\frac{\partial g}{\partial x} = 0 \qquad \text{and} \qquad \frac{\partial g}{\partial y} = 0$$

lead to the equations

$$10x + 4y - 20 = 0, \qquad 4x + 4y - 10 = 0,$$

with solution $x = \frac{5}{3}$, $y = \frac{5}{6}$. The z-coordinate of the corresponding point P is $z = -\frac{5}{6}$, and thus we have found the point $(\frac{5}{3}, \frac{5}{6}, -\frac{5}{6})$ as the *only* point on the plane that satisfies the *necessary* conditions. That is, if the given problem has an answer, this is it. From our knowledge of solid geometry we know that the problem does have an answer; hence we have found it. Of course, we may solve this same problem by strictly geometrical methods, but our purpose is not so much to solve this specific problem as it is to illustrate the *method* of solving such problems by partial differentiation. We may check our answer by noting that the vector from the origin to $P(\frac{5}{3}, \frac{5}{6}, -\frac{5}{6})$ is

$$\overrightarrow{OP} = \tfrac{5}{6}(2\mathbf{i} + \mathbf{j} - \mathbf{k}),$$

which is normal to the plane, as it should be.

REMARK 1.   The mechanics of setting $f_x = 0, f_y = 0$, and so forth may lead to a point not in the region where the function f is defined. Sometimes it is desirable to choose a different set of independent variables when this happens. We do this in the next example.

EXAMPLE 2.   Find the minimum distance from the origin to the surface $x^2 - z^2 = 1$.

Solution.   We seek to minimize

$$w = x^2 + y^2 + z^2,$$

where $x^2 = 1 + z^2$, or $z^2 = x^2 - 1$. If we eliminate z^2, we have

$$w = 2x^2 + y^2 - 1,$$

whose partial derivatives,

$$\frac{\partial w}{\partial x} = 4x, \qquad \frac{\partial w}{\partial y} = 2y,$$

are zero only at $x = 0$, $y = 0$. But then we run into trouble, for $z^2 = x^2 - 1 = -1$ means that z is imaginary when $x = 0$. In fact, the point $P(x, y, z)$ is on the surface $z^2 = x^2 - 1$ only when $|x| \geq 1$.

   If we eliminate x^2, however, and express w as a function of y and z, then the function

$$w = 1 + y^2 + 2z^2$$

has partial derivatives

$$\frac{\partial w}{\partial y} = 2y, \qquad \frac{\partial w}{\partial z} = 4z,$$

which are both zero when $y = z = 0$. This leads to

$$x^2 = 1 + z^2 = 1, \qquad x = \pm 1.$$

It is obvious from the expression $w = 1 + y^2 + 2z^2$ that $w \geq 1$ for all real values of y and z, since $y^2 + 2z^2 \geq 0$. Therefore the two points $(\pm 1, 0, 0)$ are nearer the origin than are any other points on the surface. The minimum distance from the surface to the origin is 1.

   By expressing w in terms of y and z as independent variables, we obtained variables which can take all real values

$$-\infty < y < \infty, \qquad -\infty < z < \infty.$$

The surface is a two-sheeted hyperbolic cylinder with elements parallel to the y-axis (Fig. 13–28).

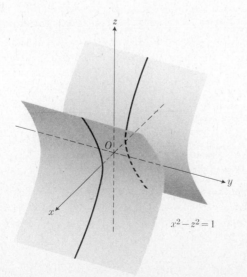

13–28   The surface $x^2 - z^2 = 1$.

Method of Lagrange Multipliers

In Example 2, we wanted to minimize the function

$$f(x, y, z) = x^2 + y^2 + z^2,$$

subject to the constraint

$$g(x, y, z) = x^2 - z^2 - 1 = 0.$$

The method of Lagrange multipliers applies to problems of this type. This is how it goes:

To minimize (or maximize) a function $f(x, y, z)$, subject to the constraint $g(x, y, z) = 0$, construct the auxiliary function

$$H(x, y, z, \lambda) = f(x, y, z) - \lambda g(x, y, z), \tag{1a}$$

and find values of x, y, z, λ for which the partial derivatives of H are all zero:

$$H_x = 0, \qquad H_y = 0, \qquad H_z = 0, \qquad H_\lambda = 0. \tag{1b}$$

We shall discuss the theory behind the method after the next problem, which demonstrates how to use it.

EXAMPLE 3. Find the point on the plane

$$2x - 3y + 5z = 19$$

that is nearest the origin, using the method of Lagrange multipliers.

Solution. As before, the function to be minimized can be taken to be the square of the distance from the origin to $P(x, y, z)$:

$$f(x, y, z) = x^2 + y^2 + z^2. \tag{2a}$$

The constraint is

$$g(x, y, z) = 2x - 3y + 5z - 19 = 0. \tag{2b}$$

We let

$$H(x, y, z, \lambda) = x^2 + y^2 + z^2 - \lambda(2x - 3y + 5z - 19). \tag{2c}$$

Then

$$H_x = 2x - 2\lambda = 0, \qquad H_y = 2y + 3\lambda = 0, \qquad H_z = 2z - 5\lambda = 0, \tag{3a}$$

and

$$H_\lambda = -g(x, y, z) = -(2x - 3y + 5z - 19) = 0. \tag{3b}$$

From Eqs. (3a), we get

$$x = \lambda, \qquad y = -\tfrac{3}{2}\lambda, \qquad z = \tfrac{5}{2}\lambda, \tag{3c}$$

and when these are substituted in Eq. (3b), or (2b), we get

$$2\lambda + \tfrac{9}{2}\lambda + \tfrac{25}{2}\lambda = 19,$$

so

$$\lambda = 1. \tag{3d}$$

Substituting $\lambda = 1$ in Eqs. (3c), we get the point $P_0 = (1, -\frac{3}{2}, \frac{5}{2})$. To see that the vector

$$\overrightarrow{OP_0} = \mathbf{i} - \tfrac{3}{2}\mathbf{j} + \tfrac{5}{2}\mathbf{k}$$

is normal to the plane

$$2x - 3y + 5z = 19,$$

we have only to divide both sides of the latter equation by 2. Therefore, $|\overrightarrow{OP_0}| = \frac{1}{2}\sqrt{38}$ is the minimum distance from the origin to the plane. (We could have found this answer using the normal vector

$$\mathbf{N} = 2\mathbf{i} - 3\mathbf{j} + 5\mathbf{k}$$

and no calculus.)

Discussion of the Method and Why It Works

We pass now to the general situation. Assume that the equation representing the constraint

$$g(x, y, z) = 0 \qquad \text{(4a)}$$

can be solved for z as a function of (x, y):

$$z = \phi(x, y), \qquad \text{(4b)}$$

throughout some neighborhood of the point $P_0(x_0, y_0)$. Assume, further, that this point minimizes the function

$$w = f(x, y, \phi(x, y)) \qquad \text{(5)}$$

that we get by substituting for z (Eq. 4b) into the function $f(x, y, z)$. For convenience, we shall use subscripts 1, 2, and 3 to denote partial derivatives of f and g with respect to the first, second, and third variables, respectively:

$$f_1(x, y, z) = f_x(x, y, z), \qquad g_1(x, y, z) = g_x(x, y, z),$$
$$f_2(x, y, z) = f_y(x, y, z), \qquad g_2(x, y, z) = g_y(x, y, z),$$
$$f_3(x, y, z) = f_z(x, y, z), \qquad g_3(x, y, z) = g_z(x, y, z).$$

Also, in the calculations that follow, we assume that

$$g_3[x, y, \phi(x, y)] \neq 0 \quad \text{near } P_0 \text{ and at } P_0.$$

We next differentiate both sides of Eq. (4a) implicitly with respect to x, holding y constant, and treating z as a differentiable function, as in Eq. (4b). This gives

$$g_1 + g_3 \frac{\partial z}{\partial x} = 0, \qquad \text{or} \qquad \frac{\partial z}{\partial x} = -\frac{g_1}{g_3}. \qquad \text{(6a)}$$

Likewise, if we differentiate with respect to y, holding x constant, we get

$$g_2 + g_3 \frac{\partial z}{\partial y} = 0, \qquad \text{or} \qquad \frac{\partial z}{\partial y} = -\frac{g_2}{g_3}. \qquad \text{(6b)}$$

In Eqs. (6a, b), the partial derivatives $g_1, g_2,$ and g_3 are to be evaluated at $(x, y, \phi(x, y))$ for (x, y) in some suitably restricted neighborhood of $P_0(x_0, y_0)$.

Now we turn our attention to the function in Eq. (5), whose extreme value is assumed to occur at P_0. The necessary condition [assuming that the righthand side of Eq. (5) is differentiable at P_0] for such a minimum or maximum is

$$f_1 + f_3 \frac{\partial \phi}{\partial x} = 0, \qquad f_2 + f_3 \frac{\partial \phi}{\partial y} = 0, \quad \text{at } P_0. \tag{7}$$

Substituting from Eqs. (6a, b) for

$$\frac{\partial z}{\partial x} = \frac{\partial \phi}{\partial x} = \frac{-g_1}{g_3}, \qquad \frac{\partial z}{\partial y} = \frac{\partial \phi}{\partial y} = \frac{-g_2}{g_3},$$

we get

$$f_1 - f_3 \left(\frac{g_1}{g_3} \right) = 0, \qquad f_2 - f_3 \left(\frac{g_2}{g_3} \right) = 0, \quad \text{at } P_0.$$

Thus at

$$(x_0, y_0, \phi(x_0, y_0)) = (x_0, y_0, z_0),$$

the following conditions hold:

$$f_1 = g_1 \left(\frac{f_3}{g_3} \right), \qquad f_2 = g_2 \left(\frac{f_3}{g_3} \right), \tag{8a}$$

and, of course,

$$f_3 = g_3 \left(\frac{f_3}{g_3} \right). \tag{8b}$$

Suppose, therefore, that we denote the ratio f_3/g_3 by λ. Then Eqs. (8a, b) can be combined into one vector equation:

$$\mathbf{i}f_1 + \mathbf{j}f_2 + \mathbf{k}f_3 = \lambda(\mathbf{i}g_1 + \mathbf{j}g_2 + \mathbf{k}g_3),$$

or

$$\nabla f = \lambda \nabla g \quad \text{at } (x_0, y_0, z_0), \tag{9}$$

and (x_0, y_0, z_0) is a point whose coordinates satisfy the constraint

$$g(x_0, y_0, z_0) = 0. \tag{10}$$

Equations (9, 10) are just the same as Eqs. (1a, b) in different form, because

$$\left.\begin{array}{l} H_x = f_x - \lambda g_x = 0 \\ H_y = f_y - \lambda g_y = 0 \\ H_z = f_z - \lambda g_z = 0 \end{array}\right\} \Leftrightarrow \nabla f = \lambda \nabla g,$$

and

$$H_\lambda = -g = 0 \Leftrightarrow g = 0.$$

REMARK 2. We could make Eq. (9) seem plausible by a geometric argument. Let us imagine that we are traveling around on the surface S, whose equation is $g = 0$, noting the values of f as we go. In particular, we note that the *level surfaces* of f (which we shall call *iso-f surfaces*) intersect the surface S in curves along which f remains constant. To find either a maximum or a minimum of f on S, we should take a route that crosses these iso-f curves in a direction in which f-values increase or decrease; specifically, if we are searching for a maximum, we should look for a direction in which f-values increase, and if we are searching for a minimum, we should look for a direction in which f-values decrease. When we have once arrived at a maximum of f on S, there will be no direction in which we can travel to get to an iso-f curve with a larger f-value. Equation (9) says that at this point ∇f and ∇g must have the same direction (or *opposite* directions, if λ is *negative*). This means that S and the surface $f = $ constant are *tangent* at that point: For a slightly smaller f-value, there would be a curve of intersection of the iso-f surface and S, and for a larger f-value, there would be no intersection. For the maximum, there is just one point at which the surface S and the iso-f surface touch, and at that point it does indeed seem plausible that the two surfaces are tangent.

REMARK 3.   If there are two constraints, say

$$g(x, y, z) = 0 \qquad \text{and} \qquad h(x, y, z) = 0,$$

we introduce two Lagrange multipliers λ and μ, and work with the auxiliary function

$$H(x, y, z, \lambda, \mu) = f(x, y, z) - \lambda g(x, y, z) - \mu h(x, y, z).$$

We then treat x, y, z, λ, μ as five independent variables for H, and set the five first-order partial derivatives of H equal to zero:

$$H_x = 0, \qquad H_y = 0, \qquad H_z = 0, \qquad H_\lambda = 0, \qquad H_\mu = 0.$$

These results are equivalent to

$$\nabla f = \lambda \nabla g + \mu \nabla h \quad \text{at } (x_0, y_0, z_0), \tag{11a}$$

$$g(x_0, y_0, z_0) = 0 \qquad \text{and} \qquad h(x_0, y_0, z_0) = 0. \tag{11b}$$

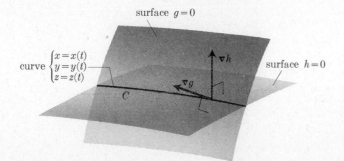

surface $g = 0$

curve $\begin{cases} x = x(t) \\ y = y(t) \\ z = z(t) \end{cases}$

∇h

surface $h = 0$

∇g

C

13–29 Vectors ∇g and ∇h are in a plane perpendicular to curve C because ∇g is normal to the surface $g = 0$, and ∇h is normal to the surface $h = 0$.

The vector equation (11a) says that the gradient of f lies in the plane of the gradients of g and h at $Q_0 = (x_0, y_0, z_0)$, and this has a fairly simple geometrical interpretation (Fig. 13–29). First, we know that ∇g is normal to the surface $g = 0$, and that ∇h is normal to the surface $h = 0$. The intersection of these two surfaces is usually a curve. On this curve, say C, we can think of x, y, and z as functions of one variable, for example, time (t) or arc length. Then $w = f(x, y, z)$ is a function of a single variable, say t, on C, and we want to find points where

$$\frac{dw}{dt} = 0.$$

We also know, from the chain rule, that

$$\frac{dw}{dt} = \nabla f \cdot \mathbf{v},$$

where

$$\mathbf{v} = \mathbf{i}\frac{dx}{dt} + \mathbf{j}\frac{dy}{dt} + \mathbf{k}\frac{dz}{dt}$$

is a vector *tangent* to C. To make $dw/dt = 0$, we therefore want to find a point Q_0 on C where ∇f is orthogonal to the tangent vector. This means, however, that ∇f should lie in a plane that is perpendicular to C at Q_0. This is just the plane that contains the two vectors $(\nabla g)_0$ and $(\nabla h)_0$, so $(\nabla f)_0$ should be a linear combination of them. Equation (11a) expresses this relationship. Equations (11b) represent the constraints that put Q_0 on C.

EXAMPLE 4. The cone $z^2 = x^2 + y^2$ is cut by the plane $z = 1 + x + y$ in a curve C. Find the points on C that are nearest to, and farthest from, the origin.

Solution. The function $f(x, y, z) = x^2 + y^2 + z^2$ is to be a minimum (or maximum) subject to the constraints

$$g(x, y, z) = x^2 + y^2 - z^2 = 0, \tag{12a}$$

$$h(x, y, z) = 1 + x + y - z = 0. \tag{12b}$$

We use Eq. (11a). For the critical points, we have

$$2x\mathbf{i} + 2y\mathbf{j} + 2z\mathbf{k} = \lambda(2x\mathbf{i} + 2y\mathbf{j} - 2z\mathbf{k}) + \mu(\mathbf{i} + \mathbf{j} - \mathbf{k}),$$

or, because components must agree,

$$\left.\begin{array}{l} 2x = 2x\lambda + \mu \\ 2y = 2y\lambda + \mu \\ 2z = -2z\lambda - \mu \end{array}\right\} \quad \begin{array}{l} \Rightarrow \quad x - y = (x - y)\lambda \\ \\ \Rightarrow \quad y + z = (y - z)\lambda \end{array}$$

The equation $x - y = (x - y)\lambda$ is satisfied if $x = y$ or if $x \neq y$ and $\lambda = 1$. This latter case cannot apply: The case $\lambda = 1$ implies $y + z = y - z$, from which it follows that $z = 0$. From Eq. (12a), however, $z = 0$ gives $x^2 + y^2 = 0$, or $x = y = 0$. But the point $(0, 0, 0)$ is not on the plane $z = 1 + x + y$. Therefore $\lambda \neq 1$, and we must have $x = y$. The intersection of this plane with the plane $z = 1 + x + y$ is a line that cuts the cone in just two points. We find these points by substituting $y = x$ and $z = 1 + 2x$:

$$x^2 + x^2 = (1 + 2x)^2, \quad 2x^2 + 4x + 1 = 0,$$

$$x = -1 \pm \tfrac{1}{2}\sqrt{2}.$$

The points are

$$A = (-1 - \sqrt{\tfrac{1}{2}}, -1 - \sqrt{\tfrac{1}{2}}, -1 - \sqrt{2}), \qquad \textbf{(13a)}$$

$$B = (-1 + \sqrt{\tfrac{1}{2}}, -1 + \sqrt{\tfrac{1}{2}}, -1 + \sqrt{2}). \qquad \textbf{(13b)}$$

In Example 4, we know that C is either an ellipse or a hyperbola. If it is an ellipse, we would conclude that B is the point on it nearest the origin, and A the point farthest from the origin. But if it is a hyperbola, then there is no point on it that is farthest away from the origin, and the points A and B are the points on the two branches that are nearest the origin. Problem 13 asks you to think about these possibilities and decide between them. It seems obvious that the critical points should satisfy the condition $x = y$ because all three of the functions f, g, and h treat x and y alike.

As a last example, we apply the method of Lagrange multipliers to find the extreme values of a function of two variables. The problem is one that can be solved by eliminating one variable by direct substitution, but the geometry of the Lagrange solution is worth looking at.

EXAMPLE 5. Find the extreme values of the function $f(x, y) = xy$ subject to the constraint

$$g(x, y) = \frac{x^2}{8} + \frac{y^2}{2} - 1 = 0.$$

Solution. We form

$$H(x, y, \lambda) = xy - \lambda\left(\frac{x^2}{8} + \frac{y^2}{2} - 1\right)$$

and find

$$H_x = y - \frac{\lambda x}{4}, \qquad H_y = x - \lambda y, \qquad H_\lambda = -\frac{x^2}{8} - \frac{y^2}{2} + 1.$$

Setting these equal to zero gives

$$y = \frac{\lambda x}{4}, \qquad x = \lambda y, \qquad x^2 + 4y^2 = 8.$$

The two equations on the left give

$$y = \frac{\lambda}{4}(\lambda y), \qquad y = \frac{\lambda^2}{4}y, \qquad \lambda = \pm 2.$$

Therefore, $x = \pm 2y$. Substituting this in the equation $x^2 + 4y^2 = 8$, we get

$$4y^2 + 4y^2 = 8,$$

$$y = \pm 1.$$

The function $f(x, y)$ takes on its extreme values at $x = \pm 2$, $y = \pm 1$. These values are $xy = 2$ and $xy = -2$.

13–30 When subjected to the constraint $g(x, y) = x^2/8 + y^2/2 - 1 = 0$, the function $f(x, y) = xy$ takes on extreme values at the four points $(\pm 2, \pm 1)$.

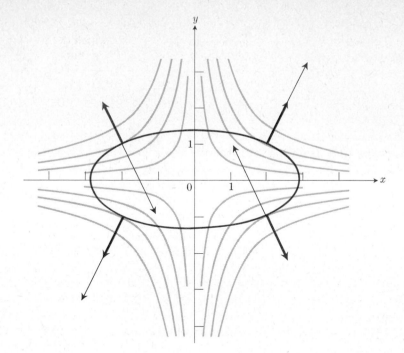

Geometric interpretation of the solution (see Fig. 13–30).   The level curves of the function $f(x, y) = xy$ are the hyperbolas $xy = c$. The farther they are from the origin, the larger the absolute value of f. We want to find the extreme values of $f(x, y)$, given that the point (x, y) also lies on the ellipse $x^2 + 4y^2 = 8$. Which hyperbolas intersecting the ellipse are farthest from the origin? The hyperbolas that just graze the ellipse, the ones that are tangent to the ellipse at the four points $(\pm 2, \pm 1)$. At these points,

a) the normal to the level curve of f is normal to the ellipse;

b) the gradient

$$\nabla f = y\mathbf{i} + x\mathbf{j}$$

is a multiple $(\lambda = \pm 2)$ of the gradient

$$\nabla g = \frac{x}{4}\mathbf{i} + y\mathbf{j}.$$

For example, at the point $(2, 1)$,

$$\nabla f = \mathbf{i} + 2\mathbf{j} \qquad \text{and} \qquad \nabla g = \tfrac{1}{2}\mathbf{i} + \mathbf{j},$$

so that $\nabla f = 2\nabla g$. At the point $(-2, 1)$,

$$\nabla f = \mathbf{i} - 2\mathbf{j} \qquad \text{and} \qquad \nabla g = -\tfrac{1}{2}\mathbf{i} + \mathbf{j},$$

so that $\nabla f = -2\nabla g$.

As mentioned earlier in this article, and in Article 13–11, the conditions that the first partial derivatives of a function be zero at a point where the function has an extreme value is only a necessary condition. It is not a sufficient condition. The partial derivatives of a function may be zero at a point that is neither a maximum nor a minimum of the function. For example, the partial derivatives of the function $z = y^2 - x^2$, which defines a surface like the one shown in Fig. 11–60, are zero at the origin, but the function clearly has no maximum or minimum value there.

As with functions of a single variable, there are second derivative tests that sometimes help to distinguish maxima and minima from each other and from other points where the first partial derivatives of a function are zero. A discussion of one such test in connection with Lagrange multipliers may be found in the appendix to Chapter III of Courant and John's *Introduction to Calculus and Analysis*, Vol. II (Wiley–Interscience, 1974). See Article 16–11, also.

PROBLEMS

1. Find the extreme values of $f(x, y) = xy$ subject to the constraint $g(x, y) = x^2 + y^2 - 10 = 0$.

2. Use the method of Lagrange multipliers to find (a) the minimum value of $x + y$, subject to the constraint $xy = 16$; (b) the maximum value of xy, subject to the constraint $x + y = 16$. Comment on the geometry of each solution.

3. Find the maximum of $f(x, y) = 9 - (x^2/4) - (y^2/4)$ subject to the constraint $g(x, y) = x + 3y - 12 = 0$. (See Fig. 13–27.)

4. Find the point on the surface $z = xy + 1$ that is nearest the origin.

5. A rectangular box, open at the top, is to hold 256 in^3. Find the dimensions of the box for which the surface area is a minimum.

6. The base of a rectangular box costs three times as much per square foot as do the sides and top. Find the relative dimensions for the most economical box of given volume.

7. Find the equation of the plane through the point (2, 1, 1) that cuts off the least volume from the first octant. (Consider only those planes whose intercepts with the coordinate axes are positive.)

8. A pentagon is composed of a rectangle surmounted by an isosceles triangle. If the area is fixed, what are the dimensions for which the perimeter is a minimum?

9. A plane of the form

$$z = Ax + By + C$$

is to be "fitted" to the following points (x_i, y_i, z_i):

$$(0, 0, 0), \quad (0, 1, 1), \quad (1, 1, 1), \quad (1, 0, -1).$$

Find the plane that minimizes the sum of squares of the deviations

$$\sum_{i=1}^{4} (Ax_i + By_i + C - z_i)^2.$$

10. Consider the geometric argument in Remark 2 for the minimization problem of Example 3.

a) Describe the family of surfaces $f = $ constant.

b) Do all of the surfaces of (a) intersect the plane $2x - 3y + 5z = 19$?

c) If a particular surface $f = k$ intersects the plane, what is the locus of intersection, geometrically? If $k' > k$, does the surface $f = k'$ also intersect the plane? In what kind of curve?

d) Does the geometric plausibility argument apply to this example?

11. Use the method of Lagrange multipliers to find the points nearest to, and farthest from, the origin and lying on the curve $x^2 + 2xy + 3y^2 = 9$ in the xy-plane.

12. Use the method of Lagrange multipliers to find the points on the surface $x^2 + y^2 + z^2 = 25$, where the function $f(x, y, z) = x + 2y + 3z$ is:

a) a minimum, **b)** a maximum.

Comment on the geometric interpretation of $\nabla f = \lambda \nabla g$ at these points.

13. In the solution of Example 4, two points A and B were located as candidates for maximum or minimum distances from the origin. Use cylindrical coordinates r, θ, z to express the equations of the cone, the plane $z = 1 + x + y$, and the cylinder that contains their curve of intersection and has elements parallel to the z-axis. Is this cylinder circular, elliptical, parabolic, or hyperbolic? (Consider its intersection with the xy-plane.) Express the distance from the origin to a point on the curve of intersection of the cone and the plane as a function of θ. Does it have a minimum? A maximum? What can you now say about the points A and B of Eqs. (13a, b) as solutions in Example 4?

14. In Example 4, the extrema for $f(x, y, z)$ on the cone $z^2 = x^2 + y^2$ and the plane $z = 1 + x + y$ were found to satisfy $y = x$ as well. Thus $z = 1 + 2x$, and the function to be made a maximum or minimum is $x^2 + y^2 + z^2 = x^2 + x^2 + (1 + 2x)^2$, which can also be written as $6(x + \frac{1}{3})^2 + \frac{1}{3}$. This is obviously a minimum when $x = -\frac{1}{3}$. But the point

we get with
$$y = x, \qquad z = 1 + 2x, \qquad x = -\tfrac{1}{3},$$
is $(-\tfrac{1}{3}, -\tfrac{1}{3}, \tfrac{1}{3})$, which is not on the cone. What's wrong? (A sketch of the situation in the plane $y = x$ may throw some light on the question.)

15. In Example 4, we can determine that, for all points on the cone $z^2 = x^2 + y^2$, the square of the distance from the origin to $P(x, y, z)$ is $w = 2(x^2 + y^2)$, which is a function of two independent variables, x and y. But if P is also to be on the plane
$$z = 1 + x + y$$
as well as the cone, then
$$(1 + x + y)^2 = x^2 + y^2.$$

Show that these points have coordinates that satisfy the equation
$$2xy + 2x + 2y + 1 = 0.$$

Interpret this equation in two ways:

a) as a curve in the xy-plane, and

b) as a set of points on a cylinder in 3-space.

Sketch the curve of (a) and find the point or points on it for which w is a minimum. Are there points on this curve for which w is a maximum? Use the information you now have to complete the discussion of Example 4.

13–12
HIGHER-ORDER DERIVATIVES

Partial derivatives of the second order are denoted by such symbols as
$$\frac{\partial^2 f}{\partial x^2}, \quad \frac{\partial^2 f}{\partial y^2}, \quad \frac{\partial^2 f}{\partial x\, \partial y}, \quad \frac{\partial^2 f}{\partial y\, \partial x}$$
or by
$$f_{xx}, \quad f_{yy}, \quad f_{yx}, \quad f_{xy},$$
where these are defined by the equations
$$\frac{\partial^2 f}{\partial x^2} = \frac{\partial}{\partial x}\left(\frac{\partial f}{\partial x}\right), \qquad \frac{\partial^2 f}{\partial x\, \partial y} = \frac{\partial}{\partial x}\left(\frac{\partial f}{\partial y}\right),$$
and so forth.

EXAMPLE. If
$$f(x, y) = x \cos y + y e^x,$$
then
$$\frac{\partial f}{\partial x} = \cos y + y e^x,$$

$$\frac{\partial}{\partial y}\left(\frac{\partial f}{\partial x}\right) = -\sin y + e^x = \frac{\partial^2 f}{\partial y\, \partial x},$$

$$\frac{\partial}{\partial x}\left(\frac{\partial f}{\partial x}\right) = y e^x = \frac{\partial^2 f}{\partial x^2},$$

$$\frac{\partial}{\partial x}\left(\frac{\partial^2 f}{\partial x^2}\right) = y e^x = \frac{\partial^3 f}{\partial x^3},$$

$$\frac{\partial}{\partial y}\left(\frac{\partial^2 f}{\partial x^2}\right) = e^x = \frac{\partial^3 f}{\partial y\, \partial x^2},$$

and so on; while

$$\frac{\partial f}{\partial y} = -x \sin y + e^x,$$

$$\frac{\partial}{\partial x}\left(\frac{\partial f}{\partial y}\right) = -\sin y + e^x = \frac{\partial^2 f}{\partial x\, \partial y},$$

$$\frac{\partial}{\partial y}\left(\frac{\partial f}{\partial y}\right) = -x \cos y = \frac{\partial^2 f}{\partial y^2},$$

$$\frac{\partial}{\partial x}\left(\frac{\partial^2 f}{\partial x\, \partial y}\right) = e^x = \frac{\partial^3 f}{\partial x^2\, \partial y},$$

and so on.

The example shows how the order of differentiation is indicated by the notation. Thus, in calculating $\partial^2 f/\partial y\, \partial x$, we differentiate first with respect to x and then with respect to y. This might also be indicated by $(f_x)_y$ or f_{xy}. Now it is a remarkable fact that the so-called "mixed" second-order partial derivatives

$$\frac{\partial^2 f}{\partial y\, \partial x} \quad \text{and} \quad \frac{\partial^2 f}{\partial x\, \partial y}$$

are generally equal, just as they are seen to be equal in the example above. That is, we arrive at the same result whether we differentiate first with respect to x and then with respect to y, or do the differentiation in the reverse order. The following theorem supports this assertion under suitable hypotheses.

Theorem. *If the function $w = f(x, y)$, together with the partial derivatives f_x, f_y, f_{xy}, and f_{yx}, is continuous, then*

$$\frac{\partial}{\partial x}\left(\frac{\partial f}{\partial y}\right) = \frac{\partial}{\partial y}\left(\frac{\partial f}{\partial x}\right).$$

Proof. Let (a, b) be a point in the interior of a rectangle R in the xy-plane on which f, f_x, f_y, f_{xy}, and f_{yx} are all continuous. Then the fact that

$$f_{xy}(a, b) = f_{yx}(a, b) \tag{1}$$

can be proved by repeated application of the Mean Value Theorem, as follows. We let h and k be numbers such that the point $(a + h, b + k)$ also lies in the rectangle R, and consider the difference

$$\Delta = F(a + h) - F(a), \tag{2}$$

where we define $F(x)$ in terms of $f(x, y)$ by the equation

$$F(x) = f(x, b + k) - f(x, b). \tag{3}$$

We apply the Mean Value Theorem to the function $F(x)$, and Eq. (2) becomes

$$\Delta = hF'(c_1), \tag{4}$$

where c_1 lies between a and $a + h$. From Eq. (3),

$$F'(x) = f_x(x, b + k) - f_x(x, b),$$

so Eq. (4) becomes

$$\Delta = h[f_x(c_1, b + k) - f_x(c_1, b)]. \tag{5}$$

Now we apply the Mean Value Theorem to the function $g(y) = f_x(c_1, y)$ and have

$$g(b + k) - g(b) = kg'(d_1) \tag{6a}$$

or

$$f_x(c_1, b + k) - f_x(c_1, b) = kf_{xy}(c_1, d_1), \tag{6b}$$

for some d_1 between b and $b + k$. By substituting this into Eq. (5), we get

$$\Delta = hkf_{xy}(c_1, d_1), \tag{7}$$

for some point (c_1, d_1) in the rectangle R' whose vertices are the four points (a, b), $(a + h, b)$, $(a + h, b + k)$, and $(a, b + k)$. (See Fig. 13–31.)

On the other hand, by substituting from Eq. (3) into Eq. (2), we may also write

$$\begin{aligned}
\Delta &= f(a + h, b + k) - f(a + h, b) - f(a, b + k) + f(a, b) \\
&= [f(a + h, b + k) - f(a, b + k)] - [f(a + h, b) - f(a, b)] \\
&= \phi(b + k) - \phi(b), \tag{8}
\end{aligned}$$

where

$$\phi(y) = f(a + h, y) - f(a, y). \tag{9}$$

The Mean Value Theorem applied to Eq. (8) now gives

$$\Delta = k\phi'(d_2), \tag{10}$$

for some d_2 between b and $b + k$. By Eq. (9),

$$\phi'(y) = f_y(a + h, y) - f_y(a, y). \tag{11}$$

Substituting from Eq. (11) into Eq. (10), we have

$$\Delta = k[f_y(a + h, d_2) - f_y(a, d_2)]. \tag{12}$$

Finally, we apply the Mean Value Theorem to the expression in brackets and get

$$\Delta = khf_{yx}(c_2, d_2), \tag{13}$$

for some c_2 between a and $a + h$.

A comparison of Eqs. (7) and (13) shows that

$$f_{xy}(c_1, d_1) = f_{yx}(c_2, d_2), \tag{14}$$

where (c_1, d_1) and (c_2, d_2) both lie in the rectangle R' (Fig. 13–31). Equation (14) is not quite the result we want, since it says only that the mixed derivative f_{xy} has the same value at (c_1, d_1) that the derivative f_{yx} has at (c_2, d_2). But the numbers h and k in our discussion may be made as small as we wish. The hypothesis that f_{xy} and f_{yz} are both continuous throughout R then

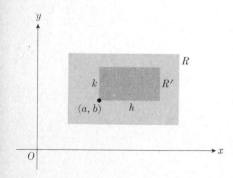

13–31 The key to proving $f_{xy}(a, b) = f_{yx}(a, b)$ is the fact that no matter how small R' is, f_{xy} and f_{yx} take on equal values somewhere inside R' (although not necessarily at the same point of R').

means that

$$f_{xy}(c_1, d_1) = f_{xy}(a, b) + \epsilon_1$$

and

$$f_{yx}(c_2, d_2) = f_{yx}(a, b) + \epsilon_2,$$

where

$$\epsilon_1, \epsilon_2 \to 0$$

as

$$h, k \to 0.$$

Hence, if we let h and $k \to 0$, we have

$$f_{xy}(a, b) = f_{yx}(a, b). \qquad \text{Q.E.D.}$$

The proof just completed hinges upon the consideration of the so-called "second difference" Δ given by Eq. (8). The reason for calling this a *second* difference is to be found from a closer examination of Eqs. (2) and (3). Note that both

$$F(a) = f(a, b + k) - f(a, b)$$

and

$$F(a + h) = f(a + h, b + k) - f(a + h, b)$$

are themselves differences ("first" differences), while

$$\Delta = F(a + h) - F(a)$$

is the difference between these first differences.

An interesting byproduct of the proof of the theorem is the fact that this second difference may, under the hypotheses of the theorem, be approximated by

$$\Delta \approx hkf_{xy}(a, b),$$

where the accuracy of the approximation depends upon the size of h and k.

If we refer once more to the example at the beginning of this article, we note not only that

$$\frac{\partial^2 f}{\partial x\, \partial y} = \frac{\partial^2 f}{\partial y\, \partial x},$$

but also that

$$\frac{\partial^3 f}{\partial x^2\, \partial y} = \frac{\partial^3 f}{\partial y\, \partial x^2}.$$

This equality may be derived from the theorem above as follows:

$$\frac{\partial^3 f}{\partial x^2\, \partial y} = \frac{\partial}{\partial x}\left(\frac{\partial^2 f}{\partial x\, \partial y}\right) = \frac{\partial}{\partial x}\left(\frac{\partial^2 f}{\partial y\, \partial x}\right)$$

$$= \frac{\partial}{\partial x}\left(\frac{\partial}{\partial y}f_x\right) = \frac{\partial}{\partial y}\left(\frac{\partial}{\partial x}f_x\right)$$

$$= \frac{\partial}{\partial y}\left(\frac{\partial^2 f}{\partial x^2}\right) = \frac{\partial^3 f}{\partial y\, \partial x^2}.$$

In fact, if all the partial derivatives that appear are continuous, the notation

$$\frac{\partial^{m+n} f}{\partial x^m \, \partial y^n}$$

may be used to denote the result of differentiating the function $f(x, y)$ m times with respect to x and n times with respect to y, the order in which these differentiations are performed being entirely arbitrary. For example, $\partial^5 f/(\partial x^2 \, \partial y^3)$ is the result of five successive differentiations, two with respect to x and three with respect to y, such as f_{xyyxy}, where the latter notation means differentiation first with respect to x, then twice with respect to y, then again with respect to x, and finally with respect to y. (The subscripts are read from left to right.)

PROBLEMS

1. If $w = \cos(x + y) + \sin(x - y)$, show that
$$\frac{\partial^2 w}{\partial x^2} = \frac{\partial^2 w}{\partial y^2}.$$

2. If $w = \ln(2x + 2y) + \tan(2x - 2y)$, show that
$$\frac{\partial^2 w}{\partial x^2} = \frac{\partial^2 w}{\partial y^2}.$$

3. If $w = f(x + y) + g(x - y)$, where $f(u)$ and $g(v)$ are twice-differentiable functions of $u = x + y$ and $v = x - y$, respectively, show that
$$\frac{\partial^2 w}{\partial x^2} = \frac{\partial^2 w}{\partial y^2} = f''(u) + g''(v).$$

(Problems 1 and 2 are special examples of this result.)

4. If c is a constant and $w = \sin(x + ct) + \cos(2x + 2ct)$, show that $(\partial^2 w/\partial t^2) = c^2(\partial^2 w/\partial x^2)$.

5. If c is a constant and
$$w = 5\cos(3x + 3ct) - 7\sinh(4x - 4ct),$$
show that $(\partial^2 w/\partial t^2) = c^2(\partial^2 w/\partial x^2)$.

6. If c is a constant and $w = f(x + ct) + g(x - ct)$, where $f(u)$ and $g(v)$ are twice-differentiable functions of $u = x + ct$ and $v = x - ct$, respectively, show that
$$\frac{\partial^2 w}{\partial t^2} = c^2 \frac{\partial^2 w}{\partial x^2} = c^2(f''(u) + g''(v)).$$

(Note that Problems 4 and 5 are special cases. The equation $(\partial^2 w/\partial t^2) = c^2(\partial^2 w/\partial x^2)$ describes the motion of a wave that travels with velocity c. See Sears, Zemansky, Young, *University Physics*, Fifth edition (1976, Addison-Wesley, Chapter 21.)

In each of the following problems (7–13), verify that V satisfies Laplace's equation

$$\frac{\partial^2 V}{\partial x^2} + \frac{\partial^2 V}{\partial y^2} + \frac{\partial^2 V}{\partial z^2} = 0.$$

7. $V = x^2 + y^2 - 2z^2$ 8. $V = 2z^3 - 3(x^2 + y^2)z$

9. $V = e^{-2y} \cos 2x$ 10. $V = \ln \sqrt{x^2 + y^2}$

11. $V = (x^2 + y^2 + z^2)^{-1/2}$ 12. $V = e^{3x + 4y} \cos 5z$

13. $V = \cos 3x \cos 4y \sinh 5z$

In each of the following problems (14–17), verify that $w_{xy} = w_{yx}$.

14. $w = e^x \sinh y + \cos(2x - 3y)$

15. $w = \ln(2x + 3y)$

16. $w = \tan^{-1}(y/x)$ 17. $w = xy^2 + x^2y^3 + x^3y^4$

18. Let $f(x, y) = x^3 y^2$. Following the notation in Eqs. (2) through (7), find:

a) $F(x)$,   b) c_1,   c) $g(y)$,

and thus verify Eq. (7) for this particular case. Also show that $f_{xy}(c_1, d_1) \to f_{xy}(a, b)$ as $(h, k) \to (0, 0)$.

19. Use the function $f = x^3 y^2$ and carry out the steps of Eqs. (8) to (13). In particular, find (c_2, d_2) and show that $f_{yx}(c_2, d_2) \to f_{xy}(a, b)$ as $(h, k) \to (0, 0)$.

13–13

EXACT DIFFERENTIALS

We have seen that on numerous occasions the result of translating a physical problem into mathematical terms is a differential equation to be integrated. In the simplest cases, we may be able to separate the variables and write the differential equation in a form such as

$$f(x)\,dx = g(y)\,dy,$$

which we can solve if we are able to evaluate $\int f(x)\, dx$ and $\int g(y)\, dy$. Sometimes, however, we are not able to separate the variables, as in the equations

$$(x^2 + y^2)\, dx + 2xy\, dy = 0 \tag{1a}$$

and

$$(x^2 + y^2)\, dx - 2xy\, dy = 0. \tag{1b}$$

More generally, we may be led to a differential equation of the form

$$M(x, y)\, dx + N(x, y)\, dy = 0, \tag{2}$$

where $M(x, y)$ and $N(x, y)$ are functions of x and y. (In most cases, these functions will be continuous and have continuous partial derivatives with respect to x and y.) The differential equation (2) can be solved quite easily, provided that it is possible to find a function

$$w = f(x, y) \tag{3}$$

such that the left side of Eq. (2) is the total differential of w. For if such is the case, then Eq. (2) becomes

$$dw = 0,$$

and the solution of this equation is simply

$$w = C,$$

and the solution of Eq. (2) is

$$f(x, y) = C,$$

where C is an arbitrary constant.

Now, expressions of the form given in Eq. (2) aren't always differentials of functions. In fact, of the two expressions in Eq. (1a, b), we shall see that the first is such a differential while the second is not.

The following terminology is commonly used: An expression

$$M(x, y)\, dx + N(x, y)\, dy \tag{4}$$

is called an *exact differential* if and only if there exists a function $w = f(x, y)$ with

$$df(x, y) = M(x, y)\, dx + N(x, y)\, dy. \tag{5}$$

If no such function exists, the expression is not an exact differential.

Three questions naturally present themselves:

a) How can we tell whether a given expression is or is not an exact differential?

b) If the expression is exact, how do we find the function $f(x, y)$ of which it is the differential?

c) If the expression is not exact, how can we solve the differential equation (2)?

In the proof of the theorem below, we shall give answers to the first two of these questions. (Differential equations are discussed in more detail in Chapter 18.)

The theorem introduces a mild restriction on the geometric nature of the

Connected and simply connected.

Connected but not simply connected.

Connected and simply connected.

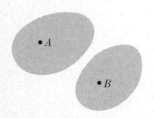

Simply connected but not connected.
No path from A to B lies entirely in
the region.

13–32   Regions.

set R on which the functions $M(x, y)$ and $N(x, y)$ are defined. Specifically, R is required to be a simply connected region. The word *region* has the technical meaning here of "connected open set." A subset of the plane is *open* if each of its points is the center of a circle whose interior lies entirely in the set. An *open* subset of the plane is *connected* if every two of its points can be joined by a path that lies entirely in the set. A subset R of the plane is *simply connected* if no simple closed curve in R surrounds points not in R. When you read "simply connected," think "no holes." (See Fig. 13–32.) You need not be concerned with these technicalities now. The plane domains on which most of the functions in this book are defined really are regions or unions of regions, and most of them are simply connected. It will not be necessary to test every function that comes along. But without these conditions on R (which are usually met in practice), or others like them, some of the most useful theorems of calculus would not be true.

Theorem. Test for exactness.   *Suppose that the functions $M(x, y)$ and $N(x, y)$ and their partial derivatives M_x, M_y, N_x, and N_y are continuous for all real values of x and y in a simply connected region R. Then a necessary and sufficient condition for*

$$M(x, y)\, dx + N(x, y)\, dy$$

to be an exact differential in R is

$$\frac{\partial M}{\partial y} = \frac{\partial N}{\partial x}.$$

Proof.   We shall first prove that the condition is necessary. Suppose the expression is an exact differential; that is, suppose a function $f(x, y)$ exists such that Eq. (5) is satisfied at all points in R. We also know that

$$df = \frac{\partial f}{\partial x}\, dx + \frac{\partial f}{\partial y}\, dy. \tag{6}$$

In Eqs. (5) and (6), dx and dy are independent variables, and we may set either dx or dy equal to zero and keep the other one different from zero. Then the only way that both equations can hold is to have

$$\frac{\partial f}{\partial x} = M(x, y), \qquad \frac{\partial f}{\partial y} = N(x, y). \tag{7}$$

Now, by the theorem of Article 13–12, we know that if M and N are continuous and have continuous partial derivatives in R, then

$$\frac{\partial}{\partial y}\left(\frac{\partial f}{\partial x}\right) = \frac{\partial}{\partial x}\left(\frac{\partial f}{\partial y}\right),$$

so that the condition

$$\frac{\partial M}{\partial y} = \frac{\partial N}{\partial x} \tag{8}$$

is a necessary condition if Eq. (7) is to be satisfied.

EXAMPLE 1. The condition given in Eq. (8) is satisfied by the expression in Eq. (1a), where

$$M = x^2 + y^2, \qquad N = 2xy.$$

Here

$$\frac{\partial M}{\partial y} = 2y = \frac{\partial N}{\partial x}.$$

We have not yet proved that this condition is sufficient, however, so we cannot at this point say that the expression is exact.

For Eq. (1b), we have

$$M = x^2 + y^2, \qquad N = -2xy$$

and

$$\frac{\partial M}{\partial y} = 2y, \qquad \frac{\partial N}{\partial x} = -2y,$$

so that

$$\frac{\partial M}{\partial y} \neq \frac{\partial N}{\partial x}.$$

Since Eq. (8) is a necessary condition, we can say that the expression in (1b) is not an exact differential.

As Example 1 suggests, it is usually a simple matter to apply the condition of Eq. (8) to test $M(x, y)\, dx + N(x, y)\, dy$ for exactness. What we have not shown yet, however, is that the condition is sufficient as well as necessary. It is here that the simple connectivity of the region R comes in, but it is also here that the argument becomes so technical that it will not be presented in full detail. We shall show how to find the function f, first in general terms, and then by example; but we will not go into the details of why one should expect the function f to exist. The full story can be found in most advanced calculus texts.

The basic fact to establish is that, if

$$\frac{\partial M}{\partial y} = \frac{\partial N}{\partial x} \quad \text{in } R,$$

then there is a function $w = f(x, y)$ whose domain includes R and which is such that

$$df = M\, dx + N\, dy.$$

We shall establish this result by showing how to find the function $f(x, y)$ and this will also answer the second question previously raised.

From Eq. (6), we see that our sought-for function must have the property expressed by Eqs. (7):

$$\frac{\partial f}{\partial x} = M(x, y), \qquad \frac{\partial f}{\partial y} = N(x, y).$$

Integrating the first of these with respect to x, we find

$$f(x, y) = \int_x M(x, y)\, dx + g(y), \tag{9}$$

where $g(y)$ represents an unknown function of y that plays the role of an arbitrary constant of integration. The integral $\int_x M(x, y)\, dx$ is an ordinary indefinite integral with respect to x with y held constant during the integration. The function $f(x, y)$ produced by Eq. (9) satisfies the condition

$$\frac{\partial f}{\partial x} = M(x, y)$$

for any choice of the function $g(y)$, because $g(y)$ acts as a constant under partial differentiation with respect to x. To see how we may satisfy the second condition, $\partial f/\partial y = N(x, y)$, we differentiate both sides of Eq. (9) with respect to y, holding x fixed, and obtain

$$\frac{\partial f}{\partial y} = \frac{\partial}{\partial y} \int_x M(x, y)\, dx + \frac{\partial g(y)}{\partial y}. \tag{10}$$

Actually, since $g(y)$ is a function of y alone, we may write dg/dy instead of $\partial g/\partial y$. We then set $\partial f/\partial y$ from Eq. (10) equal to $N(x, y)$ and have

$$N(x, y) = \frac{\partial}{\partial y} \int_x M(x, y)\, dx + \frac{dg(y)}{dy},$$

or

$$\frac{dg(y)}{dy} = N(x, y) - \frac{\partial}{\partial y} \int_x M(x, y)\, dx. \tag{11}$$

We use this differential equation to determine $g(y)$ by simply integrating its righthand member with respect to y and then substituting the result back into Eq. (9), to obtain our final answer, namely $f(x, y)$. Success of the method hinges on the fact that the expression on the righthand side of Eq. (11) *is a function of y alone, provided that the condition*

$$\frac{\partial M(x, y)}{\partial y} = \frac{\partial N(x, y)}{\partial x}$$

is satisfied. [If the righthand side of Eq. (11) depended on x as well as on y, it could not be equal to dg/dy, which involves only y.]

But how, in general, can we prove that the expression in question is independent of x? We can prove this by showing that its partial derivative with respect to x is identically zero. That is, we must calculate

$$\frac{\partial}{\partial x}\left(N(x, y) - \frac{\partial}{\partial y} \int_x M(x, y)\, dx \right) = \frac{\partial N}{\partial x} - \frac{\partial^2}{\partial x\, \partial y} \int_x M(x, y)\, dx$$

$$= \frac{\partial N}{\partial x} - \frac{\partial}{\partial y}\left(\frac{\partial}{\partial x} \int_x M(x, y)\, dx \right)$$

$$= \frac{\partial N}{\partial x} - \frac{\partial}{\partial y}(M),$$

which vanishes if it is true that

$$\frac{\partial N}{\partial x} = \frac{\partial M}{\partial y},$$

as we have assumed.

EXAMPLE 2. Find a function $f(x, y)$ whose differential is

$$df = (x^2 + y^2)\, dx + 2xy\, dy.$$

Solution. We set

$$M = x^2 + y^2, \qquad N = 2xy,$$

and note that the condition

$$\frac{\partial M}{\partial y} = \frac{\partial N}{\partial x}$$

is satisfied. We seek $f(x, y)$ such that

$$\frac{\partial f}{\partial x} = x^2 + y^2, \qquad \frac{\partial f}{\partial y} = 2xy.$$

Integrating the first of these with respect to x while holding y constant and adding $g(y)$ as our "constant of integration," we have

$$f(x, y) = \tfrac{1}{3}x^3 + y^2 x + g(y).$$

Differentiating this with respect to y with x held constant and setting the result equal to $2xy$, we have

$$2xy = 2yx + \frac{dg}{dy}, \qquad \text{or} \qquad \frac{dg}{dy} = 0,$$

so that $g(y) = C$ must be a pure constant. Hence

$$f(x, y) = \tfrac{1}{3}x^3 + y^2 x + C.$$

Note three things about Example 2:

1. The method was easy to apply.

2. We found infinitely many functions with the differential $(x^2 + y^2)\, dx + 2xy\, dy$, one for each value of C.

3. We were able to tell that $(x^2 + y^2)\, dx + 2xy\, dy$ was an exact differential *without knowing f in advance*. This and the ease of application are why the theorem of this article is so useful.

PROBLEMS

In Problems 1 through 7, determine whether the given expression is or is not an exact differential. If the expression is the differential of a function $f(x, y)$, find f.

1. $2x(x^3 + y^3)\, dx + 3y^2(x^2 + y^2)\, dy$

2. $e^y\, dx + x(e^y + 1)\, dy$

3. $(2x + y)\, dx + (x + 2y)\, dy$

4. $(\cosh y + y \cosh x)\, dx + (\sinh x + x \sinh y)\, dy$

5. $(\sin y + y \sin x)\, dx + (\cos x + x \cos y)\, dy$

6. $(1 + e^x)\, dy + e^x(y - x)\, dx$

7. $(e^{x+y} + e^{x-y})(dx + dy)$

13–14

DERIVATIVES OF INTEGRALS

From the Fundamental Theorem of integral calculus we know that if f is a continuous function on $a \le t \le b$, then

$$\frac{d}{dx} \int_a^x f(t)\,dt = f(x).$$ (1)

For example,

$$\frac{d}{dx} \int_0^x e^{-t^2}\,dt = e^{-x^2},$$

and

$$\frac{d}{dx} \int_1^x \frac{1}{t}\,dt = \frac{1}{x}, \qquad (x > 0).$$

Similarly, since

$$\int_x^b f(t)\,dt = -\int_b^x f(t)\,dt,$$

we have

$$\frac{d}{dx} \int_x^b f(t)\,dt = -f(x).$$ (2)

Equations (1) and (2) may be combined to give the following result.

Theorem. *Let f be continuous on $a \le t \le b$. Let u and v be differentiable functions of x such that $u(x)$ and $v(x)$ lie between a and b. Then*

$$\frac{d}{dx} \int_{u(x)}^{v(x)} f(t)\,dt = f(v(x))\frac{dv}{dx} - f(u(x))\frac{du}{dx}.$$ (3)

Proof. Let $F(u, v) = \int_u^v f(t)\,dt$. Then, by Eq. (1),

$$\frac{\partial F}{\partial v} = f(v),$$ (4a)

and, by Eq. (2),

$$\frac{\partial F}{\partial u} = -f(u),$$ (4b)

provided u and v lie between a and b. If u and v are differentiable functions of x, and $u(x)$, $v(x)$ are between a and b, we may apply the chain rule:

$$\frac{dF}{dx} = \frac{\partial F}{\partial u}\frac{du}{dx} + \frac{\partial F}{\partial v}\frac{dv}{dx}.$$ (5)

The result of substituting from Eqs. (4a, b) into Eq. (5) is

$$\frac{dF}{dx} = f(v)\frac{dv}{dx} - f(u)\frac{du}{dx}.$$

This establishes Eq. (3). Q.E.D.

EXAMPLE.   Verify Eq. (3) for

$$\frac{d}{dx}\int_x^{2x} \frac{1}{t}\, dt, \qquad (x > 0).$$

Solution.   Let $F(u, v) = \int_u^v (1/t)\, dt = \ln v - \ln u$. Then $\partial F/\partial u = -1/u$ and $\partial F/\partial v = 1/v$. If $u = x$ and $v = 2x$, then

$$\frac{du}{dx} = 1, \qquad \frac{dv}{dx} = 2,$$

and

$$\frac{dF}{dx} = \frac{\partial F}{\partial u}\cdot\frac{du}{dx} + \frac{\partial F}{\partial v}\cdot\frac{dv}{dx}$$

$$= -\frac{1}{u} + \frac{2}{v}$$

$$= -\frac{1}{x} + \frac{2}{2x} = 0.$$

Alternatively,

$$F(x, 2x) = \int_x^{2x} \frac{1}{t}\, dt = \ln t\,\Big]_x^{2x} = \ln 2x - \ln x$$

$$= \ln \frac{2x}{x} = \ln 2, \qquad (0 < x)$$

and

$$\frac{d}{dx} F(x, 2x) = \frac{d}{dx}(\ln 2) = 0.$$

PROBLEMS

Find the derivative, with respect to x, of each of the following (assuming $x > 0$):

1. $\int_x^{x^2} \frac{1}{t}\, dt$

2. $\int_x^{2x} \frac{1}{t^2}\, dt$

3. $\int_{2x}^{x^2} \frac{1}{t^2}\, dt$

4. $\int_0^{\sin^{-1} x} \frac{\sin t}{t}\, dt$

5. $\int_x^{x^2} \ln t\, dt$

6. If u and v are differentiable functions of x and $u(x) > 0$, show (by two different methods) that

$$\frac{d}{dx}\big[(u(x))^{v(x)}\big] = u^v \left[\frac{v}{u}\cdot\frac{du}{dx} + \frac{dv}{dx}\cdot\ln u\right].$$

Find dy/dx if:

7. $y = (e^x)^x$

8. $y = (\cosh x)^{x^2}$

9. $y = (x^2 + 1)^{1/x}$

10. $y = (4x^2 + 4x + 3)^{\int_x^{x^2}\ln t\, dt}$

REVIEW QUESTIONS AND EXERCISES

1. Let $w = f(x, y)$ define a function of two independent variables, for values of (x, y) in some region G of the xy-plane (the domain of f). Describe two geometrical ways of representing the function.

2. When is a function of two variables continuous at a point of its domain? Give an example, different from those in the text, of a function that is discontinuous at some point(s) of its domain.

3. Let $w = f(x, y)$. Define $\partial w/\partial x$ and $\partial w/\partial y$ at a point (x_0, y_0) in the domain of f.

4. When is a function of three variables continuous at a point of its domain? Give an example of a function of three independent variables that is continuous at some points of its domain and discontinuous at at least one place in its domain. Give an example that is discontinuous at all points of a surface $F(x, y, z) = 0$; at all points of a line.

5. Define the directional derivative, at a point in its domain, of a function of three independent variables. Write a formula for the directional derivative in vector form. What is the analogous formula for a function of two variables?

6. Define tangent plane, and normal line, to a surface S at a point P_0 on S. Derive equations of the tangent plane and normal line in terms of the equations of the surface.

7. Write an expression for the tangent plane approximation to the increment of a function of two independent variables. What is the corresponding expression approximating the increment of a function of three variables?

8. Define *gradient* of a scalar function. Give two properties of the gradient that you consider to be important.

9. State the chain rule for partial derivatives of functions of several variables.

10. Define the *total differential* of a function of several variables.

11. Outline a method for finding local maxima or minima of a function of two or three independent variables.

12. Outline the "method of least squares" as applied to fitting a straight line to a set of observations.

13. Describe the method of Lagrange multipliers as it applies to the problem of maximizing or minimizing a function $f(x, y, z)$,

a) subject to a constraint

$$g(x, y, z) = 0,$$

b) subject to two constraints,

$$g(x, y, z) = 0 \quad \text{and} \quad h(x, y, z) = 0.$$

14. Sketch some of the contour curves for the function $f(x, y) = 2x + 3y$. Find points on the curve C: $x^2 + xy + y^2 = 3$ that

a) maximize f, **b)** minimize f.

Does it seem reasonable on geometric grounds that the level curve of f at each one of these points is tangent to C at that point? Is it true?

MISCELLANEOUS PROBLEMS

1. Let $f(x, y) = (x^2 - y^2)/(x^2 + y^2)$ for $x^2 + y^2 \neq 0$. Is it possible to define the value of f at $x = 0$, $y = 0$, in such a way that the function would be continuous at $x = 0$, $y = 0$? Why?

2. Let the function $f(x, y)$ be defined by the relations

$$f(x, y) = \frac{\sin^2 (x - y)}{|x| + |y|} \quad \text{for} \quad |x| + |y| \neq 0, \quad f(0, 0) = 0.$$

Is f continuous at $x = 0$, $y = 0$?

3. Prove that if $f(x, y)$ is defined for all x, y, by

$$f(x, y) = \begin{cases} \dfrac{2xy}{x^2 + y^2} & \text{if} \quad (x, y) \neq (0, 0), \\ 0 & \text{if} \quad x = y = 0, \end{cases}$$

then (a) for any fixed x, $f(x, y)$ is a continuous function of y; (b) for any fixed y, $f(x, y)$ is a continuous function of x; (c) $f(x, y)$ is not continuous at $(0, 0)$; (d) $\partial f/\partial x$ and $\partial f/\partial y$ exist at $(0, 0)$ but are not continuous there. (This example shows that a function may possess partial derivatives at all points of a region, yet not be continuous in the region.) Contrast the case of a function of one variable, where the existence of a derivative implies continuity.

4. Let $f(x, y)$ be defined and continuous for all x, y (differentiability not assumed). Show that it is always possible to find arbitrarily many points (x_1, y_1), (x_2, y_2), ..., (x_n, y_n) such that the function has the same value at each of them.

5. Find the first partial derivatives of the following functions:

a) $(\sin xy)^2$, **b)** $\sin [(xy)^2]$.

6. Let α, β, γ be the direction angles of a line and consider γ as a function of α and β. Find the value of $\partial \gamma/\partial \alpha$ when $\alpha = \pi/4$, $\beta = \pi/3$, $\gamma = \pi/3$.

7. Let (r, θ) and (x, y) be polar coordinates and cartesian coordinates in the plane. Show geometrically why $\partial r/\partial x$ is not equal to $(\partial x/\partial r)^{-1}$, by appealing to the definitions of these derivatives.

8. Consider the surface whose equation is $x^3 z + y^2 x^2 + \sin (yz) + 54 = 0$. Give an equation of the tangent plane to the surface at the point $P(3, 0, -2)$, and give equations of the straight line through P normal to the surface. Determine direction cosines of the line.

9. (a) Sketch and name the surface $x^2 - y^2 + z^2 = 4$. (b) Find a vector that is normal to this surface at $(2, -3, 3)$. (c) Find equations of the surface's tangent plane and normal line at $(2, -3, 3)$.

10. (a) Find an equation of the plane tangent to the surface

$$x^3 + xy^2 + y^3 + z^3 + 1 = 0$$

at the point $(-2, 1, 2)$. (b) Find equations of the straight line perpendicular to the plane above at the point $(-2, 1, 2)$.

11. The directional derivative of a given function $w = f(x, y)$ at the point $P_0(1, 2)$ in the direction toward $P_1(2, 3)$ is $2\sqrt{2}$, and in the direction toward $P_2(1, 0)$ it is -3. Compute $\partial f/\partial x$ and $\partial f/\partial y$ at $P_0(1, 2)$, and compute the directional derivative dw/ds at $P_0(1, 2)$ in the direction toward $P_3(4, 6)$.

12. Let $z = f(x, y)$ have continuous first partial derivatives. Let C be any curve lying on the surface and passing through (x_0, y_0, z_0). Prove that the tangent line to C at (x_0, y_0, z_0) must lie wholly in the plane determined by the tangent lines to the curves C_x and C_y, where C_x is the curve of intersection of $y = y_0$ and $z = f(x, y)$, and C_y is the curve of intersection of $x = x_0$ and the surface.

13. Let $u = xyz$. Show that if x and y are the independent variables (so u and z are functions of x and y), then

$$\partial u/\partial x = xy\, (\partial z/\partial x) + yz;$$

but that if x, y, and z are the independent variables,

$$\partial u/\partial x = yz.$$

14. Let

$$\mathbf{u} = u_1\mathbf{i} + u_2\mathbf{j} + u_3\mathbf{k}$$

and

$$\mathbf{v} = v_1\mathbf{i} + v_2\mathbf{j} + v_3\mathbf{k}$$

be given constant unit vectors and let $f(x, y, z)$ be a given scalar function. Compute (a) the directional derivative $D_\mathbf{u}f$, and (b) the directional derivative $D_\mathbf{v}(D_\mathbf{u}f)$, in terms of derivatives of f and the components of $\mathbf{u}$ and $\mathbf{v}$. (Here $D_\mathbf{u}f$ denotes df/ds in the direction of $\mathbf{u}$.)

15. Consider the function $w = xyz$. (a) Compute the directional derivative of w at the point $(1, 1, 1)$ in the direction of the vector $\mathbf{i} + \mathbf{j} + \mathbf{k}$. (b) Compute the largest value of directional derivative of w at the point $(1, 1, 1)$.

16. The function $w = f(x, y)$ has, at the point $(1, 2)$, directional derivatives that are equal to $+2$ in the direction toward $(2, 2)$, and -2 in the direction toward $(1, 1)$. What is its directional derivative at $(1, 2)$ in the direction toward $(4, 6)$?

17. Given the function $f(x, y, z) = x^2 + y^2 - 3z$, what is the maximum value of the directional derivative df/ds at the point $(1, 3, 5)$?

18. Given the function

$$(x - 1)^2 + 2(y + 1)^2 + 3(z - 2)^2 - 6.$$

Find the directional derivative of the function at the point $(2, 0, 1)$ in the direction of the vector $\mathbf{i} - \mathbf{j} + 2\mathbf{k}$.

19. Find the derivative of the function

$$f(x, y, z) = x^2 - 2y^2 + z^2$$

at the point $(3, 3, 1)$ in the direction of the vector $2\mathbf{i} + \mathbf{j} - \mathbf{k}$.

20. The two equations

$$e^u \cos v - x = 0 \quad \text{and} \quad e^u \sin v - y = 0$$

define u and v as functions of x and y, say $u = u(x, y)$ and $v = v(x, y)$. Show that the angle between the two vectors

$$\left(\frac{\partial u}{\partial x}\right)\mathbf{i} + \left(\frac{\partial u}{\partial y}\right)\mathbf{j} \quad \text{and} \quad \left(\frac{\partial v}{\partial x}\right)\mathbf{i} + \left(\frac{\partial v}{\partial y}\right)\mathbf{j}$$

is constant.

21. (a) Find a vector $\mathbf{N}(x, y, z)$ normal to the surface $z = \sqrt{x^2 + y^2} + (x^2 + y^2)^{3/2}$ at the point (x, y, z) of the surface. (b) Find the cosine of the angle γ between $\mathbf{N}(x, y, z)$ and the z-axis. Find the limit of $\cos \gamma$ as $(x, y, z) \to (0, 0, 0)$.

22. Find all points (a, b, c) in space for which the spheres

$$(x - a)^2 + (y - b)^2 + (z - c)^2 = 1$$

and

$$x^2 + y^2 + z^2 = 1$$

will intersect orthogonally. (Their tangents are to be perpendicular at each point of intersection.)

23. (a) Find the gradient, at $P_0(1, -1, 3)$, of the function

$$x^2 + 2xy - y^2 + z^2.$$

(b) Find the plane that is tangent to the surface $x^2 + 2xy - y^2 + z^2 = 7$ at $P_0(1, -1, 3)$.

24. Find a unit vector normal to the surface $x^2 + y^2 = 3z$ at the point $(1, 3, \frac{10}{3})$.

25. In a flowing fluid, the density $\rho(x, y, z, t)$ depends on position and time. If

$$\mathbf{V} = \mathbf{V}(x, y, z, t)$$

is the velocity of the fluid particle at the point (x, y, z) at time t, then

$$\frac{d\rho}{dt} = \mathbf{V} \cdot \nabla\rho + \frac{\partial \rho}{\partial t} = V_1\frac{\partial \rho}{\partial x} + V_2\frac{\partial \rho}{\partial y} + V_3\frac{\partial \rho}{\partial z} + \frac{\partial \rho}{\partial t},$$

where $\mathbf{V} = V_1\mathbf{i} + V_2\mathbf{j} + V_3\mathbf{k}$. Explain the physical and geometrical meaning of this relation.

26. Find a constant a such that, at any point of intersection of the two spheres

$$(x - a)^2 + y^2 + z^2 = 3 \quad \text{and} \quad x^2 + (y - 1)^2 + z^2 = 1,$$

their tangent planes will be perpendicular to each other.

27. If the gradient of a function $f(x, y, z)$ is always parallel to the vector $x\mathbf{i} + y\mathbf{j} + z\mathbf{k}$, show that the function must assume the same value at the points $(0, 0, a)$ and $(0, 0, -a)$.

28. Let $f(P)$ denote a function defined for points P in the plane; i.e., to each point P there is attached a real number $f(P)$. Explain how one could introduce the notions of continuity and differentiability of the function and define the vector ∇f *without* introducing a coordinate system. If one introduces a polar coordinate system r, θ, $\mathbf{U}_r$, $\mathbf{U}_\theta$, what form does the vector $\nabla f(r, \theta)$ take?

29. Show that the directional derivative of

$$r = \sqrt{x^2 + y^2 + z^2}$$

equals unity in any direction at the origin, but that r does not have a gradient vector at the origin.

30. Let $\mathbf{R} = x\mathbf{i} + y\mathbf{j} + z\mathbf{k}$ and $r = |\mathbf{R}|$. (a) From its geometrical interpretation, show that $\nabla r = \mathbf{R}/r$. (b) Show that $\nabla(r^n) = nr^{n-2}\mathbf{R}$. (c) Find a function with gradient equal to $\mathbf{R}$. (d) Show that $\mathbf{R} \cdot d\mathbf{R} = r \, dr$. (e) If $\mathbf{A}$ is a constant vector, show that $\nabla(\mathbf{A} \cdot \mathbf{R}) = \mathbf{A}$.

31. If θ is the polar coordinate in the xy-plane, find the direction and magnitude of $\nabla\theta$.

32. If r_1, r_2 are the distances from the point $P(x, y)$ on an ellipse to its foci, show that the equation $r_1 + r_2 = \text{const.}$, satisfied by these distances, requires $\mathbf{U} \cdot \nabla(r_1 + r_2) = 0$, where $\mathbf{U}$ is a unit tangent to the curve. By geometrical interpretation, show that the tangent makes equal angles with the lines to the foci.

33. If A, B are fixed points and θ is the angle at $P(x, y, z)$ subtended by the line segment AB, show that $\nabla\theta$ is normal to the circle through A, B, P.

34. Find the general solution of the partial differential equations:

a) $af_x + bf_y = 0$, a, b constants, **b)** $yf_x - xf_y = 0$.

[*Hint.* Consider the geometrical meaning of the equations.]

35. When y is eliminated from the two equations $z = f(x, y)$ and $g(x, y) = 0$, the result is expressible in the form $z = h(x)$. Express the derivative $h'(x)$ in terms of $\partial f/\partial x$, $\partial f/\partial y$, $\partial g/\partial x$, $\partial g/\partial y$. Check your formula by computing $h(x)$ and $h'(x)$ explicitly in the example where $f(x, y) = x^2 + y^2$ and $g(x, y) = x^3 + y^2 - x$.

36. Suppose the equation $F(x, y, z) = 0$ defines z as a function of x and y, say $z = f(x, y)$, with derivatives $\partial f/\partial x$ and $\partial f/\partial y$. Suppose also that the same equation $F(x, y, z) = 0$ defines x as a function of y and z, say $x = g(y, z)$, with derivatives $\partial g/\partial y$ and $\partial g/\partial z$. Prove that

$$\frac{\partial g}{\partial y} = -\frac{\partial f/\partial y}{\partial f/\partial x},$$

and also express $\partial g/\partial z$ in terms of $\partial f/\partial x$ and $\partial f/\partial y$.

37. Given $z = x \sin x - y^2$, $\cos y = y \sin z$, find dx/dz.

38. If

$$z = f\left(\frac{x - y}{y}\right),$$

show that $x(\partial z/\partial x) + y(\partial z/\partial y) = 0$.

39. If the substitution $u = (x - y)/2$, $v = (x + y)/2$, changes $f(u, v)$ into $F(x, y)$, express $\partial F/\partial x$ and $\partial F/\partial y$ in terms of the derivatives of $f(u, v)$ with respect to u and v.

40. Given $w = f(x, y)$ with $x = u + v$, $y = u - v$, show that

$$\frac{\partial^2 w}{\partial u \, \partial v} = \frac{\partial^2 w}{\partial x^2} - \frac{\partial^2 w}{\partial y^2}.$$

41. Suppose $f(x, y, z)$ is a function that has continuous partial derivatives and satisfies $f(tx, ty, tz) = t^n f(x, y, z)$ for every quadruple of numbers x, y, z, t (where n is a fixed integer). Show the identity

$$\frac{\partial f}{\partial x}x + \frac{\partial f}{\partial y}y + \frac{\partial f}{\partial z}z = nf.$$

[*Hint.* Differentiate with respect to t; then set $t = 1$.]

42. The substitution $u = x + y$, $v = xy^2$ changes the function $f(u, v)$ into $F(x, y)$. Express the partial derivative $\partial^2 F/\partial x \, \partial y$ in terms of x, y, and the partial derivatives of $f(u, v)$ with respect to u, v.

43. Given $z = u(x, y) \cdot e^{ax+by}$, where $u(x, y)$ is a function of x and y such that $\partial^2 u/\partial x \, \partial y = 0$, $(a, b$ constants). Find values of a and b that will make the expression $\partial^2 z/\partial x \, \partial y - \partial z/\partial x - \partial z/\partial y + z$ identically zero.

44. Introducing polar coordinates, $x = r \cos \theta$, $y = r \sin \theta$, changes $f(x, y)$ into $g(r, \theta)$. Compute the value of the second derivative $\partial^2 g/\partial \theta^2$ at the point where $r = 2$ and $\theta = \pi/2$, given that $\partial f/\partial x = \partial f/\partial y = \partial^2 f/\partial x^2 = \partial^2 f/\partial y^2 = 1$ at that point.

45. Let $w = f(u, v)$ be a function of u, v with continuous partial derivatives, where u, v in turn are functions of independent variables, x, y, z, with continuous partial derivatives. Show that if w is regarded as a function of x, y, z, its gradient at any point (x_0, y_0, z_0) lies in a common plane with the gradients of $u = u(x, y, z)$ and $v = v(x, y, z)$.

46. Show that if a function u has first derivatives that satisfy a relation of the form $F(u_x, u_y) = 0$, and if $\partial F/\partial u_x$ and $\partial F/\partial u_y$ are not both zero, then u also satisfies $u_{xx}u_{yy} - u_{xy}^2 = 0$. [*Hint.* Differentiate $F = 0$ with respect to x and y.]

47. If $f(x, y) = 0$, find d^2y/dx^2.

48. If $F(x, y, z) = 0$, show that $(\partial x/\partial y)_z(\partial y/\partial z)_x \times (\partial z/\partial x)_y = -1$. [Here $(\partial x/\partial y)_z$ denotes that z is held constant while we compute the partial derivative of x with respect to y, etc.]

49. If $f(x, y, z) = 0$ and $z = x + y$, find dz/dx.

50. The function $v(x, t)$ is defined for $0 \leq x \leq 1$, $0 \leq t$ and satisfies the partial differential equation

$$v_t = v_x(v - x) + a v_{xx}$$

(a = constant > 0) and the boundary conditions $v(0, t) = 0$, $v(1, t) = 1$. Suppose that for each fixed t, $v(x, t)$ is a strictly increasing function of x; that is, $v_x(x, t) > 0$. Show that v and t may be introduced as independent variables and x as dependent variable, and find the partial differential equation satisfied by the function $x(v, t)$. Find also the region of definition of $x(v, t)$ and boundary values that it satisfies. By considering level curves, show geometrically why the assumption $v_x(x, t) > 0$ is necessary for the success of this transformation.

51. Let $f(x, y, z)$ be a function depending only on $r = \sqrt{x^2 + y^2 + z^2}$; that is, $f(x, y, z) = g(r)$. Prove that if $f_{xx} + f_{yy} + f_{zz} = 0$, it follows that

$$f = \left(\frac{a}{r}\right) + b,$$

where a and b are constants.

52. A function $f(x, y)$, defined and differentiable for all x, y, is said to be homogeneous of degree n (a nonnegative integer) if $f(tx, ty) = t^n f(x, y)$ for all t, x, and y. For such a function prove: (a) $x(\partial f/\partial x) + y(\partial f/\partial y) = nf(x, y)$ and express this in vector form; (b) $x^2(\partial^2 f/\partial x^2) + 2xy(\partial^2 f/\partial x\, \partial y) + y^2(\partial^2 f/\partial y^2) = n(n - 1)f$, if f has continuous second partial derivatives; (c) a homogeneous function of degree zero is a constant.

53. Prove the Mean Value Theorem for functions of two variables

$$f(x + h, y + k) - f(x, y) = f_x(x + \theta h, y + \theta k)h$$
$$+ f_y(x + \theta h, y + \theta k)k,$$
$$0 < \theta < 1,$$

with suitable assumptions about f. What assumptions? [*Hint.* Apply the Mean Value Theorem for functions of one variable to $F(t) = f(x + ht, y + kt)$.]

54. Prove the theorem: If $f(x, y)$ is defined in a region R, and f_x, f_y exist and are bounded in R, then $f(x, y)$ is continuous in R. (The assumption of boundedness is essential.)

55. Using differentials, find a reasonable approximation to the value of

$$w = xy\sqrt{x^2 + y^2}$$

at $x = 2.98$, $y = 4.04$.

56. A flat circular plate has the shape of the region $x^2 + y^2 \leq 1$. The plate (including the boundary, where $x^2 + y^2 = 1$) is heated so that the temperature T at any point (x, y) is

$$T = x^2 + 2y^2 - x.$$

Locate the hottest and coldest point of the plate and find the temperature at each of these points.

57. The temperature T at any point (x, y, z) in space is $T = 400xyz^2$. Find the highest temperature on the surface of the unit sphere

$$x^2 + y^2 + z^2 = 1.$$

58. For each of the following three surfaces, find all the values of x and y for which z is a maximum or minimum (if there are any). Give complete reasonings.

a) $x^2 + y^2 + z^2 = 3$,   **b)** $x^2 + y^2 = 2z$,
c) $x^2 - y^2 = 2z$.

59. Find the point(s) on the surface $xyz = 1$ whose distance from the origin is a minimum.

60. A closed rectangular box is to be made to hold a given volume, V in^3. The cost of the material used in the box is a cents/in^2 for top and bottom, b cents/in^2 for front and back, c cents/in^2 for the remaining two sides. What dimensions make the total cost of materials a minimum?

61. Find the maximum value of the function $xye^{-(2x+3y)}$ in the first quadrant.

62. A surface is defined by $z = x^3 + y^3 - 9xy + 27$. Prove that the only possible maxima and minima of z occur at $(0, 0)$ or $(3, 3)$. Prove that $(0, 0)$ is neither a maximum nor a minimum. Determine whether $(3, 3)$ is a maximum or a minimum.

63. Given n positive numbers $a_1, a_2, \ldots, a_n$. Find the maximum value of the expression $a_1 x_1 + a_2 x_2 + \cdots + a_n x_n$ if the variables $x_1, x_2, \ldots, x_n$ are restricted so that the sum of their squares is 1.

64. Find the minimum volume bounded by the planes $x = 0$, $y = 0$, $z = 0$, and a plane that is tangent to the ellipsoid

$$\frac{x^2}{a^2} + \frac{y^2}{b^2} + \frac{z^2}{c^2} = 1$$

at a point in the octant $x > 0$, $y > 0$, $z > 0$.

65. Among the points $P(x, y)$ on the level curve $\phi(x, y) = 0$, it is desired to find one where the function $f(x, y)$ has a (relative) maximum. Assuming that such a point, p_0, exists, show that at p_0 the vectors ∇f and $\nabla \phi$ are parallel so that there is a number λ_0 such that $(\nabla f)_0 = \lambda_0(\nabla \phi)_0$. Explain geometrically by considering the level curves of f and ϕ.

66. Let z be defined implicitly as a function of x and y by the equation $\sin(x + y) + \sin(y + z) = 1$. Compute $\partial^2 z/\partial x\, \partial y$ in terms of x, y, and z.

67. Given $z = xy^2 - y \sin x$, calculate the value of $y(\partial^2 z/\partial y\, \partial x) - \partial z/\partial x$.

68. Let $w = z \tan^{-1}(x/y)$. Compute

$$\frac{\partial^2 w}{\partial x^2} + \frac{\partial^2 w}{\partial y^2} + \frac{\partial^2 w}{\partial z^2}.$$

Figure 13–33. The surface of Problem 70. (Courtesy of Norton Starr, Amherst College.)

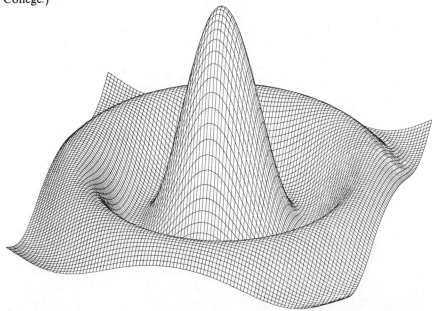

Figure 13–34. The surface of Problem 75. (Courtesy of Norton Starr, Amherst College.)

69. Show that the function satisfies the equation:

a) $\log \sqrt{x^2 + y^2}$, $f_{xx} + f_{yy} = 0$

b) $\sqrt{(x^2 + y^2 + z^2)^{-1}}$, $f_{xx} + f_{yy} + f_{zz} = 0$

c) $\int_0^{x/2\sqrt{kt}} e^{-\sigma^2}\, d\sigma$, $kf_{xx} - f_t = 0$ $(k \text{ const.})$

d) $\phi(x + at) + \psi(x - at)$, $f_{tt} = a^2 f_{xx}$

70. Consider the function defined by

$$f(x, y) = \begin{cases} xy\,\dfrac{x^2 - y^2}{x^2 + y^2}, & (x, y) \neq (0, 0), \\ 0, & (x, y) = (0, 0). \end{cases}$$

Then find $f_{yx}(0, 0)$ and $f_{xy}(0, 0)$. See Fig. 13–33.

71. Is $2x(x^3 + y^3)\, dx + 3y^2(x^2 + y^2)\, dy$ the total differential df of a function $f(x, y)$? If so, find the function.

72. Find a function $f(x, y)$ whose differential is

$$df = \left(\frac{y}{x} + e^y\right) dx + (\ln x + 2y + xe^y)\, dy,$$

or else show that no such function exists.

73. Find a function $w = f(x, y)$ such that $\partial w/\partial x = 1 + e^x \cos y$ and $\partial w/\partial y = 2y - e^x \sin y$, or else explain why no such function exists.

74. In thermodynamics the five quantities S, T, u, p, v are such that any two of them may be considered independent variables, the others then being determined. They are connected by the differential relation $T\, dS = du + p\, dv$. Show that

$$\left(\frac{\partial S}{\partial v}\right)_T = \left(\frac{\partial p}{\partial T}\right)_v \quad \text{and} \quad \left(\frac{\partial v}{\partial S}\right)_p = \left(\frac{\partial T}{\partial p}\right)_S.$$

75. Let

$$f(r, \theta) = \begin{cases} \dfrac{\sin 6r}{6r}, & r \neq 0 \\ 1, & r = 0. \end{cases}$$

(See Fig. 13–34.) Find (a) $\lim_{r \to 0} f(r, \theta)$, (b) $f_r(0, 0)$, (c) $f_\theta(r, \theta)$, $r \neq 0$.

MULTIPLE INTEGRALS

14–1

DOUBLE INTEGRALS

We shall show how to use the method of double integration to calculate the area or center of gravity of the region A (Fig. 14–1) which is bounded above by the curve $y = f_2(x)$, below by $y = f_1(x)$, on the left by the line $x = a$, and on the right by $x = b$. Before taking up the specific applications referred to, we shall first define what we mean by the double integral of a function $F(x, y)$ of two variables x and y. Then the specific applications follow at once by specializing the function $F(x, y)$ to be

a) $F(x, y) = 1$,   or   **b)** $F(x, y) = y$

for the calculation of

a) the area, or
b) the moment of the area about the x-axis.

The notation

$$\int_A \int F(x, y) \, dA, \tag{1}$$

is used to denote the double integral, over the region A, of the function $F(x, y)$.

We imagine the region A to be covered by a grid of lines parallel to the x- and y-axes. These lines divide the plane into small pieces of area

$$\Delta A = \Delta x \, \Delta y = \Delta y \, \Delta x, \tag{2}$$

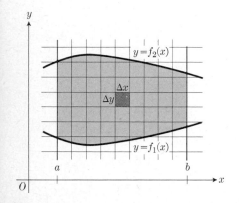

14–1   Region with rectangular grid.

some of which lie entirely within the given region, some entirely outside of the region, and some of which are intersected by the boundary of the region. We disregard all those that lie outside the region and may or may not take into account those that lie only partly inside, but we do take into consideration all the ΔA pieces that lie completely inside. We number these in some order, as

$$\Delta A_1, \quad \Delta A_2, \quad \dots, \quad \Delta A_n, \tag{3}$$

choose a point (x_k, y_k) in each ΔA_k, and form the sum

$$S_n = \sum_{k=1}^{n} F(x_k, y_k) \, \Delta A_k. \tag{4}$$

If the function $F(x, y)$ is continuous throughout A and if the curves that form the boundary of A are continuous and have a finite total length, then, as we refine the mesh width in such a way that Δx and Δy tend to zero (we may, for example, take $\Delta y = 2 \, \Delta x$ and then make $\Delta x \to 0$), the limit

$$I = \lim_{\Delta A \to 0} \sum_{k=1}^{n} F(x_k, y_k) \, \Delta A_k \tag{5}$$

exists. It is this limit that is indicated by the notation in Eq. (1).

The double integral (1) can also be interpreted as a volume, at least in the case where $F(x, y)$ is positive. Suppose, for example, that the region A is the base of a solid (Fig. 14–2) whose altitude above the point (x, y) is given by

$$z = F(x, y).$$

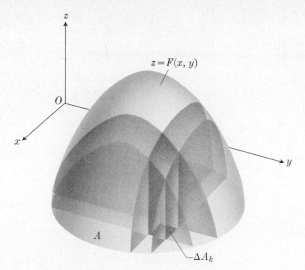

14–2   Approximating a volume by vertical prisms.

Then the term

$$F(x_k, y_k)\, \Delta A_k$$

is a reasonable approximation to the volume of that portion of the solid that rests upon the base ΔA_k. The sum S_n in Eq. (4) then gives an approximation to the total volume of the solid, and the limit in Eq. (5) gives what we call the exact volume.

Just as with integrals in one variable, the use of double integrals would be severely limited if it were necessary to calculate them directly from the definition in Eq. (5). Fortunately, it is possible to evaluate double integrals by evaluating successive single integrals. That is, in practice, the double integral in (1) is evaluated by calculating either one of the two *iterated integrals*

$$\int_A \int F(x, y)\, dx\, dy \qquad \text{or} \qquad \int_A \int F(x, y)\, dy\, dx, \qquad \textbf{(6)}$$

as we shall explain below. A theorem of analysis, which we shall not prove here, asserts that the iterated integrals (6) are equal to each other and to the double integral (1) whenever the function $F(x, y)$ is continuous over A and the boundary of A is not too complicated. The necessary conditions are fulfilled in the examples and problems in this book. [For more details see Franklin, *A Treatise on Advanced Calculus* (Dover, 1961); Chapter XI.]

The iterated integral

$$\int_A \int F(x, y)\, dy\, dx$$

is the result of:

a) integrating $\int F(x, y)\, dy$ with respect to y (with x held fixed) and evaluating the resulting integral between the limits $y = f_1(x)$ and $y = f_2(x)$; then

b) integrating the result of (a) with respect to x between the limits $x = a$ and $x = b$.

That is, we start with the innermost integral and perform successive integrations as follows:

$$\int_A \int F(x, y)\, dy\, dx = \int_a^b \left(\int_{f_1(x)}^{f_2(x)} F(x, y)\, dy \right) dx, \tag{7}$$

treating x as a constant while we perform the y integration.

We can gain some insight into the geometrical significance of Eq. (7) as follows: We may again think of a solid with base covering the region A of the xy-plane and having altitude $z = F(x, y)$ at the point (x, y) of A. (Assume, for sake of simplicity, that F is positive.) Then imagine a slice cut from the solid by planes perpendicular to the x-axis at x and at $x + dx$. We may think of this as approximated by the differential of volume given by

$$dV = A(x)\, dx,$$

where $A(x)$ is the cross-sectional area cut from the solid by the plane at x. Now this cross-sectional area (Fig. 14–3) is given by the integral

$$A(x) = \int_{f_1(x)}^{f_2(x)} z\, dy = \int_{f_1(x)}^{f_2(x)} F(x, y)\, dy,$$

where x is held fixed and the limits of integration depend upon where the cutting plane is taken. That is, the y-limits are functions of x, the functions that represent the boundary curves. Then, finally, we see that the iterated integral in Eq. (7) is the same as

$$V = \int_a^b A(x)\, dx = \int_a^b \left(\int_{f_1(x)}^{f_2(x)} F(x, y)\, dy \right) dx.$$

14–3   The area of the vertical slice shown above is

$$A(x) = \int_{f_1(x)}^{f_2(x)} F(x, y)\, dy.$$

This area is integrated from a to b to calculate the volume.

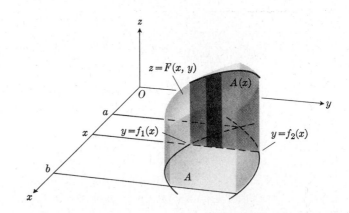

EXAMPLE 1.   Find the volume of the solid whose base is in the xy-plane and is the triangle bounded by the x-axis, the line $y = x$, and the line $x = 1$, while the top of the solid is in the plane

$$z = F(x, y) = 3 - x - y.$$

Solution. The volume dV of a representative prism of altitude z and base $dy\,dx$ is

$$dV = (3 - x - y)\,dy\,dx.$$

For any x between 0 and 1, y may vary from $y = 0$ to $y = x$ (Fig. 14–4). Hence,

$$V = \int_0^1 \int_0^x (3 - x - y)\,dy\,dx = \int_0^1 \left[3y - xy - \frac{y^2}{2}\right]_{y=0}^{y=x} dx$$

$$= \int_0^1 \left(3x - \frac{3x^2}{2}\right) dx = \frac{3x^2}{2} - \frac{x^3}{2}\bigg]_{x=0}^{x=1} = 1.$$

When the order of integration is reversed, the integral for the volume is

$$V = \int_0^1 \int_y^1 (3 - x - y)\,dx\,dy = \int_0^1 \left[3x - \frac{x^2}{2} - xy\right]_{x=y}^{x=1} dy$$

$$= \int_0^1 \left(3 - \frac{1}{2} - y - 3y + \frac{y^2}{2} + y^2\right) dy$$

$$= \int_0^1 \left(\frac{5}{2} - 4y + \frac{3}{2}y^2\right) dy = \frac{5}{2}y - 2y^2 + \frac{y^3}{2}\bigg]_{y=0}^{y=1} = 1.$$

The two integrals are equal, as they should be.

While the iterated integrals in Eq. (6) both give the value of the double integral, they may not be equally easy to compute. The next example shows one way this can happen.

EXAMPLE 2. Calculate

$$\int_A \int \frac{\sin x}{x}\,dA,$$

where A is the triangle in the xy-plane bounded by the x-axis, the line $y = x$, and the line $x = 1$.

Solution. The region of integration is the same as the one in Example 1. If we integrate first with respect to y and then with respect to x, we find

$$\int_0^1 \left(\int_0^x \frac{\sin x}{x}\,dy\right) dx = \int_0^1 \left(y\,\frac{\sin x}{x}\right]_{y=0}^{y=x}\right) dy$$

$$= \int_0^1 \sin x\,dx = -\cos(1) + 1 \approx 0.46.$$

If we reverse the order of integration, and attempt to calculate

$$\int_0^1 \int_y^1 \frac{\sin x}{x}\,dx\,dy,$$

we are stopped by the fact that $\int (\sin x/x)\,dx$ cannot be expressed in terms of elementary functions.

a)

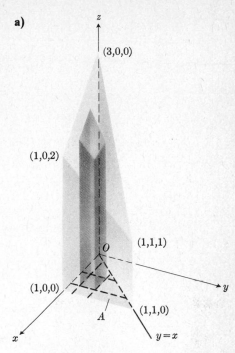

Prism with a triangular base in the xy-plane.

b)

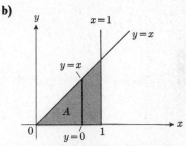

Integration limits of
$$\int_{x=0}^{x=1} \int_{y=0}^{y=x} F(x, y)\,dy\,dx$$

c)

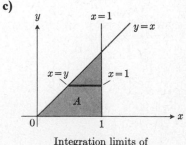

Integration limits of
$$\int_{y=0}^{y=1} \int_{x=y}^{x=1} F(x, y)\,dx\,dy$$

Figure 14–4

PROBLEMS

Evaluate each of the double integrals in Problems 1–4. Also sketch the region A over which the integration extends.

1. $\displaystyle\int_0^\pi \int_0^x x \sin y \, dy \, dx$ **2.** $\displaystyle\int_1^{\ln 8} \int_0^{\ln y} e^{x+y} \, dx \, dy$

3. $\displaystyle\int_0^\pi \int_0^{\sin x} y \, dy \, dx$ **4.** $\displaystyle\int_1^2 \int_y^{y^2} dx \, dy$

Write an equivalent double integral with the order of integration reversed for each of Problems 5–8. Check your answer by evaluating *both* double integrals. Also, sketch the region A over which the integration takes place.

5. $\displaystyle\int_0^2 \int_1^{e^x} dy \, dx$ **6.** $\displaystyle\int_0^1 \int_{\sqrt{y}}^1 dx \, dy$

7. $\displaystyle\int_0^{\sqrt{2}} \int_{-\sqrt{4-2y^2}}^{\sqrt{4-2y^2}} y \, dx \, dy$ **8.** $\displaystyle\int_{-2}^1 \int_{x^2+4x}^{3x+2} dy \, dx$

9. Find the volume of the solid whose base is the region in the xy-plane that is bounded by the parabola $y = 4 - x^2$ and the line $y = 3x$, while the top of the solid is bounded by the plane $z = x + 4$.

10. The base of a solid is the region in the xy-plane that is bounded by the circle $x^2 + y^2 = a^2$, while the top of the solid is bounded by the paraboloid $az = x^2 + y^2$. Find the volume.

14–2

AREA BY DOUBLE INTEGRATION

The simplest application of double integration is that of finding the area of a region of the xy-plane. The area is given by either of the integrals

$$A = \iint dx \, dy = \iint dy \, dx, \tag{1}$$

with proper limits of integration to be supplied. We have already illustrated how this is done for the area shown in Fig. 14–1 when the integrations are carried out in the order of first y and then x, namely,

$$A = \int_a^b \int_{f_1(x)}^{f_2(x)} dy \, dx. \tag{2}$$

If, however, the area is bounded on the left by the curve $x = g_1(y)$, on the right by $x = g_2(y)$, below by the line $y = c$, and above by the line $y = d$ (Fig. 14–5), then it is better to integrate first with respect to x [which may vary from $g_1(y)$ to $g_2(y)$] and then with respect to y. That is,

$$A = \int_c^d \int_{g_1(y)}^{g_2(y)} dx \, dy. \tag{3}$$

The first integration, with respect to x, may be visualized as adding together all the representative elements

$$dA = dx \, dy$$

that lie in a horizontal strip that extends from the curve $x = g_1(y)$ on the left to the curve $x = g_2(y)$ on the right. The evaluation of this integral gives

$$A = \int_c^d \int_{g_1(y)}^{g_2(y)} dx \, dy = \int_c^d [x]_{g_1(y)}^{g_2(y)} dy = \int_c^d [g_2(y) - g_1(y)] \, dy.$$

This latter integral could have been written down at once, since it merely expresses the area as the limit of the sum of horizontal strips of area.

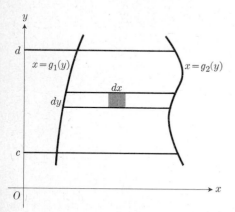

14–5   Area: $\displaystyle\int_c^d \int_{g_1(y)}^{g_2(y)} dx \, dy$.

EXAMPLE 1. The integral

$$\int_0^1 \int_{x^2}^x dy\, dx$$

represents the area of a region of the xy-plane. Sketch the region and express the same area as a double integral with the order of integration reversed.

Solution. In the inner integral, y varies from the curve $y = x^2$ to the line $y = x$. This gives the area of a vertical strip between x and $x + dx$, for values of x from $x = 0$ to $x = 1$. The region of integration is shown in Fig. 14–6. If we integrate in the other order, taking the x integration first, then x varies from the line $x = y$ to the parabola $x = \sqrt{y}$ to fill out a horizontal strip between y and $y + dy$. These strips must then be added together for values of y from 0 to 1. Hence

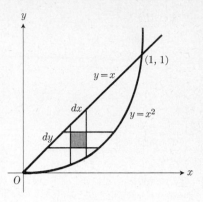

14–6 Area: $\int_0^1 \int_{x^2}^x dy\, dx$.

$$A = \int_0^1 \int_y^{\sqrt{y}} dx\, dy.$$

As a check, we evaluate the area by both integrals, and find

$$A = \int_0^1 \int_{x^2}^x dy\, dx = \int_0^1 (x - x^2)\, dx = \frac{x^2}{2} - \frac{x^3}{3}\Big]_0^1 = \frac{1}{6}$$

and

$$A = \int_0^1 \int_y^{\sqrt{y}} dx\, dy = \int_0^1 (\sqrt{y} - y)\, dy = \frac{2}{3} y^{3/2} - \frac{y^2}{2}\Big]_0^1 = \frac{1}{6}.$$

EXAMPLE 2. Find the area bounded by the parabola $y = x^2$ and the line $y = x + 2$.

Solution. The area to be found is shown in Fig. 14–7. We imagine a representative element of area

$$dA = dx\, dy = dy\, dx$$

lying in the region and ask ourselves what order of integration we should choose. We see that *horizontal* strips sometimes go from the line to the right branch of the parabola (if $1 \le y \le 4$) but sometimes go from the left branch of the parabola to its right side (if $0 \le y \le 1$). Thus integration in the order of first x and then y requires that the area be taken in two separate pieces, with the result given by

$$A = \int_0^1 \int_{-\sqrt{y}}^{\sqrt{y}} dx\, dy + \int_1^4 \int_{y-2}^{\sqrt{y}} dx\, dy.$$

On the other hand, *vertical* strips always go from the parabola as lower boundary up to the line, and the area is given by

$$A = \int_{-1}^2 \int_{x^2}^{x+2} dy\, dx.$$

Clearly, this result is simpler and is the only one we would bother to write

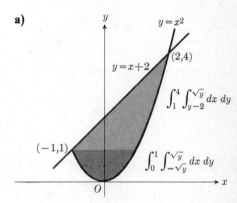

a)

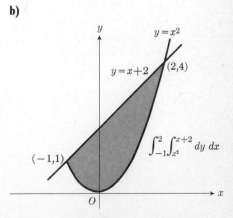

b)

14–7 Calculating the area shown above takes (a) two integrals if the first integration is with respect to x, but (b) only one if the first integration is with respect to y.

down in practice. Evaluation of this integral leads to the result

$$A = \int_{-1}^{2} y \Big]_{x^2}^{x+2} dx$$

$$= \int_{-1}^{2} (x + 2 - x^2)\, dx = \tfrac{9}{2}.$$

PROBLEMS

In each of these problems, find the area of the region bounded by the given curves and lines by means of double integration.

1. The coordinate axes and the line $x + y = a$.
2. The x-axis, the curve $y = e^x$, and the lines $x = 0, x = 1$.
3. The y-axis, the line $y = 2x$, and the line $y = 4$.
4. The curve $y^2 + x = 0$, and the line $y = x + 2$.
5. The curves $x = y^2$, $x = 2y - y^2$.
6. The semicircle $y = \sqrt{a^2 - x^2}$, the lines $x = \pm a$, and the line $y = -a$.
7. The parabola $x = y - y^2$ and the line $x + y = 0$.

The integrals in Problems 8–12 give areas of regions in the xy-plane. Sketch each region. Label each bounding curve with its equation, and give the coordinates of the boundary points where the curves intersect.

8. $\int_{0}^{1} \int_{y}^{\sqrt{y}} dx\, dy$

9. $\int_{0}^{3} \int_{-x}^{x(2-x)} dy\, dx$

10. $\int_{0}^{\pi/4} \int_{\sin x}^{\cos x} dy\, dx$

11. $\int_{-1}^{2} \int_{y^2}^{y+2} dx\, dy$

12. $\int_{-1}^{0} \int_{-2x}^{1-x} dy\, dx + \int_{0}^{2} \int_{-x/2}^{1-x} dy\, dx$

14-3

PHYSICAL APPLICATIONS

If the representative element of mass dm in a mass that is continuously distributed over some region A of the xy-plane is taken to be

$$dm = \delta(x, y)\, dy\, dx$$

$$= \delta(x, y)\, dA, \qquad (1)$$

where $\delta = \delta(x, y)$ is the density at the point (x, y) of A (Fig. 14–8), then double integration may be used to calculate:

a) the mass, $\qquad M = \iint \delta(x, y)\, dA, \qquad (2)$

b) the first moment of the mass with respect to the x-axis,

$$M_x = \iint y\, \delta(x, y)\, dA, \qquad (3a)$$

c) its first moment with respect to the y-axis,

$$M_y = \iint x\, \delta(x, y)\, dA. \qquad (3b)$$

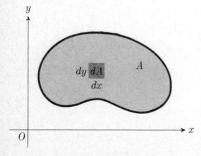

14–8 Area element $dA = dx\, dy$.

From (2) and (3) we get the coordinates of the center of mass,

$$\bar{x} = \frac{M_y}{M}, \qquad \bar{y} = \frac{M_x}{M}.$$

Other moments of importance in physical application are the *moments of inertia* of the mass. These are the *second* moments that we get by using the squares instead of the first powers of the "lever-arm" distances x and y. Thus the moment of inertia about the x-axis, denoted by I_x, is defined by

$$I_x = \iint y^2 \, \delta(x, y) \, dA. \tag{4}$$

The moment of inertia about the y-axis is

$$I_y = \iint x^2 \, \delta(x, y) \, dA. \tag{5}$$

Also of interest is the *polar moment of inertia* about the origin, I_0, given by

$$I_0 = \iint r^2 \, \delta(x, y) \, dA. \tag{6}$$

Here $r^2 = x^2 + y^2$ is the square of the distance from the origin to the representative point (x, y) in the element of mass dm.

In all of these integrals, the same limits of integration are to be supplied as would be called for if one were calculating only the area of A.

REMARK 1. When a particle of mass m is rotating about an axis in a circle of radius r with angular velocity ω and linear velocity $v = \omega r$, its kinetic energy is

$$\tfrac{1}{2}mv^2 = \tfrac{1}{2}mr^2\omega^2.$$

If a system of particles of masses $m_1, m_2, \ldots, m_n$, all rotate about the same axis with the same angular velocity ω but their respective distances from the axis of rotation are $r_1, r_2, \ldots, r_n$, then the kinetic energy of the system of particles is

$$\text{K.E.} = \tfrac{1}{2}(m_1 v_1^2 + \cdots + m_n v_n^2) = \tfrac{1}{2}\omega^2 \sum_{k=1}^{n} m_k r_k^2 = \tfrac{1}{2}\omega^2 I, \tag{7}$$

where

$$I = \sum_{k=1}^{n} m_k r_k^2 \tag{8}$$

is the *moment of inertia* of the system about the axis in question. It depends only upon the magnitudes m_k of the masses and their distances r_k from the axis. When a mass m is moving in a straight line with velocity v, its kinetic energy is $\tfrac{1}{2}mv^2$, and an amount of work equal to this must be expended to stop the object and bring it to rest. Similarly, when a system of mass is moving in a *rotational* motion (like a turning shaft), the kinetic energy it possesses is

$$\text{K.E.} = \tfrac{1}{2}I\omega^2, \tag{9}$$

and this amount of work is required to stop the rotating system. It is seen that I here plays the role that m plays in the case of motion in a straight line. In a sense, the *moment of inertia* of a large shaft is what makes it hard to start or to stop the rotation of the shaft, in the same way that the *mass* of an automobile is what makes it hard to start or to stop its motion.

If, instead of a system of discrete mass particles as in (7) and (8), we have a continuous distribution of mass in a fine wire, or spread out in a thin film or plate over an area, or distributed throughout a solid, then we may divide the total mass into small elements of mass Δm such that if r represents the distance of some *one* point of the element Δm from an axis, then *all* points of that element will be within a distance $r \pm \epsilon$ of the axis, where $\epsilon \to 0$ as the largest dimension of the elements $\Delta m \to 0$. Then we define the moment of inertia of the total mass about the axis in question to be

$$I = \lim_{\Delta m \to 0} \sum r^2 \, \Delta m = \int r^2 \, dm. \tag{10}$$

Thus, for example, the polar moment of inertia, given by Eq. (6), is the moment of inertia with respect to a z-axis through O perpendicular to the xy-plane.

In addition to its importance in connection with the kinetic energy of rotating bodies, the moment of inertia plays an important part in the theory of the deflection of beams under transverse loading, where the "stiffness factor" is given by EI, where E is Young's modulus, and I is the moment of inertia of a cross section of the beam with respect to a horizontal axis through its center of gravity. The greater the value of I, the stiffer the beam and the less it will deflect. This fact is exploited in so-called I-beams, where the flanges at the top and bottom of the beam are at relatively large distances from the center and hence correspond to large values of r^2 in Eq. (10), thereby contributing a larger amount to the moment of inertia than would be the case if the same mass were all distributed uniformly, say in a beam with a square cross section.

REMARK 2.   Moments are also of importance in statistics. The *first moment* is used in computing the mean (i.e., average) value of a given set of data. The *second moment* (which corresponds to the moment of inertia) is used in computing the variance (σ^2) or standard deviation (σ). Third and fourth moments are also used for computing statistical quantities known as skewness and kurtosis. The tth moment is defined as

$$M_t = \sum_{k=1}^{n} m_k r_k^t.$$

Here r_k ranges over the values of the statistic under consideration (e.g., r_k might represent height in quarter inches, or weight in ounces, or quiz grades in calculus in percentage points, etc.), while m_k is the number of individuals in the entire group whose "measurements" equal r_k. (For example, if 5 students get a grade of 75 on a quiz, then corresponding to $r_k = 75$ we would have $m_k = 5$.) A table of values of m_k versus r_k is called a "frequency distribution," and one refers to M_t as the tth moment of this frequency distribution. The mean value $\bar{r}$ is defined by

$$\bar{r} = \frac{\sum m_k r_k}{\sum m_k} = \frac{M_1}{m}, \tag{11}$$

where M_1 is the first moment and $m = \sum m_k$ is the total number of individuals in the "population" under consideration. The *variance* σ^2 involves the second moment about the mean. It is defined by

$$\sigma^2 = \frac{\sum (r_k - \bar{r})^2 m_k}{\sum m_k}, \qquad \text{(12a)}$$

where σ is the so-called *standard deviation*. Both the variance and standard deviation are measures of the way in which the r values tend to bunch up close to $\bar{r}$ (small values of σ) or to be spread out (large values of σ). Algebraic manipulations with (12a) permit one also to write the variance in the alternative form

$$\sigma^2 = \frac{M_2}{m} - \bar{r}^2. \qquad \text{(12b)}$$

There is a significant difference between the meaning attached to y in the case of the formula

$$A = \int_a^b y \, dx, \qquad \text{(13)}$$

meaning the area (Fig. 14–9) under a curve $y = f(x)$ from $x = a$ to $x = b$, and the meaning attached to y in these double integrals, Eqs. (2)–(6). In Eq. (13), one must replace y by $f(x)$ from the equation of the curve *before* integrating, because y means the ordinate of the point (x, y) *on* the curve $y = f(x)$. But in the case of the double integrals (2)–(6), one must *not* replace y by a function of x before integrating because the point (x, y) is, in general, a point of the element $dA = dy \, dx$ and both x and y are *independent* variables. The equations of the boundary curves of the region A enter only as the *limits of integration*. Thus:

1. In the case of *single* integrals, such as

$$A = \int_a^b y \, dx, \qquad \text{(14)}$$

we do not integrate with respect to y and hence we must substitute for it.

2. In the case of *double* integrals, such as

$$I_x = \iint y^2 \, \delta \, dy \, dx, \qquad \text{(15)}$$

we *do* integrate with respect to y and hence we do not substitute for it before performing the y integration. The equations $y = f_1(x)$ and $y = f_2(x)$ of the boundary curves are used as limits of integration and are only to be substituted after the y integration is performed.

a)

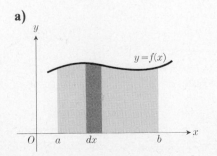

b)

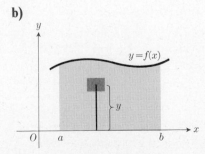

14–9 (a) To calculate $A = \int_a^b y \, dx$, substitute $f(x)$ for y before integrating. (b) To calculate $I_x = \int_a^b \int_0^{f(x)} y^2 \, \delta \, dy \, dx$, integrate with respect to y before substituting $f(x)$ for y.

EXAMPLE. A thin plate of uniform thickness and density covers the region of the xy-plane shown in Fig. 14-7. Find its moment of inertia I_y about the y-axis.

Solution. Integrating in the order of first y and then x, we have

$$I_y = \int_{-1}^{2} \int_{x^2}^{x+2} x^2 \delta \, dy \, dx$$

$$= \delta \int_{-1}^{2} x^2 y \Big]_{y=x^2}^{y=x+2} \, dx$$

$$= \delta \int_{-1}^{2} (x^3 + 2x^2 - x^4) \, dx = \tfrac{63}{20} \delta.$$

The equation

$$I_y = MR_y^2$$

defines a number

$$R_y = \sqrt{I_y/M},$$

called the *radius of gyration* with respect to the y-axis. It tells how far from the y-axis the entire mass M might be concentrated and still give the same I_y. The mass of the plate in the example above is

$$M = \int_{-1}^{2} \int_{x^2}^{x+2} \delta \, dy \, dx = \tfrac{9}{2} \delta.$$

Hence

$$R_y = \sqrt{I_y/M} = \sqrt{7/10}.$$

Note that the density δ in this problem is a constant, and hence we were able to move it outside the integral signs. If the density had been given instead as some variable function of x and y, then we would have taken this into account, in both I_y and M, by simply substituting this function for δ before integrating.

PROBLEMS

1. Find the center of gravity of the area of Problem 1, Article 14-2.

2. Find the moment of inertia, about the x-axis, of the area of Problem 2, Article 14-2. [For an area, we take $\delta = 1$.]

3. Find the polar moment of inertia, about an axis through O perpendicular to the xy-plane, for the area of Problem 3, Article 14-2.

4. Find the center of gravity of the area of Problem 4, Article 14-2.

5. Find the moment of inertia about the x-axis of the area in Problem 5, Article 14-2, if the density at (x, y) is $\delta = y + 1$.

6. Find the center of gravity of the area of Problem 6, Article 14-2, if the density at (x, y) is $\delta = y + a$.

7. Find the moment of inertia, about the x-axis, of the area of Problem 7, Article 14-2, if the density at (x, y) is $\delta = x + y$.

8. For any area in the xy-plane, show that its polar moment of inertia I_0 about an axis through O perpendicular to the xy-plane is equal to $I_x + I_y$.

Let A be a region of the plane bounded by rays $\theta = \alpha$, $\theta = \beta$, and curves $r = f_1(\theta)$, $r = f_2(\theta)$, as in Fig. 14–10. Suppose that A is completely contained in the wedge R

$$R: \quad 0 \le r \le a, \quad \alpha \le \theta \le \beta.$$

Let m and n be positive integers and take

$$\Delta r = \frac{a}{m}, \qquad \Delta \theta = \frac{\beta - \alpha}{n}.$$

14–4

POLAR COORDINATES

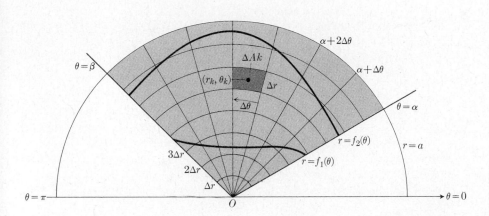

14–10 Subdivision of the region $R: 0 \le r \le a, \alpha \le \theta \le \beta$, in polar coordinates; $\Delta A_k = r_k \, \Delta \theta \, \Delta r$.

Now cover R by a grid of circular arcs with centers at O and radii Δr, $2 \, \Delta r, \ldots, m \, \Delta r$, and rays through O along $\theta = \alpha$, $\alpha + \Delta \theta$, $\alpha + 2 \, \Delta \theta, \ldots,$ $\alpha + n \, \Delta \theta = \beta$. This grid partitions R into subregions of three kinds: (a) those exterior to A, (b) those interior to A, and (c) those that intersect the boundary of A. We henceforth ignore those of the first type, but we want to include all those of the second kind, and may include some, none, or all of those of the third kind. Those that are to be included may now be numbered in some order $1, 2, 3, \ldots, N$. In the kth subregion so included, let (r_k, θ_k) be the coordinates of its center.* We multiply the value of F at each of these centers by the area of the corresponding subregion and add the products. That is, we consider the sum

$$S = \sum_{k=1}^{N} F(r_k, \theta_k) \cdot \Delta A_k$$

$$= \sum_{k=1}^{N} F(r_k, \theta_k) \cdot r_k \, \Delta \theta \, \Delta r, \tag{1}$$

since

$$\Delta A_k = r_k \, \Delta \theta \, \Delta r, \tag{2}$$

as we shall now see. The radius of the inner arc bounding ΔA_k is $r_k - \frac{1}{2} \, \Delta r$; of

---

* We mean the point halfway between the circular arcs, and on the ray that bisects them.

the outer arc, $r_k + \frac{1}{2} \Delta r$. Hence

$$\Delta A_k = \tfrac{1}{2}(r_k + \tfrac{1}{2} \Delta r)^2 \, \Delta\theta - \tfrac{1}{2}(r_k - \tfrac{1}{2} \Delta r)^2 \, \Delta\theta,$$

and simple algebra reduces this to Eq. (2).

We now imagine this process repeated over and over again with finer and finer grids, and consider the limit of the sums (1) as the diagonals of all subregions approach zero. If the function F is continuous, and the region A is bounded by continuous, rectifiable curves, the sums approach as limit the double integral of F over A:

$$\lim_{N \to \infty} \sum_{k=1}^{N} F(r_k, \theta_k) r_k \, \Delta\theta \, \Delta r = \int_A \int F(r, \theta) \, dA. \tag{3}$$

This limit may also be computed from the iterated integral on the right below:

$$\int_A \int F(r, \theta) \, dA = \int_{\theta=\alpha}^{\beta} \int_{r=f_1(\theta)}^{f_2(\theta)} F(r, \theta) r \, dr \, d\theta. \tag{4}$$

The question naturally arises whether one might first set up the double integral in Cartesian coordinates and then change to polar coordinates.

A rigorous treatment of the problem of changing the variables in a double integral may be found in Franklin, *A Treatise on Advanced Calculus*, p. 368. We shall here be content with citing the result and showing how it leads to Eq. (4) in the case of polar coordinates. In general, equations of the form

$$x = f(u, v), \qquad y = g(u, v), \tag{5}$$

may be interpreted as mapping a region A of the xy-plane into a region G of the uv-plane. Then, under suitable restrictions on the functions f and g, the following equation gives the formula for changing from xy-coordinates to uv-coordinates in a double integral, namely,

$$\int_A \int \phi(x, y) \, dx \, dy = \int_G \int \phi[f(u, v), g(u, v)] \frac{\partial(x, y)}{\partial(u, v)} \, du \, dv, \tag{6}$$

where the symbol $\partial(x, y)/\partial(u, v)$ denotes the so-called "Jacobian" of the transformation (5) and is defined by the determinant

$$\frac{\partial(x, y)}{\partial(u, v)} = \begin{vmatrix} \dfrac{\partial x}{\partial u} & \dfrac{\partial x}{\partial v} \\[2mm] \dfrac{\partial y}{\partial u} & \dfrac{\partial y}{\partial v} \end{vmatrix}. \tag{7}$$

In the case of polar coordinates, we have r and θ in place of u and v,

$$x = r \cos \theta, \qquad y = r \sin \theta,$$

and

$$\frac{\partial(x, y)}{\partial(r, \theta)} = \begin{vmatrix} \cos \theta & -r \sin \theta \\ \sin \theta & r \cos \theta \end{vmatrix} = r(\cos^2 \theta + \sin^2 \theta) = r.$$

Hence, Eq. (6) becomes

$$\iint \phi(x, y)\, dx\, dy = \iint \phi(r \cos \theta, r \sin \theta) r\, dr\, d\theta, \qquad \textbf{(8)}$$

which corresponds to Eq. (4).

EXAMPLE 1. Find the polar moment of inertia about the origin of a thin plate of density $\delta = 1$ bounded by the circle $x^2 + y^2 = 1$.

Solution

In cartesian coordinates	In polar coordinates

$$\int_{-1}^{1} \int_{-\sqrt{1-x^2}}^{\sqrt{1-x^2}} (x^2 + y^2)\, dy\, dx = \int_{0}^{2\pi} \int_{0}^{1} (r^2) r\, dr\, d\theta$$

$$= \int_{0}^{2\pi} \left[\frac{r^4}{4} \right]_{r=0}^{r=1} d\theta$$

$$= \int_{0}^{2\pi} \frac{1}{4}\, d\theta = \frac{\pi}{2}.$$

To convert from the cartesian integral to the polar integral, we took $\phi(x, y) = x^2 + y^2$ in Eq. (8), and used polar-coordinate limits that described the circle. The polar integral is much easier to evaluate than the cartesian integral.

The total area of a region is given by each of the double integrals

$$A = \iint dx\, dy = \iint r\, dr\, d\theta \qquad \textbf{(9)}$$

with appropriate limits. This means, essentially, that the given region can be divided into pieces of area

$$dA_{xy} = dx\, dy$$

by lines parallel to the x- and y-axes, or that it can be divided into pieces of area

$$dA_{r\theta} = r\, dr\, d\theta$$

by radial lines and circular arcs, and that the total area can be found by adding together all of the elements of area of either type. But it is not to be expected that the *individual pieces* dA_{xy} and $dA_{r\theta}$ will be equal. In fact, an elementary calculation shows that

$$dA_{xy} = dx\, dy = d(r \cos \theta)\, d(r \sin \theta) \neq r\, dr\, d\theta = dA_{r\theta}.$$

EXAMPLE 2. Find the moment of inertia, about the y-axis, of the area enclosed by the cardioid (see Fig. 14-11):

$$r = a(1 - \cos \theta).$$

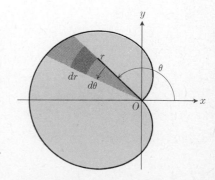

14-11 The cardioid $r = a(1 - \cos \theta)$.

Solution. It is customary to take the density as unity when working with a geometrical area. Thus we have

$$I_y = \int_A \int x^2 \, dA,$$

with

$$x = r \cos \theta, \qquad dA = r \, dr \, d\theta.$$

If we integrate first with respect to r, then, for any θ between 0 and 2π, r may vary from 0 to $a(1 - \cos \theta)$. This permits the integration to extend over those elements of area lying in the wedge between the radius lines θ and $\theta + d\theta$. Next we integrate with respect to θ from 0 to 2π to allow these wedges to cover the entire area. Hence

$$I_y = \int_0^{2\pi} \int_0^{a(1 - \cos \theta)} r^3 \cos^2 \theta \, dr \, d\theta$$

$$= \int_0^{2\pi} \frac{a^4}{4} \cos^2 \theta (1 - \cos \theta)^4 \, d\theta.$$

The evaluation of the integrals

$$\int_0^{2\pi} \cos^n \theta \, d\theta \quad (n = 2, 3, 4, 5, 6)$$

is made easier by use of the reduction formula

$$\int_0^{2\pi} \cos^n \theta \, d\theta = \frac{\cos^{n-1} \theta \sin \theta}{n} \bigg]_0^{2\pi} + \frac{n-1}{n} \int_0^{2\pi} \cos^{n-2} \theta \, d\theta$$

or, since $\sin \theta$ vanishes at both limits,

$$\int_0^{2\pi} \cos^n \theta \, d\theta = \frac{n-1}{n} \int_0^{2\pi} \cos^{n-2} \theta \, d\theta.$$

Thus

$$\int_0^{2\pi} \cos^2 \theta \, d\theta = \tfrac{1}{2} \int_0^{2\pi} d\theta = \pi,$$

$$\int_0^{2\pi} \cos^3 \theta \, d\theta = \tfrac{2}{3} \int_0^{2\pi} \cos \theta \, d\theta = \tfrac{2}{3} \sin \theta \bigg]_0^{2\pi} = 0,$$

$$\int_0^{2\pi} \cos^4 \theta \, d\theta = \frac{3}{4} \int_0^{2\pi} \cos^2 \theta \, d\theta = \frac{3\pi}{4},$$

$$\int_0^{2\pi} \cos^5 \theta \, d\theta = \frac{4}{5} \int_0^{2\pi} \cos^3 \theta \, d\theta = 0,$$

$$\int_0^{2\pi} \cos^6 \theta \, d\theta = \frac{5}{6} \int_0^{2\pi} \cos^4 \theta \, d\theta = \frac{5\pi}{8}.$$

Therefore

$$I_y = \frac{a^4}{4} \int_0^{2\pi} (\cos^2 \theta - 4 \cos^3 \theta + 6 \cos^4 \theta - 4 \cos^5 \theta + \cos^6 \theta) \, d\theta$$

$$= \frac{a^4}{4} \left[1 + \frac{18}{4} + \frac{5}{8} \right] \pi = \frac{49\pi a^4}{32}.$$

PROBLEMS

Change each of the double integrals of Problems 1–6 to an equivalent double integral in terms of polar coordinates; then evaluate the integrals thus obtained.

1. $\displaystyle\int_{-a}^{a} \int_{-\sqrt{a^2-x^2}}^{\sqrt{a^2-x^2}} dy \, dx$ **2.** $\displaystyle\int_0^a \int_0^{\sqrt{a^2-y^2}} (x^2 + y^2) \, dx \, dy$

3. $\displaystyle\int_0^{a/\sqrt{2}} \int_y^{\sqrt{a^2-y^2}} x \, dx \, dy$ **4.** $\displaystyle\int_0^{\infty} \int_0^{\infty} e^{-(x^2+y^2)} \, dx \, dy$

5. $\displaystyle\int_0^2 \int_0^x y \, dy \, dx$ **6.** $\displaystyle\int_0^{2a} \int_0^{\sqrt{2ax-x^2}} x^2 \, dy \, dx$

7. By double integration, find the area that lies inside the cardioid $r = a(1 + \cos \theta)$ and outside the circle $r = a$.

8. Find the center of gravity of the area of Problem 7.

9. Find the polar moment of inertia I_0 with respect to an axis through O perpendicular to the xy-plane, for the area of Problem 7.

10. The base of a solid is the area of Problem 7 and the top of the solid is bounded by the plane $z = x$. Find the volume.

11. Using double integration, find the total area enclosed by the lemniscate $r^2 = 2a^2 \cos 2\theta$.

12. The base of a solid is the area of Problem 11, while its top is bounded by the sphere $z = \sqrt{2a^2 - r^2}$. Find the volume.

Consider a region V, in xyz-space, completely contained within the box B bounded by the planes $x = a$, $x = b$, $y = c$, $y = d$, $z = e$, and $z = f$, with $a < b$, $c < d$, and $e < f$. Let $F(x, y, z)$ be a function whose domain includes V. Let m, n, p be positive integers, and let

14–5

TRIPLE INTEGRALS. VOLUME

$$\Delta x = \frac{b-a}{m}, \qquad \Delta y = \frac{d-c}{n}, \qquad \Delta z = \frac{f-e}{p}.$$

Divide B into mnp subregions each with dimensions Δx by Δy by Δz, by planes

$$x = a, \quad a + \Delta x, \quad a + 2\,\Delta x, \quad \ldots, \quad a + m\,\Delta x;$$

$$y = c, \quad c + \Delta y, \quad c + 2\,\Delta y, \quad \ldots, \quad c + n\,\Delta y;$$

$$z = e, \quad e + \Delta z, \quad e + 2\,\Delta z, \quad \ldots, \quad e + p\,\Delta z.$$

These subregions are of three kinds: (a) those interior to V, (b) those exterior to V, and (c) those intersecting the boundary of V. We include all those of type (a), exclude all those of type (b), and include some, none, or all those of type (c). Then we number the included subregions 1, 2, 3, ..., N. Let (x_k, y_k, z_k) be a point in the kth subregion; multiply the value of F at that point by the volume ΔV_k of the subregion, and form the sum

$$S = \sum_{k=1}^{N} F(x_k, y_k, z_k) \, \Delta V_k$$

$$= \sum_{k=1}^{N} F(x_k, y_k, z_k) \, \Delta x \, \Delta y \, \Delta z. \qquad (1)$$

Finally, suppose that the function F is continuous throughout V and on its boundary. Then, if the boundary of V is sufficiently "tame," the sums (1) have a limit as $\sqrt{(\Delta x)^2 + (\Delta y)^2 + (\Delta z)^2}$ approaches zero, and this limit is called the (Riemann) triple integral of F over V:

$$\iiint\limits_{V} F \, dV = \lim \sum_{k=1}^{N} F(x_k, y_k, z_k) \, \Delta x \, \Delta y \, \Delta z. \tag{2}$$

REMARK 1.   There are many possible interpretations of (2). If $F(x, y, z) = 1$ for all points in V, the integral is just the volume of V. If $F(x, y, z) = x$, the integral is the first moment of the volume V with respect to the yz-plane. If $F(x, y, z)$ is the density at (x, y, z), then the integral is the mass in V. If $F(x, y, z)$ is the product of the density at (x, y, z) and the square of the distance from (x, y, z) to an axis L, then the integral is the moment of inertia of the mass with respect to L.

REMARK 2.   The triple integral is seldom evaluated directly from its definition as a limit. Instead, it is usually evaluated as an iterated integral. For example, suppose V is bounded below by a surface

$$z = f_1(x, y),$$

above by the surface

$$z = f_2(x, y),$$

and laterally by a cylinder C with elements parallel to the z-axis (Fig. 14–12). Let A denote the region of the xy-plane enclosed by the cylinder C. (That is, A is the region covered by the orthogonal projection of the solid into the xy-plane.) Then the *volume* of the region V (which we shall also denote by V) can be found by evaluating the triply iterated integral

$$V = \int_A \iint_{f_1(x,y)}^{f_2(x,y)} dz \, dy \, dx. \tag{3}$$

The z-limits of integration indicate that for every (x, y) in the region A, z may extend from the lower surface $z = f_1(x, y)$ to the upper surface $z = f_2(x, y)$. The y- and x-limits of integration have not been given explicitly in Eq. (3), but are indicated as extending over the region A. The problem of supplying these limits is precisely the problem we have previously considered in connection with *double* integrals. It is usually desirable to draw the xy-projection of the solid in order to see more easily what these limits are.

In case the lateral surface of the cylinder reduces to zero (as in the example that follows), one may find the equation of the boundary of the region A by eliminating z between the two equations $z = f_1(x, y)$ and $z = f_2(x, y)$, thus obtaining an equation

$$f_1(x, y) = f_2(x, y), \tag{4}$$

which contains no z. Such an equation, interpreted as the equation of a surface in xyz-space, represents a cylinder with elements parallel to the z-axis. If we interpret it as an equation in the xy-plane, Eq. (4) represents the boundary of the region A.

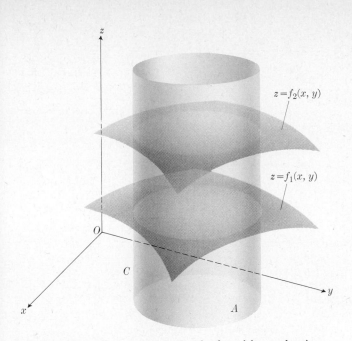

14–12 The enclosed volume can be found by evaluating

$$V = \int_A \int \int_{f_1(x,y)}^{f_2(x,y)} dz \, dy \, dx.$$

14–13 The volume between two paraboloids.

EXAMPLE. Find the volume enclosed between the two surfaces

$$z = 8 - x^2 - y^2 \quad \text{and} \quad z = x^2 + 3y^2.$$

Solution. The two surfaces (Fig. 14–13) intersect on the elliptic cylinder

$$x^2 + 2y^2 = 4.$$

The volume projects into the region A (in the xy-plane) that is enclosed by the ellipse having this same equation. In the double integral with respect to y and x over this region A, if we integrate first with respect to y, holding x and dx fixed, we see that y varies from $-\sqrt{(4-x^2)/2}$ to $+\sqrt{(4-x^2)/2}$. Then x varies from -2 to $+2$. Thus we have

$$V = \int_{-2}^{2} \int_{-\sqrt{(4-x^2)/2}}^{\sqrt{(4-x^2)/2}} \int_{x^2+3y^2}^{8-x^2-y^2} dz \, dy \, dx$$

$$= \int_{-2}^{2} \int_{-\sqrt{(4-x^2)/2}}^{\sqrt{(4-x^2)/2}} (8 - 2x^2 - 4y^2) \, dy \, dx$$

$$= \int_{-2}^{2} \left[2(8 - 2x^2) \sqrt{\frac{4-x^2}{2}} - \frac{8}{3}\left(\frac{4-x^2}{2}\right)^{3/2} \right] dx$$

$$= \frac{4\sqrt{2}}{3} \int_{-2}^{2} (4 - x^2)^{3/2} \, dx = 8\pi\sqrt{2}.$$

PROBLEMS

By triple integration, find the volume in each of the following problems.

1. The volume of the tetrahedron bounded by the plane $x/a + y/b + z/c = 1$ and the coordinate planes.

2. The volume between the cylinder $z = y^2$ and the xy-plane that is bounded by the four vertical planes $x = 0$, $x = 1$, $y = -1$, $y = 1$.

3. The volume in the first octant bounded by the planes $x + z = 1$, $y + 2z = 2$.

4. The volume in the first octant bounded by the cylinder $x = 4 - y^2$ and the planes $z = y$, $x = 0$, $z = 0$.

5. The volume enclosed by the cylinders $z = 5 - x^2$, $z = 4x^2$, and the planes $y = 0$, $x + y = 1$.

6. The volume enclosed by the cylinder $y^2 + 4z^2 = 16$ and the planes $x = 0$, $x + y = 4$.

7. The volume bounded below by the plane $z = 0$, laterally by the elliptic cylinder $x^2 + 4y^2 = 4$, and above by the plane $z = x + 2$.

8. The volume common to the two cylinders $x^2 + y^2 = a^2$ and $x^2 + z^2 = a^2$. (See Fig. 14–14.)

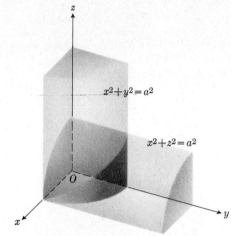

14–14 One-eighth of the volume common to the cylinders $x^2 + y^2 = a^2$, $x^2 + z^2 = a^2$.

9. The volume bounded by the elliptic paraboloids $z = x^2 + 9y^2$ and $z = 18 - x^2 - 9y^2$.

10. The volume of an ellipsoid of semiaxes a, b, c.

14–6

CYLINDRICAL COORDINATES

Instead of using an element of volume

$$dV_{xyz} = dz \, dy \, dx, \qquad (1)$$

as we have done, we may use an element

$$dV_{r\theta z} = dz \, r \, dr \, d\theta. \qquad (2)$$

Equation (2) may be visualized as giving the volume of an element having cross-sectional area $r \, dr \, d\theta$, such as that used with polar coordinates in Article 14–4, and altitude dz. Cylindrical coordinates, r, θ, z, are particularly useful in problems where there is an axis of symmetry of the solid. By proper choice of axes, this axis of symmetry may be taken to be the z-axis.

EXAMPLE. Find the center of gravity of a homogeneous solid hemisphere of radius a.

Solution. We may choose the origin at the center of the sphere and consider the hemisphere that lies above the xy-plane. (See Fig. 14–15.) The equation of the hemispherical surface is

$$z = \sqrt{a^2 - x^2 - y^2}$$

or, in terms of cylindrical coordinates,

$$z = \sqrt{a^2 - r^2}.$$

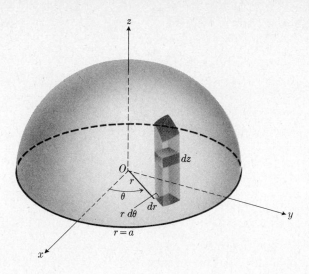

14–15 The volume element in cylindrical coordinates is $dV = dz\, r\, dr\, d\theta$.

By symmetry we have

$$\bar{x} = \bar{y} = 0.$$

We calculate $\bar{z}$:

$$\bar{z} = \frac{\iiint z\, dV}{\iiint dV} = \frac{\int_0^{2\pi} \int_0^a \int_0^{\sqrt{a^2 - r^2}} z\, dz\, r\, dr\, d\theta}{\frac{2}{3}\pi a^3} = \frac{3a}{8}.$$

PROBLEMS

By triple integration, find the volume in each of the following problems.

1. The volume bounded above by the paraboloid $z = 5 - x^2 - y^2$ and below by the paraboloid $z = 4x^2 + 4y^2$.

2. The volume that is bounded above by the paraboloid $z = 9 - x^2 - y^2$, below by the xy-plane, and that lies *outside* the cylinder $x^2 + y^2 = 1$.

3. The volume cut from the sphere $x^2 + y^2 + z^2 = 4a^2$ by the cylinder $x^2 + y^2 = a^2$.

4. The volume bounded below by the paraboloid $z = x^2 + y^2$ and above by the plane $z = 2y$.

5. The volume bounded above by the sphere $x^2 + y^2 + z^2 = 2a^2$ and below by the paraboloid $az = x^2 + y^2$.

6. The volume in the first octant bounded by the cylinder $x^2 + y^2 = a^2$ and the planes $x = a, y = a, z = 0, z = x + y$.

The mass, center of gravity, and moments of inertia of a mass M distributed over a region V of xyz-space and having density $\delta = \delta(x, y, z)$ at the point (x, y, z) of V (see Fig. 14–16) are given by integrals of the type

$$M = \iiint \delta\, dV, \tag{1}$$

$$\bar{x} = \frac{\iiint x\, \delta\, dV}{\iiint \delta\, dV}, \tag{2}$$

$$I_z = \iiint (x^2 + y^2)\, \delta\, dV, \tag{3}$$

14-7

PHYSICAL APPLICATIONS OF TRIPLE INTEGRATION

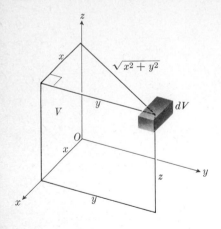

14–16 Distances of dV from the coordinate planes and the z-axis.

with similar integrals for $\bar{y}$, $\bar{z}$, I_x, and I_y. The integrals in Eqs. (1) through (3) may be evaluated as triple integrals with

$$dV = dz\, dy\, dx$$

or, if it is more convenient to use cylindrical coordinates,

$$dV = dz\, r\, dr\, d\theta.$$

Limits of integration are to be supplied so that the element of volume ranges over the volume V as discussed above.

EXAMPLE. A solid is bounded below by the xy-plane, above by the sphere $x^2 + y^2 + z^2 = 4a^2$, and laterally by the cylinder $r = 2a \cos \theta$. Find its moment of inertia I_z.

Solution. The solid lies in front of the yz-plane, as shown in Fig. 14–17. It projects orthogonally into the interior of the circle $r = 2a \cos \theta$ in the xy-plane. Taking an element of volume $dV = dz\, r\, dr\, d\theta$ enclosing a point r, θ, z, we have

$$dI_z = r^2\, dV = dz\, r^3\, dr\, d\theta.$$

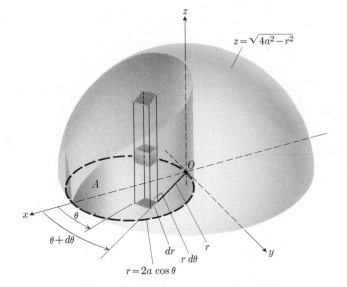

14–17 The solid bounded by the xy-plane, the sphere $x^2 + y^2 + z^2 = 4a^2$, and the cylinder $r = 2a \cos \theta$.

When we integrate with respect to z, we use as lower limit $z = 0$ (the plane) and as upper limit $z = \sqrt{4a^2 - r^2}$ (the sphere). This integral gives the moment of inertia of the elements dV in a prism extending from the xy-plane to the sphere and having its base inside the circle $r = 2a \cos \theta$. In order to add the moments of all of the prisms, we examine this region by itself to see what the appropriate r and θ limits are. If we were finding only the *area* of this region (Fig. 14–17), we would have

$$A = \int_{-\pi/2}^{\pi/2} \int_{0}^{2a \cos \theta} r\, dr\, d\theta.$$

In the present problem, we are finding the moment of inertia I_z of a solid standing on this area as a base, but *the same limits of integration* apply to the r and θ integrations. Therefore

$$I_z = \int_{-\pi/2}^{\pi/2} \int_0^{2a\cos\theta} \int_0^{\sqrt{4a^2-r^2}} dz\, r^3\, dr\, d\theta = \frac{64a^5}{15}\left[\pi - \frac{26}{15}\right].$$

PROBLEMS

1. Find the moment of inertia about the x-axis for the volume of Problem 3, Article 14–6.

2. Find the moment of inertia about the z-axis for the volume of Problem 4, Article 14–6.

3. Find the x-coordinate of the center of gravity of the volume of Problem 7, Article 14–5.

4. Find the center of gravity of the volume of Problem 3, Article 14–6.

5. Use cylindrical coordinates to find the moment of inertia of a sphere of radius a and mass M about a diameter.

6. Find the volume generated by rotating the cardioid $r = a(1 - \cos\theta)$ about the x-axis. [*Hint.* Use *double* integration. Rotate an area element dA around the x-axis to generate a volume element dV.]

7. Find the moment of inertia, about the x-axis, of the volume of Problem 6.

8. Find the moment of inertia of a right circular cone of base radius a, altitude h, and mass M about an axis through the vertex and parallel to the base.

9. Find the moment of inertia of a sphere of radius a and mass M with respect to a tangent line.

10. Find the center of gravity of that portion of the volume of the sphere $r^2 + z^2 = a^2$ that lies between the planes $\theta = -(\pi/4)$ and $\theta = \pi/4$.

11. A torus of mass M is generated by rotating a circle of radius a about an axis in its plane at distance b from the center (b greater than a). Find its moment of inertia about the axis of revolution.

In a problem where there is symmetry with respect to a point, it may be convenient to choose that point as origin and to use spherical coordinates (Fig. 14–18). These are related to the cartesian system by the equations

$$x = \rho \sin\phi \cos\theta, \qquad y = \rho \sin\phi \sin\theta, \qquad z = \rho \cos\phi. \qquad (1)$$

14–8

SPHERICAL COORDINATES

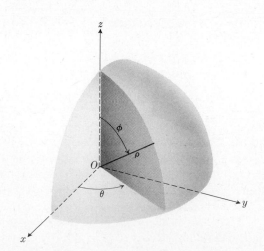

14–18 Spherical coordinates.

If we give ρ, ϕ, and θ increments $d\rho$, $d\phi$, and $d\theta$, we are led to consider the volume element (Fig. 14–19).

$$dV_{\rho\phi\theta} = d\rho \cdot \rho \, d\phi \cdot \rho \sin \phi \, d\theta = \rho^2 \sin \phi \, d\rho \, d\phi \, d\theta \qquad (2)$$

and triple integrals of the form

$$\iiint F(\rho, \phi, \theta)\rho^2 \sin \phi \, d\rho \, d\phi \, d\theta. \qquad (3)$$

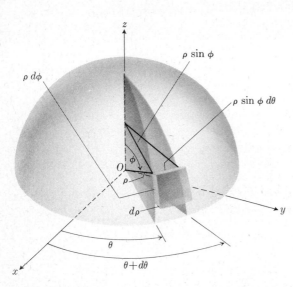

14–19 The volume element in spherical coordinates is $dV = d\rho \cdot \rho \, d\phi \cdot \rho \sin \phi \, d\theta$.

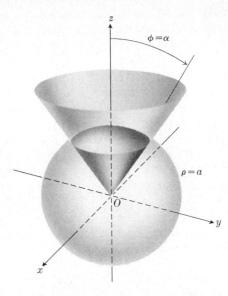

14–20 The volume cut from the sphere $\rho = a$ by the cone $\phi = \alpha$.

EXAMPLE. Find the volume cut from the sphere $\rho = a$ by the cone $\phi = \alpha$. (See Fig. 14–20.)

Solution. The volume is given by

$$V = \int_0^{2\pi} \int_0^{\alpha} \int_0^{a} \rho^2 \sin \phi \, d\rho \, d\phi \, d\theta = \frac{2\pi a^3}{3}(1 - \cos \alpha).$$

As a check, we note that the special cases $\alpha = \pi/2$ and $\alpha = \pi$ correspond to the cases of a hemisphere and a sphere, of volumes $2\pi a^3/3$ and $4\pi a^3/3$, respectively.

PROBLEMS

1. Find the volume cut from the sphere $\rho = 2$ by the plane $z = \sqrt{2}$.

2. Find the center of gravity of the volume (which resembles a filled ice cream cone) that is bounded above by the sphere $\rho = a$ and below by the cone $\phi = \pi/6$.

3. Find the volume enclosed by the surface $\rho = a(1 - \cos \phi)$. Compare with Problem 6, Article 14–7.

4. Find the radius of gyration, with respect to a diameter, of a spherical shell of mass M bounded by the spheres $\rho = a$ and $\rho = 2a$ if the density is $\delta = \rho^2$.

5. Sketch the space curve $\rho = 1$, $\phi = \theta$ for $0 \le \theta \le \pi/2$. Label the point $(\rho, \phi, \theta) = (1, 0, 0)$.

Let G be a region of the xy-plane and let the function

$$z = f(x, y), \qquad (x, y) \in G, \tag{1}$$

14–9
SURFACE AREA

together with its first partial derivatives, be continuous in G. For simplicity, suppose that the surface represented by Eq. (1) has a normal $\mathbf{N}$ that is never parallel to the xy-plane. The area of the surface may then be computed in the following way:

Divide the region G into rectangles of dimensions Δx by Δy, by a grid of lines parallel to the x- and y-axes. Project a typical rectangle of area

$$\Delta A = \Delta y \, \Delta x \tag{2}$$

vertically upward onto the surface and call the corresponding area on the surface ΔS. (See Fig. 14–21.) Choose any point Q on ΔS and consider the plane tangent to the surface at Q. Project the area ΔA vertically upward onto the plane tangent to S at Q. Call the corresponding area in the tangent plane ΔP. We use ΔP to approximate ΔS. If this procedure is carried out for all of the pieces of area ΔA lying in G, and we add all the pieces of area ΔP, the result will approximate the total surface area S. That is,

$$S \approx \sum \Delta P. \tag{3}$$

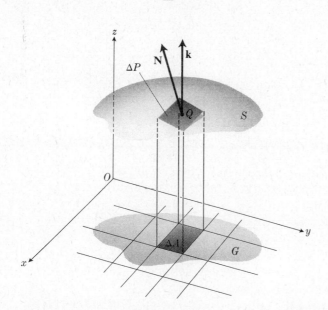

14–21 The area ΔP is the projection of ΔA in G onto the plane tangent to the surface S at the arbitrarily chosen point Q.

The approximation improves as Δx and Δy approach zero. We take the limit of the sum in (3) as the *definition of the surface area* S. That is,

$$S = \lim_{\Delta x, \Delta y \to 0} \sum_G \Delta P. \tag{4}$$

To calculate S we need an analytic expression for ΔP as a function of x, y, Δx, and Δy. Let

$$(x, y, 0), \qquad (x + \Delta x, y, 0), \qquad (x, y + \Delta y, 0),$$

and

$$(x + \Delta x, y + \Delta y, 0)$$

be the corners of the rectangle in G whose area ΔA projects onto the area ΔP in the tangent plane (Fig. 14–22). For simplicity, let Q be the point $(x, y, f(x, y))$ on the surface (1). Let $\mathbf{u}, \mathbf{v}$ be vectors from Q forming two adjacent sides of the parallelogram whose area is ΔP. Then

$$\mathbf{u} = \mathbf{i}\,\Delta x + \mathbf{k}\,f_x(x, y)\,\Delta x,$$

$$\mathbf{v} = \mathbf{j}\,\Delta y + \mathbf{k}\,f_y(x, y)\,\Delta y.$$

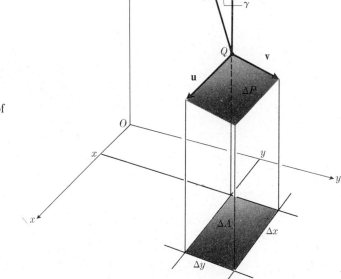

14–22   The area $\Delta P = |\mathbf{u} \times \mathbf{v}|$ is the projection of ΔA onto the tangent plane at Q: $\Delta P = \Delta A/\cos \gamma$.

A vector normal to the surface at Q, with magnitude equal to the area ΔP, is

$$\mathbf{N} = \mathbf{u} \times \mathbf{v} = \begin{vmatrix} \mathbf{i} & \mathbf{j} & \mathbf{k} \\ \Delta x & 0 & f_x(x, y)\,\Delta x \\ 0 & \Delta y & f_y(x, y)\,\Delta y \end{vmatrix}$$

$$= \Delta x\,\Delta y(-\mathbf{i}f_x(x, y) - \mathbf{j}f_y(x, y) + \mathbf{k}). \tag{5}$$

Therefore,

$$\Delta P = |\mathbf{u} \times \mathbf{v}| = \Delta x\,\Delta y\sqrt{f_x^2(x, y) + f_y^2(x, y) + 1}. \tag{6}$$

Equations (4) and (6) together say that the area of the surface S above the region G in the xy-plane is given by the integral

$$S = \int_G \int \sqrt{\left(\frac{\partial f}{\partial x}\right)^2 + \left(\frac{\partial f}{\partial y}\right)^2 + 1}\; dx\, dy. \tag{7}$$

EXAMPLE 1.   Find the surface area S of the paraboloid $z = x^2 + y^2$ below the plane $z = 1$.

Solution. The surface area S projects onto the interior G of the circle

$$x^2 + y^2 = 1,$$

in the xy-plane (Fig. 14–23). Here

$$z = f(x, y) = x^2 + y^2,$$

so that

$$\frac{\partial f}{\partial x} = 2x, \qquad \frac{\partial f}{\partial y} = 2y$$

and

$$S = \iint\limits_{x^2 + y^2 \le 1} \sqrt{4x^2 + 4y^2 + 1} \; dy \; dx. \qquad \textbf{(8)}$$

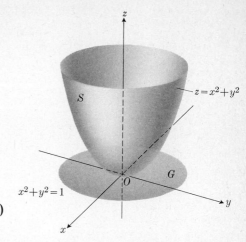

14–23 The area of the parabolic surface above is calculated in Example 1.

Now the double integral (8) is easier to evaluate in polar coordinates, since the combination $x^2 + y^2$ may be replaced by r^2. Taking the element of area to be

$$dA = r \; dr \; d\theta$$

in place of $dy \; dx$, we thus have

$$S = \iint\limits_{r^2 \le 1} \sqrt{4r^2 + 1} \, r \; dr \; d\theta$$

$$= \int_0^{2\pi} \int_0^1 \sqrt{4r^2 + 1} \, r \; dr \; d\theta = \frac{\pi}{6}(5\sqrt{5} - 1).$$

Another expression for surface area may be found by applying Eq. (12a), Article 11–9, which says that

$$(\mathbf{u} \times \mathbf{v}) \cdot \mathbf{k} = \text{area of projection of } \Delta P \text{ in } xy\text{-plane.}$$

This also agrees with Eq. (5), above, which gives

$$(\mathbf{u} \times \mathbf{v}) \cdot \mathbf{k} = \Delta x \, \Delta y = \Delta A. \qquad \textbf{(9a)}$$

From the definition of the dot product, we also know that

$$(\mathbf{u} \times \mathbf{v}) \cdot \mathbf{k} = |\mathbf{u} \times \mathbf{v}| \, |\mathbf{k}| \cos \gamma \qquad \textbf{(9b)}$$

$$= \Delta P \cos \gamma,$$

where γ is the angle between $\mathbf{N} = \mathbf{u} \times \mathbf{v}$ and $\mathbf{k}$. Equations (9a) and (9b) give the result

$$\Delta P = \frac{\Delta A}{\cos \gamma}, \qquad \textbf{(10)}$$

and from Eqs. (4) and (10) we have

$$S = \int_G \int \frac{dA}{\cos \gamma}. \qquad \textbf{(11)}$$

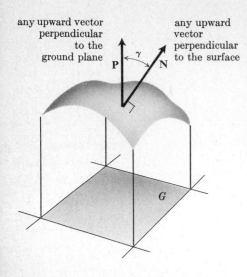

any upward vector perpendicular to the ground plane

any upward vector perpendicular to the surface

14–24 Surface area: $\iint\limits_{G} (dA/\cos \gamma)$.

Equation 11 does not depend on which particular coordinates are used in the ground plane above which the surface lies. The essential ingredient is that γ be the angle between some upward normal $\mathbf{N}$ to the surface and some upward vector $\mathbf{p}$ perpendicular to the ground plane, as shown in Fig. 14–24. If the surface is given by

$$F(x, y, z) = 0,$$

then $\pm\nabla F$ will do for $\mathbf{N}$ (Article 13–6), and we may take

$$\cos \gamma = \frac{|\nabla F \cdot \mathbf{p}|}{|\nabla F| \, |\mathbf{p}|}. \tag{12}$$

If we choose $\mathbf{p}$ to be a unit vector, then Eq. (12) simplifies to

$$\cos \gamma = \frac{|\nabla F \cdot \mathbf{p}|}{|\nabla F|}. \tag{13}$$

With this expression substituted for $\cos \gamma$ in Eq. (11), we get

$$S = \iint\limits_{G} \frac{dA}{\cos \gamma} = \iint\limits_{G} \frac{|\nabla F|}{|\nabla F \cdot \mathbf{p}|} \, dA. \tag{14}$$

EXAMPLE 2.   Evaluate Eq. (14) for the surface

$$z = f(x, y), \qquad (x, y) \in G,$$

of Eq. (1).

Solution.   We take

$$F(x, y, z) = z - f(x, y) = 0.$$

Then,

$$\nabla F = F_x\mathbf{i} + F_y\mathbf{j} + F_z\mathbf{k}$$
$$= -f_x\mathbf{i} - f_y\mathbf{j} + \mathbf{k},$$

and

$$|\nabla F| = \sqrt{f_x^2 + f_y^2 + 1}.$$

The upward unit normal to the ground plane is $\mathbf{p} = \mathbf{k}$, so that

$$\nabla F \cdot \mathbf{p} = \nabla F \cdot \mathbf{k} = 1.$$

Substituting these values for $|\nabla F|$ and $\nabla F \cdot \mathbf{p}$ in Eq. (14) gives

$$S = \iint\limits_{G} \frac{|\nabla F|}{|\nabla F \cdot \mathbf{p}|} \, dA$$

$$= \iint\limits_{G} \sqrt{f_x^2 + f_y^2 + 1} \, dx \, dy.$$

Thus we have recovered Eq. (7).

PROBLEMS

1. Use the method of Example 2 to derive the following formulas.

a) The area of a smooth surface $x = f(y, z)$ above a region G in the yz-plane is

$$S = \iint\limits_{G} \sqrt{f_y^2 + f_z^2 + 1} \; dy \; dz.$$

b) The area of a smooth surface $y = f(x, z)$ above a region G in the xz-plane is

$$S = \iint\limits_{G} \sqrt{f_x^2 + f_z^2 + 1} \; dx \; dz.$$

2. Find, by integration, the area of the triangle cut from the plane $x/a + y/b + z/c = 1$ by the coordinate planes. Check your answer by vector methods.

3. Find, by integration, the area of that portion of the surface of the sphere $x^2 + y^2 + z^2 = a^2$ that lies in the first octant.

4. Find the area of the surface of that portion of the sphere $x^2 + y^2 + z^2 = 4a^2$ that lies inside the cylinder $x^2 + y^2 = 2ax$. (Figure 14–17 shows the top half.)

5. Find the area cut from the paraboloid $z = 9 - x^2 - y^2$ by the planes $z = 0$, $z = 8$.

6. Find the area of that portion of the sphere $x^2 + y^2 + z^2 = 2a^2$ that is cut out by the upper nappe of the cone $x^2 + y^2 = z^2$.

7. Find the area cut from the plane $z = cx$ by the cylinder $x^2 + y^2 = a^2$.

8. Find the area of that portion of the cylinder $x^2 + z^2 = a^2$ that lies between the planes $y = \pm a/2$, $x = \pm a/2$.

9. Find the area cut from the surface $az = y^2 - x^2$ by the cylinder $x^2 + y^2 = a^2$.

10. Find the area of that portion of the cylinder in Problem 4 that lies inside the sphere. [*Hint.* Project the area into the xz-plane. Or use single integration, $\int h \, ds$, where h is the altitude of the cylinder and ds is the element of arc length in the xy-plane.]

REVIEW QUESTIONS AND EXERCISES

1. Define the double integral of a function of two variables. What geometric interpretation may be given to the integral?

2. List four applications of multiple integration.

3. Define *moment of inertia* and *radius of gyration*.

4. How does a double integral in polar coordinates differ from a double integral in cartesian coordinates? In what way are they alike?

5. What are the fundamental volume elements for triple integrals (a) in cartesian coordinates, (b) in cylindrical coordinates, (c) in spherical coordinates?

6. How is surface area defined? Which formula of Article 14–9 is the most general one for computing surface area, in the sense that it includes many others as special cases?

7. How would you define $\iint_S F \, dS$, when S is a surface in space and F is a function defined at points on the surface? Illustrate when S is the hemisphere

$$z = \sqrt{1 - x^2 - y^2},$$
$$x^2 + y^2 \leq 1,$$

and

$$F(x, y, z) = z.$$

What is the geometrical interpretation of $\iint z \, dS$?

MISCELLANEOUS PROBLEMS

1. Reverse the order of integration and evaluate $\int_0^4 \int_{-\sqrt{4-y}}^{(y-4)/2} dx \, dy$.

2. Sketch the region over which the integral $\int_0^1 \int_{\sqrt{y}}^{2-\sqrt{y}} xy \, dx \, dy$ is to be evaluated and find its value.

3. The integral $\int_{-1}^{1} \int_{x^2}^{1} dy \, dx$ represents the area of a region of the xy-plane. Sketch the region and express the same area as a double integral with the order of integration reversed.

4. The base of a pile of sand covers the region in the xy-plane that is bounded by the parabola $x^2 + y = 6$ and the line $y = x$. The depth of the sand above the point (x, y)

is x^2. Sketch the base of the sand pile and a representative element of volume dV, and find the volume of sand in the pile by double integration.

5. In setting up a double integral for the volume V under the paraboloid $z = x^2 + y^2$ and above a certain region R of the xy-plane, the following sum of iterated integrals was obtained:

$$V = \int_0^1 \left(\int_0^y (x^2 + y^2) \, dx \right) dy + \int_1^2 \left(\int_0^{2-y} (x^2 + y^2) \, dx \right) dy.$$

Sketch the region R in the xy-plane and express V as an iterated integral in which the order of integration is reversed.

6. By change of order of integration, show that the following double integral can be reduced to a single integral

$$\int_0^x du \int_0^u e^{m(x-t)}f(t)\, dt = \int_0^x (x-t)e^{m(x-t)}f(t)\, dt.$$

Similarly, it can be shown that

$$\int_0^x dv \int_0^v du \int_0^u e^{m(x-t)}f(t)\, dt = \int_0^x \frac{(x-t)^2}{2!}\, e^{m(x-t)}f(t)\, dt.$$

Evaluate integrals for the case $f(t) = \cos at$. (This example illustrates that such reductions usually make calculation easier.)

7. Sometimes a multiple integral with variable limits may be changed into one with constant limits. By changing the order of integration, show that

$$\int_0^1 f(x)\, dx \int_0^x \log(x-y)f(y)\, dy$$

$$= \int_0^1 f(y)\, dy \int_y^1 \log(x-y)\ f(x)\, dx$$

$$= \tfrac{1}{2} \int_0^1 \int_0^1 \log|x-y|\, f(x)\ f(y)\, dx\, dy.$$

8. Evaluate the integral

$$\int_0^\infty \frac{e^{-ax} - e^{-bx}}{x}\, dx.$$

[*Hint.* Use the relation

$$\frac{e^{-ax} - e^{-bx}}{x} = \int_a^b e^{-xy}\, dy$$

to form a double integral, and evaluate it by change of the order of integration.]

9. By double integration, find the center of gravity of that part of the area of the circle $x^2 + y^2 = a^2$ contained in the first quadrant.

10. Determine the centroid of the plane area that is given in polar coordinates by $0 \le r \le a$, $-\alpha \le \theta \le \alpha$.

11. Find the centroid of the area bounded by the lines $\theta = 0°$ and $\theta = 45°$, and by the circles $r = 1$ and $r = 2$.

12. By double integration, find the center of gravity of the area between the parabola $x + y^2 - 2y = 0$ and the line $x + 2y = 0$.

13. For a solid body of constant density, having its center of gravity at the origin, show that the moment of inertia about an axis parallel to Oz through (x_0, y_0) is equal to the moment of inertia about Oz plus $M(x_0^2 + y_0^2)$, where M is the mass of the body.

14. Find the moment of inertia of the angle section shown in Fig. 14–25, (a) with respect to the horizontal base; (b) with respect to a horizontal line through its centroid.

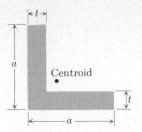

Figure 14–25

15. Show that, for a uniform elliptic lamina of semiaxes a, b, the moment of inertia about an axis in its plane through the center of the ellipse making an angle α with the axis of length $2a$ is $\tfrac{1}{4}M(a^2 \sin^2 \alpha + b^2 \cos^2 \alpha)$, where M is the mass of the lamina.

16. A counterweight of a flywheel has the form of the smaller segment cut from a circle of radius a by a chord at a distance b from the center $(b < a)$. Find the area of this counterweight and its polar moment of inertia about the center of the circle.

17. The radius of gyration of a body with volume V is defined by $K = \sqrt{I/V}$, where K and its moment of inertia I are referred to the same axis. Consider an ellipse $(x^2/a^2) + (y^2/b^2) = 1$ revolving about the x-axis to generate an ellipsoid. Find the radius of gyration of the ellipsoid with respect to the x-axis.

18. Find the radii of gyration about $\theta = 0$ and $\theta = \pi/2$ for the area of a loop of the curve $r^2 = a^2 \cos 2\theta$, $(a > 0)$.

19. The hydrostatic pressure at a depth y in a fluid is wy. Taking the x-axis in the surface of the fluid and the y-axis vertically downward, consider a semicircular lamina, radius a, completely immersed with its bounding diameter horizontal, uppermost, and at a depth c. Show that the depth of the center of pressure is

$$\frac{3\pi a^2 + 32ac + 12\pi c^2}{4(4a + 3\pi c)}.$$

The center of pressure is defined as the point where the entire hydrostatic force could be concentrated so as to produce the same first moment of force.

20. Show that

$$\iint \frac{\partial^2 F(x, y)}{\partial x\, \partial y}\, dx\, dy$$

over the rectangle $x_0 \le x \le x_1$, $y_0 \le y \le y_1$, is

$$F(x_1, y_1) - F(x_0, y_1) - F(x_1, y_0) + F(x_0, y_0).$$

21. Change the following double integral to an equivalent double integral in polar coordinates, and sketch the region of integration.

$$\int_{-a}^a \int_0^{\sqrt{a^2-y^2}} x\, dx\, dy.$$

22. A customary method of evaluating the improper integral $I = \int_0^\infty e^{-x^2}\,dx$ is to calculate its square,

$$I^2 = \left(\int_0^\infty e^{-x^2}\,dx\right)\left(\int_0^\infty e^{-y^2}\,dy\right) = \int_0^\infty \int_0^\infty e^{-(x^2+y^2)}\,dx\,dy.$$

Introduce polar coordinates in the last expression and show that

$$I = \int_0^\infty e^{-x^2}\,dx = \frac{\sqrt{\pi}}{2}.$$

23. By transformation of variables $u = x - y$, $v = y$, show that

$$\int_0^\infty e^{-sx}\,dx \int_0^x f(x-y, y)\,dy = \int_0^\infty \int_0^\infty e^{-s(u+v)}f(u, v)\,du\,dv.$$

24. How must a, b, c be chosen in order that $\int_{-\infty}^\infty \int_{-\infty}^\infty e^{-(ax^2+2bxy+cy^2)}\,dx\,dy = 1$? [*Hint.* Introduce the transformation

$$\xi = \alpha x + \beta y, \qquad \eta = \gamma x + \delta y$$

where $(\alpha\delta - \beta\gamma)^2 = ac - b^2$; then

$$ax^2 + 2bxy + cy^2 = \xi^2 + \eta^2.]$$

25. Find the area enclosed by the lemniscate $r^2 = 2a^2 \cos 2\theta$. Also find the moment of inertia of this area about the y-axis.

26. Evaluate the integral

$$\iint \frac{dx\,dy}{(1 + x^2 + y^2)^2}$$

taken (a) over one loop of the lemniscate $(x^2 + y^2)^2 - (x^2 - y^2) = 0$, (b) over the triangle with vertices $(0, 0)$, $(2, 0)$, $(1, \sqrt{3})$. [*Hint.* Transform to polar coordinates.]

27. Show, by transforming to polar coordinates, that

$$K(a) = \int_0^{a\sin\beta} dy \int_{y\cot\beta}^{\sqrt{a^2-y^2}} \ln(x^2 + y^2)\,dx = a^2\beta(\ln a - \tfrac{1}{2}),$$

where $0 < \beta < \pi/2$. Changing the order of integration, what expression do you obtain?

28. Find the volume bounded by the cylinder $y = \cos x$ and the planes

$$z = y, \qquad x = 0, \qquad x = \pi/2, \qquad \text{and} \qquad z = 0.$$

29. Find the center of mass of the homogeneous pyramid whose base is the square enclosed by the lines $x = 1$, $x = -1$, $y = 1$, $y = -1$, in the plane $z = 0$, and whose vertex is at the point $(0, 0, 1)$.

30. Find the volume bounded above by the sphere $x^2 + y^2 + z^2 = 2a^2$ and below by the paraboloid $az = x^2 + y^2$.

31. Find the volume bounded by the surfaces

$$z = x^2 + y^2 \qquad \text{and} \qquad z = \tfrac{1}{2}(x^2 + y^2 + 1).$$

32. Determine by triple integration the volume enclosed by the two surfaces $x = y^2 + z^2$ and $x = 1 - y^2$.

33. Find the moment of inertia, with respect to the z-axis, of a solid that is bounded below by the paraboloid $3az = x^2 + y^2$ and above by the sphere $x^2 + y^2 + z^2 = 4a^2$, if its density is constant.

34. Find by integration the volume of the ellipsoid

$$\frac{x^2}{a^2} + \frac{y^2}{b^2} + \frac{z^2}{c^2} = 1.$$

35. Evaluate the integral $\iiint |xyz|\,dx\,dy\,dz$ taken throughout the ellipsoid $x^2/a^2 + y^2/b^2 + z^2/c^2 \le 1$. [*Hint.* Introduce new coordinates:

$$x = a\xi, \qquad y = b\eta, \qquad z = c\zeta.]$$

36. Two cylinders of radius a have their axes along the x- and y-axes, respectively. Find the volume that they have in common.

37. The volume of a certain solid is given by the triple integral

$$\int_0^2 \left[\int_0^{\sqrt{2x-x^2}} \left(\int_{-\sqrt{4-x^2-y^2}}^{\sqrt{4-x^2-y^2}} dz \right) dy \right] dx.$$

(a) Describe the solid by giving the equations of all the surfaces that form its boundary. (b) Express the volume as a triple integral in cylindrical coordinates. Give the limits of integration explicitly, but do not evaluate the integral.

38. A square hole of side $2b$ is cut symmetrically through a sphere of radius a $(a > b\sqrt{2})$. Find the volume removed.

39. A hole is bored through a sphere, the axis of the hole being a diameter of the sphere. The volume of the solid remaining is given by the integral

$$V = 2\int_0^{2\pi} \int_0^{\sqrt{3}} \int_1^{\sqrt{4-z^2}} r\,dr\,dz\,d\theta,$$

(a) By inspecting the given integral, determine the radius of the hole and the radius of the sphere. (b) Calculate the numerical value of the integral.

40. Set up an equivalent triple integral in rectangular coordinates. (Arrange the order so that the first integration is with respect to z, the second with respect to y, and the last with respect to x.)

$$\int_0^{\pi/2} \int_1^{\sqrt{3}} \int_1^{\sqrt{4-r^2}} r^3 \sin\theta \cos\theta\, z^2\,dz\,dr\,d\theta.$$

41. Find the volume bounded by the plane $z = 0$, the cylinder $x^2 + y^2 = a^2$, and the cylinder $az = a^2 - x^2$.

42. Find the volume of that portion of the sphere $r^2 + z^2 = a^2$ that is inside the cylinder $r = a \sin \theta$. (Here r, θ, z are cylindrical coordinates.)

43. Find the moment of inertia, about the z-axis, of the volume that is bounded above by the sphere $\rho = a$ and below by the cone $\phi = \pi/3$. (ρ, ϕ, θ are spherical coordinates.)

44. Find the volume enclosed by the surface $\rho = a \sin \phi$, in spherical coordinates.

45. Find the moment of inertia of the solid of constant density δ bounded by two concentric spheres of radii a and b ($a < b$), about a diameter.

46. Let S be a solid homogeneous sphere of radius a, constant density δ, mass $M = \frac{4}{3}\pi a^3 \delta$. Let P be a particle of mass m situated at distance b ($b > a$) from the center of S. According to Newton, the force of gravitational attraction of the sphere for P is given by the equation

$$\mathbf{F} = \gamma m \iiint \frac{\mathbf{u} \, \delta \, dV}{r^2},$$

where γ is the gravitational constant, $\mathbf{u}$ is a unit vector in the direction from P toward the volume element dV in S, r^2 is the square of the distance from P to dV, and the integration is extended throughout S. Take the origin at the center of the sphere and P at $(0, 0, b)$ on the z-axis, and show that $\mathbf{F} = -(\gamma Mm/b^2)\mathbf{k}$. [*Remark.* This result shows that the force is the same as it would be if all the mass of the sphere were concentrated at its center.]

47. The density at P, a point of a solid sphere of radius a and center O, is given to be

$$\rho_0\{1 + \epsilon \cos \theta + \tfrac{1}{2}\epsilon^2(3 \cos \theta - 1)\},$$

where θ is the angle OP makes with a fixed radius OQ, and ρ_0 and ϵ are constants. Find the average density of the sphere.

48. Find the area of the surface $y^2 + z^2 = 2x$ cut off by the plane $x = 1$.

49. Find the area cut from the plane $x + y + z = 1$ by the cylinder $x^2 + y^2 = 1$.

50. Find the area above the xy-plane cut from the cone $x^2 + y^2 = z^2$ by the cylinder $x^2 + y^2 = 2ax$.

51. Find the surface area of that portion of the sphere $r^2 + z^2 = a^2$ that is inside the cylinder $r = a \sin \theta$. (r, θ, z are cylindrical coordinates.)

52. The cylinder $x^2 + y^2 = 2x$ cuts out a portion of a surface S from the upper nappe of the cone $x^2 + y^2 = z^2$. Compute the value of the surface integral

$$\iint_S (x^4 - y^4 + y^2z^2 - z^2x^2 + 1) \, dS.$$

53. The sphere $x^2 + y^2 + z^2 = 25$ is cut by the plane $z = 3$, the smaller portion cut off forming a solid V, which is bounded by a closed surface S_0 made up of two parts, the spherical part S_1 and the planar part S_2. If $(\cos \alpha)\mathbf{i} + (\cos \beta)\mathbf{j} + (\cos \gamma)\mathbf{k}$ is the unit outer normal of S_0, find the value of the surface integral

$$\iint_S (xz \cos \alpha + yz \cos \beta + \cos \gamma) \, dS$$

(a) if S is the spherical cap S_1; (b) if S is the planar base S_2; (c) if S is the complete boundary S_0.

54. Obtain the double integral expressing the surface area cut from the cylinder $z = a^2 - y^2$ by the cylinder $x^2 + y^2 = a^2$, and reduce this double integral to a definite single integral with respect to the variable y.

55. A square hole of side $2\sqrt{2}$ is cut symmetrically through a sphere of radius 2. Show that the area of the surface removed is $16\pi(\sqrt{2} - 1)$.

56. A torus surface is generated by moving a sphere of unit radius whose center travels on a closed plane circle of radius 2. Calculate the area of this surface.

57. Calculate the area of the surface $(x^2 + y^2 + z^2)^2 = x^2 - y^2$. [*Hint.* Use polar coordinates.]

58. Calculate the area of the spherical part of the boundary of the region

$$x^2 + y^2 + z^2 = r^2, \quad x^2 + y^2 - rx \geq 0, \quad x^2 + y^2 + rx \geq 0.$$

[*Hint.* Integrate first with respect to x and y.]

59. Prove that the potential of a circular disk of mass m per unit area, and of radius a, at a point distant h from the center and on the normal to the disk through the center, is $2\pi m(\sqrt{(a^2 + h^2)} - h)$. (The potential at a point P due to a mass Δm at Q is $\Delta m/r$, where r is the distance from P to Q.)

60. Find the attraction, at the vertex, of a solid right circular cone of mass M, height h, and radius of base a. (The attraction at P due to a mass Δm at Q is $(\Delta m/r^2)\mathbf{u}$, where r is the distance from P to Q, and $\mathbf{u}$ is a unit vector in the direction of $\overrightarrow{PQ}$.)

61. The solid angle sustained by a surface Σ bounded by a closed curve is defined with respect to the origin as

$$\Omega = \left| \iint_\Sigma \frac{\cos \theta}{r^2} \, dS \right|,$$

where the area element dS is located at the end of the position vector $\mathbf{R}$, θ is the angle between $\mathbf{R}$ and the normal to dS, and $r = |\mathbf{R}|$. Show that, in cartesian coordinates,

$$\Omega = \left| \iint_\Sigma \frac{x \, dy \, dz + y \, dz \, dx + z \, dx \, dy}{(x^2 + y^2 + z^2)^{3/2}} \right|.$$

62. Prove by direct integration that

$$\int_{-\infty}^{\infty} \int_{-\infty}^{\infty} \frac{dx \, dy}{(x^2 + y^2 + 1)^{3/2}} = 2\pi.$$

Interpret this integral as a solid angle sustained by a surface. What surface is this?

63. Show that the average distance of the points of the surface of a sphere of radius a from a point on the surface is $4a/3$.

15

VECTOR ANALYSIS

15–1

INTRODUCTION: VECTOR FIELDS

Suppose that a certain region G of 3-space is occupied by a moving fluid: air, for example, or water. We may imagine that the fluid is made up of an infinite number of particles, and that at time t, the particle that is in position P at that instant has a velocity $\mathbf{v}$. If we stay at P and observe new particles that pass through it, we shall probably see that they have different velocities. This would surely be true, for example, in turbulent motions caused by high winds or stormy seas. Again, if we could take a picture of the velocities of particles at different places at the same instant, we would expect to find that these velocities vary from place to place. Thus the velocity at position P at time t is, in general, a function of both position and time:

$$\mathbf{v} = \mathbf{F}(x, y, z, t). \tag{1}$$

Equation (1) indicates that the velocity $\mathbf{v}$ is a vector function $\mathbf{F}$ of the four independent variables x, y, z, and t. Such functions have many applications, particularly in treatments of flows of material. In hydrodynamics, for example, if $\delta = \delta(x, y, z, t)$ is the *density* of the fluid at (x, y, z) at time t, and we take $\mathbf{F} = \mathbf{i}u + \mathbf{j}v + \mathbf{k}w$ to be the velocity expressed in terms of components, then we are able to derive the Euler partial differential equation of continuity of motion:

$$\frac{\partial \delta}{\partial t} + \frac{\partial(\delta u)}{\partial x} + \frac{\partial(\delta v)}{\partial y} + \frac{\partial(\delta w)}{\partial z} = 0.$$

(We are not prepared to deal with this subject* in any detail; we mention it as one important field in which the ideas presented in this chapter are applied.) Such functions are also applied in physics and electrical engineering; for example, in the study of propagation of electromagnetic waves. Also, much current research activity in applied mathematics has to do with such functions.

Steady-State Flows

In this chapter, we shall deal only with those flows for which the velocity function, Eq. (1), does not depend on the time t. Such flows are called steady-state flows. They exemplify *vector fields*.

Definition.   *If, to each point P in some region G, a vector $\mathbf{F}(P)$ is assigned, the collection of all such vectors is called a vector field.*

In addition to the vector fields that are associated with fluid flows, there are vector *force* fields that are associated with gravitational attraction, magnetic force fields, electric fields, and purely mathematical fields.

EXAMPLE 1.   Imagine an idealized fluid flowing with steady-state flow in a long cylindrical pipe of radius a, so that particles at distance r from the long axis are moving parallel to the axis with speed $|\mathbf{v}| = a^2 - r^2$ (Fig. 15–1). Describe this field by a formula for $\mathbf{v}$.

---

*   Some of the laws of hydrodynamics can be found in the article "Hydromechanics" in the *Encyclopaedia Britannica*.

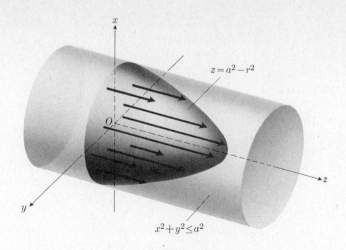

15–1 The flow of fluid in a long cylindrical pipe. The vectors $\mathbf{v} = (a^2 - r^2)\mathbf{k}$ inside the cylinder have their bases in the xy-plane and their tips on the paraboloid $z = a^2 - r^2$.

Solution. Let the z-axis lie along the axis of the pipe, with positive direction in the direction of the flow. Then, in the usual way, introduce a righthanded cartesian coordinate system with unit vectors along the axes. By hypothesis, the $\mathbf{k}$-component of the flow is the only one different from zero, so

$$\mathbf{v} = (a^2 - r^2)\mathbf{k} = (a^2 - x^2 - y^2)\mathbf{k}$$

for points inside the pipe. This vector field is not defined outside the cylinder $x^2 + y^2 = a^2$. If we were to draw the velocity vectors at all points in the disk

$$x^2 + y^2 \leq a^2, \qquad z = 0,$$

their tips would describe the surface

$$z = a^2 - r^2$$

(cylindrical coordinates) for $z \geq 0$. Since this field does not depend on z, a similar figure would illustrate the flow field across any cross section of the pipe made by a plane perpendicular to its axis.

EXAMPLE 2. In another flow, a fluid is rotating about the z-axis with constant angular velocity ω. Hence every particle at a distance r from the z-axis and in a plane perpendicular to the z-axis traces a circle of radius r, and each such particle has constant speed $|\mathbf{v}| = \omega r$. Describe this field by writing an equation for the velocity at $P(x, y, z)$.

Solution. (See Fig. 15–2.) Each particle travels in a circle parallel to the xy-plane. Therefore it is convenient to begin by looking at the projection of such a circle onto this plane. The point $P(x, y, z)$ in space projects onto the image point $P'(x, y, 0)$, and the velocity vector $\mathbf{v}$ of a particle at P projects onto the velocity vector $\mathbf{v}'$ of a particle at P'. We assume that the motion is in the positive, or counterclockwise, direction, as indicated in the figure. The position vector of P' is $\mathbf{R}' = \mathbf{i}x + \mathbf{j}y$, and the vectors $-\mathbf{i}y + \mathbf{j}x$ and $\mathbf{i}y - \mathbf{j}x$ are both perpendicular to $\mathbf{R}'$. All three of these vectors have magnitude

$$\sqrt{x^2 + y^2} = r.$$

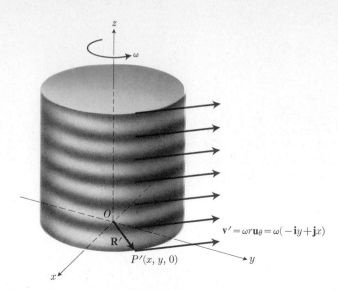

15–2 A steady flow parallel to the xy-plane, with constant angular velocity ω in the positive direction.

The velocity vector we want has magnitude ωr, is perpendicular to $\mathbf{R}'$, and points in the direction of motion. When x and y are both positive (that is, when the particle is in the first quadrant), the velocity should have a negative **i**-component and a positive **j**-component. The vector that has these properties is

$$\mathbf{v}' = \omega r \mathbf{u}_\theta = \omega(-\mathbf{i}y + \mathbf{j}x). \tag{2a}$$

This formula can be verified for P' in the other three quadrants as well; for example, in the third quadrant both x and y are negative, so Eq. (2a) gives a vector with a positive **i**-component and a negative **j**-component, which is correct. Also, because the motion of P is in a circle parallel to that described by P', and has the same velocity, we have

$$\mathbf{v} = \omega(-\mathbf{i}y + \mathbf{j}x) \tag{2b}$$

for any point in the fluid.

EXAMPLE 3. A fluid has a velocity vector, at every point in space, that is the sum of a constant velocity vector parallel to the z-axis and a rotational velocity vector given by Eq. (2b). Describe the field.

Solution. Let the constant component parallel to the z-axis be $c\mathbf{k}$. Then the resultant field is

$$\mathbf{v} = \omega(-\mathbf{i}y + \mathbf{j}x) + c\mathbf{k}. \tag{3}$$

EXAMPLE 4. The gravitational force field induced at the point $P(x, y, z)$ in space by a mass M that is taken to lie at an origin is defined to be the force with which M would attract a particle of *unit* mass at P. Describe this field mathematically, assuming the inverse-square law.

Solution. Because we are now assuming that both M and the unit mass at P are *point* masses, we don't have to integrate anything; we just write down the force:

$$\mathbf{F} = \frac{GM(1)}{|\overrightarrow{OP}|^2}\mathbf{u}, \tag{4a}$$

where G is the gravitational constant, and

$$\mathbf{u} = -\frac{\overrightarrow{OP}}{|\overrightarrow{OP}|}$$

is a unit vector directed *from P toward O*. The position vector of P is $\overrightarrow{OP} = \mathbf{i}x + \mathbf{j}y + \mathbf{k}z$, so we find that

$$\mathbf{F} = \frac{-GM(\mathbf{i}x + \mathbf{j}y + \mathbf{k}z)}{(x^2 + y^2 + z^2)^{3/2}} \tag{4b}$$

gives the gravitational force field in question. Its graph would consist of infinitely many vectors, one starting from each point P (except the origin), and pointing straight toward the origin. If P is near the origin, the associated vector is longer than for points farther away from O. For points P on a ray through the origin, the $\mathbf{F}$-vectors would lie along that same ray, and decrease in length in proportion to the square of the distance from O. Figure 15–3 is a partial representation of this field. As you look at the figure, however, you should also imagine that an $\mathbf{F}$-vector is attached to *every* point $P \neq O$, and not just to those shown. At points on the surface of the sphere $|\overrightarrow{OP}| = a$, the vectors all have the same length, and all point toward the center of the sphere.

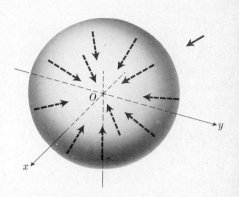

15–3 Some of the vectors of the gravitational field of Example 4.

Mathematically, a vector field $\mathbf{F}(x, y, z)$ need not be a velocity field or a force field. One easy way to construct another kind of vector field is to apply the gradient operator to a scalar function.

EXAMPLE 5. Suppose that the temperature T at each point $P(x, y, z)$ in some region of space is

$$T = 100 - x^2 - y^2 - z^2, \tag{5a}$$

and that $\mathbf{F}(x, y, z)$ is defined to be the gradient of T:

$$\mathbf{F} = \nabla T. \tag{5b}$$

Find this vector field and discuss some of its properties.

Solution. From the definition of grad T we have

$$\mathbf{F} = \nabla T = \operatorname{grad} T = \mathbf{i}\frac{\partial T}{\partial x} + \mathbf{j}\frac{\partial T}{\partial y} + \mathbf{k}\frac{\partial T}{\partial z}$$

$$= -2x\mathbf{i} - 2y\mathbf{j} - 2z\mathbf{k} \tag{5c}$$

$$= -2\mathbf{R},$$

where

$$\mathbf{R} = \overrightarrow{OP} = \mathbf{i}x + \mathbf{j}y + \mathbf{k}z$$

is the position vector of $P(x, y, z)$. This field is like a central force field, all vectors $\mathbf{F}$ being directed toward the origin. At points on a sphere with $|\overrightarrow{OP}|$

equal to a constant, the magnitude of the field vectors is a constant equal to twice the radius of the sphere. So, to represent the field, we could construct any sphere with center at O and draw a vector from any point P on the surface straight through O to the other side of the sphere. The collection of all such vectors, for points in the domain of the function T of Eq. (5a), constitutes the *gradient field* of this particular scalar function.

REMARK.   An *isothermal* surface for Eq. (5a) is any surface on which T is constant. For Example 5, such a surface would be any sphere with center at the origin and radius $\sqrt{100 - T}$. Our calculation of $\mathbf{F} = \nabla T = -2\mathbf{R}$ has verified that the gradient of T at P is *normal* to the isothermal surface through P, because the diameter of such a spherical surface is always normal to the surface. [See Fig. 13–21(b) for the general picture of grad f normal to the surface $f =$ constant.]

PROBLEMS

1. In Example 1, where is the speed (a) the greatest? (b) the least?

2. Suppose the density of the fluid is $\delta =$ constant at $P(x, y, z)$ in Example 1. Explain why the double integral

$$\int_0^a \int_0^{2\pi} \delta(a^2 - r^2)r \, d\theta \, dr$$

represents the *mass transport* (amount of mass per unit of time) flowing across the surface

$$x^2 + y^2 \le a^2, \qquad z = 0.$$

Evaluate the integral.

3. In Example 2, the position vector of P is

$$\mathbf{R} = \mathbf{R}' + z\mathbf{k}.$$

Show that for the motion described, it is correct to say that

$$\frac{d\mathbf{R}}{dt} = \mathbf{v} = \frac{d\mathbf{R}'}{dt} = \mathbf{v}'.$$

4. Describe, in words, the motion of the fluid discussed in Example 3. What path in space is described by a particle of the fluid that goes through the point $A(a, 0, 0)$ at time $t = 0$? Prove your result by integrating the vector equation

$$\frac{d\mathbf{R}}{dt} = \omega(-\mathbf{i}y + \mathbf{j}x) + c\mathbf{k}.$$

You may find cylindrical coordinates helpful.

5. In Example 4, suppose that the mass M is at the point (x_0, y_0, z_0) rather than at the origin. How should Eq. (4b) be modified to describe this new gravitational force field?

In Problems 6 through 10, find the gradient fields $\mathbf{F}(x, y, z) = \nabla f$ for the given functions f.

6. $f(x, y, z) = x^2 \exp(2y + 3z)$
7. $f(x, y, z) = \ln(x^2 + y^2 + z^2)$
8. $f(x, y, z) = \tan^{-1}(xy/z)$
9. $f(x, y, z) = 2x - 3y + 5z$
10. $f(x, y, z) = (x^2 + y^2 + z^2)^{n/2}$

15–2

SURFACE INTEGRALS

We know how to calculate the area of a surface in space by projecting it onto one of the coordinate planes and integrating a suitable function over this shadow region. For a surface described by

$$z = f(x, y) \tag{1}$$

that projects into a region R in the xy-plane, the surface area is

$$\iint_R \sqrt{1 + f_x^2 + f_y^2} \, dx \, dy. \tag{2}$$

The development in Article 14–9 also showed that we could interpret the integrand

$$g(x, y) = \sqrt{1 + f_x^2 + f_y^2} \tag{3a}$$

as the amount by which we need to multiply the area of a small portion of R to obtain the area of the corresponding small portion of a tangent plane approximating the surface at $P(x, y, f(x, y))$. In such cases, it is customary to use differential notation and simply write

$$d\sigma = g(x, y)\, dA, \tag{3b}$$

where we consider $d\sigma$ to be an element of surface area in the tangent plane that approximates the corresponding portion $\Delta\sigma$ of the surface itself. This is precisely analogous to taking

$$ds = \sqrt{1 + f_x^2}\, dx$$

as an approximation of a portion Δs of arc length of a curve. Furthermore, just as $\int ds$ gives the length of a curve, so $\iint d\sigma$ gives the area of a surface. The dA in Eq. (3b) represents an element of area $dx\, dy$, or $r\, d\theta\, dr$, in the xy-plane, and Eq. (2) could be written as

$$\iint_S d\sigma = \iint_R g(x, y)\, dA. \tag{4}$$

The symbol S under the integrals on the lefthand side in Eq. (4) symbolizes the surface in space over which we integrate, just as R on the righthand side symbolizes that region of the xy-plane over which the calculations are made according to Eq. (2).

We often want to evaluate such an integral as

$$\iint_S h(x, y, z)\, d\sigma, \tag{5}$$

and understand its meaning and applications. For example, if h gives the charge density per unit area in some electrostatic field, then this integral could be interpreted as total charge on the surface S; or, if h represents the amount of fluid flowing in the direction of the normal to S at $P(x, y, z)$ per unit area, per unit time, then the integral could be interpreted as the total fluid flow across S per unit time. Many other interpretations are possible, some of which will be brought out in examples and problems. You may encounter others in your studies in physics or engineering, or in other courses in mathematics.

Definition of the Surface Integral as a Limit of Sums

Although you should have no difficulty interpreting and using the surface integral indicated by (5), we ought first to give a mathematical definition of it. As in a discussion of surface area, therefore, we consider a surface consisting of those points $P(x, y, z)$ whose coordinates satisfy

$$z = f(x, y) \qquad \text{for} \quad (x, y) \in R, \tag{6}$$

where R is a closed, bounded region of the xy-plane. We assume that f and its first partial derivatives f_x and f_y are continuous functions throughout R

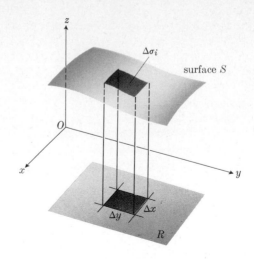

15–4   The surface S in space projects onto the region R in the xy-plane. A subregion of S with area $\Delta\sigma$ projects onto a subregion of R with area $\Delta x \, \Delta y$:

$$\iint\limits_{S} h(x, y, z)\, d\sigma = \lim \sum h(x_i, y_i, z_i)\, \Delta\sigma_i.$$

and on its boundary. We subdivide the region R into a finite number N of nonoverlapping subregions. We can do this, for example, by lines parallel to the y-axis spaced Δx apart, and lines parallel to the x-axis spaced Δy apart. When these subregions of R are projected vertically upward on the surface S (see Fig. 15–4), they induce a subdivision of S into N subregions. Let the areas of these subregions be numbered

$$\Delta\sigma_1, \quad \Delta\sigma_2, \quad \dots, \quad \Delta\sigma_N. \tag{7}$$

Next, we suppose that a point $P_i(x_i, y_i, z_i)$ is chosen on the surface in the ith subregion, and the product

$$h(x_i, y_i, z_i)\, \Delta\sigma_i$$

is formed for each i from 1 through N. Now consider the sum

$$\sum_{i=1}^{N} h(x_i, y_i, z_i)\, \Delta\sigma_i. \tag{8}$$

If such sums as (8) have a common limit L as the number N tends to infinity and the largest dimension of the subregions of R tends to zero, independently of the way in which the points P_i are selected within the subregions $\Delta\sigma_i$ on the surface, then that limit is called the *surface integral* of h over S, and it is represented by the notation (5). Although we shall not prove it here, it is true that for surfaces S of the type described, and for continuous functions h, the limit does exist as specified. We now turn to the practical matter of evaluating such surface integrals.

Evaluation of Surface Integrals

Continuing with the assumptions about S and h just mentioned, we see that the area $\Delta\sigma_i$ in the sum (8) is approximated by

$$g(x_i, y_i)\, \Delta A_i,$$

where g is the function defined by Eq. (3a) and ΔA_i is the area of the ith subregion of R. For the subregions completely inside R, away from the boundary, we could take $\Delta A_i = \Delta x\, \Delta y$; but for subregions along the boundary, we might (at least in theory) compute ΔA_i itself by a separate double integration in the xy-plane. However, as $\Delta x \to 0$ and $\Delta y \to 0$, if the boundary of R is a curve of finite arc length, these broken subregions can, in fact, simply be ignored. We do this, and let N denote the number of little rectangles that lie completely inside the boundary of R. The sum (8) is thus to be replaced by a sum of the form

$$\sum_{i=1}^{N} h(x_i,\, y_i,\, z_i)g(x_i,\, y_i)\, \Delta x\, \Delta y,$$

with $z_i = f(x_i, y_i)$, and g as given by Eq. (3a). Let Δx and Δy approach zero in this last sum: Then the approximations we have used for $\Delta\sigma_i$ become more and more accurate, and the limit is the same as

$$\iint_R h[x, y, f(x, y)]g(x, y)\, dx\, dy, \qquad\qquad \textbf{(9)}$$

where

$$g(x, y) = \sqrt{1 + f_x^2 + f_y^2}.$$

As a practical procedure for evaluating the surface integral (5), replace z by its value $f(x, y)$ on the surface, and replace $d\sigma$ by

$$d\sigma = \sqrt{1 + f_x^2 + f_y^2}\, dA,$$

where dA is $dx\, dy$, $dy\, dx$, or $r\, d\theta\, dr$, and evaluate the resulting double integral over the region R in the xy-plane into which S projects.

EXAMPLE 1.   Evaluate $\iint z\, d\sigma$ over the hemisphere

$$z = \sqrt{a^2 - x^2 - y^2}, \qquad x^2 + y^2 \le a^2.$$

Solution

$$\frac{\partial z}{\partial x} = \frac{-x}{z}, \qquad \frac{\partial z}{\partial y} = \frac{-y}{z}.$$

Hence

$$d\sigma = \sqrt{1 + (x^2/z^2) + (y^2/z^2)}\, dA$$

$$= \frac{a}{z}\, dA,$$

because $x^2 + y^2 + z^2 = a^2$ on S. Since the integrand is $z\, d\sigma = a\, dA$, we can omit substituting the radical expression for z, and simply get

$$\iint_S z\, d\sigma = \iint_R a\, dA$$

$$= a(\pi a^2) = \pi a^3.$$

We skip the detailed evaluation of the double integral of dA over the interior of the circle $r = a$ in the plane, because we know it is just the area πa^2.

EXAMPLE 2. Evaluate $\iint (x^2 + y^2)\, d\sigma$ over hemisphere S of Example 1.

Solution. From Example 1, we have

$$d\sigma = \frac{a}{z}\, dA,$$

and so our integral is

$$\iint_S (x^2 + y^2)\, d\sigma = \iint_R (x^2 + y^2)(a/z)\, dA,$$

with

$$z = \sqrt{a^2 - x^2 - y^2}.$$

This integral is an obvious candidate for polar coordinates, with

$$x^2 + y^2 = r^2, \qquad dA = r\, dr\, d\theta, \qquad z = \sqrt{a^2 - r^2}.$$

Thus we obtain

$$\iint_S (x^2 + y^2)\, d\sigma = \int_0^{2\pi} \int_0^a \frac{ar^3\, dr\, d\theta}{(a^2 - r^2)^{1/2}}.$$

The r-integration is done using the substitutions

$$u = (a^2 - r^2)^{1/2}, \qquad u^2 = a^2 - r^2,$$
$$r^2 = a^2 - u^2, \qquad r\, dr = -u\, du,$$

so that

$$\int r^3(a^2 - r^2)^{-1/2}\, dr = -\int (a^2 - u^2)u^{-1}u\, du$$

$$= -a^2 u + \tfrac{1}{3}u^3.$$

If $r = 0$, then $u = a$, and if $r = a$, then $u = 0$; and with another two or three simple steps, we get

$$2\pi a(a^3 - \tfrac{1}{3}a^3) = \tfrac{4}{3}\pi a^4$$

as the final answer.

REMARK 1. There is a very easy way to check this result: If we were to integrate $x^2 + y^2$ over the entire sphere, we should get twice what we get for the integral over the top half. Also, because the sphere has so much symmetry, we see that

$$\iint x^2\, d\sigma = \iint y^2\, d\sigma = \iint z^2\, d\sigma$$

$$= \tfrac{1}{3} \iint (x^2 + y^2 + z^2)\, d\sigma,$$

if all integrals are extended over the entire surface of the sphere. But we can easily evaluate the last of these four integrals without integration, because

$x^2 + y^2 + z^2 = a^2$ is constant on the sphere: We have

$$\iint a^2 \, d\sigma = a^2 \iint d\sigma = a^2(4\pi a^2) = 4\pi a^4.$$

For Example 2, we have to multiply this by $\frac{1}{3}$, then by 2 (for $x^2 + y^2$), and finally by $\frac{1}{2}$, because we want the value of the integral over a hemisphere. The result of this multiplication is $\frac{4}{3}\pi a^4$, which agrees with our earlier calculation.

REMARK 2.   If the equation of a surface S has the form $F(x, y, z) = 0$, we can let

$$\mathbf{N} = \mathbf{i}F_x + \mathbf{j}F_y + \mathbf{k}F_z$$

be a normal to S, and then take $d\sigma = dA/|\cos \phi|$, where ϕ is an angle between $\mathbf{N}$ and a vector normal to the plane onto which S is projected. If we project S into the xy-plane, we then take dA to be equal to $dx\, dy$, and ϕ to be the angle between $\mathbf{N}$ and $\mathbf{k}$, so that

$$d\sigma = \left(\frac{\sqrt{F_x^2 + F_y^2 + F_z^2}}{|F_z|} \right) dx \, dy. \tag{10}$$

(See Fig. 15–5.) To evaluate the surface integral

$$\iint\limits_S h(x, y, z) \, d\sigma,$$

we use the equation of the surface to eliminate z in the integrand and in Eq. (10), thereby obtaining a function of x and y to be integrated, as usual, over the projection in the xy-plane. Two other equations can be derived from Eq. (10) by simply permuting the letters x, y, and z. These can be used whenever it is easier to work with the projection of S onto one of the other coordinate planes.

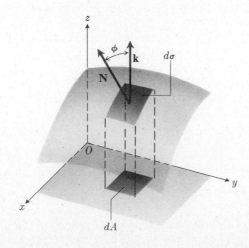

15–5 The element of area $d\sigma$ on the surface S and the element of area dA in the xy-plane satisfy the relation $d\sigma = dA/|\cos \phi|$, where ϕ is the angle between $\mathbf{N} = \mathbf{i}F_x + \mathbf{j}F_y + \mathbf{k}F_z$ and $\mathbf{k}$.

PROBLEMS

In Problems 1 through 3, explain briefly, with reference to the definition of the surface integral as a limit, why the stated result should be true if c is a constant and F and G are continuous functions.

1. $\displaystyle\iint_S c \, d\sigma = c \times (\text{area of } S)$

2. $\displaystyle\iint_S [F(x, y, z) + G(x, y, z)] \, d\sigma$

$$= \iint_S F(x, y, z) \, d\sigma + \iint_S G(x, y, z) \, d\sigma$$

3. $\displaystyle\iint_S cF(x, y, z) \, d\sigma = c \iint_S F(x, y, z) \, d\sigma$

4. (*Spherical coordinates.*) Suppose that the surface of the hemisphere in Example 1 is subdivided by arcs of great circles on which the spherical coordinate θ remains constant (meridians of longitude), and by circles parallel to the xy-plane on which ϕ remains constant (parallels of latitude). Let the angular spacings be $\Delta\theta$ and $\Delta\phi$, respectively. Express the integral of Example 1 in the form

$$\lim_{\substack{\Delta\theta \to 0 \\ \Delta\phi \to 0}} \sum F(\theta, \phi) \, \Delta\theta \, \Delta\phi = \iint F(\theta, \phi) \, d\theta \, d\phi,$$

with appropriate limits of integration, and evaluate. (*Hint.* You should get

$$d\sigma = (r \, d\theta) \cdot (\rho \, d\phi) = \rho^2 \, \sin \phi \, d\theta \, d\phi,$$

where ρ, ϕ, θ are spherical coordinates.)

In Problems 5 and 6, let $h(x, y, z) = x + y + z$ and let S be the portion of the plane $z = 2x + 3y$ for which $x \geq 0, y \geq 0$, $x + y \leq 2$.

5. Evaluate $\iint_S h \, d\sigma$ by projecting S into the xy-plane. Sketch the projection.

6. Evaluate $\iint_S h \, d\sigma$ by projecting S into the yz-plane. Sketch the projection and its boundaries.

In Problems 7 through 10, you are asked to evaluate integrals of the form

$$\iint_S \mathbf{F} \cdot \mathbf{n} \, d\sigma$$

for specific vector fields $\mathbf{F}$, given that S, lying in the first octant, is one-eighth of the sphere $x^2 + y^2 + z^2 = a^2$, and $\mathbf{n}$ is a unit vector normal to S and pointing away from the origin. (Thus both $\mathbf{F}$ and $\mathbf{n}$ are vector functions of position on the sphere.)

7. $\mathbf{F} = \mathbf{n}$ **8.** $\mathbf{F} = -\mathbf{i}y + \mathbf{j}x$

9. $\mathbf{F} = z\mathbf{k}$ **10.** $\mathbf{F} = \mathbf{i}x + \mathbf{j}y$

15-3

LINE INTEGRALS

Suppose that C is a directed curve in space from A to B, and that $w = w(x, y, z)$ is a scalar function of position that is continuous in a region D that contains C. Figure 15–6 illustrates such a directed curve. It is the locus of points (x, y, z) such that

$$x = f(t), \qquad y = g(t), \qquad z = h(t), \qquad t_A \leq t \leq t_B. \tag{1}$$

We assume that the functions f, g, h are continuous and have bounded and piecewise-continuous first derivatives on $[t_A, t_B]$. It is a theorem of higher mathematics that the object to be defined below, $\int_C w \, ds$, does not actually depend on the particular parametrization of C: All parametrizations satisfying the hypotheses stated for f, g, h give the same answer. Indeed, it is possible to define the integral without reference to parametric equations, but evaluations of line integrals are almost always carried out in terms of some parametrization or other. So we proceed as follows:

We divide the interval $[t_A, t_B]$ into N subintervals of lengths

$$\Delta t_1, \quad \Delta t_2, \quad \ldots, \quad \Delta t_N.$$

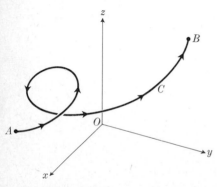

15–6 The directed curve C from A to B.

The points of subdivision also correspond to points on C which divide it into subarcs of lengths

$$\Delta s_1, \quad \Delta s_2, \quad \ldots, \quad \Delta s_N.$$

Let $P_i(x_i, y_i, z_i)$ be an arbitrary point on the ith subarc, and form the sum

$$\sum_{i=1}^{N} w(x_i, y_i, z_i) \, \Delta s_i. \qquad (2)$$

If these sums have a limit L, as $N \to \infty$ and the largest $\Delta t_i \to 0$, and if this limit is the same for *all* ways of subdividing $[t_A, t_B]$ and all choices of the points P_i, then we call this limit the *line integral* of w along C from A to B, and express it by the notation

$$\int_C w \, ds = \lim \sum_{i=1}^{N} w(x_i, y_i, z_i) \, \Delta s_i. \qquad (3a)$$

It is also a theorem that, under the hypotheses stated for w and C, the line integral exists, and is the same as

$$\int_{t_A}^{t_B} w[f(t), g(t), h(t)] \sqrt{[f'(t)]^2 + [g'(t)]^2 + [h'(t)]^2} \, dt. \qquad (3b)$$

Although we shall not prove this theorem, we shall show how line integrals are evaluated in practice, and illustrate some of their physical applications. Although Eq. (3b) looks quite complicated, it is just the result of substituting the parametric equations for x, y, z in w and using the standard formula for ds. In our first example, we use a curve in the xy-plane for which the formula simplifies a bit.

EXAMPLE 1. Let C be the line segment from $A(0, 0)$ to $B(1, 1)$, and let $w = x + y^2$. Evaluate $\int_C w \, ds$ for two different parametrizations of C.

Solution 1. If we let

$$x = t \quad \text{and} \quad y = t, \quad 0 \le t \le 1,$$

then we get

$$\int_C w \, ds = \int_0^1 (t + t^2)\sqrt{1 + 1} \, dt$$

$$= \sqrt{2} \left[\frac{t^2}{2} + \frac{t^3}{3} \right]_0^1 = \frac{5\sqrt{2}}{6}.$$

Solution 2. As a second parametrization of the given segment of the line $y = x$, we let

$$x = \sin t \quad \text{and} \quad y = \sin t, \quad 0 \le t \le \pi/2,$$

and get

$$\int_C w \, ds = \int_0^{\pi/2} (\sin t + \sin^2 t)\sqrt{2 \cos^2 t} \, dt$$

$$= \sqrt{2} \left[\frac{\sin^2 t}{2} + \frac{\sin^3 t}{3} \right]_0^{\pi/2} = \frac{5\sqrt{2}}{6}.$$

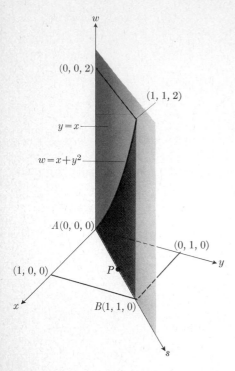

15–7 Area in the plane $y = x$ under the surface $w = x + y^2$ for $0 \le x \le 1$.

REMARK 1.   The line integral of Example 1 can be interpreted as the area of the region R that lies in the plane $y = x$, above the plane $w = 0$, and under the surface $w = x + y^2$. We can, in fact, introduce an s-axis along the intersection of the planes $w = 0$ and $y = x$, as shown in Fig. 15–7. The s-coordinate of the point $P(x, x, 0)$ between $A(0, 0, 0)$ and $B(1, 1, 0)$ on C is

$$s = \sqrt{x^2 + x^2} = x\sqrt{2}.$$

Thus we can use the arc length s itself as parameter for C:

$$x = \frac{s}{\sqrt{2}}, \qquad y = \frac{s}{\sqrt{2}}, \qquad 0 \le s \le \sqrt{2}.$$

The upper boundary of R is the intersection of the surface $w = x + y^2$ and the plane $y = x$. In the sw-plane, this curve has equation

$$w = \frac{s}{\sqrt{2}} + \frac{s^2}{2},$$

and the area of R is given by

$$\int_C w \, ds = \int_0^{\sqrt{2}} \left(\frac{s}{\sqrt{2}} + \frac{s^2}{2} \right) ds$$

$$= \frac{s^2}{2\sqrt{2}} + \frac{s^3}{6} \bigg]_0^{\sqrt{2}} = \frac{1}{\sqrt{2}} + \frac{2\sqrt{2}}{6} = \frac{5\sqrt{2}}{6}.$$

Whenever C is a *plane* curve, we can interpret the line integral $\int_C w \, ds$ as the area of a portion of a cylinder (or as the difference between areas above and below C, if w has both positive and negative values along C). Even if C is curved, one can at least think of measuring the distance s along C, starting with $s = 0$ at A and increasing to $s = \ell$ at B, where ℓ is the length of arc of C from A to B. Because s increases along C, there is one and only one point on C for any value of $s \in [0, \ell]$, and we can imagine the parametric equations of C being given in terms of s; say,

$$x = x(s), \qquad y = y(s), \qquad z = z(s), \qquad 0 \le s \le \ell.$$

Then, along C, $w = w[x(s), y(s), z(s)]$ is a function of s: $w = \phi(s)$. The way in which the line integral is defined as a limit of sums ensures that $\int_C w \, ds$ is just the integral of this function ϕ with respect to s:

$$\int_C w \, ds = \int_0^\ell \phi(s) \, ds. \tag{4}$$

Equation (4) also suggests that we can think of the cylinder as having the plane curve C as base, and the curve $w = \phi(s)$ as upper boundary. We can then flatten the cylinder so that C becomes the segment $[0, \ell]$ of the s-axis in an sw-plane. Figure 15–8 illustrates this idea.

Line Integrals and Work

If the point of application of a force

$$\mathbf{F} = \mathbf{i}M(x, y, z) + \mathbf{j}N(x, y, z) + \mathbf{k}P(x, y, z) \tag{5}$$

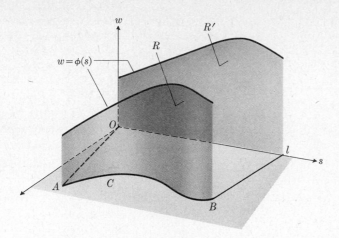

15–8 The region R above the curve C on the cylindrical surface maps onto the region R' in the sw-plane.

moves along a curve C from a point $A(a_1, a_2, a_3)$ to a point $B(b_1, b_2, b_3)$, then the work done by the force is

$$W = \int_C \mathbf{F} \cdot d\mathbf{R}, \tag{6}$$

where

$$\mathbf{R} = \mathbf{i}x + \mathbf{j}y + \mathbf{k}z \tag{7}$$

is the vector from the origin to the point (x, y, z), and

$$d\mathbf{R} = \frac{d\mathbf{R}}{ds}\, ds = \mathbf{i}\, dx + \mathbf{j}\, dy + \mathbf{k}\, dz. \tag{8}$$

If we calculate the dot product of the vectors $\mathbf{F}$ and $d\mathbf{R}$ from Eqs. (5) and (8), then we may write Eq. (6) in the alternative form

$$W = \int_C M\, dx + N\, dy + P\, dz, \tag{9}$$

where M, N, and P are functions of x, y, and z, and the subscript C on the integral refers to the curve C along which the integral is taken. Such an integral as Eq. (9) is also called a line integral (*curve integral* would perhaps be a more descriptive name). Because

$$\frac{d\mathbf{R}}{ds} = \mathbf{T} = \text{unit tangent vector,}$$

Eq. (6) is just another way of saying that the work is the value of the line integral along C of the *tangential component* of the force field $\mathbf{F}$. This tangential component is a scalar function, say w, of position along C:

$$w = \mathbf{F} \cdot \mathbf{T} = w(x, y, z).$$

Therefore

$$W = \int_C \mathbf{F} \cdot d\mathbf{R} = \int_C \mathbf{F} \cdot \mathbf{T}\, ds = \int_C w(x, y, z)\, ds.$$

This is just the kind of line integral defined by Eq. (3a), but the form of the integral in Eq. (9) suggests another way of evaluating it.

To evaluate the integral in (9) we might express the equations of C in terms of a parameter t:

$$x = x(t), \qquad y = y(t), \qquad z = z(t), \tag{10}$$

such that the curve is described from A to B as t varies from a value t_1 to a value t_2. Then *all* quantities in the integral may be expressed in terms of one variable t and the result evaluated in the usual manner as a definite integral with respect to t from t_1 to t_2. In general, the value of the integral depends on the path C as well as on its endpoints.

EXAMPLE 2.   A force is given by

$$\mathbf{F} = \mathbf{i}(x^2 - y) + \mathbf{j}(y^2 - z) + \mathbf{k}(z^2 - x),$$

and its point of application moves from the origin O to the point $A(1, 1, 1)$,
 a) along the straight line OA, and
 b) along the curve

$$x = t, \qquad y = t^2, \qquad z = t^3, \qquad 0 \le t \le 1.$$

Find the work done in the two cases.

Solution.   **a)** Equations for the line OA are

$$x = y = z.$$

The integral to be evaluated is

$$W = \int_C (x^2 - y)\, dx + (y^2 - z)\, dy + (z^2 - x)\, dx,$$

which, for the path OA, becomes

$$W = \int_0^1 3(x^2 - x)\, dx = -\tfrac{1}{2}.$$

b) Along the curve, we get

$$W = \int_0^1 2(t^4 - t^3)t\, dt + 3(t^6 - t)t^2\, dt = -\tfrac{29}{60}.$$

Now, under certain conditions, the line integral between two points A and B is independent of the path C joining them. That is, the integral in Eq. (6) has the same value for any two paths C_1 and C_2 joining A and B. This happens when the force field $\mathbf{F}$ is a *gradient field*, that is, when

$$\mathbf{F}(x, y, z) = \nabla f = \mathbf{i}\frac{\partial f}{\partial x} + \mathbf{j}\frac{\partial f}{\partial y} + \mathbf{k}\frac{\partial f}{\partial z},$$

for some differentiable function f. We state this as a formal theorem and prove the sufficiency and necessity of the conditions, with some interpolated remarks.

Theorem 1. *Let **F** be a vector field with components M, N, P, that are contin-uous throughout some connected region D. Then a necessary and sufficient condition for the integral*

$$\int_A^B \mathbf{F} \cdot d\mathbf{R}$$

to be independent of the path joining the points A and B in D is that there exist a differentiable function f such that

$$\mathbf{F} = \nabla f = \mathbf{i}\frac{\partial f}{\partial x} + \mathbf{j}\frac{\partial f}{\partial y} + \mathbf{k}\frac{\partial f}{\partial z} \tag{11}$$

throughout D.

Proof. Sufficiency. First, we suppose that Eq. (11) is satisfied, and then consider A and B to be two points in D (see Fig. 15–9). Suppose that C is any piecewise smooth curve joining A and B:

$$x = x(t), \qquad y = y(t), \qquad z = z(t), \qquad t_1 \le t \le t_2.$$

Along $C, f = f[x(t), y(t), z(t)]$ is a function of t to which we may apply the chain rule to differentiate with respect to t:

$$\frac{df}{dt} = \frac{\partial f}{\partial x}\frac{dx}{dt} + \frac{\partial f}{\partial y}\frac{dy}{dt} + \frac{\partial f}{\partial z}\frac{dz}{dt}$$

$$= \nabla f \cdot \left(\mathbf{i}\frac{dx}{dt} + \mathbf{j}\frac{dy}{dt} + \mathbf{k}\frac{dz}{dt}\right)$$

$$= \nabla f \cdot \frac{d\mathbf{R}}{dt}. \tag{12a}$$

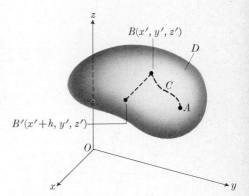

15–9 A piecewise smooth curve C joining points A and B in the region D of Theorem 1.

Because Eq. (11) holds, we also have

$$\mathbf{F} \cdot d\mathbf{R} = \nabla f \cdot d\mathbf{R} = \nabla f \cdot \frac{d\mathbf{R}}{dt} dt = \frac{df}{dt} dt. \tag{12b}$$

We now use this result to integrate $\mathbf{F} \cdot d\mathbf{R}$ along C from A to B:

$$\int_C \mathbf{F} \cdot d\mathbf{R} = \int_{t_1}^{t_2} \frac{df}{dt} dt$$

$$= \int_{t_1}^{t_2} \frac{d}{dt} f[x(t), y(t), z(t)] \, dt$$

$$= f[x(t), y(t), z(t)]_{t_1}^{t_2}$$

$$= f[x(t_2), y(t_2), z(t_2)] - f[x(t_1), y(t_1), z(t_1)]$$

$$= f(B) - f(A).$$

Therefore, if $\mathbf{F} = \nabla f$, we have the result

$$\int_A^B \mathbf{F} \cdot d\mathbf{R} = \int_A^B \nabla f \cdot d\mathbf{R} = f(B) - f(A). \tag{13}$$

The value of the integral $f(B) - f(A)$ does not depend on the path C at all. Equation (13) is the space analog of the Fundamental Theorem of Integral Calculus (see Article 4–8):

$$\int_a^b f'(x)\,dx = f(b) - f(a).$$

The only difference is that we have $\nabla f \cdot d\mathbf{R}$ in place of $f'(x)\,dx$. This analogy suggests that perhaps there is also a space analog of the fact that any continuous function of a single real variable is the derivative with respect to x of its integral from a to x (again, see Article 4–8). In other words, if we define a function f by the rule

$$f(x', y', z') = \int_A^{(x',y',z')} \mathbf{F} \cdot d\mathbf{R}, \tag{14a}$$

perhaps it will be true that

$$\nabla f = \mathbf{F}. \tag{14b}$$

Equation (14b) is indeed true when the righthand side of Eq. (14a) is path-independent, and the proof of this fact will complete our theorem.

Proof. *Necessity.* We now assume that the line integral in (14a) is path-independent, and prove that $\mathbf{F} = \nabla f$ for the function f defined by Eq. (14a). We first write $\mathbf{F}$ in terms of its **i**-, **j**-, and **k**-components:

$$\mathbf{F}(x, y, z) = \mathbf{i}M(x, y, z) + \mathbf{j}N(x, y, z) + \mathbf{k}P(x, y, z), \tag{15}$$

and fix the points A and $B(x', y', z')$ in D. To establish Eq. (14b), we need to show that *the equalities*

$$\frac{\partial f}{\partial x} = M, \qquad \frac{\partial f}{\partial y} = N, \qquad \frac{\partial f}{\partial z} = P \tag{16}$$

hold at each point of D. In what follows, we either assume that D is an open set, so that all of its points are interior points, or we restrict our attention to interior points.

The point $B(x', y', z')$ is the center of some small sphere whose interior lies entirely inside D. We let $h \neq 0$ be small enough so that all points on the ray from B to $B'(x' + h, y', z')$ lie in D (see Fig. 15–9), and consider the difference quotient

$$\frac{f(x' + h, y', z') - f(x', y', z')}{h} = \frac{1}{h} \int_B^{B'} \mathbf{F} \cdot d\mathbf{R}. \tag{17}$$

Since the integral does not depend on a particular path, we choose one convenient for our purpose:

$$x = x' + th, \qquad y = y', \qquad z = z', \qquad 0 \le t \le 1,$$

along which neither y nor z varies, and along which $d\mathbf{R} = \mathbf{i}\,dx = \mathbf{i}h\,dt$. When this is substituted into Eq. (17), along with $\mathbf{F}$ from Eq. (15), we get

$$\frac{f(x' + h, y', z') - f(x', y', z')}{h} = \frac{1}{h} \int_0^1 M(x' + ht, y', z')h\,dt$$

$$= \int_0^1 M(x' + ht, y', z')\,dt. \tag{18}$$

By hypothesis, **F** is continuous, so each component is a continuous function. Thus, given any $\epsilon > 0$, there is a $\delta > 0$ such that

$$\left| M(x' + ht, y', z') - M(x', y', z') \right| < \epsilon \qquad \text{when} \qquad |ht| < \delta.$$

This implies that when $|h| < \delta$, the integral in Eq. (18) also differs from

$$\int_0^1 M(x', y', z')\, dt = M(x', y', z') \tag{19}$$

by less than ϵ. The equality in (19) follows from the fact that the integrand is a constant, and

$$\int_0^1 dt = 1.$$

Therefore, as $h \to 0$ in Eq. (18), the righthand side has as limit $M(x', y', z')$, so the lefthand side must have the same limit. That, however, is just the partial derivative of f with respect to x at $B(x', y', z')$. Therefore

$$\frac{\partial f}{\partial x} = M \tag{20}$$

holds at each interior point of D.

Equation (20) is the first of the three equalities, Eqs. (16), that are needed to establish Eq. (14b). Proofs of the remaining two equalities in (16) are very similar, and you are asked to prove one of them in Problem 7. One sets up a difference quotient like Eq. (17), but takes

$$B' = (x', y' + h, z') \qquad \text{or} \qquad B' = (x', y', z' + h).$$

In other words, from B, one integrates along a path parallel to the y-axis or parallel to the z-axis. On the former path, $d\mathbf{R} = \mathbf{j}h\, dt$, and on the latter, $d\mathbf{R} = \mathbf{k}h\, dt$. This concludes the proof.

EXAMPLE 3. Find a function f such that

if $$\mathbf{F} = 2x\mathbf{i} + 2y\mathbf{j} + 2z\mathbf{k}, \tag{21a}$$

then $$\mathbf{F} = \nabla f. \tag{21b}$$

Solution.   We might be lucky and guess

$$f(x, y, z) = x^2 + y^2 + z^2, \tag{22}$$

because $2x$, $2y$, $2z$ are its partial derivatives with respect to x, y, and z. But if we weren't so inspired, then we might try something like Eq. (14a). In the first place, the functions $2x$, $2y$, $2z$ are everywhere continuous, so the region D can be all of space. Of course we don't know, until *after* we find that **F** is a gradient, that the integral in (14a) is path-independent, but we proceed on faith (or at least with hope). The choice of A is up to us, so we make life easy for ourselves by taking $A = (0, 0, 0)$. For the path of integration from A to $B(x', y', z')$, we take the line segment

$$x = x't, \qquad y = y't, \qquad z = z't, \qquad 0 \le t \le 1,$$

along which

$$d\mathbf{R} = (x'\mathbf{i} + y'\mathbf{j} + z'\mathbf{k})\, dt$$

and

$$\mathbf{F} \cdot d\mathbf{R} = (2xx' + 2yy' + 2zz')\,dt$$
$$= (2x'^2 + 2y'^2 + 2z'^2)t\,dt.$$

Therefore, when we substitute into Eq. (14a), we get

$$f(x', y', z') = \int_{(0,0,0)}^{(x',y',z')} \mathbf{F} \cdot d\mathbf{R}$$
$$= [x'^2 + y'^2 + z'^2] \int_0^1 2t\,dt$$
$$= x'^2 + y'^2 + z'^2.$$

If we delete the primes, this equation is identical with Eq. (22).

REMARK 2.   The upper limit of integration in Eq. (14a) is an arbitrary point in the domain of $\mathbf{F}$, but we use (x', y', z') to designate it, rather than (x, y, z), because the latter is used for the running point that covers the arc C from A to B during the integration. After we have completed the computation of $f(x', y', z')$, we then delete the primes to express the result as $f(x, y, z)$. The analog in one dimension would be

$$\ln x' = \int_1^{x'} \frac{1}{x}\,dx.$$

We must be careful not to confuse the variable of integration x with the limit of integration x'. We distinguished between these two things in a slightly different manner in Eq. (1), Article 6–4, where we wrote

$$\ln x = \int_1^x \frac{1}{t}\,dt.$$

Our purpose there was the same as it is here, however: to maintain a notational difference between the variable *upper limit* and the *variable of integration*.

REMARK 3.   So far we have only the criterion

$$\mathbf{F} = \nabla f$$

for deciding whether

$$\int_A^B \mathbf{F} \cdot d\mathbf{R}$$

is path-independent. We shall discover another criterion in Eqs. (26) below. If we follow the method indicated by Eq. (14a) and illustrated in Example 3 for a field $\mathbf{F}$ that is *not* path-independent, then we should discover, on trying to verify that $\mathbf{F} = \nabla f$, that it isn't so. The next example illustrates exactly this situation.

EXAMPLE 4.   Show that there is no function f such that

$$\mathbf{F} = \nabla f \quad \text{if} \quad \mathbf{F} = y\mathbf{i} - x\mathbf{j}.$$

Solution.   Here's one way to show it: If there were such a function f, then

$$\frac{\partial f}{\partial x} = y \qquad \text{and} \qquad \frac{\partial f}{\partial y} = -x,$$

from which we would get

$$\frac{\partial^2 f}{\partial y\,\partial x} = \frac{\partial(y)}{\partial y} = 1 \neq \frac{\partial^2 f}{\partial x\,\partial y} = \frac{\partial(-x)}{\partial x} = -1.$$

But we should have $f_{xy} = f_{yx}$, because

$$f_x = y \qquad \text{and} \qquad f_y = -x$$

are everywhere continuously differentiable. This contradiction shows that no such f exists.

Another method would be to compute $\int \mathbf{F} \cdot d\mathbf{R}$ between two points, say $A(0, 0, 0)$ and $B(1, 1, 0)$, along two different paths. If the answers turn out to be the same, we haven't proved a thing. But if they turn out to be different, then we know that $\mathbf{F}$ is not a gradient field. Problem 5 asks you to do this for two specific paths.

A third method is to proceed blithely with Eq. (14a), and get a function f that satisfies Eq. (14a) for a particular path, but that fails to satisfy $\mathbf{F} = \nabla f$. Once again we would choose an origin $A = (0, 0, 0)$ and let $B = (x', y', z')$, and then integrate along the segment

$$x = x't, \qquad y = y't, \qquad z = z't, \qquad 0 \le t \le 1.$$

We would get

$$\begin{aligned}
\mathbf{F} \cdot d\mathbf{R} &= (y\mathbf{i} - x\mathbf{j}) \cdot (\mathbf{i}\,dx + \mathbf{j}\,dy + \mathbf{k}\,dz) \\
&= y\,dx - x\,dy \\
&= (y't)(x'\,dt) - (x't)(y'\,dt) \\
&= t(x'y' - x'y')\,dt = 0\,dt.
\end{aligned}$$

Therefore Eq. (14a) produces

$$f(x', y', z') = 0 \qquad \text{for all } (x', y', z').$$

This constant function obviously won't have a gradient equal to $y\mathbf{i} - x\mathbf{j}$. In Problem 6 you are asked to explain why this also means that no other function exists whose gradient is the given $\mathbf{F}$.

Conservative Fields

When $\mathbf{F}$ is a force field such that the work integral from A to B is the same for all paths joining them, the field is said to be *conservative*. Theorem 1 therefore shows that a force field is *conservative* if and only if it is a *gradient* field:

$$\mathbf{F} \text{ is conservative} \quad \Leftrightarrow \quad \mathbf{F} = \nabla f. \tag{23}$$

If the field $\mathbf{F}$ is conservative, the integrand in the work integral,

$$\mathbf{F} \cdot d\mathbf{R} = M\,dx + N\,dv + P\,dz. \tag{24a}$$

is an *exact differential*. By this we mean that there is a function f whose total differential is equal to the given integrand:

$$df = M \, dx + N \, dy + P \, dz, \qquad \textbf{(24b)}$$

which holds if and only if

$$M = \frac{\partial f}{\partial x}, \qquad N = \frac{\partial f}{\partial y}, \qquad P = \frac{\partial f}{\partial z}. \qquad \textbf{(25)}$$

In Article 13–13, we discussed exact differentials of functions $f(x, y)$ of two variables. The criterion for an exact differential stated in the theorem of that article is easily extended to functions of three or more variables. For functions of three variables, it goes as follows.

Theorem 2. *Let $M(x, y, z)$, $N(x, y, z)$, and $P(x, y, z)$ be continuous, together with their first-order partial derivatives. Then a necessary condition for the expression*

$$M \, dx + N \, dy + P \, dz$$

to be an exact differential is that the following equations all be satisfied:

$$\frac{\partial M}{\partial y} = \frac{\partial N}{\partial x}, \qquad \frac{\partial M}{\partial z} = \frac{\partial P}{\partial x}, \qquad \frac{\partial N}{\partial z} = \frac{\partial P}{\partial y}. \qquad \textbf{(26)}$$

This theorem is a straightforward extension of the theorem of Article 13–13 from the two-dimensional to the three-dimensional case. We shall omit the proof, since it is similar to the proof of the earlier theorem.

EXAMPLE 5. Suppose

$$\mathbf{F} = \mathbf{i}(e^x \cos y + yz) + \mathbf{j}(xz - e^x \sin y) + \mathbf{k}(xy + z).$$

Is $\mathbf{F}$ conservative? If so, find f such that $\mathbf{F} = \nabla f$.

Solution. We apply the test of Eqs. (26) to the expression

$$\mathbf{F} \cdot d\mathbf{R} = (e^x \cos y + yz) \, dx + (xz - e^x \sin y) \, dy + (xy + z) \, dz.$$

We let

$$M = e^x \cos y + yz, \qquad N = xz - e^x \sin y, \qquad P = xy + z,$$

and calculate

$$\frac{\partial M}{\partial z} = y = \frac{\partial P}{\partial x}, \qquad \frac{\partial N}{\partial z} = x = \frac{\partial P}{\partial y}, \qquad \frac{\partial M}{\partial y} = -e^x \sin y + z = \frac{\partial N}{\partial x}.$$

The theorem tells us that there may be a function $f(x, y, z)$ such that

$$\mathbf{F} \cdot d\mathbf{R} = df.$$

We would find f by integrating the system of equations

$$\frac{\partial f}{\partial x} = e^x \cos y + yz, \qquad \frac{\partial f}{\partial y} = xz - e^x \sin y, \qquad \frac{\partial f}{\partial z} = xy + z. \qquad \textbf{(27)}$$

We integrate the first of these with respect to x, holding y and z constant, and add an arbitrary function $g(y, z)$ as the "constant of integration"; we thus obtain

$$f(x, y, z) = e^x \cos y + xyz + g(y, z). \tag{28}$$

Next we differentiate this with respect to y and set it equal to $\partial f/\partial y$ as given by the second of Eqs. (27):

$$xz - e^x \sin y = -e^x \sin y + xz + \frac{\partial g}{\partial y},$$

or

$$\frac{\partial g(y, z)}{\partial y} = 0. \tag{29}$$

Integrating Eq. (29) with respect to y, holding z constant, and adding an arbitrary function $h(z)$ as constant of integration, we obtain

$$g(y, z) = h(z). \tag{30}$$

We substitute this into Eq. (28) and then calculate $\partial f/\partial z$, which we compare with the third of Eqs. (27). We find that

$$xy + z = xy + \frac{dh(z)}{dz} \quad \text{or} \quad \frac{dh(z)}{dz} = z,$$

so that

$$h(z) = \frac{x^2}{2} + C.$$

Hence we may write Eq. (28) as

$$f(x, y, z) = e^x \cos y + xyz + (z^2/2) + C.$$

Then, for this function, it is easy to see that

$$\mathbf{F} = \nabla f.$$

A function $f(x, y, z)$ that has the property that its gradient gives the force vector $\mathbf{F}$ is called a "potential" function. (Sometimes a minus sign is introduced. For example, the electric intensity of a field is the negative of the potential gradient in the field. See Sears, Zemansky, Young, *University Physics* (Fifth edition); Addison-Wesley, 1976; pp. 446–447.)

PROBLEMS

1. In Example 1, let C be given by
$$x = t^2, \quad y = t^2, \quad 0 \le t \le 1,$$
and evaluate $\int_C w \, ds$ for $w = x + y^2$.

2. In Example 1, let C be given by $x = f(t) = y$, where $f(0) = 0$ and $f(1) = 1$. Show that if $f'(t)$ is continuous on $[0, 1]$, then $\int_C w \, ds = (5\sqrt{2})/6$, no matter what the particular function f may be.

3. Evaluate $\int \mathbf{F} \cdot d\mathbf{R}$ around the circle
$$x = \cos t, \quad y = \sin t, \quad z = 0, \quad 0 \le t \le 2\pi$$
for the force given in Example 2.

4. In Example 3, evaluate $\int \mathbf{F} \cdot d\mathbf{R}$ along a curve C lying on the sphere $x^2 + y^2 + z^2 = a^2$. Do you need to know anything more about C? Why?

5. Assume $\mathbf{F} = y\mathbf{i} - x\mathbf{j}$, as in Example 4, and take $A = (0, 0, 0)$, $B = (1, 1, 0)$. Evaluate $\int \mathbf{F} \cdot d\mathbf{R}$ for:

a) $x = y = t$, $0 \leq t \leq 1$;

b) $x = t$, $y = t^2$, $0 \leq t \leq 1$.

Comment on the meaning of your answers.

6. In Example 4, when we considered $\mathbf{F} = y\mathbf{i} - x\mathbf{j}$, we found a function $f(x', y', z') = 0$ which expresses the value of the integral

$$\int_{(0,0,0)}^{(x',y',z')} \mathbf{F} \cdot d\mathbf{R}$$

along the line segment from $(0, 0, 0)$ to an arbitrary point (x', y', z'). Using this result, and the first half of the proof of Theorem 1, prove that if $\mathbf{F}$ were a gradient field, say $\mathbf{F} = \nabla g$, then $g - f = \text{constant}$. From this, show that no such g exists for the given $\mathbf{F}$.

7. Using the notations of Eqs. (14a) and (15), show that $\partial f/\partial y = N$ holds at each point of D if $\mathbf{F}$ is continuous and if the integral in (14a) is path-independent in D.

8. Let $\rho = (x^2 + y^2 + z^2)^{1/2}$. Show that

$$\nabla(\rho^n) = n\rho^{n-2}\mathbf{R},$$

where $\mathbf{R} = \mathbf{i}x + \mathbf{j}y + \mathbf{k}z$. Is there a value of n for which $\mathbf{F} = \nabla(\rho^n)$ represents the "inverse-square law" field? If so, what is this value of n?

In Problems 9 through 13, find the work done by the given force $\mathbf{F}$ as the point of application moves from $(0, 0, 0)$ to $(1, 1, 1)$,

a) along the straight line $x = y = z$;

b) along the curve $x = t$, $y = t^2$, $z = t^4$; and

c) along the x-axis to $(1, 0, 0)$, then in a straight line to $(1, 1, 0)$, and from there in a straight line to $(1, 1, 1)$.

9. $\mathbf{F} = 2x\mathbf{i} + 3y\mathbf{j} + 4z\mathbf{k}$

10. $\mathbf{F} = \mathbf{i}x \sin y + \mathbf{j} \cos y + \mathbf{k}(x + y)$

11. $\mathbf{F} = \mathbf{i}(y + z) + \mathbf{j}(z + x) + \mathbf{k}(x + y)$

12. $\mathbf{F} = e^{y+2z}(\mathbf{i} + \mathbf{j}x + 2\mathbf{k}x)$

13. $\mathbf{F} = \mathbf{i}y \sin z + \mathbf{j}x \sin z + \mathbf{k}xy \cos z$

In Problems 14 through 17, find a function $f(x, y, z)$ such that $\mathbf{F} = \text{grad } f$ for the $\mathbf{F}$ given in the exercise named.

14. Problem 9   **15.** Problem 11

16. Problem 12   **17.** Problem 13

18. If A and B are given, prove that the line integral

$$\int_A^B (z^2 \, dx + 2y \, dy + 2xz \, dz)$$

is independent of the path of integration.

19. If $\mathbf{F} = y\mathbf{i} + x\mathbf{j}$, evaluate the line integral $\int_A^B \mathbf{F} \cdot d\mathbf{R}$ along the straight line from $A(1, 1, 1)$ to $B(3, 3, 3)$.

20. If $\mathbf{F} = \mathbf{i}x^2 + \mathbf{j}yz + \mathbf{k}y^2$, compute $\int_A^B \mathbf{F} \cdot d\mathbf{R}$, where $A = (0, 0, 0)$, $B = (0, 3, 4)$, along the straight line connecting these points.

21. Let C denote the plane curve whose vector equation is

$$\mathbf{r}(t) = (e^t \cos t)\mathbf{i} + (e^t \sin t)\mathbf{j}.$$

Evaluate the line integral

$$\int \frac{x \, dx + y \, dy}{(x^2 + y^2)^{3/2}}$$

along that arc of C from the point $(1, 0)$ to the point $(e^{2\pi}, 0)$.

22. If the density $\rho(x, y, z)$ of a fluid is a function of the pressure $p(x, y, z)$, and

$$\phi(x, y, z) = \int_{p_0}^{p} (dp/\rho),$$

where p_0 is constant, show that $\nabla\phi = \nabla p/\rho$.

23. If $\mathbf{F} = y\mathbf{i}$, show that the line integral $\int_A^B \mathbf{F} \cdot d\mathbf{R}$ along an arc AB in the xy-plane is equal to an area bounded by the x-axis, the arc, and the ordinates at A and B.

Remark. Despite similarity of appearance and identity of value, the integral of this problem and the integral of earlier calculus are conceptually distinct. The latter is a line integral for which the path lies along the x-axis.

24. The "curl" of a vector field

$$\mathbf{F} = \mathbf{i}f(x, y, z) + \mathbf{j}g(x, y, z) + \mathbf{k}h(x, y, z)$$

is defined to be del cross $\mathbf{F}$; that is,

$$\text{curl } \mathbf{F} \equiv \nabla \times \mathbf{F} \equiv \begin{vmatrix} \mathbf{i} & \mathbf{j} & \mathbf{k} \\ \dfrac{\partial}{\partial x} & \dfrac{\partial}{\partial y} & \dfrac{\partial}{\partial z} \\ f & g & h \end{vmatrix},$$

or

$$\text{curl } \mathbf{F} \equiv \mathbf{i}\left(\frac{\partial h}{\partial y} - \frac{\partial g}{\partial z}\right) + \mathbf{j}\left(\frac{\partial f}{\partial z} - \frac{\partial h}{\partial x}\right) + \mathbf{k}\left(\frac{\partial g}{\partial x} - \frac{\partial f}{\partial y}\right),$$

and the "divergence" of a vector field

$$\mathbf{V} = \mathbf{i}u(x, y, z) + \mathbf{j}v(x, y, z) + \mathbf{k}w(x, y, z)$$

is defined to be del dot $\mathbf{V}$; that is,

$$\text{div } \mathbf{V} \equiv \nabla \cdot \mathbf{V} \equiv \frac{\partial u}{\partial x} + \frac{\partial v}{\partial y} + \frac{\partial w}{\partial z}.$$

If the components f, g, h of $\mathbf{F}$ are functions that possess continuous mixed partial derivatives

$$\frac{\partial^2 h}{\partial x \, \partial y}, \quad \ldots,$$

show that

$$\text{div (curl } \mathbf{F}) = 0.$$

25. Assume the notation of Problem 24.

a) Prove that if ϕ is a scalar function of x, y, z, then

$$\text{curl (grad } \phi) = \nabla \times (\nabla\phi) = 0.$$

b) State in terms of the vector field $\nabla \times \mathbf{F}$ how you would express the condition that $\mathbf{F} \cdot d\mathbf{r}$ be an exact differential.

Prove the following results: If

$$\mathbf{r} = x\mathbf{i} + y\mathbf{j} + z\mathbf{k},$$

c) div $(\phi\mathbf{F}) \equiv \nabla \cdot (\phi\mathbf{F}) = \phi\nabla \cdot \mathbf{F} + \mathbf{F} \cdot \nabla\phi$;

d) $\nabla \times (\phi\mathbf{F}) = \phi\nabla \times \mathbf{F} + (\nabla\phi) \times \mathbf{F}$;

e) $\nabla \cdot (\mathbf{F}_1 \times \mathbf{F}_2) = \mathbf{F}_2 \cdot \nabla \times \mathbf{F}_1 - \mathbf{F}_1 \cdot \nabla \times \mathbf{F}_2$;

f) $\nabla \cdot \mathbf{r} = 3$ and $\nabla \times \mathbf{r} = 0$.

In this article, we turn our attention to two-dimensional vector fields of the form

$$\mathbf{F} = \mathbf{i}M(x, y) + \mathbf{j}N(x, y). \tag{1}$$

Figure 15–10 shows how such a two-dimensional vector field might look in space. In the figure, for example, $\mathbf{F}$ might represent a fluid flow in which each particle travels in a circle parallel to the xy-plane in such a way that all particles on a given line perpendicular to the xy-plane travel with the same velocity. Example 1 provides another instance, that of an electric field with field strength

$$\mathbf{E} = \frac{\mathbf{i}x + \mathbf{j}y}{x^2 + y^2}. \tag{2}$$

Note that this formulation is like the righthand side of Eq. (1), with

$$M(x, y) = \frac{x}{x^2 + y^2}, \qquad N(x, y) = \frac{y}{x^2 + y^2}.$$

The essential features of a two-dimensional field are (1) the vectors in $\mathbf{F}$ are all parallel to one plane, which we have taken to be the xy-plane, and (2) in every plane parallel to the xy-plane, the field is the same as it is in that plane. In Eq. (1), the field has a zero $\mathbf{k}$-component everywhere, which makes the vectors parallel to the xy-plane. The $\mathbf{i}$- and $\mathbf{j}$-components do not depend on z, so they are the same in all planes parallel to the xy-plane.

EXAMPLE 1. An infinitely long, thin, straight wire has a uniform electric charge density δ_0. Using Coulomb's law, find the electric field intensity around the wire due to this charge.

Solution. From a physics textbook,* we find that *Coulomb's law* is an inverse-square law. It says that the force acting on a positive test charge q_0 placed at a distance r from a positive *point charge* q is directed away from q and has magnitude $(4\pi\epsilon_0)^{-1}(qq_0)/r^2$, where ϵ_0 is a certain constant called the *permittivity*. For the charged wire, we have a distributed charge instead of a point charge, but we handle it in the familiar way: We replace this distributed charge by a large number of tiny elements, add, and take limits.

15–4

TWO-DIMENSIONAL FIELDS: LINE INTEGRALS IN THE PLANE AND THEIR RELATION TO SURFACE INTEGRALS ON CYLINDERS

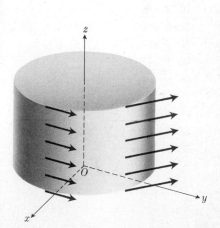

15–10 A two-dimensional vector field in space.

---

*   For example, Sears, Zemansky, Young, *University Physics* (Fifth edition, 1976), p. 412.

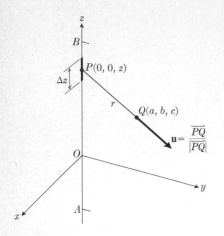

15–11 According to Coulomb's law, a charge $\delta_0\,\Delta z$ at $P(0, 0, z)$ produces a field $\Delta\mathbf{F}$ on a test charge q at $Q(a, b, c)$.

More specifically, suppose that the wire runs along the z-axis from $-\infty$ to $+\infty$. Take a long but finite piece of the wire and divide it into a lot of small segments. One of these is indicated in Fig. 15–11, with its center at $P(0, 0, z)$, and its length equal to Δz. We assume that Δz is so small that we can treat the charge $\delta_0\,\Delta z$ on this segment of the wire as a point charge at P. Now let $Q(a, b, c)$ be any point not on the z-axis, and let $\Delta\mathbf{F}$ denote the force at Q due to the point charge at P:

$$\Delta\mathbf{F} = \frac{\delta_0 q_0}{4\pi\epsilon_0}\frac{\Delta z\mathbf{u}}{a^2 + b^2 + (c - z)^2}, \tag{3a}$$

where $\mathbf{u}$ is a unit vector having the direction of $\overrightarrow{PQ}$:

$$\mathbf{u} = \frac{\mathbf{i}a + \mathbf{j}b + \mathbf{k}(c - z)}{[a^2 + b^2 + (c - z)^2]^{1/2}}. \tag{3b}$$

When we add the vector forces $\Delta\mathbf{F}$ for pieces of wire between $z = A$ and $z = B$ and take the limit as $\Delta z \to 0$, we get an integral of the form

$$\frac{\delta_0 q_0}{4\pi\epsilon_0}\int_A^B \frac{\mathbf{i}a + \mathbf{j}b + \mathbf{k}(c - z)}{[a^2 + b^2 + (c - z)^2]^{3/2}}\,dz. \tag{3c}$$

The denominator of the integrand behaves about like $|z|^3$ as $|z| \to \infty$, so the three component integrals in (3c) converge as $A \to -\infty$ and $B \to \infty$. As our final integral representation of the field, therefore, we get

$$\mathbf{F} = \frac{\delta_0 q_0}{4\pi\epsilon_0}\int_{-\infty}^{+\infty} \frac{\mathbf{i}a + \mathbf{j}b + \mathbf{k}(c - z)}{[a^2 + b^2 + (c - z)^2]^{3/2}}\,dz. \tag{4}$$

There are three separate integrals, but two are essentially the same except for the constant coefficients a and b, and the third is zero. It is easy to do the integration by making the substitutions

$$\sqrt{a^2 + b^2} = m,$$

$$z - c = m\tan\theta, \qquad \theta = \tan^{-1}\left(\frac{z - c}{m}\right),$$

$$dz = m\sec^2\theta\,d\theta,$$

and observing that the limits for θ are from $-\pi/2$ to $\pi/2$. In Problem 1 you are asked to finish these calculations and to show that the following result is correct:

$$\mathbf{F} = \frac{\delta_0 q_0}{2\pi\epsilon_0}\left(\frac{\mathbf{i}a + \mathbf{j}b}{a^2 + b^2}\right). \tag{5}$$

We observe that the result is a two-dimensional field that does not depend on $\mathbf{k}$ or on c. If we write the resultant field strength $\mathbf{E} = \mathbf{F}/q_0$ as a function of position (x, y, z) instead of (a, b, c), we have

$$\mathbf{E} = k_0\left(\frac{\mathbf{i}x + \mathbf{j}y}{x^2 + y^2}\right), \qquad \text{where } k_0 = \frac{\delta_0}{2\pi\epsilon_0}. \tag{6}$$

REMARK 1. There is also a fluid-flow interpretation for the field in Eq. (6) (or Eq. 2). To arrive at that interpretation, imagine a long, thin pipe running along the z-axis, and perforated with a very large number of little holes through which it supplies fluid at a constant rate. (It helps to be a bit vague about the actual physics of this: Don't try to be too literal-minded.) In other words, the z-axis is to be thought of as a *source* from which water flows radially outward and so produces a velocity field that is characterized by

$$\mathbf{v} = f(r)\mathbf{u}_r, \tag{7a}$$

where $\mathbf{u}_r$ is the usual unit vector associated with the cylindrical coordinates r, θ, z, and $f(r)$ is a function of r alone. Thus the velocity is all perpendicular to the z-axis, and it is independent of both θ and z. (These are our present interpretations of the phrases "at a constant rate" and "radially outward.") Now consider the amount of fluid that flows out through the cylinder $r = a$ between the planes $z = 0$ and $z = 1$ in a short interval of time, from t to $t + \Delta t$. According to the law expressed by Eq. (7a), every particle of water that is on the surface $r = a$ moves radially outward a distance Δr, which is approximately $f(a)\,\Delta t$. Thus the volume of fluid that crosses the boundary $r = a$ between $z = 0$ and $z = 1$ in this time interval is approximately the volume between the cylinders $r = a$ and $r = a + f(a)\,\Delta t$, or $2\pi a f(a)\,\Delta t$. If we multiply this by the density δ_1, we get the *mass* transported through a unit length of the cylinder $r = a$ in the interval from t to $t + \Delta t$:

$$\Delta m \approx \delta_1 2\pi a f(a)\,\Delta t. \tag{7b}$$

If we divide both sides of Eq. (7b) by Δt and take the limit as $\Delta t \to 0$, we get the *rate* at which fluid is flowing across the unit length of the cylinder $r = a$:

$$\frac{dm}{dt} = \delta_1 2\pi a f(a). \tag{7c}$$

For an incompressible fluid such as water, all fluid that flows across the cylinder $r = a$ flows across the cylinder $r = b$ as well (unless, of course, there are other sources or sinks between the two cylinders). Therefore, for the model under discussion, the rate of mass transport given by Eq. (7c) is independent of a, and its value for any radius $r = a$ is the same as for $r = 1$:

$$\delta_1 2\pi f(1) = \delta_1 2\pi a f(a). \tag{7d}$$

From Eq. (7d), we get

$$f(a) = f(1)/a \qquad \text{for any } a > 0.$$

Writing r in place of a and substituting C for $f(1)$, we can rewrite the velocity field (7a) in the form

$$\mathbf{v} = (C/r)\mathbf{u}_r. \tag{8}$$

If we recall that the position vector in cylindrical coordinates is

$$\mathbf{R} = \overrightarrow{OP} = r\mathbf{u}_r + \mathbf{k}z$$

and that this must also be equal to $\mathbf{R} = \mathbf{i}x + \mathbf{j}y + \mathbf{k}z$, then we conclude that

$$r\mathbf{u}_r = \mathbf{i}x + \mathbf{j}y, \qquad \text{or} \qquad \mathbf{u}_r = \frac{\mathbf{i}x + \mathbf{j}y}{r},$$

where

$$r = \sqrt{x^2 + y^2}. \qquad (9)$$

Therefore, Eqs. (6) and (8) describe the same field if $C = k_0$.

REMARK 2.   Instead of interpreting the two-dimensional vector fields as we have done in 3-space, we can interpret them simply as fields in the xy-plane itself. Then r in Eqs. (8) and (9) is just the distance from the origin to the point $P(x, y)$ in the plane, and the unit vector is

$$\mathbf{u}_r = \frac{(\mathbf{i}x + \mathbf{j}y)}{r} = \mathbf{i} \cos \theta + \mathbf{j} \sin \theta,$$

where $r > 0$ and θ measures the angle from the positive x-axis to the position vector $\overrightarrow{OP}$. Equation (8) then describes a vector field in the plane that is directed radially outward and whose strength decreases like $1/r$ as r increases. We still use the language of flow across boundaries, but in this interpretation the boundary would be a *curve* in the plane, rather than a unit length of a cylinder. Equation (7d) would be interpreted as saying that the amount of fluid flowing across the unit circle $r = 1$ per unit time is equal to the amount of fluid flowing across the circle $r = a$ in the same time. (This describes conditions after the flow has reached steady state, not during the transient phase.)

We can easily go back and forth between the two interpretations of two-dimensional fields, but henceforth we shall usually treat them as existing just in the xy-plane and ignore the fact that we can project the field onto any plane parallel to the xy-plane and thereby go to the 3-space view.

EXAMPLE 2.   Given the velocity field $\mathbf{v} = (\mathbf{i}x + \mathbf{j}y)/r^2$, calculate the mass-transport rate across the line segment AB joining the points $A(1, 0)$ and $B(0, 1)$.

Solution.   Let δ denote the density factor by which we multiply the area of a region to get the mass of fluid in that region. (We assume the density to be constant.) Consider a segment of the line having length Δs, with its center at $P(x, y)$ on AB. In Remark 3 below, we see that the mass of fluid Δm that flows across the segment in time Δt is given, approximately, by

$$\Delta m \approx (\mathbf{v} \cdot \mathbf{n})(\Delta t \, \Delta s) \, \delta, \qquad (10)$$

where $\mathbf{n}$ is a unit vector normal to the line AB at P, and pointing away from the origin:

$$\mathbf{n} = \frac{\mathbf{i} + \mathbf{j}}{\sqrt{2}}$$

If we divide both sides of Eq. (10) by Δt, then sum for all the pieces Δs of the segment AB, and take the limit as $\Delta s \to 0$, we get the *average rate* of mass transport across AB:

$$\frac{\Delta M}{\Delta t} \approx \int_{AB} \delta(\mathbf{v} \cdot \mathbf{n}) \, ds.$$

Finally, letting $\Delta t \to 0$ and substituting for $\mathbf{v}$, $\mathbf{n}$, and ds, with

$$x = t, \qquad y = 1 - t, \qquad 0 \le t \le 1$$

as parametrization of the segment AB, we get as the *instantaneous* mass-transport rate

$$\frac{dM}{dt} = \delta \int_0^1 \frac{x+y}{r^2\sqrt{2}} (\sqrt{2}\ dt)$$

$$= \delta \int_0^1 \frac{dt}{t^2 + (1-t)^2} \tag{11a}$$

$$= \delta(\pi/2). \tag{11b}$$

[In Exercise 2 you are asked to verify that the integral in (11a) yields the result (11b).]

REMARK 3.   The terms on the righthand side of Eq. (10) are explained this way (see Fig. 15-12): The quantity $\mathbf{v}\,\Delta t$ is, very nearly, the vector displacement of all particles of fluid that were on the segment Δs at time t; hence those particles have swept over a parallelogram with dimensions Δs and $|\mathbf{v}\,\Delta t|$. The $\mathbf{n}$-component of $\mathbf{v}\,\Delta t$ is the altitude h of this parallelogram. Its area is therefore approximately

$$(\mathbf{v}\,\Delta t) \cdot \mathbf{n} \text{ times } \Delta s,$$

and the mass of fluid that fills this parallelogram is what flows across the tiny segment Δs between t and $t + \Delta t$.

This same line of reasoning would apply to flows in the xy-plane in general. It leads to the result

$$\frac{dM}{dt} = \int_C \delta(\mathbf{v} \cdot \mathbf{n})\ ds, \tag{12}$$

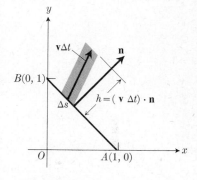

15-12   Fluid that flows across Δs in time Δt fills the parallelogram whose altitude is $h = (\mathbf{v}\,\Delta t) \cdot \mathbf{n}$.

where dM/dt is the *rate* at which mass is being transported across the curve C, in the direction of the unit normal vector $\mathbf{n}$. One can interpret M as the amount of mass that has crossed C up to time t.

If the oppositely directed normal $\mathbf{n}' = -\mathbf{n}$ is substituted in place of $\mathbf{n}$ in the integral in Eq. (12), the sign of the answer changes. This just means that if flow in one direction across C is considered to be in the positive sense, then flow in the opposite direction is then considered to be negative. If C is a simple closed curve, we usually choose $\mathbf{n}$ to point outward. In Eqs. (11a, b), we chose the normal to point away from the origin; we got a positive answer because the flow in the first quadrant is generally upward and to the right for the given $\mathbf{v}$.

To simplify further discussion, we take

$$\delta\mathbf{v} = \mathbf{F}(x, y)$$

in Eq. (12), and call the resulting integral the *flux* of $\mathbf{F}$ across C:

$$\text{Flux of } \mathbf{F} \text{ across } C = \int_C \mathbf{F} \cdot \mathbf{n}\ ds. \tag{13}$$

We shall use this terminology even when the field $\mathbf{F}$ has nothing to do with a fluid flow, but you may wish to keep the fluid-flow interpretation in mind too.

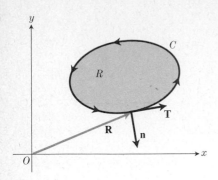

15–13 The position vector $\mathbf{R} = \mathbf{i}x + \mathbf{j}y$, the unit tangent vector $\mathbf{T} = d\mathbf{R}/ds$, and the unit normal vector $\mathbf{n} = \mathbf{T} \times \mathbf{k}$.

The curve C in Eq. (13) is to have a direction along it that is called the *positive* direction. For theoretical purposes, we find it convenient to use the arc length s, measured from some arbitrary point on C. Then s should *increase* as we proceed in the positive direction along C. (We assume that C is piecewise smooth enough to have a tangent.) Then the position vector $\mathbf{R} = \mathbf{i}x + \mathbf{j}y$ has derivative $d\mathbf{R}/ds = \mathbf{T}$, where $\mathbf{T}$ is a *unit tangent vector* pointing in the positive direction along C. (At a cusp or corner on C, the tangent will not exist, but this won't matter for most of our applications that involve integrals.) Because we often want the flux integral to represent flow outward from a region R bounded by a simple closed curve C, we choose the counterclockwise direction on C as positive, and choose the *outward*-pointing unit normal vector as $\mathbf{n}$. From Fig. 15–13, we can see that, because

$$\mathbf{T} = \frac{dx}{ds}\mathbf{i} + \frac{dy}{ds}\mathbf{j}, \tag{14a}$$

for the indicated choice of $\mathbf{n}$ we should choose $\mathbf{n} = \mathbf{T} \times \mathbf{k}$, so that

$$\mathbf{n} = \frac{dy}{ds}\mathbf{i} - \frac{dx}{ds}\mathbf{j}. \tag{14b}$$

As a check, it is easy to see that the dot product of the vectors in Eqs. (14a) and (14b) is zero, that both have unit length, and that when $\mathbf{T}$ points upward and to the right, $\mathbf{n}$ has a positive $\mathbf{i}$-component and a negative $\mathbf{j}$-component. If we proceed around the curve C in the direction in which $\mathbf{T}$ points, with the interior toward our left, then $\mathbf{n}$, as given by Eq. (14b), points to our right, as it should.

We now use Eq. (14b) to write the flux integral. We assume that

$$\mathbf{F}(x, y) = \mathbf{i}M(x, y) + \mathbf{j}N(x, y).$$

Then it follows that

$$\text{Flux across } C = \int_C \mathbf{F} \cdot \mathbf{n} \, ds$$

$$= \int_C \left(M\frac{dy}{ds} - N\frac{dx}{ds} \right) ds \tag{15}$$

$$= \int_C (M\, dy - N\, dx).$$

The virtue of the final integral in Eq. (15) is this: It can be evaluated using *any* reasonable parametrization of C; we aren't restricted to using the arc length s, provided we integrate in the positive direction along C.

EXAMPLE 3. Find the flux of the field

$$\mathbf{F} = 2x\mathbf{i} - 3y\mathbf{j}$$

outward across the ellipse

$$x = \cos t, \qquad y = 4 \sin t, \qquad 0 \le t \le 2\pi.$$

Solution. By Eq. (15), for the flux we have

$$\int_C (M \, dy - N \, dx) = \int_C (2x \, dy + 3y \, dx)$$

$$= \int_0^{2\pi} (8 \cos^2 t - 12 \sin^2 t) \, dt$$

$$= \int_0^{2\pi} [4(1 + \cos 2t) - 6(1 - \cos 2t)] \, dt$$

$$= -4\pi.$$

The negative answer just means that the net flux is inward.

REMARK 4.   The integral that we have just evaluated was set up as a flux integral, but it can also be interpreted as a work integral of the form

$$\int_C \mathbf{G} \cdot d\mathbf{R} = \int_C (3y\mathbf{i} + 2x\mathbf{j}) \cdot (\mathbf{i} \, dx + \mathbf{j} \, dy).$$

Conversely, any work integral in the plane can be reinterpreted as a flux integral of a related field. Problem 7 asks you to supply the details.

PROBLEMS

1. In Example 1, complete the calculations that lead from Eq. (4) to Eq. (5).

2. Evaluate

$$\int_0^1 \frac{dt}{2t^2 - 2t + 1}$$

by changing it to

$$\int_0^1 \frac{2 \, dt}{(2t - 1)^2 + 1}$$

and making a change of variables. You will thereby verify the answer given in Eq. (11b).

3. Find the rate of mass transport outward across the circle $r = a$ for the (velocity) flow field of Example 2. [The calculations are trivial if you interpret Eq. (12) correctly.]

4. In a three-dimensional velocity field, let S be a closed surface bounding a region D in its interior. Explain why

$$\iint_S \delta(\mathbf{v} \cdot \mathbf{n}) \, d\sigma$$

can be interpreted as the rate of mass transport outward through S if $\mathbf{n}$ is the outward-pointing unit vector normal to S.

In Problems 5 and 6, use the result of Problem 4 to find the rate of mass transport outward through the surface given, if the flow vector $\mathbf{F} = \delta\mathbf{v}$ is:

a) $\mathbf{F} = -\mathbf{i}y + \mathbf{j}x$,

b) $\mathbf{F} = (x^2 + y^2 + z^2)^{-3/2}(\mathbf{i}x + \mathbf{j}y + \mathbf{k}z)$.

5. S is the sphere $x^2 + y^2 + z^2 = a^2$.

6. S is the closed cylinder $x^2 + y^2 = a^2$, $-h \le z \le h$, plus the end disks $z = \pm h$, $x^2 + y^2 \le a^2$.

7. Suppose that C is a directed curve with unit tangent and normal vectors $\mathbf{T}$ and $\mathbf{n}$ related as in the text, and suppose that $\mathbf{F}$ and $\mathbf{G}$ are two-dimensional fields:

$$\mathbf{F}(x, y) = \mathbf{i}M(x, y) + \mathbf{j}N(x, y),$$

$$\mathbf{G}(x, y) = -\mathbf{i}N(x, y) + \mathbf{j}M(x, y).$$

Show that

$$\int_C \mathbf{F} \cdot \mathbf{n} \, ds = \int_C \mathbf{G} \cdot \mathbf{T} \, ds.$$

Which integral represents work? Which represents flux?

15-5

GREEN'S THEOREM

This theorem asserts that under suitable conditions the line integral

$$\oint (M\, dx + N\, dy) \tag{1}$$

around a simple closed curve C in the xy-plane is equal to the double integral

$$\iint_R \left(\frac{\partial N}{\partial x} - \frac{\partial M}{\partial y} \right) dx\, dy \tag{2}$$

over the region R that lies inside C.

NOTATION.   The symbol $\oint$ is used only when the curve C is *closed*.

EXAMPLE 1.   Let C be the circle $x = a \cos\theta$, $y = a \sin\theta$, $0 \le \theta \le 2\pi$, and let $M = -y$, $N = x$. Then (1) is

$$\oint_C (-y\, dx + x\, dy) = \int_0^{2\pi} a^2(\sin^2\theta + \cos^2\theta)\, d\theta = 2\pi a^2,$$

and the double integral (2) is

$$\iint_{x^2+y^2 \le a^2} 2\, dx\, dy = 2\int_{\theta=0}^{2\pi} \int_0^a r\, dr\, d\theta = 2\pi a^2.$$

Both integrals equal twice the area inside the circle.

Green's theorem.   *Let C be a simple closed curve in the xy-plane such that a line parallel to either axis cuts C in at most two points. Let M, N, $\partial N/\partial x$, and $\partial M/\partial y$ be continuous functions of (x, y) inside and on C. Let R be the region inside C. Then*

$$\oint M\, dx + N\, dy = \iint_R \left[\frac{\partial N}{\partial x} - \frac{\partial M}{\partial y} \right] dx\, dy. \tag{3}$$

DISCUSSION.   We indicate that the line integral on the left side of Eq. (3) is to be taken counterclockwise, the usual positive direction in the plane. We did this automatically in Example 1 by letting θ vary from 0 to 2π in the parametric representation of the circle. Figure 15–14 shows a curve C made up of two parts,

$$C_1: \quad a \le x \le b, \qquad y_1 = f_1(x),$$
$$C_2: \quad b \ge x \ge a, \qquad y_2 = f_2(x).$$

We use this notation in the proof.

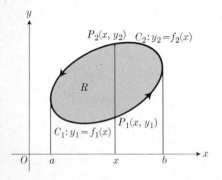

15–14 The boundary curve C, made up of C_1: $y = f_1(x)$ and C_2: $y = f_2(x)$.

Proof.   Consider the double integral of $\partial M/\partial y$ over R in Fig. 15–14. For any x between a and b, we first integrate with respect to y from $y_1 = f_1(x)$ to

$y_2 = f_2(x)$ and obtain

$$\int_{y_1}^{y_2} \frac{\partial M}{\partial y}\, dy = M(x, y)\Big]_{y = f_1(x)}^{y = f_2(x)} \tag{4}$$
$$= M(x, f_2(x)) - M(x, f_1(x)).$$

Next we integrate this with respect to x from a to b:

$$\int_a^b \int_{f_1(x)}^{f_2(x)} \frac{\partial M}{\partial y}\, dy\, dx = \int_a^b \{M(x, f_2(x)) - M(x, f_1(x))\}\, dx$$

$$= -\int_b^a M(x, f_2(x))\, dx - \int_a^b M(x, f_1(x))\, dx$$

$$= -\int_{C_2} M\, dx - \int_{C_1} M\, dx$$

$$= -\oint_C M\, dx.$$

Therefore

$$\oint_C M\, dx = \iint_R \left(-\frac{\partial M}{\partial y} \right) dx\, dy. \tag{5}$$

Equation (5) is half the result we need for Eq. (3). Problem 1 asks you to derive the other half, by integrating $\partial N/\partial x$ first with respect to x and then with respect to y, as suggested by Fig. 15–15. This shows the curve C of Fig. 15–14, decomposed into the two directed parts,

$$C_1': \quad c \le y \le d, \qquad x = g_1(y),$$
$$C_2': \quad d \ge y \ge c, \qquad x = g_2(y).$$

The result of this double integration is expressed by

$$\oint_C N\, dy = \iint_R \frac{\partial N}{\partial x}\, dx\, dy. \tag{6}$$

Combining Eqs. (5) and (6), we get Eq. (3). This concludes the proof.

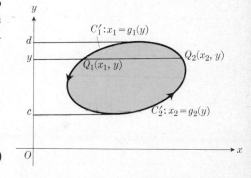

15–15 The boundary curve C', made up of $C_1': x_1 = g_1(y)$ and $C_2': x_2 = g_2(y)$.

EXAMPLE 2. Use Green's theorem to find the area enclosed by the ellipse

$$x = a \cos \theta, \qquad y = b \sin \theta, \qquad 0 \le \theta \le 2\pi.$$

Solution. If we take $M = -y$, $N = x$, as in Example 1, and apply Green's theorem, we obtain

$$\oint M\, dx + N\, dy = \int_{\theta = 0}^{2\pi} -y\, dx + x\, dy$$

$$= \int_0^{2\pi} ab(\sin^2 \theta + \cos^2 \theta)\, d\theta$$

$$= \int_0^{2\pi} ab\, d\theta = 2\pi ab,$$

and

$$\iint_R \left(\frac{\partial N}{\partial x} - \frac{\partial M}{\partial y} \right) dx \, dy = \iint_R 2 \, dx \, dy$$

$$= 2 \times (\text{area inside ellipse}).$$

Therefore

$$\text{Area inside ellipse} = \tfrac{1}{2} \oint (-y \, dx + x \, dy)$$

$$= \pi ab.$$

Corollary to Green's theorem. *If C is a simple closed curve such that a line parallel to either axis cuts it in at most two points, then the area enclosed by C is equal to*

$$\tfrac{1}{2} \oint_C (x \, dy - y \, dx).$$

Proof. If we take $M = -y/2$, $N = x/2$, we obtain

$$\oint_C (\tfrac{1}{2}x \, dy - \tfrac{1}{2}y \, dx) = \iint_R (\tfrac{1}{2} + \tfrac{1}{2}) \, dx \, dy \qquad (7)$$

$$= \text{Area of } R.$$

REMARK 1.   Green's theorem may apply to curves and regions that don't meet all of the requirements stated in it. For example, C could be a rectangle, as shown in Fig. 15–16. Here C is considered as composed of four directed parts:

$$C_1: \quad y = c, \qquad a \le x \le b,$$
$$C_2: \quad x = b, \qquad c \le y \le d,$$
$$C_3: \quad y = d, \qquad b \ge x \ge a,$$
$$C_4: \quad x = a, \qquad d \ge y \ge c.$$

The lines $x = a$ and $x = b$ intersect C in more than two points, and so do the boundaries $y = c$ and $y = d$.

Proceeding as in the proof of Eq. (6), we have

$$\int_{y=c}^d \int_{x=a}^b \frac{\partial N}{\partial x} \, dx \, dy = \int_c^d [N(b, y) - N(a, y)] \, dy$$

$$= \int_c^d N(b, y) \, dy + \int_d^c N(a, y) \, dy$$

$$= \int_{C_2} N \, dy + \int_{C_4} N \, dy. \qquad (8)$$

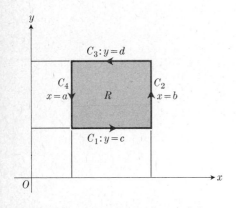

15–16 The rectangle made up of the four segments C_1, C_2, C_3, C_4.

Because y is constant along C_1 and C_3,

$$\int_{C_1} N \, dy = \int_{C_3} N \, dy = 0,$$

so we can add

$$\int_{C_1} N \, dy + \int_{C_3} N \, dy$$

to the righthand side of Eq. (8) without changing the equality. Doing so, we have

$$\int_c^d \int_a^b \frac{\partial N}{\partial x} \, dx \, dy = \oint_C N \, dy. \tag{9}$$

Similarly we could show that

$$\int_a^b \int_c^d \frac{\partial M}{\partial y} \, dy \, dx = -\oint_C M \, dx. \tag{10}$$

Subtracting (10) from (9), we again arrive at

$$\oint_C M \, dx + N \, dy = \iint_R \left(\frac{\partial N}{\partial x} - \frac{\partial M}{\partial y} \right) dx \, dy.$$

Regions such as those shown in Fig. 15–17 can be handled with no greater difficulty. Equation (3) still applies. It also applies to the horseshoe-shaped region R shown in Fig. 15–18, as we see by putting together the regions R_1 and R_2 and their boundaries. Green's theorem applies to C_1, R_1, and to C_2, R_2, yielding

$$\int_{C_1} M \, dx + N \, dy = \iint_{R_1} \left(\frac{\partial N}{\partial x} - \frac{\partial M}{\partial y} \right) dx \, dy,$$

$$\int_{C_2} M \, dx + N \, dy = \iint_{R_2} \left(\frac{\partial N}{\partial x} - \frac{\partial M}{\partial y} \right) dx \, dy.$$

When we add, the line integral along the y-axis from b to a for C_1 cancels the integral over the same segment but in the opposite direction for C_2. Hence

$$\oint_C (M \, dx + N \, dy) = \iint_R \left(\frac{\partial N}{\partial x} - \frac{\partial M}{\partial y} \right) dx \, dy,$$

where C consists of the two segments of the x-axis from $-b$ to $-a$ and from a to b, and of the two semicircles, and where R is the region inside C.

The device of adding line integrals over separate boundaries to build up an integral over a single boundary can be extended to any finite number of

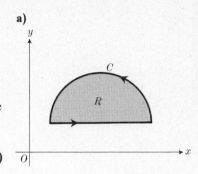

a)

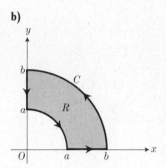

b)

15–17 Other regions to which Green's theorem applies.

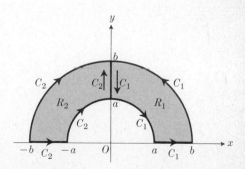

15–18 A region R that combines regions R_1 and R_2.

subregions. In Fig. 15–19(a), let C_1 be the boundary of the region R_1 in the first quadrant. Similarly for the other three quadrants: C_i is the boundary of the region R_i, $i = 1, 2, 3, 4$. By Green's theorem,

$$\oint_C M \, dx + N \, dy = \iint_{R_i} \left(\frac{\partial N}{\partial x} - \frac{\partial M}{\partial y} \right) dx \, dy. \tag{11}$$

We add Eqs. (11) for $i = 1, 2, 3, 4$, and get

$$\oint_{r=b} (M \, dx + N \, dy) + \oint_{r=a} (M \, dx + N \, dy) = \iint_{a \le r \le b} \left(\frac{\partial N}{\partial x} - \frac{\partial M}{\partial y} \right) dx \, dy. \tag{12}$$

Equation (12) says that the double integral of

$$\left(\frac{\partial N}{\partial x} - \frac{\partial M}{\partial y} \right) dx \, dy$$

over the annular ring R is equal to the line integral of $M \, dx + N \, dy$ over the *entire* boundary of R, in that *direction* along the boundary that keeps the region R on one's left as one progresses. Figure 15–19(b) shows R and its boundary (two concentric circles) and the positive direction on the boundary.

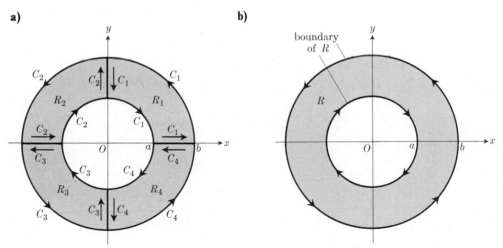

15–19 The annular region R combines four smaller regions.

EXAMPLE 3. Verify that Eq. (3) holds if

$$M = \frac{-y}{x^2 + y^2}, \qquad N = \frac{x}{x^2 + y^2},$$

$$R = \{(x, y): h^2 \le x^2 + y^2 \le 1\},$$

where $0 < h < 1$.

Solution. (See Fig. 15–20.) The boundary of R consists of the circle C_1:

$$x = \cos \theta, \qquad y = \sin \theta, \qquad 0 \le \theta \le 2\pi,$$

around which we shall integrate counterclockwise, and the circle C_h:

$$x = h \cos \phi, \qquad y = h \sin \phi, \qquad 2\pi \geq \phi \geq 0,$$

around which we shall integrate in the clockwise direction. Note that the origin is not included in R, because h is positive. For all $(x, y) \neq (0, 0)$, the functions M and N and their partial derivatives are continuous. Moreover,

$$\frac{\partial M}{\partial y} = \frac{(x^2 + y^2)(-1) + y(2y)}{(x^2 + y^2)^2} = \frac{y^2 - x^2}{(x^2 + y^2)^2} = \frac{\partial N}{\partial x},$$

so

$$\iint_R \left(\frac{\partial N}{\partial x} - \frac{\partial M}{\partial y} \right) dx\, dy = \iint_R 0\, dx\, dy = 0.$$

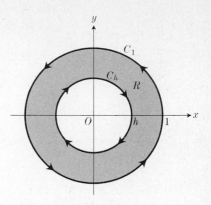

15–20 Green's theorem may be applied to the annulus R by integrating along the boundaries as shown.

The line integral is

$$\int_C M\, dx + N\, dy = \oint_{C_1} \frac{x\, dy - y\, dx}{x^2 + y^2} + \oint_{C_h} \frac{x\, dy - y\, dx}{x^2 + y^2}$$

$$= \int_0^{2\pi} (\cos^2 \theta + \sin^2 \theta)\, d\theta + \int_{2\pi}^0 \frac{h^2(\cos^2 \phi + \sin^2 \phi)\, d\phi}{h^2}$$

$$= 2\pi - 2\pi = 0.$$

REMARK 2. In Example 3, the functions M and N are discontinuous at $(0, 0)$, so we cannot immediately apply Green's theorem to C_1: $x^2 + y^2 = 1$, and all of the region inside it. We must delete the origin, which we did by excluding points inside C_h.

REMARK 3. In Example 3, we could replace the outer circle C_1 by an ellipse or any other simple closed curve Γ that lies outside C_h (for some positive h). The result would be

$$\oint_\Gamma (M\, dx + N\, dy) + \oint_{C_h} (M\, dx + N\, dy) = 0,$$

which leads to the conclusion

$$\oint_\Gamma \frac{x\, dy - y\, dx}{x^2 + y^2} = 2\pi.$$

This result is easily accounted for if we change to polar coordinates for Γ:

$$x = r \cos \theta, \qquad y = r \sin \theta,$$

$$dx = -r \sin \theta\, d\theta + \cos \theta\, dr,$$

$$dy = r \cos \theta\, d\theta + \sin \theta\, dr.$$

For then

$$\frac{x\, dy - y\, dx}{x^2 + y^2} = \frac{r^2(\cos^2 \theta + \sin^2 \theta)\, d\theta}{r^2} = d\theta;$$

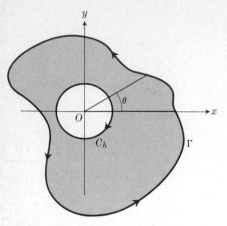

15–21 The region bounded by the circle C_h and the curve Γ.

and θ increases by 2π as we progress once around Γ counterclockwise (see Fig. 15–21).

Green's Theorem in Vector Form

Let

$$\mathbf{F} = M\mathbf{i} + N\mathbf{j} + P\mathbf{k} \qquad \text{and} \qquad \mathbf{R} = x\mathbf{i} + y\mathbf{j}.$$

Then the lefthand side of Eq. (3) is given by

$$\oint_C \mathbf{F} \cdot d\mathbf{R} = \oint_C (M\,dx + N\,dy).$$

To express the righthand side of Eq. (3) in vector form, we use the symbolic vector operator

$$\nabla = \mathbf{i}\,\frac{\partial}{\partial x} + \mathbf{j}\,\frac{\partial}{\partial y} + \mathbf{k}\,\frac{\partial}{\partial z}.$$

We met the del operator in Article 13–6, where we saw that if

$$w = f(x, y, z)$$

is a differentiable scalar function, then ∇w is the gradient of w:

$$\text{grad } w = \nabla w = \mathbf{i}\,\frac{\partial w}{\partial x} + \mathbf{j}\,\frac{\partial w}{\partial y} + \mathbf{k}\,\frac{\partial w}{\partial z}.$$

Other uses of the del operator are given in Problem 24, Article 15–3, where the curl of a vector $\mathbf{F}$ is defined to be del cross $\mathbf{F}$. Hence, if $\mathbf{F} = M\mathbf{i} + N\mathbf{j} + P\mathbf{k}$, then

$$\text{curl } \mathbf{F} = \nabla \times \mathbf{F} = \begin{vmatrix} \mathbf{i} & \mathbf{j} & \mathbf{k} \\ \dfrac{\partial}{\partial x} & \dfrac{\partial}{\partial y} & \dfrac{\partial}{\partial z} \\ M & N & P \end{vmatrix}$$

$$= \mathbf{i}\left(\frac{\partial P}{\partial y} - \frac{\partial N}{\partial z}\right) + \mathbf{j}\left(\frac{\partial M}{\partial z} - \frac{\partial P}{\partial x}\right) + \mathbf{k}\left(\frac{\partial N}{\partial x} - \frac{\partial M}{\partial y}\right).$$

The component of curl $\mathbf{F}$ that is normal to the region R in the xy-plane is

$$(\nabla \times \mathbf{F}) \cdot \mathbf{k} = \frac{\partial N}{\partial x} - \frac{\partial M}{\partial y}.$$

Hence Green's theorem can be written in vector form as

$$\oint_C \mathbf{F} \cdot d\mathbf{R} = \iint_R (\nabla \times \mathbf{F}) \cdot d\mathbf{A}, \tag{13}$$

where $d\mathbf{A} = \mathbf{k}\,dx\,dy$ is a vector normal to the region R and of magnitude $|d\mathbf{A}| = dx\,dy$. In words, Green's theorem states that the integral around C of the tangential component of $\mathbf{F}$ is equal to the integral, over the region R bounded by C, of the component of curl $\mathbf{F}$ that is normal to R; this integral, specifically, is the flux through R of curl $\mathbf{F}$. We shall later extend this result to more general curves and surfaces in a formulation that is known as Stokes's theorem.

There is a second, *normal*, vector form for Green's theorem. It involves the gradient operator $\mathbf{V}$ in another form, one that produces the *divergence*. Now the integrand of the line integral of Eq. (13) is the *tangential* component of the field $\mathbf{F}$ because

$$\mathbf{F} \cdot d\mathbf{R} = \left(\mathbf{F} \cdot \frac{d\mathbf{R}}{ds} \right) ds = (\mathbf{F} \cdot \mathbf{T}) \, ds.$$

As in Article 15–4, if we let

$$\mathbf{F} = \mathbf{i}M(x, y) + \mathbf{j}N(x, y),$$

and let $\mathbf{G}$ be the orthogonal field given by

$$\mathbf{G} = \mathbf{i}N(x, y) - \mathbf{j}M(x, y),$$

then it follows that

$$\mathbf{F} \cdot \mathbf{T} = \mathbf{G} \cdot \mathbf{n} = M\frac{dx}{ds} + N\frac{dy}{ds}$$

because

$$\mathbf{T} = \mathbf{i}\frac{dx}{ds} + \mathbf{j}\frac{dy}{ds}, \qquad \mathbf{n} = \mathbf{i}\frac{dy}{ds} - \mathbf{j}\frac{dx}{ds}.$$

Therefore Green's theorem, which says that

$$\oint_C (M \, dx + N \, dy) = \iint_R \left[\frac{\partial N}{\partial x} - \frac{\partial M}{\partial y} \right] dx \, dy,$$

also says that

$$\oint_C \mathbf{G} \cdot \mathbf{n} \, ds = \iint_R \mathbf{V} \cdot \mathbf{G} \, dx \, dy, \qquad (14)$$

where

$$\mathbf{V} \cdot \mathbf{G} = \operatorname{div} \mathbf{G} = \frac{\partial N}{\partial x} + \frac{\partial(-M)}{\partial y}.$$

In words, Eq. (14) says that the line integral of the *normal* component of any vector field $\mathbf{G}$ around the boundary of a region R in which $\mathbf{G}$ is continuous and has continuous partial derivatives is equal to the double integral of the *divergence* of $\mathbf{G}$ over R. In the next article, we shall extend this result to three-dimensional vector fields and discuss the physical interpretation of the divergence. For such vector fields

$$\mathbf{F}(x, y, z) = \mathbf{i}M(x, y, z) + \mathbf{j}N(x, y, z) + \mathbf{k}P(x, y, z),$$

the *divergence* is defined to be

$$\operatorname{div} \mathbf{F} = \mathbf{V} \cdot \mathbf{F} = \frac{\partial M}{\partial x} + \frac{\partial N}{\partial y} + \frac{\partial P}{\partial z}. \qquad (15)$$

PROBLEMS

1. Supply the details necessary to establish Eq. (6).

2. Supply the steps necessary to establish Eq. (10).

In Problems 3 through 7, C is the circle $x^2 + y^2 = a^2$ and R is C plus its interior. Verify that

$$\oint_C M\, dx + N\, dy = \iint_R \left(\frac{\partial N}{\partial x} - \frac{\partial M}{\partial y} \right) dx\, dy,$$

given the condition stated in each problem.

3. $M = x$, $N = y$ **4.** $M = N = xy$

5. $M = -x^2 y$, $N = xy^2$ **6.** $M = N = e^{x+y}$

7. $M = y$, $N = 0$

8. Suppose that

$$R = \{(x, y): 0 \le y \le \sqrt{a^2 - x^2}, \quad -a \le x \le a\},$$

and that C is the boundary of R.

a) Sketch R and C.

b) Write out the proof of Green's formula for this region.

Definition. *A region R is said to be simply connected if every simple closed curve lying in R can be continuously contracted to a point without its touching any part of the boundary of R. Examples are the interiors of circles, ellipses, cardioids, and rectangles; and, in three dimensions, the region between two concentric spheres. (The annular ring in Fig. 15–20 is not simply connected.)*

9. Show, by a geometric argument, that Green's formula, Eq. (3), holds for any simply connected region R whose boundary is a simple closed curve C, provided R can be decomposed into a finite number of nonoverlapping regions $R_1, R_2, \ldots, R_n$ with boundaries $C_1, C_2, \ldots, C_n$ of a type for which the formula (3) is true for each R_i and C_i, $i = 1, \ldots, n$.

10. Suppose R is a region in the xy-plane, C is its boundary, and the area of R is given by

$$A(R) = \oint_C \tfrac{1}{2}(x\, dy - y\, dx).$$

Suppose the equations $x = f(u, v)$, $y = g(u, v)$ map R and C in a continuous and one-to-one manner onto a region R' and curve C', respectively, in the uv-plane. Use Green's formula to show that

$$\iint_R dx\, dy = \iint_{R'} \begin{vmatrix} f_u & f_v \\ g_u & g_v \end{vmatrix} du\, dv$$

$$= \iint_R \left(\frac{\partial f}{\partial u} \frac{\partial g}{\partial v} - \frac{\partial f}{\partial v} \frac{\partial g}{\partial u} \right) du\, dv.$$

[*Hint*. Note that

$$\iint_R dx\, dy = \tfrac{1}{2} \int_C (x\, dy - y\, dx)$$

$$= \frac{1}{2} \int_{C'} \left[f(u, v) \left(\frac{\partial g}{\partial u} du + \frac{\partial g}{\partial v} dv \right) \right.$$

$$\left. - g(u, v) \left(\frac{\partial f}{\partial u} du + \frac{\partial f}{\partial v} dv \right) \right],$$

and apply Green's formula to C' and R'.]

In Problems 11 and 12, with C as given, evaluate the line integrals by applying Green's formula.

11. C is the triangle bounded by $x = 0$, $x + y = 1$, $y = 0$:

$$\int_C (y^2\, dx + x^2\, dy).$$

12. C is the boundary of $0 \le x \le \pi$, $0 \le y \le \sin x$:

$$\int_C (3y\, dx + 2x\, dy).$$

13. Rewrite Eq. (14) in nonvector notation for a vector field $\mathbf{F} = \mathbf{i} M(x, y) + \mathbf{j} N(x, y)$ in place of $\mathbf{G}$. (In other words, first write it in vector form with $\mathbf{F}$ in place of $\mathbf{G}$, and then translate the result into nonvector notation.)

THE DIVERGENCE THEOREM

This theorem states that under appropriate conditions, the triple integral

$$\iiint_D \operatorname{div} \mathbf{F}\, dV \tag{1}$$

is equal to the double integral

$$\iint_S \mathbf{F} \cdot \mathbf{n}\, d\sigma. \tag{2}$$

Here $\mathbf{F} = \mathbf{i}M + \mathbf{j}N + \mathbf{k}P$, with M, N, and P continuous functions of (x, y, z) that have continuous first-order partial derivatives:

$$\text{div } \mathbf{F} = \frac{\partial M}{\partial x} + \frac{\partial N}{\partial y} + \frac{\partial P}{\partial z};$$

$\mathbf{n} \, d\sigma$ is a vector element of surface area directed along the unit outer normal vector $\mathbf{n}$; and S is the surface enclosing the region D. We shall first show that (1) and (2) are equal if D is some convex region with no holes, such as the interior of a sphere, or a cube, or an ellipsoid, and if S is a piecewise smooth surface. In addition, we assume that the projection of D into the xy-plane is a simply connected region R_{xy} and that any line perpendicular to the xy-plane at an interior point of R_{xy} intersects the surface S in at most two points, producing surfaces S_1 and S_2:

$$S_1: \quad z_1 = f_1(x, y), \quad (x, y) \text{ in } R_{xy},$$

$$S_2: \quad z_2 = f_2(x, y), \quad (x, y) \text{ in } R_{xy},$$

with $z_1 \leq z_2$. Similarly for the projection of D onto the other coordinate planes.

If we write the unit normal vector $\mathbf{n}$ in terms of its direction cosines, as

$$\mathbf{n} = \mathbf{i} \cos \alpha + \mathbf{j} \cos \beta + \mathbf{k} \cos \gamma,$$

then

$$\mathbf{F} \cdot (\mathbf{n} \, d\sigma) = (\mathbf{F} \cdot \mathbf{n}) \, d\sigma = (M \cos \alpha + N \cos \beta + P \cos \gamma) \, d\sigma; \qquad \text{(3)}$$

and the divergence theorem states that

$$\iiint\limits_{D} \left(\frac{\partial M}{\partial x} + \frac{\partial N}{\partial y} + \frac{\partial P}{\partial z} \right) dx \, dy \, dz = \iint\limits_{S} (M \cos \alpha + N \cos \beta + P \cos \gamma) \, d\sigma. \qquad \text{(4)}$$

We see that both sides of Eq. (4) are additive with respect to M, N, and P, and that our task is to prove

$$\iiint \frac{\partial M}{\partial x} dx \, dy \, dz = \iint M \cos \alpha \, d\sigma, \qquad \text{(5a)}$$

$$\iiint \frac{\partial N}{\partial y} dx \, dy \, dz = \iint N \cos \beta \, d\sigma, \qquad \text{(5b)}$$

$$\iiint \frac{\partial P}{\partial z} dx \, dy \, dz = \iint P \cos \gamma \, d\sigma. \qquad \text{(5c)}$$

We shall establish (5c) in detail.

Figure 15–22 illustrates the projection of D into the xy-plane. The surface S consists of the *upper part*

$$S_2: \quad z = f_2(x, y), \quad (x, y) \text{ in } R_{xy},$$

and the *lower part*:

$$S_1: \quad z = f_1(x, y), \quad (x, y) \text{ in } R_{xy}.$$

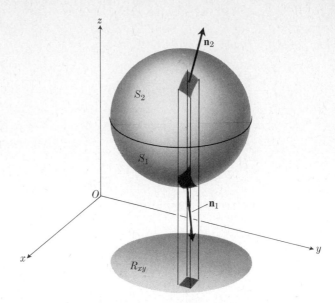

15-22   Regions S_1 and S_2 project onto R_{xy}.

On the surface S_2, the outer normal has a positive **k**-component, and

$$\cos \gamma_2 \, d\sigma_2 = dx \, dy \tag{6a}$$

is the projection of $d\sigma$ into R_{xy}. On the surface S_1, the outer normal has a negative **k**-component, and

$$\cos \gamma_1 \, d\sigma_1 = -dx \, dy. \tag{6b}$$

Therefore we can evaluate the surface integral on the righthand side of Eq. (5c):

$$\iint P \cos \gamma \, d\sigma = \iint\limits_{S_2} P_2 \cos \gamma_2 \, d\sigma_2 + \iint\limits_{S_1} P_1 \cos \gamma_1 \, d\sigma_1$$

$$= \iint\limits_{R_{xy}} P(x, y, z_2) \, dx \, dy - \iint\limits_{R_{xy}} P(x, y, z_1) \, dx \, dy$$

$$= \iint\limits_{R_{xy}} [P(x, y, z_2) - P(x, y, z_1)] \, dx \, dy$$

$$= \iint\limits_{R_{xy}} \left[\int_{z_1}^{z_2} \frac{\partial P}{\partial z} \, dz \right] dx \, dy$$

$$= \iiint\limits_{D} \frac{\partial P}{\partial z} \, dz \, dx \, dy. \tag{7}$$

Thus we have established Eq. (5c). Proofs for (5a) and (5b) follow the same pattern; or just permute x, y, z; M, N, P; α, β, γ, in order, and get those results from (5c) by renaming the axes. Finally, by addition of (5a, b, c), we get Eq. (4):

$$\iiint_D \text{div } \mathbf{F} \, dV = \iint_S \mathbf{F} \cdot \mathbf{n} \, d\sigma. \tag{8}$$

EXAMPLE 1. Verify Eq. (8) for the sphere

$$x^2 + y^2 + z^2 = a^2$$

if

$$\mathbf{F} = \mathbf{i}x + \mathbf{j}y + \mathbf{k}z.$$

Solution

$$\text{div } \mathbf{F} = \frac{\partial x}{\partial x} + \frac{\partial y}{\partial y} + \frac{\partial z}{\partial z} = 3,$$

so

$$\iiint_D \text{div } \mathbf{F} \, dV = \iiint_D 3 \, dV = 3(\tfrac{4}{3}\pi a^3) = 4\pi a^3.$$

To find a unit vector **n** normal to the surface S, we first write the equation of S in the form $f(x, y, z) = 0$, and then (see Article 13–6) use

$$\mathbf{n} = \pm \frac{\text{grad } f}{|\text{grad } f|}.$$

Here

$$f(x, y, z) = x^2 + y^2 + z^2 - a^2;$$

the outer unit normal is

$$\mathbf{n} = \frac{2(x\mathbf{i} + y\mathbf{j} + z\mathbf{k})}{\sqrt{4(x^2 + y^2 + z^2)}} = \frac{x\mathbf{i} + y\mathbf{j} + z\mathbf{k}}{a},$$

and

$$\mathbf{F} \cdot \mathbf{n} \, d\sigma = \frac{x^2 + y^2 + z^2}{a} \, d\sigma = \frac{a^2}{a} \, d\sigma = a \, d\sigma,$$

because $x^2 + y^2 + z^2 = a^2$ on the surface. Therefore

$$\iint_S \mathbf{F} \cdot d\boldsymbol{\sigma} = \iint_S a \, d\sigma = a(4\pi a^2) = 4\pi a^3.$$

EXAMPLE 2. Show that Eq. (8) holds for the cube with faces in the planes

$$x = x_0, \qquad x = x_0 + h,$$
$$y = y_0, \qquad y = y_0 + h,$$
$$z = z_0, \qquad z = z_0 + h,$$

where h is a positive constant.

Solution. We compute $\iint \mathbf{F} \cdot \mathbf{n} \, d\sigma$ as the sum of the integrals over the six faces separately. We begin with the two faces perpendicular to the x-axis. For the face $x = x_0$ and the face $x = x_0 + h$, respectively, we have the first and second lines of the following table.

Range of integration	Outward unit normal	$\iint (\mathbf{F} \cdot \mathbf{n}) \, d\sigma$
$y_0 \le y \le y_0 + h,\ z_0 \le z \le z_0 + h$	$-\mathbf{i}$	$-\iint M(x_0, y, z) \, dy \, dz$
$y_0 \le y \le y_0 + h,\ z_0 \le z \le z_0 + h$	$\mathbf{i}$	$+\iint M(x_0 + h, y, z) \, dy \, dz$

The sum of the surface integrals over these two faces is

$$\iint (\mathbf{F} \cdot \mathbf{n}) \, d\sigma = \iint [M(x_0 + h, y, z) - M(x_0, y, z)] \, dy \, dz$$

$$= \iint \left(\int_{x_0}^{x_0 + h} \frac{\partial M}{\partial x} \, dx \right) dy \, dz$$

$$= \iiint_D \frac{\partial M}{\partial x} \, dV.$$

Similarly the sum of the surface integrals over the two faces perpendicular to the y-axis is equal to

$$\iiint (\partial N / \partial y) \, dV;$$

and the sum of the surface integrals over the other two faces is equal to $\iiint (\partial P / \partial z) \, dV$. Hence the surface integral over the six faces is equal to the sum of the three volume integrals, and Eq. (8) holds for the cube:

$$\iint_S \mathbf{F} \cdot \mathbf{n} \, d\sigma = \iiint_D \left(\frac{\partial M}{\partial x} + \frac{\partial N}{\partial y} + \frac{\partial P}{\partial z} \right) dV$$

$$= \iiint_D \operatorname{div} \mathbf{F} \, dV.$$

REMARK 1. The divergence theorem can be extended to more complex regions that can be split up into a finite number of simple regions of the type discussed, and to regions that can be defined by certain limiting processes. For example, suppose D is the region between two concentric spheres, and $\mathbf{F}$ has continuously differentiable components throughout D and on the bounding surfaces. Split D by an equatorial plane and apply the divergence theorem to each half separately. The top half, D_1, is shown in Fig. 15–23. The surface that bounds D_1 consists of an outer hemisphere, a plane washer-shaped base, and an inner hemisphere. The divergence theorem says that

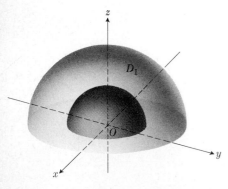

15–23 Upper half of the region between two spheres.

$$\iiint_{D_1} \operatorname{div} \mathbf{F} \, dV_1 = \iint_{S_1} \mathbf{F} \cdot \mathbf{n}_1 \, d\sigma_1. \tag{9a}$$

The unit normal $\mathbf{n}_1$ that points outward from D_1 points away from the origin along the outer surface, points down along the flat base, and points toward the origin along the inner surface. Next apply the divergence theorem to D_2, as shown in Fig. 15–24:

$$\iiint\limits_{D_2} \text{div } \mathbf{F} \, dV_2 = \iint\limits_{S_2} \mathbf{F} \cdot \mathbf{n}_2 \, d\sigma_2. \tag{9b}$$

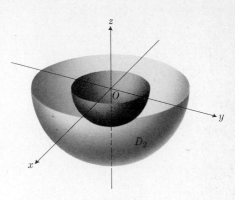

As we follow $\mathbf{n}_2$ over S_2, pointing outward from D_2, we see that $\mathbf{n}_2$ points upward along the flat surface in the xy-plane, points away from the origin on the outer sphere, and points toward the origin on the inner sphere. When we add (9a) and (9b), the surface integrals over the flat base cancel because of the opposite signs of $\mathbf{n}_1$ and $\mathbf{n}_2$. We thus arrive at the result

$$\iiint\limits_{D} \text{div } \mathbf{F} \, dV = \iint\limits_{S} \mathbf{F} \cdot \mathbf{n} \, d\sigma, \tag{10}$$

15–24   Lower half of the region between two spheres.

with D the region between the spheres, S the boundary of D consisting of two spheres, and $\mathbf{n}$ the unit normal to S directed outward from D.

EXAMPLE 3.   Verify Eq. (10) for the region

$$1 \le x^2 + y^2 + z^2 \le 4$$

if

$$\mathbf{F} = -\frac{\mathbf{i}x + \mathbf{j}y + \mathbf{k}z}{\rho^3}, \qquad \rho = \sqrt{x^2 + y^2 + z^2}.$$

Solution.   Observe that

$$\frac{\partial \rho}{\partial x} = \frac{x}{\rho}$$

and

$$\frac{\partial}{\partial x}(x\rho^{-3}) = \rho^{-3} - 3x\rho^{-4}\frac{\partial \rho}{\partial x} = \frac{1}{\rho^3} - \frac{3x^2}{\rho^5}.$$

Thus, throughout the region $1 \le \rho \le 2$, all functions considered are continuous, and

$$\text{div } \mathbf{F} = \frac{-3}{\rho^3} + \frac{3}{\rho^5}(x^2 + y^2 + z^2) = -\frac{3}{\rho^3} + \frac{3\rho^2}{\rho^5} = 0.$$

Therefore

$$\iiint\limits_{D} \text{div } \mathbf{F} \, dV = 0. \tag{11}$$

On the outer sphere ($\rho = 2$), the positive unit normal is

$$\mathbf{n} = \frac{\mathbf{i}x + \mathbf{j}y + \mathbf{k}z}{\rho},$$

and

$$\mathbf{F} \cdot \mathbf{n} \, d\sigma = -\frac{x^2 + y^2 + z^2}{\rho^4} \, d\sigma = -\frac{1}{\rho^2} \, d\sigma.$$

Hence

$$\iint_{\rho=2} \mathbf{F} \cdot \mathbf{n} \, d\sigma = -\tfrac{1}{4} \iint_{\rho=2} d\sigma$$

$$= -\tfrac{1}{4} \cdot 4\pi\rho^2 = -\pi\rho^2 = -4\pi. \tag{12a}$$

On the inner sphere ($\rho = 1$), the positive unit normal points toward the origin; its equation is

$$\mathbf{n} = \frac{-(\mathbf{i}x + \mathbf{j}y + \mathbf{k}z)}{\rho}.$$

Hence

$$\mathbf{F} \cdot \mathbf{n} \, d\sigma = +\frac{x^2 + y^2 + z^2}{\rho^4} = \frac{1}{\rho^2} \, d\sigma.$$

Thus

$$\iint_{\rho=1} \mathbf{F} \cdot \mathbf{n} \, d\sigma = \iint_{\rho=1} \frac{1}{\rho^2} d\sigma$$

$$= \frac{1}{\rho^2} \cdot 4\pi\rho^2 = 4\pi. \tag{12b}$$

The sum of (12a) and (12b) is the surface integral over the complete boundary of D:

$$-4\pi + 4\pi = 0,$$

which agrees with (11), as it should.

REMARK 2. We can also conclude that if div $\mathbf{F}$ is continuous at a point Q, then

$$(\text{div } \mathbf{F})_Q = \lim_{\rho \to 0} \left(\frac{3}{4\pi\rho^3} \iint_S \mathbf{F} \cdot \mathbf{n} \, d\sigma \right). \tag{13}$$

Here S is a sphere of radius ρ centered at Q. We take D to be the interior of such a sphere and apply the divergence theorem. The argument is this: If div $\mathbf{F}$ is continuous at Q, then its average value throughout V approaches the value at Q as $\rho \to 0$:

$$\lim_{\rho \to 0} \left(\frac{1}{\tfrac{4}{3}\pi\rho^3} \iiint_V \text{div } \mathbf{F} \, dV \right) = (\text{div } \mathbf{F})_Q.$$

We substitute

$$\iint_S \mathbf{F} \cdot \mathbf{n}\, d\sigma \qquad \text{for} \qquad \iiint_D \text{div } \mathbf{F}\, dV$$

to get Eq. (13). Equation (13) can be taken as the definition of div **F**, and often is. Such a definition has the advantage of being coordinate-free. If one starts with Eq. (13) as a definition, one can then prove the divergence theorem and the coordinate representation of div **F** as

$$\frac{\partial F_x}{\partial x} + \frac{\partial F_y}{\partial y} + \frac{\partial F_z}{\partial z}.$$

However, we take Eq. (13) as a derived result, and see that it leads to the following interpretation of div **F**. Suppose **v** is the velocity field of a moving fluid, and δ is the density. If $\mathbf{F} = \delta\mathbf{v}$, then **F** specifies the mass flow per unit of time, and $\mathbf{F} \cdot \mathbf{n}$ is the component of flow normal to S; hence

$$\iint_S \mathbf{F} \cdot \mathbf{n}\, d\sigma$$

gives the net rate of flow per unit time from the region bounded by S. If we divide this by the volume of that region (that is, by $\frac{4}{3}\pi\rho^3$, assuming that S is a sphere of radius ρ), then the result is the net outflow per unit of time, per unit volume. Thus $(\text{div }\mathbf{F})_Q$ is the strength of the *source* at Q, if there is one. (A *sink* corresponds to a negative value of the divergence.) If we multiply $(\text{div }\mathbf{F})_Q$ by ΔV, the result is approximately the rate of flow out from ΔV per unit time (say, in pounds per second).

For an incompressible fluid ($\delta = $ constant), if there are no sources or sinks in a region D, then the flow into D over its entire boundary just balances the flow out, so that the net flow is zero:

$$\iint_S \mathbf{F} \cdot \mathbf{n}\, d\sigma = 0.$$

Equation (13) then leads to the conclusion that

$$\text{div } \mathbf{F} = \text{div } (\delta\mathbf{v}) = \delta \text{ div } \mathbf{v} = 0$$

at each interior point of D. In words, the divergence of the velocity of an incompressible fluid is zero in a region where there are no sources or sinks.

PROBLEMS

In Problems 1 through 5, verify the divergence theorem for the cube with center at the origin and faces in the planes $x = \pm 1$, $y = \pm 1$, $z = \pm 1$, and **F** as given.

1. $\mathbf{F} = 2\mathbf{i} + 3\mathbf{j} + 4\mathbf{k}$ 2. $\mathbf{F} = \mathbf{i}x + \mathbf{j}y + \mathbf{k}z$

3. $\mathbf{F} = \mathbf{i}yz + \mathbf{j}xz + \mathbf{k}xy$

4. $\mathbf{F} = \mathbf{i}(x - y) + \mathbf{j}(y - z) + \mathbf{k}(x - y)$

5. $\mathbf{F} = \mathbf{i}x^2 + \mathbf{j}y^2 + \mathbf{k}z^2$

In Problems 6 through 10, compute both

$$\iiint_D \text{div } \mathbf{F}\, dV \qquad \text{and} \qquad \iint_S \mathbf{F} \cdot \mathbf{n}\, d\sigma$$

directly. Compare the results with the divergence theorem expressed by Eq. (8), given that

$$\mathbf{F} = \mathbf{i}(x + y) + \mathbf{j}(y + z) + \mathbf{k}(z + x),$$

and given that S bounds the region D given in the problem.

6. $0 \le z \le 4 - x^2 - y^2, \quad 0 \le x^2 + y^2 \le 4$

7. $-4 + x^2 + y^2 \le z \le 4 - x^2 - y^2, \quad 0 \le x^2 + y^2 \le 4$

8. $0 \le x^2 + y^2 \le 9, \quad 0 \le z \le 5$

9. $0 \le x^2 + y^2 + z^2 \le a^2$

10. $|x| \le 1, \quad |y| \le 1, \quad |z| \le 1$

11. A function f is said to be *harmonic* in a region D if, throughout D,

$$\frac{\partial^2 f}{\partial x^2} + \frac{\partial^2 f}{\partial y^2} + \frac{d^2 f}{\partial z^2} = 0.$$

Suppose f is harmonic throughout D, S is the boundary of D, $\mathbf{n}$ is the positive unit normal on S, and $\partial f / \partial n$ is the directional derivative of f in the direction of $\mathbf{n}$. Prove that

$$\iint\limits_S \frac{\partial f}{\partial n}\, d\sigma = 0.$$

(*Hint.* Let $\mathbf{F} = \operatorname{grad} f$.)

12. Prove that if f is harmonic in D (see Problem 11), then

$$\iint\limits_S f \frac{\partial f}{\partial n}\, d\sigma = \iiint\limits_D |\operatorname{grad} f|^2\, dV.$$

(*Hint.* Let $\mathbf{F} = f \operatorname{grad} f$.)

13. A function of two variables is harmonic in a region R of the xy-plane if

$$\frac{\partial^2 f}{\partial x^2} + \frac{\partial^2 f}{\partial y^2} = 0$$

throughout R. Let f be

a) the real part, or   **b)** the imaginary part

of $(x + iy)^3$, where $i = \sqrt{-1}$ and x and y are real. Prove that f is harmonic in the entire xy-plane in both (a) and (b).

STOKES'S THEOREM

Stokes's theorem is an extension of Green's theorem in vector form to surfaces and curves in three dimensions. It says that the line integral

$$\oint \mathbf{F} \cdot d\mathbf{R} \tag{1}$$

is equal to the surface integral

$$\iint\limits_S (\operatorname{curl} \mathbf{F}) \cdot \mathbf{n}\, d\sigma, \tag{2}$$

under suitable restrictions (i) on the vector

$$\mathbf{F} = \mathbf{i}M + \mathbf{j}N + \mathbf{k}P, \tag{3}$$

(ii) on the simple closed curve C:

$$x = f(t), \qquad y = g(t), \qquad z = h(t), \qquad 0 \le t \le 1, \tag{4}$$

(iii) on the surface

$$S: \phi(x, y, z) = 0 \tag{5}$$

bounded by C.

EXAMPLE 1. Let S be the hemisphere

$$z = \sqrt{4 - x^2 - y^2}, \qquad 0 \le x^2 + y^2 \le 4, \tag{6}$$

lying above the xy-plane, with center at the origin. The boundary of this hemisphere is the circle C:

$$z = 0, \qquad x^2 + y^2 = 4. \tag{7}$$

Let

$$\mathbf{F} = \mathbf{i}y - \mathbf{j}x. \tag{8}$$

The integrand in the line integral (1) is

$$\mathbf{F} \cdot d\mathbf{R} = \mathbf{F} \cdot (\mathbf{i}\,dx + \mathbf{j}\,dy + \mathbf{k}\,dz)$$

$$= y\,dx - x\,dy. \tag{9}$$

By Green's theorem for *plane* curves and surfaces, we have

$$\oint \mathbf{F} \cdot d\mathbf{r} = \oint_C (y\,dx - x\,dy)$$

$$= \iint\limits_{x^2 + y^2 \le 4} -2\,dx\,dy \tag{10}$$

$$= -8\pi.$$

To evaluate the surface integral (2), we need to compute

$$\text{curl } \mathbf{F} = \mathbf{i}\left(\frac{\partial P}{\partial y} - \frac{\partial N}{\partial z}\right) + \mathbf{j}\left(\frac{\partial M}{\partial z} - \frac{\partial P}{\partial x}\right) + \mathbf{k}\left(\frac{\partial N}{\partial x} - \frac{\partial M}{\partial y}\right), \tag{11}$$

where

$$M = y, \qquad N = -x, \qquad P = 0. \tag{12}$$

Substituting from (12) into (11), we get

$$\text{curl } \mathbf{F} = -2\mathbf{k}. \tag{13}$$

The unit outer normal to the hemisphere of Eq. (6) is

$$\mathbf{n} = \frac{\mathbf{i}x + \mathbf{j}y + \mathbf{k}z}{\sqrt{x^2 + y^2 + z^2}} = \frac{\mathbf{i}x + \mathbf{j}y + \mathbf{k}z}{2}. \tag{14}$$

Therefore

$$\text{curl } \mathbf{F} \cdot \mathbf{n}\,d\sigma = -z\,d\sigma. \tag{15}$$

For element of surface area $d\sigma$ (Article 14–9), we use

$$d\sigma = \sqrt{1 + \left(\frac{\partial z}{\partial x}\right)^2 + \left(\frac{\partial z}{\partial y}\right)^2}\,dx\,dy, \tag{16}$$

with

$$\frac{\partial z}{\partial x} = \frac{-x}{\sqrt{4 - x^2 - y^2}} \qquad \text{and} \qquad \frac{\partial z}{\partial y} = \frac{-y}{\sqrt{4 - x^2 - y^2}},$$

or

$$\frac{\partial z}{\partial x} = \frac{-x}{z} \qquad \text{and} \qquad \frac{\partial z}{\partial y} = \frac{-y}{z}. \tag{17}$$

From (15), (16), and (17), we get

$$\operatorname{curl} \mathbf{F} \cdot \mathbf{n} \, d\sigma = -z \, d\sigma = -z \sqrt{1 + \frac{x^2}{z^2} + \frac{y^2}{z^2}} \, dx \, dy. \tag{18}$$

Therefore

$$\iint_S \operatorname{curl} \mathbf{F} \cdot \mathbf{n} \, d\sigma = \iint_{x^2 + y^2 \le 4} -2 \, dx \, dy = -8\pi, \tag{19}$$

which agrees with the result found for the line integral in Eq. (10).

REMARK 1.   In this example, the surface integral (19) taken over the *hemisphere* turns out to have the same value as a surface integral taken over the *plane base* of that hemisphere. The underlying reason for this equality is that both surface integrals are equal to the line integral around the circle that is their common boundary.

REMARK 2.   In Stokes's theorem, we require that the surface be *orientable* and *simply connected*. By "simply connected," once again, we mean that any simple closed curve lying on the surface can be continuously contracted to a point (while staying on the surface) without its touching any part of the boundary of S. By "orientable," we mean that it is possible to consistently assign a unique direction, called *positive*, at each point of S, and that there exists a unit normal **n** pointing in this direction. As we move about over the surface S without touching its boundary, the direction cosines of the unit vector **n** should vary continuously. Also, when we return to the starting position, **n** should return to its initial direction. This rules out such a surface as a Möbius strip, which can be constructed by taking a rectangular strip of paper *abcd*, giving the end *bc* a single twist to interchange the positions of the vertices *b* and *c*, and then pasting the ends of the strip together so as to bring vertices *a* and *c* together, and also *b* and *d* (see Fig. 15–25). The resulting surface is nonorientable because a unit normal vector (think of the shaft of a thumbtack) can be continuously moved around the surface with-

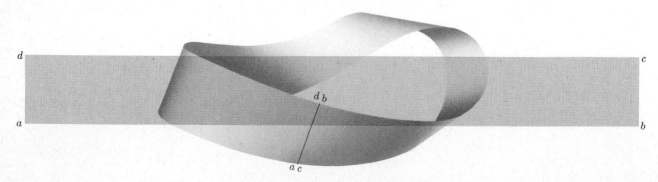

15–25   The construction of a Möbius strip.

out its touching the boundary of the surface, and in such a way that when it is returned to its initial position it will point in a direction *exactly opposite* to its initial direction.

REMARK 3.   We also want C to have a positive direction that is related to the positive direction on S. We imagine a simple closed curve Γ on S, near the boundary C (see Fig. 15–26), and let **n** be normal to S at some point inside Γ. We then assign to Γ a positive direction, the counterclockwise direction as viewed by an observer who is at the end of **n** and looking down. (Note that such a direction keeps the interior of Γ on the observer's left as he progresses around Γ. We could equally well have specified **n**'s direction by this condition.) Now we move Γ about on S until it touches and is tangent to C. The direction of the positive tangent to Γ at this point of common tangency we shall take to be the positive direction along C. It is a consequence of the orientability of S that a consistent assignment of positive direction along C is induced by this process. The same positive direction is assigned all the way around C, no matter where on S the process is begun. This would not be true of the (nonorientable) Möbius strip.

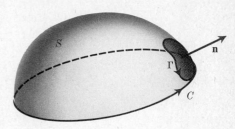

15-26   Orientation of the boundary of an oriented surface.

Stokes's Theorem.   *Let S be a smooth, simply connected, orientable surface bounded by a simple closed curve C. Let*

$$\mathbf{F} = \mathbf{i}M + \mathbf{j}N + \mathbf{k}P, \tag{20}$$

*where M, N, and P are continuous functions of (x, y, z), together with their first-order partial derivatives, throughout a region D containing S and C in its interior. Let **n** be a positive unit vector normal to S, and let the positive direction around C be the one induced by the positive orientation of S. Then*

$$\oint_C \mathbf{F} \cdot d\mathbf{R} = \iint_S \operatorname{curl} \mathbf{F} \cdot \mathbf{n} \, d\sigma, \tag{21a}$$

where

$$d\mathbf{R} = \mathbf{i}\, dx + \mathbf{j}\, dy + \mathbf{k}\, dz = \mathbf{T}\, ds \tag{21b}$$

and

$$\mathbf{n}\, d\sigma = (\mathbf{i} \cos \alpha + \mathbf{j} \cos \beta + \mathbf{k} \cos \gamma)\, d\sigma. \tag{21c}$$

Proof for a polyhedral surface S.   Let the surface S be a polyhedral surface consisting of a finite number of plane regions. (This polyhedral surface S might resemble a Buckminster Fuller geodesic dome.) We apply Green's theorem to each separate panel of S. There are two types of panels:

1. those that are surrounded on all sides by other panels, and
2. those that have one or more edges that are not adjacent to other panels.

Let Δ be part of the boundary of S that consists of those edges of the type 2 panels that are not adjacent to other panels. In Fig. 15–27, the triangles ABE, BCE, and CDE represent a part of S, with $ABCD$ part of the boundary Δ. Applying Green's theorem to the three triangles in turn and adding the results, we get

$$\left(\oint_{ABE} + \oint_{BCE} + \oint_{CDE} \right) \mathbf{F} \cdot d\mathbf{R} = \left(\iint_{ABE} + \iint_{BCE} + \iint_{CDE} \right) \operatorname{curl} \mathbf{F} \cdot \mathbf{n} \, d\sigma. \tag{22}$$

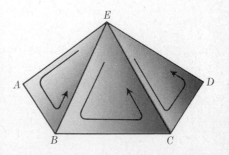

15-27   Part of a polyhedral surface.

The three line integrals on the lefthand side of Eq. (22) combine into a single line integral taken around the periphery *ABCDE*, because the integrals along interior segments cancel in pairs. For example, the integral along the segment *BE* in triangle *ABE* is opposite in sign to the integral along the same segment in triangle *EBC*. Similarly for the segment *CE*. Hence (22) reduces to

$$\oint_{ABCDE} \mathbf{F} \cdot d\mathbf{R} = \iint_{ABCDE} \text{curl } \mathbf{F} \cdot \mathbf{n} \, d\sigma.$$

In general, when we apply Green's theorem to all the panels and add the results, we get

$$\oint_{\Delta} \mathbf{F} \cdot d\mathbf{R} = \iint_{S} \text{curl } \mathbf{F} \cdot \mathbf{n} \, d\sigma. \tag{23}$$

This is Stokes's theorem for a polyhedral surface *S*.

REMARK 4.   A rigorous proof of Stokes's theorem for more general surfaces is beyond the level of a beginning calculus course. (See, for example, Buck, *Advanced Calculus*, or Apostol, *Mathematical Analysis*.) However, the following intuitive argument shows why one would expect Eq. (21a) to be true. Imagine a sequence of polyhedral surfaces

$$S_1, \quad S_2, \quad \ldots,$$

and their corresponding boundaries $\Delta_1, \Delta_2, \ldots$. The surface S_n should be constructed in such a way that its boundary Δ_n is inscribed in or tangent to *C*, the boundary of *S*, and so that the length of Δ_n approaches the length of *C* as $n \to \infty$. *C* needs to be rectifiable if this is to hold. The faces of S_n might be polygonal regions, approximating pieces of *S*, and such that the area of S_n approaches the area of *S* as $n \to \infty$. *S* also needs to have finite area. Assuming that *M*, *N*, *P*, and their partial derivatives are continuous in a region *D* containing *S* and *C*, it is plausible to expect that

$$\oint_{\Delta_n} \mathbf{F} \cdot d\mathbf{R} \qquad \text{approaches} \qquad \oint_{C} \mathbf{F} \cdot d\mathbf{R}$$

and that

$$\iint_{S_n} \text{curl } \mathbf{F} \cdot \mathbf{n} \, d\sigma_n \qquad \text{approaches} \qquad \iint_{S} \text{curl } \mathbf{F} \cdot \mathbf{n} \, d\sigma$$

as $n \to \infty$. But if

$$\oint_{\Delta_n} \mathbf{F} \cdot d\mathbf{R} \to \oint_{C} \mathbf{F} \cdot d\mathbf{R} \tag{24a}$$

and

$$\iint_{S_n} \text{curl } \mathbf{F} \cdot \mathbf{n} \, d\sigma \to \iint_{S} \text{curl } \mathbf{F} \cdot \mathbf{n} \, d\sigma, \tag{24b}$$

and if the lefthand sides of (24a) and (24b) are equal by Stokes's theorem for polyhedra, we then have equality of their limits.

EXAMPLE 2.   Let S be the portion of the paraboloid $z = 4 - x^2 - y^2$ that lies above the plane $z = 0$. Let C be their curve of intersection, and let

$$\mathbf{F} = \mathbf{i}(z - y) + \mathbf{j}(z + x) - \mathbf{k}(x + y).$$

Compute

$$\oint_C \mathbf{F} \cdot d\mathbf{R} \qquad \text{and} \qquad \iint_S \text{curl } \mathbf{F} \cdot \mathbf{n} \, d\sigma$$

and compare with Eq. (21a).

Solution.   The curve C lies in the xy-plane; it is the circle $x^2 + y^2 = 4$. We introduce a parameter θ such that

$$x = 2 \cos \theta, \qquad y = 2 \sin \theta, \qquad 0 \le \theta \le 2\pi.$$

Along C, we have

$$\mathbf{F} \cdot d\mathbf{R} = (z - y) \, dx + (z + x) \, dy - (x + y) \, dz,$$

or, since $z = 0$, $x = 2 \cos \theta$, $y = 2 \sin \theta$,

$$\mathbf{F} \cdot d\mathbf{R} = -y \, dx + x \, dy - 2 \sin \theta \cdot (-2 \sin \theta \, d\theta) + 2 \cos \theta \cdot (2 \cos \theta \, d\theta)$$

$$= 4 \, d\theta$$

and

$$\oint_C \mathbf{F} \cdot d\mathbf{R} = \int_0^{2\pi} 4 \, d\theta = 8\pi.$$

For the surface integral, we compute

$$\text{curl } \mathbf{F} = \begin{vmatrix} \mathbf{i} & \mathbf{j} & \mathbf{k} \\ \dfrac{\partial}{\partial x} & \dfrac{\partial}{\partial y} & \dfrac{\partial}{\partial z} \\ z - y & z + x & -x - y \end{vmatrix}$$

$$= -2\mathbf{i} + 2\mathbf{j} + 2\mathbf{k}.$$

For a positive unit normal on the surface

$$S: \quad f(x, y, z) = z - 4 + x^2 + y^2 = 0,$$

we take

$$\mathbf{n} = \frac{\text{grad } f}{|\text{grad } f|} = \frac{2x\mathbf{i} + 2y\mathbf{j} + \mathbf{k}}{\sqrt{4x^2 + 4y^2 + 1}}.$$

The projection of S onto the xy-plane is the region

$$x^2 + y^2 \le 4,$$

and for element of surface area $d\sigma$, we take

$$d\sigma = \sqrt{\left(\frac{\partial z}{\partial x}\right)^2 + \left(\frac{\partial z}{\partial y}\right)^2 + 1} \; dx \; dy$$

$$= \sqrt{4x^2 + 4y^2 + 1} \; dx \; dy.$$

Thus

$$\iint\limits_{S} \text{curl } \mathbf{F} \cdot \mathbf{n} \; d\sigma = \iint\limits_{x^2+y^2 \leq 4} (-4x + 4y + 2) \; dx \; dy \qquad (\alpha)$$

$$= \iint\limits_{x^2+y^2 \leq 4} 2 \; dx \; dy = 8\pi, \qquad (\beta)$$

where (β) follows from (α) because odd powers of x or y integrate to zero over the interior of the circle.

REMARK 5.   Stokes's theorem can also be extended to a surface S that has one or more holes in it (like a curved slice of Swiss cheese), in a way exactly analogous to Green's theorem: The surface integral over S of the *normal component* of curl $\mathbf{F}$ is equal to the line integral around all the boundaries of S (including boundaries of the holes) of the *tangential component* of $\mathbf{F}$, where the boundary curves are to be traced in the positive direction induced by the positive orientation of S.

REMARK 6.   Stokes's theorem provides the following vector interpretation for curl $\mathbf{F}$. As in the discussion of divergence, let $\mathbf{v}$ be the velocity field of a moving fluid, δ the density, and $\mathbf{F} = \delta\mathbf{v}$. Then

$$\oint_{C} \mathbf{F} \cdot \mathbf{T} \; ds$$

is a measure of the *circulation* of fluid around the closed curve C. By Stokes's theorem, this circulation is also equal to the flux of curl $\mathbf{F}$ through a surface S spanning C:

$$\oint_{C} \mathbf{F} \cdot d\mathbf{R} = \iint\limits_{S} \text{curl } \mathbf{F} \cdot \mathbf{n} \; d\sigma.$$

Suppose we fix a point Q and a direction $\mathbf{u}$ at Q. Let C be a circle of radius ρ, with center at Q, whose plane is normal to $\mathbf{u}$. If curl $\mathbf{F}$ is continuous at Q, then the average value of the $\mathbf{u}$-component of curl $\mathbf{F}$ over the circular disk bounded by C approaches the $\mathbf{u}$-component of curl $\mathbf{F}$ at Q as $\rho \to 0$:

$$(\text{curl } \mathbf{F} \cdot \mathbf{u})_Q = \lim_{\rho \to 0} \frac{1}{\pi\rho^2} \iint\limits_{S} \text{curl } \mathbf{F} \cdot \mathbf{u} \; d\sigma. \qquad \textbf{(25)}$$

If we replace the double integral on the righthand side of Eq. (25) by the circulation, we get

$$(\text{curl } \mathbf{F} \cdot \mathbf{u})_Q = \lim_{\rho \to 0} \frac{1}{\pi\rho^2} \oint_C \mathbf{F} \cdot d\mathbf{R}. \qquad (26)$$

The lefthand side of Eq. (26) is a maximum at Q when $\mathbf{u}$ has the same direction as curl $\mathbf{F}$. When ρ is small, the righthand side of Eq. (26) is approximately equal to

$$\frac{1}{\pi\rho^2} \oint_C \mathbf{F} \cdot d\mathbf{R},$$

which is the circulation around C divided by the area of the disk. Suppose that a small paddle wheel, of radius ρ, is introduced into the fluid at Q, with its axle directed along $\mathbf{u}$. The circulation of the fluid around C will affect the rate of spin of the paddle wheel. The wheel will spin fastest when the circulation integral is maximized; therefore it will spin fastest when the axle of the paddle wheel points in the direction of curl $\mathbf{F}$. (See Fig. 15–28.)

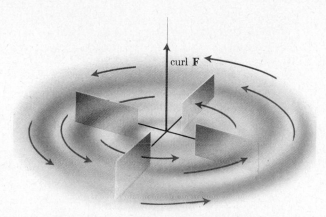

15–28 The paddle-wheel interpretation of curl $\mathbf{F}$.

EXAMPLE 3.   A fluid of constant density δ rotates around the z-axis with velocity $\mathbf{v} = \omega(\mathbf{j}x - \mathbf{i}y)$, where ω is a positive constant. If $\mathbf{F} = \delta\mathbf{v}$, find curl $\mathbf{F}$, and comment.

Solution

$$\mathbf{F} = \delta\omega(\mathbf{j}x - \mathbf{i}y),$$

and

$$\text{curl } \mathbf{F} = \begin{vmatrix} \mathbf{i} & \mathbf{j} & \mathbf{k} \\ \dfrac{\partial}{\partial x} & \dfrac{\partial}{\partial y} & \dfrac{\partial}{\partial z} \\ -\delta\omega y & \delta\omega x & 0 \end{vmatrix} = 2\,\delta\omega\mathbf{k}.$$

The work done by a force equal to $\mathbf{F}$, as the point of application moves around a circle C of radius ρ, is

$$\oint_C \mathbf{F} \cdot d\mathbf{R}.$$

If C is in a plane parallel to the xy-plane, Stokes's theorem gives the result

$$\oint_C \mathbf{F} \cdot d\mathbf{R} = \iint_S \operatorname{curl} \mathbf{F} \cdot \mathbf{n}\, d\sigma = \iint 2\, \delta\omega \mathbf{k} \cdot \mathbf{k}\, dx\, dy$$

$$= (2\, \delta\omega)(\pi\rho^2).$$

We note that

$$(\operatorname{curl} \mathbf{F}) \cdot \mathbf{k} = 2\, \delta\omega = \frac{1}{\pi\rho^2} \oint_C \mathbf{F} \cdot d\mathbf{r},$$

in agreement with Eq. (26) with $\mathbf{u} = \mathbf{k}$.

PROBLEMS

In Problems 1 through 4, verify the result of Stokes's theorem for the vector

$$\mathbf{F} = \mathbf{i}(y^2 + z^2) + \mathbf{j}(x^2 + z^2) + \mathbf{k}(x^2 + y^2)$$

for the given surface S and boundary C.

1. S: $z = \sqrt{1 - x^2}$, $-1 \le x \le 1$, $-2 \le y \le 2$,
   $y = 2$, $0 \le z \le \sqrt{1 - x^2}$, $-1 \le x \le 1$,
   $y = -2$, $0 \le z \le \sqrt{1 - x^2}$, $-1 \le x \le 1$;
   C: $z = 0$,
   $x = \pm 1$, $-2 \le y \le 2$,
   $y = \pm 2$, $-1 \le x \le 1$

2. The surface S is the surface of the upper half of the cube with one vertex at $(1, 1, 1)$, center at the origin, and edges parallel to the axes; the curve C is the intersection of S with the xy-plane.

3. The surface S is as in Problem 2, with a hole cut out of the top face by the circular disk whose cylindrical coordinates satisfy

$$z = 1, \qquad 0 \le r \le \cos\theta, \qquad -\tfrac{1}{2}\pi \le \theta \le \tfrac{1}{2}\pi.$$

(The circle $z = 1$, $r = \cos\theta$ becomes part of the boundary of S.)

4. The surface S is the surface (excluding the face in the yz-plane) of a pyramid with vertices at the origin O and at $A(1, 0, 0)$, $B(0, 1, 0)$, and $D(0, 0, 1)$; the boundary curve C is the triangle OBD in the yz-plane.

5. Suppose $\mathbf{F} = \operatorname{grad} \phi$ is the gradient of a scalar function ϕ having continuous second-order partial derivatives

$$\frac{\partial^2 \phi}{\partial x^2}, \quad \frac{\partial^2 \phi}{\partial x\, \partial y}, \quad \cdots$$

throughout a simply connected region D that contains the surface S and its boundary C in the interior of D. What constant value does

$$\oint_C \mathbf{F} \cdot d\mathbf{R}$$

have in such circumstances? Explain.

6. Let $\phi = (x^2 + y^2 + z^2)^{-1/2}$. Let V be the spherical shell $1 \le x^2 + y^2 + z^2 \le 4$. Let $\mathbf{F} = \operatorname{grad} \phi$. If $1 < a < 2$ and C is the circle $z = 0$, $x^2 + y^2 = a^2$, show that

$$\oint_C \mathbf{F} \cdot d\mathbf{R} = 0$$

a) by direct evaluation of the integral, and
b) by applying Stokes's theorem with S the hemisphere

$$z = \sqrt{a^2 - x^2 - y^2}, \qquad x^2 + y^2 \le a^2.$$

7. If the components of $\mathbf{F}$ have continuous second-order partial derivatives of all types, prove that

$$\operatorname{div}(\operatorname{curl} \mathbf{F}) = 0.$$

8. Use the result of Problem 7 and the divergence theorem to show that

$$\iint_S \operatorname{curl} \mathbf{F} \cdot \mathbf{n}\, d\sigma = 0$$

if the components of $\mathbf{F}$ have continuous second-order derivatives and S is a closed surface like a sphere, an ellipsoid, or a cube.

9. By Stokes's theorem, if S_1 and S_2 are two oriented surfaces having the same positively oriented curve C as boundary, then

$$\iint_{S_1} \operatorname{curl} \mathbf{F} \cdot \mathbf{n}_1\, d\sigma_1 = \oint_C \mathbf{F} \cdot d\mathbf{r} = \iint_{S_2} \operatorname{curl} \mathbf{F} \cdot \mathbf{n}_2\, d\sigma_2.$$

Deduce that

$$\iint_S \operatorname{curl} \mathbf{F} \cdot \mathbf{n}\, d\sigma$$

has the same value for all oriented surfaces S that span C and that induce the same positive direction on C.

10. Use Stokes's theorem to deduce that if $\operatorname{curl} \mathbf{F} = \mathbf{0}$ throughout a simply connected region D, then

$$\int_{P_1}^{P_2} \mathbf{F} \cdot d\mathbf{R}$$

has the same value for all simple paths lying in D and joining P_1 and P_2. In other words, $\mathbf{F}$ is conservative.

REVIEW QUESTIONS AND EXERCISES

1. What is a vector field? Give an example of a two-dimensional vector field; of a three-dimensional field.

2. What is the velocity vector field for a fluid rotating about the x-axis if the angular velocity is a constant ω and the flow is counterclockwise as viewed by an observer at (1, 0, 0) looking toward (0, 0, 0)?

3. Give examples of gradient fields

a) in the plane,   **b)** in space.

State a property that gradient fields have and other fields do not.

4. If $\mathbf{F} = \nabla f$ is a gradient field, S is a level surface for f, and C is a curve on S, why is it true (or not true) that $\int_C \mathbf{F} \cdot d\mathbf{R} = 0$?

5. Suppose that S is a portion of a level surface of a function $f(x, y, z)$. How could you select an orientation (if S is orientable) on S such that

$$\iint_S \nabla f \cdot \mathbf{n} \, d\sigma = \iint_S |\nabla f| \, d\sigma?$$

Why is the hypothesis that S is a level surface of f important?

6. If $f(x, y, z) = 2x - 3y + e^z$, and C is any smooth curve

from $A(0, 0, 0)$ to $(1, 2, \ln 3)$, what is the value of $\int_C \nabla f \cdot d\mathbf{R}$? Why doesn't the answer depend on C?

7. Write a formula for a vector field $\mathbf{F}(x, y, z)$ such that $\mathbf{F} = f(\rho)\mathbf{R}$, where $\rho = |\mathbf{R}|$ and $\mathbf{R} = i x + j y + k z$, if it is true that

a) $\mathbf{F}$ is directed radially outward from the origin and $|\mathbf{F}| = \rho^{-n}$,

b) $\mathbf{F}$ is directed toward the origin and $|\mathbf{F}| = 2$,

c) $\mathbf{F}$ is a gravitational attraction field for a mass M at the origin in which an inverse-*cube* law applies. (Don't worry about the possible nonexistence of such a field.)

8. Give one physical and one geometrical interpretation for a surface integral

$$\iint_S h \, d\sigma.$$

9. State both the normal form and the tangential form of Green's theorem in the plane.

10. State the divergence theorem and show that it applies to the region D described by $1 \le |\mathbf{R}| \le 2$, assuming that S is the total boundary of this region, $\mathbf{n}$ is directed away from D at each point, and $\mathbf{F} = \nabla(1/|\mathbf{R}|)$, $\mathbf{R} = i x + j y + k z$.

MISCELLANEOUS PROBLEMS

In Problems 1 through 4, describe the vector fields in words and with graphs.

1. $\mathbf{F} = x i + y j + z k$ **2.** $\mathbf{F} = -x i - y j - z k$

3. $\mathbf{F} = (x - y) i + (x + y) j$

4. $\mathbf{F} = (x i + y j)/(x^2 + y^2)$

In Problems 5 through 8, evaluate the surface integrals

$$\iint_S h \, d\sigma$$

for the given functions and surfaces.

5. The surface S is the hemisphere $x^2 + y^2 + z^2 = a^2$, $z \ge 0$, and $h(x, y, z) = x + y$.

6. The surface S is the portion of the plane $z = x + y$ for which $x \ge 0$, $y \ge 0$, $z \le \pi$, and

$$h(x, y, z) = \sin z.$$

7. The surface S is $z = 4 - x^2 - y^2$, $z \ge 0$; $h = z$.

8. The surface S is the sphere $\rho = a$, and $h = z^2$. (You might do the upper and lower hemispheres separately and add; or use spherical coordinates and not project the surface.)

For the functions and surfaces given in Problems 9 through

12, evaluate

$$\iint_S \frac{\partial f}{\partial n} \, d\sigma,$$

where $\partial f/\partial n$ is the directional derivative of f in the direction of the normal $\mathbf{n}$ in the sense specified.

9. The surface S is the sphere $x^2 + y^2 + z^2 = a^2$, $\mathbf{n}$ is directed outward on S, and $f = x^2 + y^2 + z^2$.

10. The surface and normal are as in Exercise 9, and $f = (x^2 + y^2 + z^2)^{-1}$.

11. The surface S is the portion of the plane

$$z = 2x + 3y$$

for which $x \ge 0$, $y \ge 0$, $z \le 5$, $\mathbf{n}$ has a positive $\mathbf{k}$-component, and $f = x + y + z$.

12. The surface S is the one-eighth of the sphere $x^2 + y^2 + z^2 = a^2$ that lies in the first octant, $\mathbf{n}$ is directed inward with respect to the sphere, and

$$f = \ln (x^2 + y^2 + z^2)^{1/2}.$$

In Problems 13 through 20, evaluate the line integrals

$$\int_C \mathbf{F} \cdot d\mathbf{R}$$

for the given fields $\mathbf{F}$ and paths C.

13. The field $\mathbf{F} = x\mathbf{i} + y\mathbf{j}$ and the circle C:

$$x = \cos t, \qquad y = \sin t, \qquad 0 \le t \le 2\pi.$$

14. The field $\mathbf{F} = -y\mathbf{i} + x\mathbf{j}$ and C as in Problem 13.

15. The field $\mathbf{F} = (x - y)\mathbf{i} + (x + y)\mathbf{j}$ and the circle C in Problem 13.

16. The field $\mathbf{F} = x\mathbf{i} + y\mathbf{j} + z\mathbf{k}$ and the ellipse C, in which the plane $z = 2x + 3y$ cuts the cylinder $x^2 + y^2 = 12$, counterclockwise as viewed from the positive end of the z-axis looking toward the origin.

17. The field $\mathbf{F} = \mathbf{V}(xy^2z^3)$ and C as in Problem 16.

18. The field $\mathbf{F} = \mathbf{V}x(x\mathbf{i} + y\mathbf{j} + z\mathbf{k})$ and C as in Problem 13.

19. The field $\mathbf{F}$ as in Problem 18 and C the line segment from the origin to the point $(1, 2, 3)$.

20. The field $\mathbf{F}$ as in Problem 17 and C the line segment from $(1, 1, 1)$ to $(2, 1, -1)$.

21. Heat flows from a hotter body to a cooler body. In three-dimensional heat flow, the fundamental equation for the rate at which heat flows out of D is

$$\iint_S K \frac{\partial u}{\partial n} d\sigma = \iiint_D c\delta \frac{\partial u}{\partial t} dV. \tag{1}$$

The symbolism in this equation is as follows:

$u = u(x, y, z, t)$ the temperature at the point (x, y, z) at time t,

K the thermal conductivity coefficient,

δ the mass density,

c the specific heat coefficient. This is the amount of heat required to raise one unit of mass of the material of the body one degree,

S the boundary surface of the region D,

$\dfrac{\partial u}{\partial n}$ the directional derivative in the direction of the outward normal to S.

How is $\partial u/\partial n$ related to the *gradient* of the temperature? In which direction (described in words) does $\mathbf{V}u$ point? Why does the lefthand side of Eq. (1) appear to make sense as a measure of the rate of flow? Now look at the righthand side of Eq. (1): If ΔV is a small volume element in D, what does $\delta \Delta V$ represent? If the temperature of this element changes by an amount Δu in time Δt, what is

a) the amount,   **b)** the average rate

of change of heat in the element? In words, what does the right side of Eq. (1) represent physically? Is it reasonable to interpret Eq. (1) as saying that the rate at which heat flows out through the boundary of D is equal to the rate at which heat is being supplied from D?

22. Assuming Eq. (1), Problem 21, and assuming that there is no heat source or sink in D, derive the equation

$$\mathbf{V} \cdot (K\mathbf{V}u) = c\delta \frac{\partial u}{\partial t} \tag{2}$$

as the equation that must be satisfied at each point in D.

Suggestion. Apply the divergence theorem to the lefthand side of Eq. (1), and make D be a sphere of radius ϵ; then let $\epsilon \to 0$.

23. Assuming the result of Problem 22, and assuming that K, c, and δ are constants, deduce that the condition for steady-state temperature in D is Laplace's equation

$$\mathbf{V}^2 u = 0, \qquad \text{or} \qquad \text{div (grad } u) = 0.$$

In higher mathematics, the symbol Δ is used for the *Laplace operator*:

$$\Delta u = \frac{\partial^2 u}{\partial x^2} + \frac{\partial^2 u}{\partial y^2} + \frac{\partial^2 u}{\partial z^2}.$$

Thus, in this notation,

$$\Delta u = \mathbf{V}^2 u = \mathbf{V} \cdot \mathbf{V}u = \text{div (grad } u).$$

Using the divergence theorem, and assuming that the functions u and v and their first- and second-order partial derivatives are continuous in the regions considered, verify the formulas in Problems 24 through 27. Assume that S is the boundary surface of the simply connected region D.

24. $\displaystyle \iint_S u\mathbf{V}v \cdot d\sigma = \iiint_D [u\,\Delta v + (\mathbf{V}u) \cdot (\mathbf{V}v)]\,dV$

25. $\displaystyle \iint_S \left(u\frac{\partial v}{\partial n} - v\frac{\partial u}{\partial n} \right) d\sigma = \iiint_D (u\,\Delta v - v\,\Delta u)\,dV$

Suggestion. Use the result of Problem 24 as given and in the form you get by interchanging u and v.

26. $\displaystyle \iint_S u\frac{\partial u}{\partial n} d\sigma = \iiint_D [u\,\Delta u + |\mathbf{V}u|^2]\,dV$

Suggestion. Use the result of Problem 24 with $v = u$.

27. $\displaystyle \iint_S \frac{\partial u}{\partial n} d\sigma = \iiint_D \Delta u\,dV$

Suggestion. Use the result of Problem 25 with $v = -1$.

28. A function u is *harmonic* in a region D if and only if it satisfies *Laplace's equation* $\Delta u = 0$ throughout D. Use the identity in Exercise 26 to deduce that if u is harmonic in D and either $u = 0$ or $\partial u/\partial n = 0$ at all points on the surface S that is the boundary of D, then $\mathbf{V}u = \mathbf{0}$ throughout D, and therefore u is constant throughout D.

29. The result of Problem 28 can be used to establish the uniqueness of solutions of Laplace's equation in D, provided that either (i) the value of u is prescribed at each point on S, or (ii) the value of $\partial u/\partial n$ is prescribed at each point of S. This is done by supposing that u_1 and u_2 are harmonic in D and that both satisfy the same boundary conditions, and then letting $u = u_1 - u_2$. Complete this uniqueness proof.

30. Problems 21 through 23 deal with heat flow. Assume that K, c, and δ are constant and that the temperature $u = u(x, y, z)$ does not vary with time. Use the results of Problems 23 and 27 to conclude that the net rate of outflow of heat through the surface S is zero.

Note. This result might apply, for example, to the region D between two concentric spheres if the inner one were maintained at 100° and the outer one at 0°, so that heat would flow into D through the inner surface and out through the outer surface at the same rate.

31. Let $\rho = (x^2 + y^2 + z^2)^{1/2}$. Show that
$$u = C_1 + \frac{C_2}{\rho}$$
is harmonic where $\rho > 0$, if C_1 and C_2 are constants. Find values of C_1 and C_2 so that the following boundary conditions are satisfied:

a) $u = 100$ when $\rho = 1$, and $u = 0$ when $\rho = 2$;

b) $u = 100$ when $\rho = 1$, and $\partial u/\partial n = 0$ when $\rho = 2$.

Note. Part (a) refers to a steady-state heat flow problem that is like the one discussed at the end of Problem 30; part (b) refers to an insulated boundary on the sphere $\rho = 2$.

INFINITE SERIES

16-1

INTRODUCTION

The division of $1 - x^{n+1}$ by $1 - x$ results in the equation

$$\frac{1 - x^{n+1}}{1 - x} = 1 + x + x^2 + \cdots + x^n. \tag{1}$$

But when $|x|$ is small enough for x^{n+1} to be omitted from the numerator on the left without disturbing the results of some practical application, we may replace the equality (1) by the approximation

$$\frac{1}{1 - x} \approx 1 + x + x^2 + \cdots + x^n. \tag{2}$$

When $|x| < 1$, this approximation can be used in computing, as an alternative to division by $x - 1$.

Just how reliable this approximation is depends on how small x is and on how large we take n. In general, when $|x| < 1$, the more terms we add the better the approximation becomes, and it is natural to ask what would happen if we could just keep on adding. As long as we kept $|x| < 1$, so that the successive powers of x in (2) became smaller and smaller, couldn't we actually write

$$\frac{1}{1 - x} = 1 + x + x^2 + \cdots + x^n + \cdots ? \tag{3}$$

The answer is "Yes." For functions like $1/(1 - x)$ that have derivatives of all orders, we can write equalities like the one in (3) if we are careful about the domain of x and about what we mean by the sum of infinitely many terms.

The study of such sums, of what functions they represent on what domains, of how we can compute with them, and of what we can do with such sums that we could not do before we had them, is what this chapter is about. We will see why, for example, the approximation

$$\sin x \approx x - \frac{x^3}{6} \tag{4}$$

underestimates $\sin x$ by less than 0.0003 when $0 \leq x \leq 0.5$. And we will at last be able to find convenient expressions for estimating integrals like $\int_0^1 \sin x^2 \, dx$.

The way we proceed is to define an infinite sum like

$$1 + x + x^2 + x^3 + \cdots \tag{5}$$

for each x to be the limiting value of a sequence of partial sums

$$\begin{array}{ccc} \text{First} & \text{Second} & \text{Third} \\ 1 + x, & 1 + x + x^2, & 1 + x + x^2 + x^3, \quad \ldots \end{array} \tag{6}$$

The additions within the partial sums pose no problem because there are only finitely many of them at each stage, so that it only remains to make clear what we mean by the limit of a sequence of such sums. This is best done by studying sequences in their own right; in the next article, therefore, we address the questions of what we mean by a sequence and the limit of a sequence, and of how to tell when a sequence has a limit.

We begin our study of sequences with a definition.

Definition 1. *A **sequence** is a function whose domain is the set of positive integers.*

Sequences are defined by rules the way other functions are, typical rules being

$$a(n) = n - 1, \qquad a(n) = 1 - \frac{1}{n}, \qquad a(n) = \frac{\ln n}{n^2}. \qquad \textbf{(1)}$$

To signal the fact that the domains are restricted to the set of positive integers, it is conventional to use a letter like n from the middle of the alphabet for the independent variable instead of the x, y, z, and t used so widely in other contexts. The formulas in the defining rules, however, like the ones above, are often valid for domains much larger than the set of positive integers. This can prove to be an advantage, as we shall see at the end of this article.

The numbers in the range of a sequence are called the *terms* of the sequence, the number $a(n)$ being called the *nth term*, or the term with *index n*. For example, if $a(n) = (n + 1)/n$, then the terms are:

First term   Second term   Third term   *nth* term

$$a(1) = 2, \qquad a(2) = \frac{3}{2}, \qquad a(3) = \frac{4}{3}, \qquad \ldots, \qquad a(n) = \frac{n + 1}{n}, \qquad \ldots \qquad \textbf{(2)}$$

When we use the simpler notation a_n for $a(n)$, the sequence in (2) becomes

$$a_1 = 2, \qquad a_2 = \tfrac{3}{2}, \qquad a_3 = \tfrac{4}{3}, \qquad \ldots, \qquad a_n = \frac{n + 1}{n}, \qquad \ldots \qquad \textbf{(3)}$$

To describe sequences, we often write the first few terms as well as a formula for the *n*th term.

EXAMPLE 1

We write:	For the sequence whose defining rule is:
$0, \quad 1, \quad 2, \quad \ldots, \quad n - 1, \quad \ldots$	$a_n = n - 1$
$1, \quad \dfrac{1}{2}, \quad \dfrac{1}{3}, \quad \ldots, \quad \dfrac{1}{n}, \quad \ldots$	$a_n = \dfrac{1}{n}$
$1, \quad -\dfrac{1}{2}, \quad \dfrac{1}{3}, \quad -\dfrac{1}{4}, \quad \ldots, \quad (-1)^{n+1}\dfrac{1}{n}, \quad \ldots$	$a_n = (-1)^{n+1}\dfrac{1}{n}$
$0, \quad \dfrac{1}{2}, \quad \dfrac{3}{4}, \quad \ldots, \quad 1 - \dfrac{1}{n}, \quad \ldots$	$a_n = 1 - \dfrac{1}{n}$
$0, \quad -\dfrac{1}{2}, \quad \dfrac{3}{4}, \quad -\dfrac{4}{5}, \quad \ldots, \quad (-1)^{n+1}\left(1 - \dfrac{1}{n}\right), \quad \ldots$	$a_n = (-1)^{n+1}\left(1 - \dfrac{1}{n}\right)$
$3, \quad 3, \quad 3, \quad \ldots, \quad 3, \quad \ldots$	$a_n = 3$

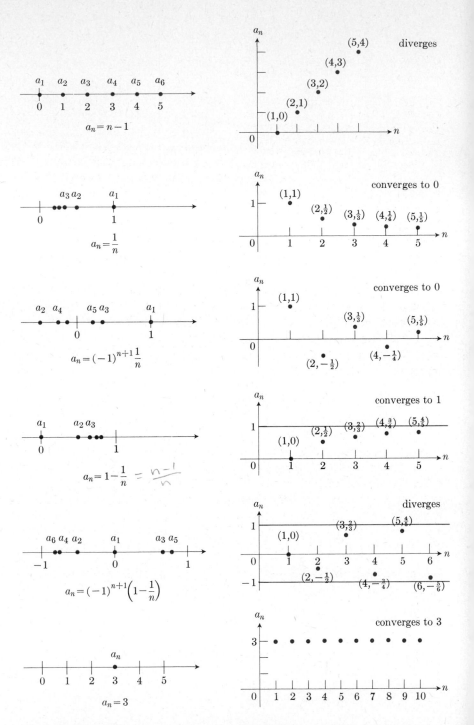

16–1 The sequences of Example 1 are graphed here in two different ways: by plotting the numbers a_n on a horizontal axis, and by plotting the points (n, a_n) in the coordinate plane.

We can, of course, use set notation to describe sequences, writing:

$\{(n, a_n)\}$ The sequence whose ordered pairs are (n, a_n)

or even

$\{a_n\}$ The sequence a_n

when such an abbreviation will not cause trouble. Both choices of notation lead to graphs, for we can either plot the ordered pairs (n, a_n) in the coordinate plane, or plot the numbers a_n on a single axis (shown as a horizontal axis in Fig. 16–1). Plotting just the number a_n has the advantage of simplicity. A potential disadvantage, however, is the fact that several a_n's may turn out to be the same for different values of n, as they are in the sequence defined by the rule $a_n = 3$, in which every term is 3. The points (n, a_n) are distinct for different values of n.

As Fig. 16–1 shows, the sequences of Example 1 exhibit different kinds of behavior. The sequences $\{1/n\}$, $\{(-1)^{n+1}(1/n)\}$, and $\{1 - 1/n\}$ seem to approach single limiting values as n increases, and the sequence $\{3\}$ is already at a limiting value from the very first. On the other hand, terms of the sequence $\{(-1)^{n+1}(1 - 1/n)\}$ seem to accumulate near two different values, -1 and 1, while the terms of $\{n - 1\}$ get larger and larger and do not accumulate anywhere.

To distinguish sequences that approach a unique limiting value L, as n increases, from those that do not, we say that they *converge*, according to the following definition.

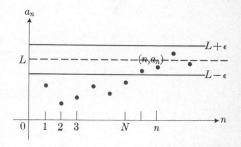

Definition 2.   *The sequence $\{(n, a_n)\}$ converges to the number L if to every positive number ϵ there corresponds an index N such that*

$$|a_n - L| < \epsilon \quad \textit{for all} \quad n > N. \tag{4}$$

In other words, $\{(n, a_n)\}$ converges to L if, for every positive ϵ, there is an index N such that all the terms after the Nth lie within ϵ of L. (See Fig. 16–2, and look once more at the sequences in Fig. 16–1.) We indicate the fact that $\{(n, a_n)\}$ converges to L by writing

$$\lim_{n \to \infty} a_n = L \quad \text{or} \quad a_n \to L \quad \text{as } n \to \infty,$$

and we call L the *limit* of the sequence $\{a_n\}$. If no such limit exists, we say that $\{a_n\}$ *diverges*.

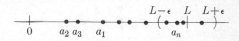

16–2 $a_n \to L$ if L is a horizontal asymptote of $\{(n, a_n)\}$. In this figure, all the a_n's after a_N are within ϵ of L.

EXAMPLE 2. $\{1/n\}$ converges to 0.

To see why, we begin by writing down the inequality (4), with $a_n = 1/n$ and $L = 0$. This gives

$$|a_n - L| = \left| \frac{1}{n} - 0 \right| = \frac{1}{n} < \epsilon, \tag{5}$$

and therefore we seek an integer N such that

$$\frac{1}{n} < \epsilon \quad \text{for all} \quad n > N. \tag{6}$$

Certainly

$$\frac{1}{n} < \epsilon \qquad \text{for all} \quad n > \frac{1}{\epsilon}, \tag{7}$$

but there is no reason to expect $1/\epsilon$ to be an integer. This minor difficulty is easily overcome: We just choose any integer $N > 1/\epsilon$. Then every index n greater than N will automatically be greater than $1/\epsilon$. In short, for this choice of N we can guarantee (6). The criterion set forth in Definition 2 for convergence to 0 is satisfied.

EXAMPLE 3.   If k is any number, then the constant sequence $\{k\}$, defined by $a_n = k$ for all n, converges to k.

When we take both $a_n = k$ and $L = k$ on the left of the inequality in (4), we find

$$|a_n - L| = |k - k| = 0, \tag{8}$$

which is less than every positive ϵ for every $n \geq 1$.

EXAMPLE 4.   The sequence $\{(-1)^{n+1}(1 - 1/n)\}$ diverges. To see why, pick a positive ϵ smaller than 1 so that the bands shown in Fig. 16–3 about the lines $y = 1$ and $y = -1$ do not overlap. Any $\epsilon < 1$ will do. Convergence to 1 would require every point of the graph from some index on to lie inside the upper band, but this will never happen. As soon as a point (n, a_n) lies in the upper band, every alternate point starting with $(n + 1, a_{n+1})$ will lie in the lower band. Likewise, the sequence cannot converge to -1. On the other hand, because the terms of the sequence get increasingly close to 1 and -1 alternately, they never accumulate near any other value.

$$a_n = (-1)^{n+1}\left(1 - \frac{1}{n}\right)$$

Neither the ϵ interval about 1 nor the ϵ interval about -1 contains a complete tail of the sequence.

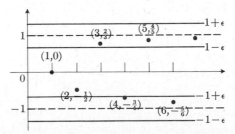

16–3   The sequence $\{(-1)^{n+1}[1 - (1/n)]\}$ diverges.

Neither of the ϵ bands shown here contains all the points (n, a_n) from some index onward.

REMARK 1.   A *tail* of a sequence $\{a_n\}$ is the collection of all the terms whose indices are greater than some index N; in other words, one of the sets $\{a_n \,|\, n > N\}$. Another way to say $a_n \to L$ is to say that every ϵ-interval about L contains a tail. As Example 4 suggests, a sequence cannot have more than one limit. There cannot be two different numbers with the property that every ϵ-interval about each one contains a complete tail.

REMARK 2.   The behavior of the sequence $\{(-1)^{n+1}(1 - 1/n)\}$ is qualitatively different from that of $\{n - 1\}$, which diverges because it outgrows every real number L. We describe the behavior of $\{n - 1\}$ by writing

$$\lim_{n \to \infty} (n - 1) = \infty.$$

In speaking of infinity as a limit of a sequence $\{a_n\}$, we do not mean that the difference between a_n and infinity becomes small as n increases. We mean that a_n becomes numerically large as n increases.

REMARK 3.   Some sequences are defined *iteratively*, by giving a rule for computing the nth term from earlier terms in the sequence, and stating how to start the sequence. For example, Newton's method for finding a solution of an equation $f(x) = 0$ is to guess a first approximation x_1 and then to use the formula

$$x_{n+1} = x_n - \frac{f(x_n)}{f'(x_n)}$$

to generate, by iteration, a sequence $\{x_n\}$. In favorable circumstances, the sequence converges to a number L which satisfies the equation $f(L) = 0$. As a second example, setting

$$a_1 = 1, \qquad a_2 = 1,$$

and

$$a_n = a_{n-1} + a_{n-2} \qquad \text{for} \quad n \geq 3$$

defines a Fibonacci sequence:

$$1, \quad 1, \quad 2, \quad 3, \quad 5, \quad 8, \quad 13, \quad 21, \quad \ldots.$$

REMARK 4.   Iteration is used as a method for solving many kinds of problems by computer. The technique is to start with a first approximation, use that to compute a second approximation, use the second to get a third, and so on. The idea is to generate a sequence whose terms approximate the solution with increasing accuracy.

The study of limits of sequences would be a cumbersome business if every question about convergence had to be answered by applying Definition 2 directly, as we have had to do so far. Fortunately there are three theorems that will make this process largely unnecessary from now on. The first two are the ones with which we began the study of limits of functions in Chapter 1. We restate them here in the notation of sequences.

Theorem 1. *If* $A = \lim_{n \to \infty} a_n$ *and* $B = \lim_{n \to \infty} b_n$ *both exist and are finite, then*

i) $\lim \{a_n + b_n\} = A + B$,

ii) $\lim \{ka_n\} = kA$ (*k any number*),

iii) $\lim \{a_n \cdot b_n\} = A \cdot B$,

iv) $\lim \left\{\dfrac{a_n}{b_n}\right\} = \dfrac{A}{B}$,   *provided* $B \neq 0$ *and* b_n *is never* 0,

it being understood that all of the limits are to be taken as $n \to \infty$.

By combining Theorem 1 with Examples 2 and 3, we can proceed immediately to

$$\lim_{n \to \infty} -\frac{1}{n} = -1 \cdot \lim_{n \to \infty} \frac{1}{n} = -1 \cdot 0 = 0,$$

$$\lim_{n \to \infty} \left(1 - \frac{1}{n}\right) = \lim_{n \to \infty} 1 - \lim_{n \to \infty} \frac{1}{n} = 1 - 0 = 1,$$

$$\lim_{n \to \infty} \frac{5}{n^2} = 5 \cdot \lim_{n \to \infty} \frac{1}{n} \cdot \lim_{n \to \infty} \frac{1}{n} = 5 \cdot 0 \cdot 0 = 0,$$

$$\lim_{n \to \infty} \frac{4 - 7n^6}{n^6 + 3} = \lim_{n \to \infty} \frac{(4/n^6) - 7}{1 + (3/n^6)} = \frac{-7}{1} = -7.$$

A corollary of Theorem 1 that will be useful later on is that every nonzero multiple of a divergent sequence is divergent.

Corollary. *If the sequence* $\{a_n\}$ *diverges, and if c is any number different from* 0, *then the sequence* $\{ca_n\}$ *diverges.*

Proof of the corollary. Suppose, on the contrary, that $\{ca_n\}$ converges. Then, by taking $k = 1/c$ in part (ii) of Theorem 1, we see that the sequence

$$\left\{\frac{1}{c} \cdot ca_n\right\} = \{a_n\}$$

converges. Thus $\{ca_n\}$ cannot converge unless $\{a_n\}$ converges. If $\{a_n\}$ does not converge, then $\{ca_n\}$ does not converge.   Q.E.D.

The next theorem is the sequence version of the *Sandwich Theorem* of Article 1–10.

Theorem 2. *If* $a_n \leq b_n \leq c_n$ *for all n beyond some index N, and if* $\lim a_n = \lim c_n = L$, *then* $\lim b_n = L$ *also.*

An immediate consequence of Theorem 2 is that, if $|b_n| \leq c_n$ and $c_n \to 0$, then $b_n \to 0$ because $-c_n \leq b_n \leq c_n$. We use this fact in the next example.

EXAMPLE 5

$$\frac{\cos n}{n} \to 0 \qquad \text{because} \quad 0 \leq \left|\frac{\cos n}{n}\right| = \frac{|\cos n|}{n} \leq \frac{1}{n}.$$

EXAMPLE 6

$$\frac{1}{2^n} \to 0 \qquad \text{because} \quad 0 \le \frac{1}{2^n} \le \frac{1}{n}.$$

EXAMPLE 7

$$(-1)^n \frac{1}{n} \to 0 \qquad \text{because} \quad 0 \le \left|(-1)^n \frac{1}{n}\right| \le \frac{1}{n}.$$

The application of Theorems 1 and 2 is broadened by a theorem that says that the result of applying a continuous function to a convergent sequence is again a convergent sequence. We state the theorem without proof.

Theorem 3. *If $a_n \to L$ and if f is a function that is continuous at L and defined at all the a_n's, then $f(a_n) \to f(L)$.*

EXAMPLE 8. Because $\sqrt{x}$ is continuous at 1 and $(n + 1)/n \to 1$,

$$\sqrt{\frac{n+1}{n}} \to \sqrt{1} = 1.$$

EXAMPLE 9. Because 2^x is continuous at 0 and $1/n \to 0$,

$$\sqrt[n]{2} = 2^{1/n} \to 2^0 = 1.$$

L'Hôpital's rule can be used to determine the limits of some sequences. The next example shows how.

EXAMPLE 10. Find $\lim_{n \to \infty} (\ln n)/n$.

Solution. The function $(\ln x)/x$ is defined for all $x \ge 1$ and agrees with the given sequence on the positive integers. Therefore $\lim_{n \to \infty} (\ln n)/n$ will equal $\lim_{x \to \infty} (\ln x)/x$ if the latter exists. A single application of l'Hôpital's rule shows that

$$\lim_{x \to \infty} \frac{\ln x}{x} = \lim_{x \to \infty} \frac{1/x}{1} = \frac{0}{1} = 0.$$

We conclude that $\lim_{n \to \infty} (\ln n)/n = 0$.

When we use l'Hôpital's rule to find the limit of a sequence, we often treat n as a continuous real variable, and differentiate directly with respect to n. This saves us from having to rewrite the formula for a_n as we did in Example 10.

EXAMPLE 11. Find $\lim_{n \to \infty} (2^n/5n)$.

Solution. By l'Hôpital's rule,

$$\lim_{n \to \infty} \frac{2^n}{5n} = \lim_{n \to \infty} \frac{2^n \cdot \ln 2}{5} = \infty.$$

PROBLEMS

Write a_1, a_2, a_3, and a_4 for each of the following sequences $\{a_n\}$. Determine which of the sequences converge and which diverge. Find the limit of each sequence that converges.

1. $a_n = \dfrac{1-n}{n^2}$ **2.** $a_n = \dfrac{n}{2^n}$

3. $a_n = \left(\dfrac{1}{3}\right)^n$ **4.** $a_n = \dfrac{1}{n!}$

5. $a_n = \dfrac{(-1)^{n+1}}{2n-1}$ **6.** $a_n = 2 + (-1)^n$

7. $a_n = \cos \dfrac{n\pi}{2}$ **8.** $a_n = 8^{1/n}$

9. $a_n = \dfrac{(-1)^{n-1}}{\sqrt{n}}$ **10.** $a_n = \sin^2 \dfrac{1}{n} + \cos^2 \dfrac{1}{n}$

Determine which of the following sequences $\{a_n\}$ converge and which diverge. Find the limit of each sequence that converges.

11. $a_n = \dfrac{1}{10n}$ **12.** $a_n = \dfrac{n}{10}$

13. $a_n = 1 + \dfrac{(-1)^n}{n}$ **14.** $a_n = \dfrac{1 + (-1)^n}{n}$

15. $a_n = (-1)^n \left(1 - \dfrac{1}{n}\right)$ **16.** $a_n = 1 + (-1)^n$

17. $a_n = \dfrac{2n+1}{1-3n}$ **18.** $a_n = \dfrac{n^2 - n}{2n^2 + n}$

19. $a_n = \sqrt{\dfrac{2n}{n+1}}$ **20.** $a_n = \dfrac{\sin n}{n}$

21. $a_n = \sin \pi n$ **22.** $a_n = \sin \left(\dfrac{\pi}{2} + \dfrac{1}{n}\right)$

23. $a_n = n\pi \cos n\pi$ **24.** $a_n = \dfrac{\sin^2 n}{2^n}$

25. $a_n = \dfrac{n^2}{(n+1)^2}$ **26.** $a_n = \dfrac{\sqrt{n-1}}{\sqrt{n}}$

27. $a_n = \dfrac{1 - 5n^4}{n^4 + 8n^3}$ **28.** $a_n = \sqrt[n]{3^{2n+1}}$

29. $a_n = \tanh n$ **30.** $a_n = \dfrac{\ln n}{\sqrt{n}}$

31. $a_n = \dfrac{2(n+1)+1}{2n+1}$ **32.** $a_n = \dfrac{(n+1)!}{n!}$

33. $a_n = 5$ **34.** $a_n = 5^n$

35. $a_n = (0.5)^n$ **36.** $a_n = \dfrac{10^{n+1}}{10^n}$

37. $a_n = \dfrac{n^n}{(n+1)^{n+1}}$ **38.** $a_n = (0.03)^{1/n}$

39. $a_n = \sqrt{2 - \dfrac{1}{n}}$ **40.** $a_n = 2 + (0.1)^n$

41. $a_n = \dfrac{3^n}{n^3}$ **42.** $a_n = \dfrac{\ln(n+1)}{n+1}$

43. $a_n = \ln n - \ln(n+1)$ **44.** $a_n = \dfrac{1 - 2^n}{2^n}$

45. $a_n = \dfrac{n^2 - 2n + 1}{n-1}$ **46.** $a_n = \dfrac{n + (-1)^n}{n}$

47. $a_n = \left(-\dfrac{1}{2}\right)^n$ **48.** $a_n = \dfrac{\ln n}{\ln 2n}$

49. $a_n = \tan^{-1} n$ **50.** $a_n = \sinh(\ln n)$

51. $a_n = n \sin \dfrac{1}{n}$ **52.** $a_n = \dfrac{2n + \sin n}{n + \cos 5n}$

53. $a_n = \dfrac{n^2}{2n-1} \sin \dfrac{1}{n}$ **54.** $a_n = n\left(1 - \cos \dfrac{1}{n}\right)$

55. Show that $\lim_{n \to \infty} (n!/n^n) = 0$.

[*Hint.* Expand the numerator and denominator and compare the quotient with $1/n$.]

56. (*Calculator*) The formula $x_{n+1} = (x_n + a/x_n)/2$ is the one produced by Newton's method to generate a sequence of approximations to the positive solution of $x^2 - a = 0$, $a > 0$. Starting with $x_1 = 1$ and $a = 3$, use the formula to calculate successive terms of the sequence until you have approximated $\sqrt{3}$ as accurately as your calculator permits.

57. (*Calculator*) If your calculator has a square-root key, enter $x = 10$ and take successive square roots to approximate the terms of the sequence $10^{1/2}$, $10^{1/4}$, $10^{1/8}$, ..., continuing as far as your calculator permits. Repeat, with $x = 0.1$. Try other positive numbers above and below 1. When you have enough evidence, guess the answers to these questions: Does $\lim_{n \to \infty} x^{1/n}$ exist when $x > 0$? Does it matter what x is?

58. (*Calculator*) If you start with a reasonable value of x_1, then the rule $x_{n+1} = x_n + \cos x_n$ will generate a sequence that converges to $\pi/2$. Figure 16–4 shows why. The convergence is rapid. With $x_1 = 1$, calculate x_2, x_3, and x_4. Find out what happens when you start with $x_1 = 5$. Remember to use radians.

59. Suppose that $f(x)$ is defined for all $0 \le x \le 1$, that f is differentiable at $x = 0$, and that $f(0) = 0$. Define a sequence $\{a_n\}$ by the rule $a_n = nf(1/n)$. Show that $\lim a_n = f'(0)$.

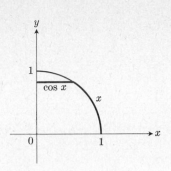

16–4 The length $\pi/2$ of the circular arc is approximated by $x + \cos x$.

Use the result of Problem 59 to find the limits of the sequences in Problems 60 and 61.

60. $a_n = n \tan^{-1} \dfrac{1}{n}$ **61.** $a_n = n(e^{1/n} - 1)$

62. Prove that a sequence $\{a_n\}$ cannot have two different limits L and L'. [*Hint.* Take $\epsilon = \frac{1}{2}|L - L'|$ in Eq. (4).]

63. Prove that, if f is a function that is defined for $x > 0$, and if $\lim_{x \to \infty} f(x) = L$, then $\lim_{n \to \infty} f(n) = L$. [*Hint.* If $|f(x) - L| < \epsilon$ for all x beyond some x_0, then $|f(x) - L| < \epsilon$ for all x beyond some integer $N > x_0$.]

64. Prove Theorem 2.

65. Prove Theorem 3.

Some limits arise so frequently that they are worth special attention. In this article we investigate these limits and look at examples in which they occur.

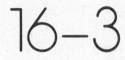

LIMITS THAT ARISE FREQUENTLY

1. $\displaystyle\lim_{n \to \infty} \frac{\ln n}{n} = 0$ **2.** $\displaystyle\lim_{n \to \infty} \sqrt[n]{n} = 1$

3. $\displaystyle\lim_{n \to \infty} x^{1/n} = 1$ $(x > 0)$ **4.** $\displaystyle\lim_{n \to \infty} x^n = 0$ $(|x| < 1)$

5. $\displaystyle\lim_{n \to \infty} \left(1 + \frac{x}{n}\right)^n = e^x$ (any x)   **6.** $\displaystyle\lim_{n \to \infty} \frac{x^n}{n!} = 0$ (any x)

Calculation of the Limits

1. $\displaystyle\lim_{n \to \infty} \frac{\ln n}{n} = 0$

This limit was calculated in Example 10 of Article 16–2.

2. $\displaystyle\lim_{n \to \infty} \sqrt[n]{n} = 1$

Let $a_n = n^{1/n}$. Then

$$\ln a_n = \ln n^{1/n} = \frac{1}{n} \ln n \to 0, \tag{1}$$

so that, by applying Theorem 3 of Article 16–2 to $f(x) = e^x$, we have

$$a_n = n^{1/n} = e^{\ln a_n} \to e^0 = 1. \tag{2}$$

3. $\displaystyle\lim_{n \to \infty} x^{1/n} = 1$, if $x > 0$

Let $a_n = x^{1/n}$. Then

$$\ln a_n = \ln x^{1/n} = \frac{1}{n} \ln x \to 0, \tag{3}$$

because x remains fixed while n gets large. Thus, again by Theorem 3, with $f(x) = e^x$,

$$a_n = x^{1/n} = e^{\ln a_n} \to e^0 = 1. \tag{4}$$

4. $\displaystyle\lim_{n \to \infty} x^n = 0$, if $|x| < 1$

Our scheme here is to show that the criteria of Definition 2 of Article 16–2 are satisfied, with $L = 0$. That is, we will show that to each $\epsilon > 0$ there corresponds an index N so large that

$$|x^n| < \epsilon \qquad \text{for} \quad n > N. \tag{5}$$

Since $\epsilon^{1/n} \to 1$, while $|x| < 1$, there is an index N for which

$$|x| < \epsilon^{1/N}. \tag{6}$$

In other words,

$$|x^N| = |x|^N < \epsilon. \tag{7}$$

This is the index we seek, because

$$|x^n| < |x^N| \qquad \text{for} \quad n > N. \tag{8}$$

Combining (7) and (8) produces

$$|x^n| < |x^N| < \epsilon \qquad \text{for} \quad n > N, \tag{9}$$

which is just what we needed to show.

5. $\displaystyle\lim_{n \to \infty}\left(1 + \frac{x}{n}\right)^n = e^x$ (any x)

Let

$$a_n = \left(1 + \frac{x}{n}\right)^n.$$

Then

$$\ln a_n = \ln\left(1 + \frac{x}{n}\right)^n = n \ln\left(1 + \frac{x}{n}\right) \to x,$$

as we can see by the following application of l'Hôpital's rule, in which we differentiate with respect to n:

$$\lim_{n \to \infty} n \ln\left(1 + \frac{x}{n}\right) = \lim_{n \to \infty} \frac{\ln\left(1 + x/n\right)}{1/n}$$

$$= \lim_{n \to \infty} \frac{\left(\dfrac{1}{1 + x/n}\right) \cdot \left(-\dfrac{x}{n^2}\right)}{-1/n^2}$$

$$= \lim_{n \to \infty} \frac{x}{1 + x/n} = x.$$

Thus,

$$a_n = \left(1 + \frac{x}{n}\right)^n = e^{\ln a_n} \to e^x.$$

6. $\displaystyle\lim_{n \to \infty} \frac{x^n}{n!} = 0$ (any x)

Since

$$-\frac{|x|^n}{n!} \le \frac{x^n}{n!} \le \frac{|x|^n}{n!},$$

all we really need to show is that $|x|^n/n! \to 0$. The first step is to choose an integer $M > |x|$, so that

$$\frac{|x|}{M} < 1 \quad \text{and} \quad \left(\frac{|x|}{M}\right)^n \to 0.$$

We then restrict our attention to values of $n > M$. For these values of n, we can write

$$\frac{|x|^n}{n!} = \frac{|x|^n}{1 \cdot 2 \cdots M \cdot \underbrace{(M+1)(M+2)\cdots n}_{(n-M) \text{ factors}}}$$

$$\le \frac{|x|^n}{M! \, M^{n-M}} = \frac{|x|^n M^M}{M! \, M^n} = \frac{M^M}{M!}\left(\frac{|x|}{M}\right)^n.$$

Thus,

$$0 \le \frac{|x|^n}{n!} \le \frac{M^M}{M!}\left(\frac{|x|}{M}\right)^n.$$

Now, the constant $M^M/M!$ does not change with n. Thus the Sandwich Theorem tells us that

$$\frac{|x|^n}{n!} \to 0 \quad \text{because} \quad \left(\frac{|x|}{M}\right)^n \to 0. \qquad \text{Q.E.D.}$$

A large number of limits can be found directly from the six limits we have just calculated.

EXAMPLES

1. If $|x| < 1$, then $x^{n+4} = x^4 \cdot x^n \to x^4 \cdot 0 = 0$.

2. $\sqrt[n]{2n} = \sqrt[n]{2}\,\sqrt[n]{n} \to 1 \cdot 1 = 1$.

3. $\left(1 + \dfrac{1}{n}\right)^{2n} = \left[\left(1 + \dfrac{1}{n}\right)^n\right]^2 \to e^2$.

4. $\dfrac{100^n}{n!} \to 0$

5. $\dfrac{x^{n+1}}{(n+1)!} = \dfrac{x}{(n+1)} \cdot \dfrac{x^n}{n!} \to 0 \cdot 0 = 0.$

Still other limits can be calculated by using logarithms or l'Hôpital's rule, as in the calculations of limits (2), (3), and (5) at the beginning of this article.

EXAMPLE 6. Find $\lim_{n \to \infty} (\ln (3n + 5)/n)$.

Solution. By l'Hôpital's rule,

$$\lim_{n \to \infty} \frac{\ln (3n + 5)}{n} = \lim_{n \to \infty} \frac{3/(3n + 5)}{1} = 0.$$

EXAMPLE 7. Find $\lim_{n \to \infty} \sqrt[n]{3n + 5}$.

Solution. Let

$$a_n = \sqrt[n]{3n + 5} = (3n + 5)^{1/n}.$$

Then,

$$\ln a_n = \ln (3n + 5)^{1/n} = \frac{\ln (3n + 5)}{n} \to 0,$$

as in Example 6. Therefore,

$$a_n = e^{\ln a_n} \to e^0 = 1,$$

by Theorem 3 of Article 16–2.

PROBLEMS

Determine which of the following sequences $\{a_n\}$ converge and which diverge. Find the limit of each sequence that converges.

1. $a_n = \dfrac{1 + \ln n}{n}$

2. $a_n = \dfrac{\ln n}{3n}$

3. $a_n = \dfrac{(-4)^n}{n!}$

4. $a_n = \sqrt[n]{10n}$

5. $a_n = (0.5)^n$

6. $a_n = \dfrac{1}{(0.9)^n}$

7. $a_n = \left(1 + \dfrac{7}{n}\right)^n$

8. $a_n = \left(\dfrac{n+5}{n}\right)^n$

9. $a_n = \dfrac{\ln (n + 1)}{n}$

10. $a_n = \sqrt[n]{n + 1}$

11. $a_n = \dfrac{n!}{10^{6n}}$

12. $a_n = \dfrac{1}{\sqrt{2^n}}$

13. $a_n = \sqrt[2n]{n}$

14. $a_n = (n + 4)^{1/(n + 4)}$

15. $a_n = \dfrac{1}{3^{2n-1}}$

16. $a_n = \ln \left(1 + \dfrac{1}{n}\right)^n$

17. $a_n = \left(\dfrac{n}{n + 1}\right)^n$

18. $a_n = \left(1 + \dfrac{1}{n}\right)^{-n}$

19. $a_n = \dfrac{\ln (2n + 1)}{n}$

20. $a_n = \sqrt[n]{2n + 1}$

21. $a_n = \sqrt[n]{\dfrac{x^n}{2n + 1}}, \quad x > 0$

22. $a_n = \sqrt[n]{n^2}$

23. $a_n = \sqrt[n]{n^2 + n}$

24. $a_n = \dfrac{3^n \cdot 6^n}{2^{-n} \cdot n!}$

25. $a_n = \left(\dfrac{3}{n}\right)^{1/n}$

26. $a_n = \sqrt[n]{4^n n}$

27. $a_n = \left(1 - \dfrac{1}{n}\right)^n$

28. $a_n = \left(1 - \dfrac{1}{n^2}\right)^n$

29. $a_n = \dfrac{1}{n} \displaystyle\int_1^n \dfrac{1}{x}\,dx$ **30.** $a_n = \displaystyle\int_1^n \dfrac{1}{x^p}\,dx, \quad p > 1$

(*Calculator*) In Problems 31–33, use a calculator to find a value of N such that the given inequality is satisfied for $n \geq N$.

31. $\left| \sqrt[n]{0.5} - 1 \right| < 10^{-3}$ **32.** $\left| \sqrt[n]{n} - 1 \right| < 10^{-3}$

33. $\dfrac{2^n}{n!} < 10^{-9}$

[*Hint.* If you do not have a factorial key, then write

$$\frac{2^n}{n!} = \left(\frac{2}{1}\right)\left(\frac{2}{2}\right)\cdots\left(\frac{2}{n}\right).$$

That is, calculate successive terms by multiplying by 2 and dividing by the next value of n.]

Infinite series are sequences of a special kind.

Definition

1. *If $\{a_n\}$ is a sequence, and*

$$s_n = a_1 + a_2 + \cdots + a_n,$$

*then the sequence $\{s_n\}$ is called an **infinite series.***
2. *Instead of $\{s_n\}$ we usually use the notation*

$$\sum_{n=1}^{\infty} a_n$$

for the series, because it shows how the sums s_n are to be constructed.
3. *The number a_n is called the nth* term *of the series (it is still the nth term of the sequence $\{a_n\}$) and the number s_n is the nth **partial sum** of the series.*
4. *If the sequence $\{s_n\}$ of partial sums converges to a finite limit L, we say that the series $\sum_{n=1}^{\infty} a_n$ **converges** to L or that its **sum** is L, and we write*

$$\sum_{n=1}^{\infty} a_n = L \qquad or \qquad a_1 + a_2 + \cdots + a_n + \cdots = L.$$

If no such limit exists, that is if $\{s_n\}$ diverges, we say that the series $\sum_{n=1}^{\infty} a_n$ **diverges.**

We shall illustrate the method of finding the sum of an infinite series with the repeating decimal

$$0.3333 \ldots = \frac{3}{10} + \frac{3}{100} + \frac{3}{1000} + \frac{3}{10{,}000} + \cdots$$

$$s_1 = \frac{3}{10},$$

$$s_2 = \frac{3}{10} + \frac{3}{10^2},$$

$$\vdots$$

$$s_n = \frac{3}{10} + \frac{3}{10^2} + \cdots + \frac{3}{10^n}.$$

16-4

INFINITE SERIES

We can obtain a simple expression for s_n in closed form as follows: We multiply both sides of the equation for s_n by $\frac{1}{10}$ and obtain

$$\frac{1}{10}\,s_n = \frac{3}{10^2} + \frac{3}{10^3} + \cdots + \frac{3}{10^n} + \frac{3}{10^{n+1}}.$$

When we subtract this from s_n, we have

$$s_n - \frac{1}{10}\,s_n = \frac{3}{10} - \frac{3}{10^{n+1}} = \frac{3}{10}\left(1 - \frac{3}{10^n}\right).$$

Therefore,

$$\frac{9}{10}\,s_n = \frac{3}{10}\left(1 - \frac{1}{10^n}\right),$$

$$s_n = \frac{3}{9}\left(1 - \frac{1}{10^n}\right).$$

As $n \to \infty$, $\left(\frac{1}{10}\right)^n \to 0$ and

$$\lim_{n \to \infty} s_n = \frac{3}{9} = \frac{1}{3}.$$

We therefore say that the sum of the infinite series

$$\frac{3}{10^1} + \frac{3}{10^2} + \frac{3}{10^3} + \cdots + \frac{3}{10^n} + \cdots$$

is $\frac{1}{3}$, and we write

$$\sum_{n=1}^{\infty} \frac{3}{10^n} = \frac{1}{3}.$$

A repeating decimal is a special kind of *geometric series*.

Definition. *A series of the form*

$$a + ar + ar^2 + ar^3 + \cdots + ar^{n-1} + \cdots \tag{1}$$

*is called a **geometric series**. The ratio of any term to the one before it is r.*

The ratio r can be positive, as in

$$1 + \frac{1}{2} + \frac{1}{4} + \cdots + \frac{1}{2^{n-1}} + \cdots, \tag{2}$$

or negative, as in

$$1 - \frac{1}{3} + \frac{1}{9} - \cdots + (-1)^n \frac{1}{3^{n-1}} + \cdots. \tag{3}$$

The sum of the first n terms of (1) is

$$s_n = a + ar + ar^2 + \cdots + ar^{n-1}. \tag{4}$$

Multiplying both sides of (4) by r gives

$$rs_n = ar + ar^2 + \cdots + ar^{n-1} + ar^n. \tag{5}$$

When we subtract (5) from (4), nearly all the terms cancel on the right side, leaving

$$s_n - rs_n = a - ar^n,$$

or

$$(1 - r)s_n = a(1 - r^n). \tag{6}$$

If $r \neq 1$, we may divide (6) by $(1 - r)$ to obtain

$$s_n = \frac{a(1 - r^n)}{1 - r}, \qquad r \neq 1. \tag{7a}$$

On the other hand, if $r = 1$ in (4), we get

$$s_n = na, \qquad r = 1. \tag{7b}$$

We are interested in the limit as $n \to \infty$ in Eqs. (7a) and (7b). Clearly, (7b) has no finite limit if $a \neq 0$. If $a = 0$, the series (1) is just

$$0 + 0 + 0 + \cdots,$$

which converges to the sum zero.

If $r \neq 1$, we use (7a). In the right side of (7a), n appears only in the expression r^n. This approaches zero as $n \to \infty$ if $|r| < 1$. Therefore,

$$\lim_{n \to \infty} s_n = \lim_{n \to \infty} \frac{a(1 - r^n)}{1 - r}$$

$$= \frac{a}{1 - r}, \qquad \text{if} \quad |r| < 1. \tag{8}$$

If $|r| > 1$, then $|r^n| \to \infty$, and (1) diverges.

The remaining case is where $r = -1$. Then $s_1 = a$, $s_2 = a - a = 0$, $s_3 = a$, $s_4 = 0$, and so on. If $a \neq 0$, this sequence of partial sums has no limit as $n \to \infty$, and the series (1) diverges.

We have thus proved the following theorem.

Theorem 1. The geometric series theorem. *If $|r| < 1$, the geometric series*

$$a + ar + ar^2 + \cdots + ar^{n-1} + \cdots$$

converges to $a/(1 - r)$. If $|r| \geq 1$, the series diverges unless $a = 0$. If $a = 0$, the series converges to 0.

EXAMPLE 1. A ball is dropped from a meters above a flat surface. Each time the ball hits after falling a distance h, it rebounds a distance rh, where r is a positive number less than one. Find the total distance the ball travels up and down.

Solution. (See Fig. 16–5.) The distance is given by the series

$$s = a + 2ar + 2ar^2 + 2ar^3 + \cdots$$

The terms following the first term form a geometric series of sum $2ar/(1 - r)$.

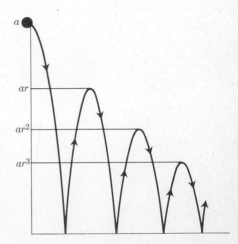

16–5 The height of each rebound is reduced by the factor r.

Hence the distance is

$$s = a + \frac{2ar}{1 - r} = a \frac{1 + r}{1 - r}.$$

For instance, if a is 6 meters and $r = \frac{2}{3}$, the distance is

$$s = 6 \frac{1 + \frac{2}{3}}{1 - \frac{2}{3}} = 30 \text{ m}.$$

EXAMPLE 2. If we take $a = 1$ and $r = x$ in the geometric series theorem, we obtain

$$\frac{1}{1 - x} = 1 + x + x^2 + \cdots + x^{n-1} + \cdots, \qquad |x| < 1, \tag{9}$$

which is the result we sought in Article 16–1.

To find the sum of the geometric series of Theorem 1, we first found a closed expression for s_n and then used our experience with sequences to find $\lim_{n \to \infty} s_n$. We use the same procedure in the next example.

EXAMPLE 3. Determine whether $\sum_{n=1}^{\infty} [1/(n(n + 1))]$ converges. If it does, find the sum.

Solution. We begin by looking for a pattern in the sequence of partial sums that might lead us to a closed expression for s_k. The key to success here, as in the integration

$$\int \frac{dx}{x(x + 1)} = \int \frac{dx}{x} - \int \frac{dx}{x + 1},$$

is the use of partial fractions:

$$\frac{1}{k(k + 1)} = \frac{1}{k} - \frac{1}{k + 1}.$$

This permits us to write the partial sum

$$\sum_{n=1}^{k} \frac{1}{n(n + 1)} = \frac{1}{1 \cdot 2} + \frac{1}{2 \cdot 3} + \cdots + \frac{1}{k \cdot (k + 1)}$$

as

$$s_k = \left(\frac{1}{1} - \frac{1}{2} \right) + \left(\frac{1}{2} - \frac{1}{3} \right) + \cdots + \left(\frac{1}{k} - \frac{1}{k + 1} \right).$$

By removing parentheses on the right, and combining terms, we find that

$$s_k = 1 - \frac{1}{k + 1} = \frac{k}{k + 1}. \tag{12}$$

From this formulation of s_k, we see immediately that $s_k \to 1$. Therefore the series does converge, and

$$\sum_{n=1}^{\infty} \frac{1}{n(n+1)} = 1. \tag{13}$$

There are, of course, other series that diverge besides geometric series with $|r| \geq 1$.

EXAMPLE 4

$$\sum_{n=1}^{\infty} n^2 = 1 + 4 + 9 + \cdots + n^2 + \cdots$$

diverges because the partial sums grow beyond every number L. The number $s_n = 1 + 4 + 9 + \cdots + n^2$ is greater than or equal to n^2 at each stage.

EXAMPLE 5

$$\sum_{n=1}^{\infty} \frac{n+1}{n} = \frac{2}{1} + \frac{3}{2} + \frac{4}{3} + \cdots + \frac{n+1}{n} + \cdots$$

The sequence of partial sums eventually outgrows every preassigned number: each term is greater than 1, so the sum of n terms is greater than n.

A series can diverge without having its partial sums become large. For instance, the partial sums may oscillate between two extremes, as they do in the next example.

EXAMPLE 6. $\sum_{n=1}^{\infty} (-1)^{n+1}$ diverges because its partial sums alternate between 1 and 0:

$$s_1 = (-1)^2 = 1,$$
$$s_2 = (-1)^2 + (-1)^3 = 1 - 1 = 0,$$
$$s_3 = (-1)^2 + (-1)^3 + (-1)^4 = 1 - 1 + 1 = 1,$$

and so on.

The next theorem provides a quick way to detect the kind of divergence that occurred in Examples 4, 5, and 6.

Theorem 2. *The nth-term test for divergence. If* $\lim_{n \to \infty} a_n \neq 0$, *or if* $\lim_{n \to \infty} a_n$ *fails to exist, then* $\sum_{n=1}^{\infty} a_n$ *diverges.*

When we apply Theorem 2 to the series in Examples 4, 5, and 6, we find that:

$$\sum_{n=1}^{\infty} n^2 \qquad\qquad \text{diverges because } n^2 \to \infty;$$

$$\sum_{n=1}^{\infty} \frac{n+1}{n} \qquad\qquad \text{diverges because } \frac{n+1}{n} > 1 \quad \text{for every index } n;$$

$$\sum_{n=1}^{\infty} (-1)^{n+1} \qquad \text{diverges because } \lim_{n \to \infty} (-1)^{n+1} \text{ does not exist.}$$

Proof of the theorem. We prove Theorem 2 by showing that if $\sum a_n$ converges, then $\lim_{n \to \infty} a_n = 0$. Let

$$s_n = a_1 + a_2 + \cdots + a_n,$$

and suppose that $\sum a_n$ converges to S; that is

$$s_n \to S.$$

Then, corresponding to any preassigned number $\epsilon > 0$, there is an index N such that all the terms of the sequence $\{s_n\}$ after the Nth one lie between $S - (\epsilon/2)$ and $S + (\epsilon/2)$. Hence, no two of them may differ by as much as ϵ. That is, if m and n are both greater than N, then

$$\left| s_n - s_m \right| < \epsilon.$$

In particular, this inequality holds if $m = n - 1$ and $n > N + 1$, so that

$$\left| s_n - s_{n-1} \right| = \left| a_n \right| < \epsilon \qquad \text{when} \quad n > N + 1.$$

Since ϵ was any positive number whatsoever, this means that

$$\lim_{n \to \infty} a_n = 0. \qquad\qquad\qquad \text{Q.E.D.}$$

Because of how it is proved, Theorem 2 is often stated in the following shorter way.

Theorem 3. *If $\sum_{n=1}^{\infty} a_n$ converges, then $a_n \to 0$.*

A word of caution. Theorem 3 does *not* say that if $a_n \to 0$ then $\sum a_n$ converges. The series $\sum a_n$ may diverge even though $a_n \to 0$. Thus, $\lim a_n = 0$ is a necessary, but not a sufficient condition for the series $\sum a_n$ to converge.

EXAMPLE 7. The series

$$1 + \underbrace{\frac{1}{2} + \frac{1}{2}}_{2 \text{ terms}} + \underbrace{\frac{1}{4} + \frac{1}{4} + \frac{1}{4} + \frac{1}{4}}_{4 \text{ terms}} + \underbrace{\frac{1}{8} + \frac{1}{8} + \cdots + \frac{1}{8}}_{8 \text{ terms}} + \underbrace{\frac{1}{2^n} + \frac{1}{2^n} + \cdots + \frac{1}{2^n}}_{2^n \text{ terms}} + \cdots$$

diverges even though its terms form a sequence that converges to 0.

Whenever we have two convergent series we can add them, subtract them, and multiply them by constants, to make other convergent series. The next theorem gives the details.

Theorem 4. *If* $A = \sum_{n=1}^{\infty} a_n$ *and* $B = \sum_{n=1}^{\infty} b_n$ *both exist and are finite, then*

i) $\displaystyle\sum_{n=1}^{\infty} (a_n + b_n) = A + B;$

ii) $\displaystyle\sum_{n=1}^{\infty} ka_n = k \sum_{n=1}^{\infty} a_n = kA$ (*k any number*).

Proof of the theorem.   Let

$$A_n = a_1 + a_2 + \cdots + a_n, \qquad B_n = b_1 + b_2 + \cdots + b_n.$$

Then the partial sums of $\sum_{n=1}^{\infty} (a_n + b_n)$ are:

$$\begin{aligned}
S_n &= (a_1 + b_1) + (a_2 + b_2) + \cdots + (a_n + b_n) \\
&= (a_1 + \cdots + a_n) + (b_1 + \cdots + b_n) \\
&= A_n + B_n.
\end{aligned}$$

Since $A_n \to A$ and $B_n \to B$, we have $S_n \to A + B$. The partial sums of $\sum_{n=1}^{\infty} (ka_n)$ are:

$$\begin{aligned}
S_n &= ka_1 + ka_2 + \cdots + ka_n \\
&= k(a_1 + a_2 + \cdots + a_n) \\
&= kA_n,
\end{aligned}$$

which converge to kA.   Q.E.D.

REMARK 1.   If you think there should be two more parts of Theorem 4 to match those of Theorem 1, Article 16–2, see Problems 44–46. Also, see Problem 41, Article 16–5, and Problem 39, Article 16–7.

Part (ii) of Theorem 4 says that every multiple of a convergent series converges. A companion to this is the next corollary, which says that every *nonzero* multiple of a divergent series diverges.

Corollary.   *If* $\sum_{n=1}^{\infty} a_n$ *diverges, and if c is any number different from* 0, *then the series of multiples* $\sum_{n=1}^{\infty} ca_n$ *diverges.*

Proof of the corollary.   Suppose, to the contrary, that $\sum_{n=1}^{\infty} ca_n$ actually converges. Then, when we take $k = 1/c$ in part (ii) of Theorem 4 we find that

$$\frac{1}{c} \cdot \sum_{n=1}^{\infty} ca_n = \sum_{n=1}^{\infty} \frac{1}{c} \cdot ca_n = \sum_{n=1}^{\infty} a_n$$

converges. That is, $\sum_{n=1}^{\infty} ca_n$ cannot converge unless $\sum_{n=1}^{\infty} a_n$ also converges. Thus, if $\sum_{n=1}^{\infty} a_n$ diverges, then $\sum_{n=1}^{\infty} ca_n$ must diverge.   Q.E.D.

REMARK 2. An immediate consequence of Theorem 4 is that, if $A = \sum_{n=1}^{\infty} a_n$ and $B = \sum_{n=1}^{\infty} b_n$, then

$$\sum (a_n - b_n) = \sum a_n + \sum (-1)b_n = \sum a_n - \sum b_n = A - B. \tag{14}$$

The series $\sum_{n=1}^{\infty} (a_n - b_n)$ is called the *difference* of $\sum_{n=1}^{\infty} a_n$ and $\sum_{n=1}^{\infty} b_n$, while $\sum_{n=1}^{\infty} (a_n + b_n)$ is called their *sum*.

EXAMPLE 8

a) $\displaystyle\sum_{n=1}^{\infty} \frac{4}{2^{n-1}} = 4 \sum_{n=1}^{\infty} \frac{1}{2^{n-1}} = 4 \frac{1}{1 - \frac{1}{2}} = 8;$

b) $\displaystyle\sum_{n=0}^{\infty} \frac{3^n - 2^n}{6^n} = \sum_{n=0}^{\infty} \left(\frac{1}{2^n} - \frac{1}{3^n} \right)$

$$= \sum_{n=0}^{\infty} \frac{1}{2^n} - \sum_{n=0}^{\infty} \frac{1}{3^n}$$

$$= \frac{1}{1 - \frac{1}{2}} - \frac{1}{1 - \frac{1}{3}}$$

$$= 2 - \tfrac{3}{2}$$

$$= \tfrac{1}{2}.$$

REMARK 3.   A finite number of terms can always be deleted from or added to a series without altering its convergence or divergence. If $\sum_{n=1}^{\infty} a_n$ converges and k is an index greater than 1, then $\sum_{n=k}^{\infty} a_n$ converges, and

$$\sum_{n=1}^{\infty} a_n = a_1 + a_2 + \cdots + a_{k-1} + \sum_{n=k}^{\infty} a_n. \tag{15}$$

Conversely, if $\sum_{n=k}^{\infty} a_n$ converges for any $k > 1$, then $\sum_{n=1}^{\infty} a_n$ converges and the sums continue to be related as in Eq. (15). Thus, for example,

$$\sum_{n=1}^{\infty} \frac{1}{5^n} = \frac{1}{5} + \frac{1}{25} + \frac{1}{125} + \sum_{n=4}^{\infty} \frac{1}{5^n} \tag{16}$$

and

$$\sum_{n=4}^{\infty} \frac{1}{5^n} = \sum_{n=1}^{\infty} \frac{1}{5^n} - \frac{1}{5} - \frac{1}{25} - \frac{1}{125}. \tag{17}$$

Note that while the addition or removal of a finite number of terms from a series has no effect on the convergence or divergence of the series, these operations can change the *sum* of a convergent series.

REMARK 4.   The indexing of the terms of a series can be changed without altering convergence of the series. For example, the geometric series that starts with

$$1 + \frac{1}{2} + \frac{1}{4} + \cdots$$

can be described as

$$\sum_{n=0}^{\infty} \frac{1}{2^n} \quad \text{or} \quad \sum_{n=-4}^{\infty} \frac{1}{2^{n+4}} \quad \text{or} \quad \sum_{n=5}^{\infty} \frac{1}{2^{n-5}}. \tag{18}$$

The partial sums remain the same no matter what indexing is chosen, so that we are free to start indexing with whatever integer we want. Preference is usually given to an indexing that leads to a simple expression. In Example 8(b) we chose to start with $n = 0$ instead of $n = 1$, because this allowed us to describe the series we had in mind as:

$$\sum_{n=0}^{\infty} \frac{3^n - 2^n}{6^n} \quad \text{instead of} \quad \sum_{n=1}^{\infty} \frac{3^{n-1} - 2^{n-1}}{6^{n-1}}. \tag{19}$$

PROBLEMS

In Problems 1 through 8, find a closed expression for the sum s_n of the first n terms of each series. Then compute the sum of the series if the series converges.

1. $\dfrac{1}{2 \cdot 3} + \dfrac{1}{3 \cdot 4} + \dfrac{1}{4 \cdot 5} + \cdots + \dfrac{1}{(n+1)(n+2)} + \cdots$

2. $\ln \dfrac{1}{2} + \ln \dfrac{2}{3} + \ln \dfrac{3}{4} + \cdots + \ln \dfrac{n}{n+1} + \cdots$

3. $1 + e^{-1} + e^{-2} + \cdots + e^{-(n-1)} + \cdots$

4. $1 - \dfrac{1}{2} + \dfrac{1}{4} - \dfrac{1}{8} + \cdots + (-1)^{n-1} \dfrac{1}{2^{n-1}} + \cdots$

5. $1 - 2 + 4 - 8 + \cdots + (-1)^{n-1} 2^{n-1} + \cdots$

6. $2 + \dfrac{2}{3} + \dfrac{2}{9} + \dfrac{2}{27} + \cdots + \dfrac{2}{3^{n-1}} + \cdots$

7. $\dfrac{9}{100} + \dfrac{9}{100^2} + \dfrac{9}{100^3} + \cdots + \dfrac{9}{100^n} + \cdots$

8. $1 + 2 + 3 + \cdots + n + \cdots$

9. The series in Problem 1 can be described as

$$\sum_{n=1}^{\infty} \frac{1}{(n+1)(n+2)}.$$

It can also be described as a summation beginning with $n = -1$:

$$\sum_{n=-1}^{\infty} \frac{1}{(n+3)(n+4)}.$$

Describe the series as a summation beginning with
a) $n = -2$ b) $n = 0$ c) $n = 5$.

10. A ball is dropped from a height of 4 m. Each time it strikes the pavement after falling from a height of h meters, it rebounds to a height of $0.75h$ meters. Find the total distance traveled up and down by the ball.

In Problems 11 through 14, write out the fourth partial sum of each series. Then find the sum of the series.

11. $\displaystyle\sum_{n=0}^{\infty} \frac{1}{4^n}$

12. $\displaystyle\sum_{n=2}^{\infty} \frac{1}{4^n}$

13. $\displaystyle\sum_{n=1}^{\infty} \frac{7}{4^n}$

14. $\displaystyle\sum_{n=0}^{\infty} (-1)^n \frac{5}{4^n}$

Find the sum of each series.

15. $\displaystyle\sum_{n=0}^{\infty} \left(\frac{5}{2^n} + \frac{1}{3^n} \right)$

16. $\displaystyle\sum_{n=0}^{\infty} \left(\frac{5}{2^n} - \frac{1}{3^n} \right)$

17. $\displaystyle\sum_{n=0}^{\infty} \left(\frac{2^n}{5^n} \right)$

18. $\displaystyle\sum_{n=0}^{\infty} \left(\frac{2^{n+1}}{5^n} \right)$

Use partial fractions to find the sum of each series.

19. $\displaystyle\sum_{n=1}^{\infty} \frac{4}{(4n-3)(4n+1)}$

20. $\displaystyle\sum_{n=1}^{\infty} \frac{1}{(4n-3)(4n+1)}$

21. $\displaystyle\sum_{n=3}^{\infty} \frac{4}{(4n-3)(4n+1)}$

22. $\displaystyle\sum_{n=1}^{\infty} \frac{2n+1}{n^2(n+1)^2}$

23. a) Express the repeating decimal

$$0.234\ 234\ 234 \ldots$$

as an infinite series, and give the sum as a ratio p/q of two integers.
b) Is it true that *every* repeating decimal is a rational number p/q? Give a reason for your answer.

24. Express the decimal number

$$1.24\ 123\ 123\ 123 \ldots,$$

which begins to repeat after the first three figures, as a rational number p/q.

In Problems 25 through 38, determine whether each series converges or diverges. If it converges, find the sum.

25. $\displaystyle\sum_{n=0}^{\infty} \left(\frac{1}{\sqrt{2}}\right)^n$

26. $\displaystyle\sum_{n=1}^{\infty} \ln \frac{1}{n}$

27. $\displaystyle\sum_{n=1}^{\infty} (-1)^{n+1} \frac{3}{2^n}$

28. $\displaystyle\sum_{n=1}^{\infty} (\sqrt{2})^n$

29. $\displaystyle\sum_{n=0}^{\infty} \cos n\pi$

30. $\displaystyle\sum_{n=0}^{\infty} \frac{\cos n\pi}{5^n}$

31. $\displaystyle\sum_{n=0}^{\infty} e^{-2n}$

32. $\displaystyle\sum_{n=1}^{\infty} \frac{n^2+1}{n}$

33. $\displaystyle\sum_{n=1}^{\infty} (-1)^{n+1} n$

34. $\displaystyle\sum_{n=1}^{\infty} \frac{2}{10^n}$

35. $\displaystyle\sum_{n=0}^{\infty} \frac{2^n-1}{3^n}$

36. $\displaystyle\sum_{n=1}^{\infty} \left(1-\frac{1}{n}\right)^n$

37. $\displaystyle\sum_{n=0}^{\infty} \frac{n!}{1000^n}$

38. $\displaystyle\sum_{n=0}^{\infty} \frac{1}{x^n}, \quad |x| > 1$

In Problems 39 and 40, the equalities are instances of Theorem 1. Give the value of a and of r in each case.

39. $\displaystyle\frac{1}{1+x} = \sum_{n=0}^{\infty} (-1)^n x^n, \quad |x| < 1$

40. $\displaystyle\frac{1}{1+x^2} = \sum_{n=0}^{\infty} (-1)^n x^{2n}, \quad |x| < 1$

41. Figure 16–6 shows the first five of an infinite series of squares. The outermost square has an area of 4, and each of the other squares is obtained by joining the midpoints of the sides of the square before it. Find the sum of the areas of all the squares.

42. Find a closed-form expression for the nth partial sum of the series $\sum_{n=1}^{\infty} (-1)^{n+1}$.

43. Show by example that the term-by-term sum of two divergent series may converge.

44. Find convergent geometric series $A = \sum_{n=1}^{\infty} a_n$ and $B = \sum_{n=1}^{\infty} b_n$ that illustrate the fact that $\sum_{n=1}^{\infty} a_n \cdot b_n$ may converge without being equal to $A \cdot B$.

45. Show by example that $\sum_{n=1}^{\infty} (a_n/b_n)$ may diverge even though $\sum_{n=1}^{\infty} a_n$ and $\sum_{n=1}^{\infty} b_n$ converge and no $b_n = 0$.

46. Show by example that $\sum_{n=1}^{\infty} (a_n/b_n)$ may converge to something other than A/B even when $A = \sum_{n=1}^{\infty} a_n$, $B = \sum_{n=1}^{\infty} b_n \neq 0$, and no $b_n = 0$.

47. Show that if $\sum_{n=1}^{\infty} a_n$ converges, and $a_n \neq 0$ for all n, then $\sum_{n=1}^{\infty} (1/a_n)$ diverges.

48. a) Verify by long division that

$$\frac{1}{1+t} = 1 - t + t^2 - t^3 + \cdots + (-1)^n t^n + \frac{(-1)^{n+1} t^{n+1}}{1+t}.$$

b) By integrating both sides of the equation in part (a) with respect to t, from 0 to x, show that

$$\ln(1+x) = x - \frac{x^2}{2} + \frac{x^3}{3} - \frac{x^4}{4} + \cdots + (-1)^n \frac{x^{n+1}}{n+1} + R,$$

where

$$R = (-1)^{n+1} \int_0^x \frac{t^{n+1}}{1+t}\, dt.$$

c) If $x > 0$, show that

$$|R| \leq \int_0^x t^{n+1}\, dt = \frac{x^{n+2}}{n+2}.$$

[*Hint.* As t varies from 0 to x, $1 + t \geq 1$.]

d) If $x = \frac{1}{2}$, how large should n be in part (c) above if we want to be able to guarantee that $|R| < 0.001$? Write a polynomial that approximates $\ln(1+x)$ to this degree of accuracy for $0 \leq x \leq \frac{1}{2}$.

e) If $x = 1$, how large should n be in part (c) above if we want to be able to guarantee that $|R| < 0.001$?

49. (*Calculator*) The concentration in the blood resulting from a single dose of a drug normally decreases with time as the drug is eliminated from the body. Doses may therefore be repeated to maintain the concentration. One model for the effect of repeated doses gives the residual concentration just before the $(n+1)$st dose as:

$$R_n = C_0 e^{-kt_0} + C_0 e^{-2kt_0} + \cdots + C_0 e^{-nkt_0},$$

where C_0 = concentration achievable by a single dose (mg/ml), k = the *elimination constant* (hr^{-1}), and t_0 = time between doses (hr). See Fig. 16–7.

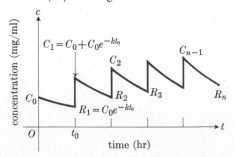

16–7   One possible effect of repeated doses on the concentration of a drug in the bloodstream.

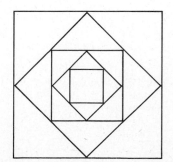

Figure 16–6

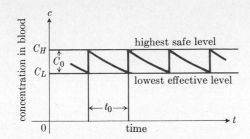

16–8 Safe and effective concentrations of a drug. C_0 is the change in concentration produced by one dose; t_0 is the time between doses.

a) Write R_n in closed form, and find $R = \lim_{n \to \infty} R_n$.

b) Calculate R_1 and R_{10} for $C_0 = 1$ mg/ml, $k = 0.1$ hr^{-1}, and $t_0 = 10$ hr. How good an estimate of R is R_{10}?

c) If $k = 0.01$ hr^{-1} and $t_0 = 10$ hr, find the smallest n such that $R_n > \frac{1}{2}R$.

d) If a drug is known to be ineffective below a concentration C_L and harmful above some higher concentration C_H, one needs to find values of C_0 and t_0 that will produce a concentration that is safe (not above C_H) but effective (not below C_L). See Fig. 16–8. We therefore want to find values of C_0 and t_0 for which

$$R = C_L \qquad \text{and} \qquad C_0 + R = C_H.$$

Thus $C_0 = C_H - C_L$. Show that, when these values are substituted in the equation for R obtained in (a), the resulting equation simplifies to:

$$t_0 = \frac{1}{k} \ln \frac{C_H}{C_L}.$$

To reach an effective level rapidly, one might administer a "loading" dose that would produce a concentration of C_H mg/ml. This could be followed every t_0 hours by a dose that raises the concentration by $C_0 = C_H - C_L$ mg/ml.

e) If $k = 0.05$ hr^{-1} and the highest safe concentration is e times the lowest safe concentration, find the length of time between doses that will assure safe and effective concentrations.

f) Given $C_H = 2$ mg/ml, $C_L = 0.5$ mg/ml, and $k = 0.02$ hr^{-1}, determine a scheme for administering the drug.

g) Suppose that $k = 0.2$ hr^{-1} and that the smallest effective concentration is 0.03 mg/ml. A single dose that produces a concentration of 0.1 mg/ml is administered. About how long will the drug remain effective?

(This problem was adapted from Horelick and Koont's *Prescribing Safe and Effective Dosage*, Project UMAP, Education Development Center, Newton, MA, 1977.)

In this article we will study series that do not have negative terms. The reason for this restriction is that the partial sums of these series always form increasing sequences, and increasing sequences that are bounded above always converge, as we will see. Thus, to show that a series of nonnegative terms converges, we need only show that there is some number beyond which the partial sums never go.

It may at first seem to be a drawback that this approach establishes the fact of convergence without actually producing the sum of the series in question. Surely it would be better to compute sums of series directly from nice formulas for their partial sums. But in most cases such formulas are not available, and in their absence we have to turn instead to a two-step procedure of first establishing convergence and then approximating the sum. In this article and the next, we focus on the first of these two steps.

Surprisingly enough it is not a severe restriction to begin our study of convergence with the temporary exclusion of series that have one or more negative terms, for it is a fact, as we shall see in the next article, that a series $\sum_{n=1}^{\infty} a_n$ will converge whenever the corresponding series of absolute values $\sum_{n=1}^{\infty} |a_n|$ converges. Thus, once we know that

$$\sum_{n=1}^{\infty} \frac{1}{n^2} = 1 + \frac{1}{4} + \frac{1}{9} + \frac{1}{16} + \frac{1}{25} + \cdots \qquad \textbf{(1)}$$

16–5

TESTS FOR CONVERGENCE OF SERIES WITH NONNEGATIVE TERMS

converges, we will know that *all* of the series like

$$1 - \frac{1}{4} + \frac{1}{9} - \frac{1}{16} + \frac{1}{25} + \cdots \tag{2}$$

and

$$-1 - \frac{1}{4} + \frac{1}{9} + \frac{1}{16} - \frac{1}{25} - \cdots, \tag{3}$$

that can be obtained from (1) by changing the sign of one or more terms, also converge! We might not know at first what they converge to, but at least we know they converge, and that is a first and necessary step towards estimating their sums.

Suppose now that $\sum_{n=1}^{\infty} a_n$ is an infinite series that has no negative terms. That is, $a_n \geq 0$ for every n. Then, when we calculate the partial sums s_1, s_2, s_3, and so on, we see that each one is greater than or equal to its predecessor because $s_{n+1} = s_n + a_n$. That is,

$$s_1 \leq s_2 \leq s_3 \leq \cdots \leq s_n \leq s_{n+1} \leq \cdots. \tag{4}$$

A sequence $\{s_n\}$ like the one in (4), with the property that $s_n \leq s_{n+1}$ for every n, is called an *increasing* sequence. The cardinal principle governing increasing sequences is contained in the following theorem.

Theorem 1. *Let $s_1, s_2, s_3, \ldots$ be an increasing sequence of real numbers. Then one or the other of the following alternatives must hold:*

A. *The terms of the sequence are all less than or equal to some finite constant M. In this case, the sequence has a finite limit L which is also less than or equal to M.*

B. *The sequence diverges to plus infinity; that is, the numbers in the sequence $\{s_n\}$ ultimately exceed every preassigned number, no matter how large.*

When all of the terms of a sequence $\{s_n\}$ are less than or equal to some finite constant M, we say that the sequence is *bounded from above*, and we call the number M an *upper bound* for the sequence. In these terms, Theorem 1 says:

A. Every increasing sequence that is bounded from above converges.

B. Every increasing sequence that is *not* bounded from above becomes infinite.

Note that the theorem does not tell us how to find the limit L when it exists.

We shall not prove Theorem 1, but we may gain an intuitive appreciation of the result by plotting the points $(1, s_1)$, $(2, s_2)$, $\ldots$, (n, s_n), $\ldots$, in the xy-plane (Fig. 16–9). Then if there is a line $y = M$ such that *none* of the points (n, s_n) lies above this line, it is intuitively clear that there is a *lowest* such line. That is, there is a line

$$y = L$$

such that none of the points lies above it but such that there are points (n, s_n) that lie above any *lower* line

$$y = L - \epsilon,$$

where ϵ is any positive number. Analytically, this means that the number L

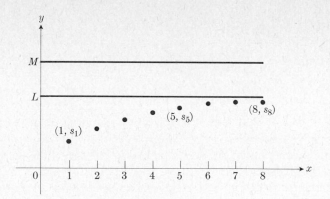

16-9 When the terms of an increasing sequence have an upper bound M, they have a limit $L \leq M$.

has the properties (a) $s_n \leq L$ for *all* values of n, (b) given any $\epsilon > 0$, there exists at least one integer N such that

$$s_N > L - \epsilon.$$

Then the fact that $\{s_n\}$ is an increasing sequence tells us further that

$$s_n \geq s_N > L - \epsilon \qquad \text{for all} \quad n \geq N.$$

This means that *all* the numbers s_n, beyond the Nth one in the sequence, lie within ϵ distance of L. This is precisely the condition for L to be the limit of the sequence s_n,

$$L = \lim_{n \to \infty} s_n.$$

Alternative B of the theorem is what happens when there are points (n, s_n) above any given line $y = M$, no matter how large M may be.

Let us now apply Theorem 1 to the convergence of infinite series of nonnegative numbers. If $\sum a_n$ is such a series, its sequence of partial sums $\{s_n\}$ is an increasing sequence. Therefore, $\{s_n\}$, and hence $\sum a_n$, will converge if and only if the numbers s_n have an upper bound. The question is how to find out in any particular instance whether the s_n's do have an upper bound.

Sometimes we can show that the s_n's are bounded above by showing that each one is less than or equal to the corresponding partial sum of a series that is already known to converge. The next example shows how this can happen.

EXAMPLE 1

$$\sum_{n=0}^{\infty} \frac{1}{n!} = 1 + \frac{1}{1!} + \frac{1}{2!} + \frac{1}{3!} + \cdots \tag{5}$$

converges because its terms are all positive and less than or equal to the corresponding terms of

$$1 + \sum_{n=0}^{\infty} \frac{1}{2^n} = 1 + 1 + \frac{1}{2} + \frac{1}{2^2} + \cdots. \tag{6}$$

To see how this relationship between these two series leads to an upper bound for the partial sums of $\sum_{n=0}^{\infty} (1/n!)$, let

$$s_n = 1 + \frac{1}{1!} + \frac{1}{2!} + \cdots + \frac{1}{n!},$$

and observe that, for each n,

$$s_n \leq 1 + 1 + \frac{1}{2} + \frac{1}{2^2} + \cdots + \frac{1}{2^n} < 1 + \sum_{n=0}^{\infty} \frac{1}{2^n} = 1 + \frac{1}{1 - \frac{1}{2}} = 3. \quad (7)$$

Thus the partial sums of $\sum_{n=0}^{\infty} (1/n!)$ are all less than 3. Therefore, $\sum_{n=0}^{\infty} (1/n!)$ converges.

Just because 3 is an upper bound for the partial sums of $\sum_{n=0}^{\infty} (1/n!)$ we cannot conclude that the series converges to 3. The series actually converges to $e = 2.71828 \ldots$.

We established the convergence of the series in Example 1 by comparing it with a series that was already known to converge. This kind of comparison is typical of a procedure called the *comparison test* for convergence of series of nonnegative terms.

Comparison Test for Series of Nonnegative Terms

Let $\sum_{n=1}^{\infty} a_n$ be a series that has no negative terms.

A. *Test for **convergence** of $\sum a_n$. The series $\sum a_n$ converges if there is a convergent series of nonnegative terms $\sum c_n$ with $a_n \leq c_n$ for all n.*

B. *Test for **divergence** of $\sum a_n$. The series $\sum a_n$ diverges if there is a divergent series of nonnegative terms $\sum d_n$ with $a_n \geq d_n$ for all n.*

To see why the test works, we need only observe that in (A) the partial sums of $\sum a_n$ are bounded above by $M = \sum c_n$, while in (B) the partial sums of $\sum a_n$, being greater than or equal to the corresponding partial sums of a divergent series of nonnegative terms, eventually exceeds every preassigned number.

To apply the comparison test to a series, we do not have to include the early terms of the series. We can start the test with any index N, provided we include all the terms of the series being tested from there on.

EXAMPLE 2.   The convergence of the series

$$5 + \frac{2}{3} + 1 + \frac{1}{7} + \frac{1}{2} + \frac{1}{3!} + \frac{1}{4!} + \cdots + \frac{1}{k!} + \cdots$$

can be established by ignoring the first four terms and comparing the remainder of the series from the fifth term on (the fifth term is $\frac{1}{2}$) with the convergent series

$$\sum_{n=1}^{\infty} \frac{1}{2^n} = \frac{1}{2} + \frac{1}{4} + \frac{1}{8} + \cdots$$

To apply the comparison test we need to have on hand a list of series that are known to converge and a list of series that are known to diverge. Our next example adds a divergent series to the list.

EXAMPLE 3. The *harmonic series*

$$\sum_{n=1}^{\infty} \frac{1}{n} = 1 + \frac{1}{2} + \frac{1}{3} + \frac{1}{4} + \cdots$$

diverges.

To see why, we represent the terms of the series as the areas of rectangles each of base unity and having altitudes $1, \frac{1}{2}, \frac{1}{3}, \ldots$, as in Fig. 16–10. The sum of the first n terms of the series,

$$s_n = 1 + \frac{1}{2} + \frac{1}{3} + \cdots + \frac{1}{n},$$

represents the sum of n rectangles each of which is somewhat greater than the area underneath the corresponding portion of the curve $y = 1/x$. Thus s_n is greater than the area under this curve between $x = 1$ and $x = n + 1$:

$$s_n > \int_{1}^{n+1} \frac{dx}{x} = \ln (n + 1).$$

Therefore $s_n \to +\infty$ because $\ln (n + 1) \to +\infty$. The series

$$1 + \frac{1}{2} + \frac{1}{3} + \cdots + \frac{1}{n} + \cdots$$

diverges to plus infinity.

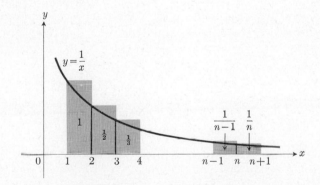

16–10 $\quad 1 + \frac{1}{2} + \frac{1}{3} + \cdots + \frac{1}{n} > \int_{1}^{n+1} \frac{1}{x} \, dx = \ln (n + 1).$

REMARK 1. The harmonic series $\sum_{n=1}^{\infty} (1/n)$ is another series whose divergence cannot be detected by the nth-term test for divergence. The series diverges in spite of the fact that $1/n \to 0$.

REMARK 2. We know that every nonzero multiple of a divergent series diverges (Corollary of Theorem 4 in the preceding article). Therefore, the divergence of the harmonic series implies the divergence of series like

$$\sum_{n=1}^{\infty} \frac{1}{2n} = \frac{1}{2} + \frac{1}{4} + \frac{1}{6} + \frac{1}{8} + \cdots$$

and

$$\sum_{n=1}^{\infty} \frac{1}{100n} = \frac{1}{100} + \frac{1}{200} + \frac{1}{300} + \frac{1}{400} + \cdots.$$

In Example 3 we deduced the divergence of the harmonic series by comparing its sequence of partial sums with a divergent sequence of integrals. This comparison is a special case of a general comparison process called the *integral test*, a test that gives criteria for convergence as well as for divergence of series whose terms are positive.

The Integral Test

Let the function $y = f(x)$, *obtained by introducing the continuous variable x in place of the discrete variable n in the nth term of the positive series*

$$\sum_{n=1}^{\infty} a_n,$$

be a decreasing function of x for $x \geq 1$. *Then the series and the integral*

$$\int_{1}^{\infty} f(x)\, dx$$

both converge or both diverge.

Proof. We start with the assumption that f is a decreasing function with $f(n) = a_n$ for every n. This leads us to observe that the rectangles in Fig. 16–11(a), which have areas $a_1, a_2, \ldots, a_n$, collectively enclose more area than that under the curve $y = f(x)$ from $x = 1$ to $x = n + 1$. That is,

$$\int_{1}^{n+1} f(x)\, dx \leq a_1 + a_2 + \cdots + a_n.$$

In Fig. 16–11(b) the rectangles have been faced to the left instead of to the right. If we momentarily disregard the first rectangle, of area a_1, we see that

$$a_2 + a_3 + \cdots + a_n \leq \int_{1}^{n} f(x)\, dx.$$

If we include a_1, we have

$$a_1 + a_2 + \cdots + a_n \leq a_1 + \int_{1}^{n} f(x)\, dx.$$

Combining these results, we have

$$\int_{1}^{n+1} f(x)\, dx \leq a_1 + a_2 + \cdots + a_n \leq a_1 + \int_{1}^{n} f(x)\, dx. \tag{8}$$

If the integral $\int_{1}^{\infty} f(x)\, dx$ is finite, the righthand inequality shows that

$$\sum_{n=1}^{\infty} a_n$$

a)

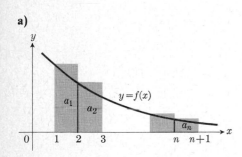

b)

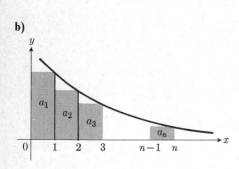

16–11 $\displaystyle \int_{1}^{n+1} f(x)\, dx \leq a_1 + a_2 + \cdots + a_n$

$\displaystyle \leq a_1 + \int_{1}^{n} f(x)\, dx.$

is also finite. But if $\int_1^\infty f(x)\,dx$ is infinite, then the lefthand inequality shows that the series is also infinite. Hence the series and the integral are both finite or both infinite.

EXAMPLE 4. *The p-series.* If p is a real constant, the series

$$\sum_{n=1}^\infty \frac{1}{n^p} = \frac{1}{1^p} + \frac{1}{2^p} + \frac{1}{3^p} + \cdots + \frac{1}{n^p} + \cdots$$

converges if $p > 1$ and diverges if $p \le 1$. To prove this, let

$$f(x) = \frac{1}{x^p}.$$

Then, if $p > 1$, we have

$$\int_1^\infty x^{-p}\,dx = \lim_{b\to\infty} \frac{x^{-p+1}}{-p+1}\bigg|_1^b = \frac{1}{p-1},$$

which is finite. Hence the p-series converges if p is greater than one.

If $p = 1$, we have

$$1 + \frac{1}{2} + \frac{1}{3} + \cdots + \frac{1}{n} + \cdots,$$

which we already know diverges. Or, by the integral test,

$$\int_1^\infty x^{-1}\,dx = \lim_{b\to\infty} \ln x \bigg|_1^b = +\infty,$$

and, since the integral diverges, the series does likewise.

Finally, if $p < 1$, then the terms of the p-series are greater than the corresponding terms of the divergent harmonic series. Hence the p-series diverges, by the comparison test.

Thus, we have convergence for $p > 1$, but divergence for every other value of p.

Estimation of Remainders by Integrals

The difference $R_n = L - s_n$ between the sum of a convergent series and its nth partial sum is called a *remainder* or a *truncation error*. Since R_n itself is given as an infinite series, which, in principle, is as difficult to evaluate as the original series, you might think that there would be no advantage in singling out R_n for attention. But sometimes even a crude estimate for R_n can lead to an estimate of L that is closer to L than s_n is.

Suppose, for example, that we are interested in learning the numerical value of the series

$$\sum_{k=1}^\infty \frac{1}{k^2} = \frac{1}{1^2} + \frac{1}{2^2} + \frac{1}{3^2} + \cdots$$

This is a p-series with $p = 2$, and hence is known to converge. This means that the sequence of partial sums

$$s_n = \frac{1}{1^2} + \frac{1}{2^2} + \cdots + \frac{1}{n^2}$$

has a limit L. If we want to know L to a couple of decimal places, we might try to find an integer n such that the corresponding *finite* sum s_n differs from L by less, say, than 0.005. Then we would use this s_n in place of L, to two decimals. If we write

$$L = \sum_{k=1}^{\infty} \frac{1}{k^2} = \frac{1}{1^2} + \frac{1}{2^2} + \cdots + \frac{1}{n^2} + \frac{1}{(n+1)^2} + \cdots,$$

we see that

$$R_n = L - s_n = \frac{1}{(n+1)^2} + \cdots.$$

We estimate the error R_n by comparing it with the area under the curve

$$y = \frac{1}{x^2}$$

from $x = n$ to ∞.

From Fig. 16–12 we see that

$$R_n < \int_n^{\infty} \frac{1}{x^2}\,dx = \frac{1}{n},$$

which tells us that, by taking 200 terms of the series, we can be sure that the difference between the sum L of the entire series and the sum s_{200} of these 200 terms will be less than 0.005.

A somewhat closer estimate of R_n results from using the trapezoidal rule to approximate the area under the curve in Fig. 16–12. Let us write u_k for $1/k^2$ and consider the trapezoidal approximation

$$T_n = \sum_{k=n}^{\infty} \tfrac{1}{2}(u_k + u_{k+1}) = \tfrac{1}{2}(u_n + u_{n+1}) + \tfrac{1}{2}(u_{n+1} + u_{n+2}) + \cdots$$

$$= \tfrac{1}{2}u_n + u_{n+1} + u_{n+2} + \cdots = \tfrac{1}{2}u_n + R_n.$$

Now since the curve $y = 1/x^2$ is concave upward,

$$T_n > \int_n^{\infty} \frac{1}{x^2}\,dx = \frac{1}{n},$$

and we have

$$R_n = T_n - \frac{1}{2}u_n > \frac{1}{n} - \frac{1}{2n^2}.$$

16–12 The rectilinear area R_n is

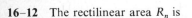

$$\frac{1}{(n+1)^2} + \frac{1}{(n+2)^2} + \frac{1}{(n+3)^2} + \cdots < \int_n^{\infty} \frac{dx}{x^2}.$$

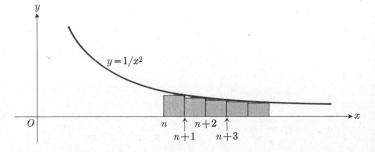

We now know that

$$\frac{1}{n} > R_n > \frac{1}{n} - \frac{1}{2n^2},$$

and $L = s_n + R_n$ may be estimated as follows:

$$s_n + \frac{1}{n} > L > s_n + \frac{1}{n} - \frac{1}{2n^2}. \tag{9}$$

Thus, by using $s_n + 1/n$ in place of s_n to estimate L, we shall be making an error which is numerically less than $1/(2n^2)$. By taking $n \geq 10$, this error is then made less than 0.005. The difference in time required to compute the sum of 10 terms versus 200 terms is sufficiently great to make this sharper analysis of practical importance.

What we have done in the case of this specific example may be done in any case where the graph of the function $y = f(x)$ is concave upward as in Fig. 16–12. We find that when $\int_n^\infty f(x)\,dx$ exists,

$$u_1 + u_2 + \cdots + u_n + \int_n^\infty f(x)\,dx \tag{10}$$

tends to overestimate the value of the series, but by an amount that is less than $u_n/2$.

Ratio Test and Root Test

It is not always possible to tell whether a particular series converges by using the comparison test. We might not be able to find a series to compare it with. Nor is it always possible to use the integral test to answer whatever questions of convergence then remain unanswered. The terms of the series might not decrease as n increases, or we might not find a formula for the nth term that we can integrate. What we really need is an intrinsic test for convergence, one that can be applied to the series without outside help, so to speak. The next two tests are intrinsic in this sense. They are also easy to apply, and they succeed on a wide variety of series. The first of these is the *ratio test*, for series with positive terms.

The Ratio Test

Let $\sum a_n$ be a series with positive terms, and suppose that

$$\lim_{n \to \infty} \frac{a_{n+1}}{a_n} = \rho \qquad \text{(Greek letter rho)}.$$

Then,

a) *the series* ***converges*** *if $\rho < 1$;*
b) *the series* ***diverges*** *if $\rho > 1$;*
c) *the series* ***may converge or it may diverge*** *if $\rho = 1$.*

Proof. a) Assume first that $\rho < 1$ and let r be a number between ρ and 1. Then the number

$$\epsilon = r - \rho$$

is positive. Since

$$\frac{a_{n+1}}{a_n} \to \rho,$$

a_{n+1}/a_n must lie within ϵ of ρ when n is large enough, say, for all $n \geq N$. In particular,

$$\frac{a_{n+1}}{a_n} < \rho + \epsilon = r, \qquad \text{when } n > N.$$

That is,

$$a_{N+1} < ra_N,$$

$$a_{N+2} < ra_{N+1} < r^2 a_N,$$

$$a_{N+3} < ra_{N+2} < r^3 a_N,$$

$$\vdots$$

$$a_{N+m} < ra_{N+m-1} < r^m a_N,$$

and

$$\sum_{n=1}^{\infty} a_n = a_1 + a_2 + \cdots + a_{N-1} + a_N + a_{N+1} + \cdots$$

$$< a_1 + a_2 + \cdots + a_{N-1} + a_N(1 + r + r^2 + \cdots). \qquad \textbf{(11)}$$

Since $|r|$ is less than one, the geometric series $1 + r + r^2 + \cdots$ converges and the right side of the inequality (11) is finite. Therefore the series on the left converges, by the comparison test.

b) Next, suppose $\rho > 1$. Then, from some index M on, we have

$$\frac{a_{n+1}}{a_n} > 1$$

or

$$a_M < a_{M+1} < a_{M+2} < \cdots.$$

Hence, the terms of the series do not approach 0 as n becomes infinite, and the series diverges, by the nth-term test.

c) Finally, the two series

$$\sum_{n=1}^{\infty} \frac{1}{n} \qquad \text{and} \qquad \sum_{n=1}^{\infty} \frac{1}{n^2}$$

show that, when $\rho = 1$, some other test for convergence must be used.

For $\displaystyle\sum_{n=1}^{\infty} \frac{1}{n}$: $\qquad \rho = \dfrac{1/(n+1)}{1/n} = \dfrac{n}{n+1} \to 1;$

For $\displaystyle\sum_{n=1}^{\infty} \frac{1}{n^2}$: $\qquad \rho = \dfrac{1/(n+1)^2}{1/n^2} = \left(\dfrac{n}{n+1}\right)^2 \to 1^2 = 1.$

In both cases $\rho = 1$, yet the first series diverges while the second converges.   Q.E.D.

EXAMPLE 5. For the series $\sum_{n=0}^{\infty} (2^n + 5)/3^n$,

$$\frac{a_{n+1}}{a_n} = \frac{(2^{n+1} + 5)/3^{n+1}}{(2^n + 5)/3^n} = \frac{1}{3} \cdot \frac{2^{n+1} + 5}{2^n + 5} = \frac{1}{3} \cdot \left(\frac{2 + 5 \cdot 2^{-n}}{1 + 5 \cdot 2^{-n}}\right) \to \frac{1}{3} \cdot \frac{2}{1} = \frac{2}{3}.$$

The series converges because $\rho = \frac{2}{3}$ is less than 1.

This does *not* mean that $\frac{2}{3}$ is the sum of the series. In fact,

$$\sum_{n=0}^{\infty} \frac{2^n + 5}{3^n} = \sum_{n=0}^{\infty} \left(\frac{2}{3}\right)^n + \sum_{n=0}^{\infty} \frac{5}{3^n} = \frac{1}{1 - \frac{2}{3}} + \frac{5}{1 - \frac{1}{3}} = 10\frac{1}{2}.$$

EXAMPLE 6. For what values of x does the series

$$x + \frac{x^3}{3} + \frac{x^5}{5} + \frac{x^7}{7} + \cdots + \frac{x^{2n-1}}{2n-1} + \cdots \tag{12}$$

converge?

Solution. The nth term of the series is

$$a_n = \frac{x^{2n-1}}{2n-1}.$$

We consider first the case where x is positive. Then the series is a positive series and

$$\frac{a_{n+1}}{a_n} = \frac{(2n-1)x^2}{(2n+1)} \to x^2.$$

The ratio test therefore tells us that the series converges if x is positive and less than one and diverges if x is greater than one.

Since only odd powers of x occur in the series, we see that the series simply changes sign when x is replaced by $-x$. Therefore the series also converges for $-1 < x \le 0$ and diverges for $x < -1$. The series converges to zero when $x = 0$.

We know, thus far, that the series

$$\text{converges for } |x| < 1,$$

$$\text{diverges for } \quad |x| > 1,$$

but we don't know what happens when $|x| = 1$. To test at $x = 1$, we apply the integral test to the series

$$1 + \frac{1}{3} + \frac{1}{5} + \frac{1}{7} + \cdots + \frac{1}{2n-1} + \cdots,$$

which we get by taking $x = 1$ in the series (12). The companion integral is

$$\int_1^{\infty} \frac{dx}{2x-1} = \frac{1}{2} \ln (2x-1) \Big|_1^{\infty} = \infty.$$

Hence the series diverges to $+\infty$ when $x = 1$. It diverges to $-\infty$ when $x = -1$. Therefore the only values of x for which the given series converges are $-1 < x < 1$.

REMARK.   When $\rho < 1$, the ratio test is also useful in estimating the truncation error that results from using

$$s_N = a_1 + a_2 + \cdots + a_N$$

as an approximation to the sum of a convergent series of positive terms

$$S = a_1 + a_2 + \cdots + a_N + (a_{N+1} + \cdots);$$

for, if we know that

$$r_1 \le \frac{a_{n+1}}{a_n} \le r_2 \qquad \text{for} \quad n \ge N, \tag{13}$$

where r_1 and r_2 are constants that are both less than one, then the inequalities

$$r_1 a_n \le a_{n+1} \le r_2 a_n \qquad (n = N, N + 1, N + 2, \ldots)$$

enable us to deduce that

$$a_N(r_1 + r_1^2 + r_1^3 + \cdots) \le \sum_{n=N+1}^{\infty} a_n \le a_N(r_2 + r_2^2 + r_2^3 + \cdots). \tag{14}$$

The two geometric series have sums

$$r_1 + r_1^2 + r_1^3 + \cdots = \frac{r_1}{1 - r_1},$$

$$r_2 + r_2^2 + r_2^3 + \cdots = \frac{r_2}{1 - r_2}.$$

Hence, the error

$$R_N = \sum_{n=N+1}^{\infty} a_n$$

lies between

$$a_N \frac{r_1}{1 - r_1} \qquad \text{and} \qquad a_N \frac{r_2}{1 - r_2}.$$

That is,

$$a_N \frac{r_1}{1 - r_1} \le S - s_n \le a_N \frac{r_2}{1 - r_2} \tag{15}$$

if

$$0 \le r_1 \le \frac{a_{n+1}}{a_n} \le r_2 < 1 \qquad \text{for} \quad n \ge N.$$

The second of the two intrinsic tests we referred to earlier is called the *root test*.

The Root Test

Let $\sum a_n$ be a series with no negative terms, and suppose that

$$\sqrt[n]{a_n} \to \rho.$$

Then,

a) *the series **converges** if $\rho < 1$*
b) *the series **diverges** if $\rho > 1$*
c) *the test is **not conclusive** if $\rho = 1$.*

Proof. **a)** Suppose that $\rho < 1$, and choose an $\epsilon > 0$ so small that $\rho + \epsilon < 1$ also. Since $\sqrt[n]{a_n} \to \rho$, the terms $\sqrt[n]{a_n}$ eventually get closer than ϵ to ρ. In other words,

$$\sqrt[n]{a_n} < \rho + \epsilon$$

for n sufficiently large, or

$$a_n < (\rho + \epsilon)^n \qquad \text{for} \quad n \geq N.$$

Now,

$$\sum_{n=N}^{\infty} (\rho + \epsilon)^n,$$

a geometric series with ratio $(\rho + \epsilon) < 1$, converges. By comparison,

$$\sum_{n=N}^{\infty} a_n$$

converges, from which it follows that

$$\sum_{n=1}^{\infty} a_n = a_1 + \cdots + a_{N-1} + \sum_{n=N}^{\infty} a_n$$

converges.

b) Suppose that $\rho > 1$. Then, for all indices beyond some index M, we have

$$\sqrt[n]{a_n} > 1,$$

so that

$$a_n > 1 \qquad \text{for} \quad n > M,$$

and the terms of the series do not converge to 0. The series therefore diverges by the nth-term test.

c) The series $\sum_{n=1}^{\infty} (1/n)$ and $\sum_{n=1}^{\infty} (1/n^2)$ show that the test is not conclusive when $\rho = 1$. The first series diverges and the second converges, but in both cases $\sqrt[n]{a_n} \to 1$.   Q.E.D.

EXAMPLE 7.   For the series $\sum_{n=1}^{\infty} (1/n^n)$,

$$\sqrt[n]{\frac{1}{n^n}} = \frac{1}{n} \to 0.$$

The series converges.

EXAMPLE 8.   For the series $\sum_{n=1}^{\infty} (2^n/n^2)$,

$$\sqrt[n]{\frac{2^n}{n^2}} = \frac{2}{\sqrt[n]{n^2}} = \frac{2}{(\sqrt[n]{n})^2} \to \frac{2}{1^2} = 2.$$

The series diverges.

EXAMPLE 9. For the series $\sum_{n=1}^{\infty} (1 - 1/n)^n = 0 + \frac{1}{4} + \frac{8}{27} + \cdots,$

$$\sqrt[n]{\left(1 - \frac{1}{n}\right)^n} = \left(1 - \frac{1}{n}\right) \to 1.$$

Because $\rho = 1$, the root test is not conclusive. However, if we apply the nth-term test for divergence, we find that

$$\left(1 - \frac{1}{n}\right)^n = \left(1 + \frac{-1}{n}\right)^n \to e^{-1} = \frac{1}{e}.$$

The series diverges.

We now have five tests for divergence and convergence of infinite series:
1. The nth-term test for divergence (applies to all series).
2. **A)** The comparison test for convergence (nonnegative series);
   B) The comparison test for divergence (nonnegative series).
3. The integral test (positive decreasing series).
4. The ratio test (positive series).
5. The root test (nonnegative series).

These tests can be applied to settle questions about the convergence or divergence of series of nonpositive or negative terms. Just factor -1 from the series in question, and test the resulting series of nonnegative or positive terms.

EXAMPLE 10

$$\sum_{n=1}^{\infty} -\frac{1}{n} = -1 \cdot \sum_{n=1}^{\infty} \frac{1}{n} \qquad \text{diverges.}$$

EXAMPLE 11

$$\sum_{n=0}^{\infty} -\frac{1}{2^n} = -1 \cdot \sum_{n=0}^{\infty} \frac{1}{2^n} = -1 \cdot 2 = -2.$$

PROBLEMS

In each of the following problems, determine whether the given series converges or diverges. In each case, give a reason for your answer.

1. $\sum_{n=1}^{\infty} \frac{1}{10^n}$

2. $\sum_{n=1}^{\infty} \frac{n}{n+2}$

3. $\sum_{n=1}^{\infty} \frac{\sin^2 n}{2^n}$

4. $\sum_{n=1}^{\infty} \frac{5}{n}$

5. $\sum_{n=1}^{\infty} \frac{n^3}{2^n}$

6. $\sum_{n=1}^{\infty} -\frac{1}{8^n}$

7. $\sum_{n=1}^{\infty} \frac{\ln n}{n}$

8. $\sum_{n=1}^{\infty} \frac{1}{n\sqrt{n}}$

9. $\sum_{n=1}^{\infty} \frac{2^n}{3^n}$

10. $\sum_{n=0}^{\infty} \frac{-2}{n+1}$

11. $\sum_{n=1}^{\infty} \frac{1}{1 + \ln n}$

12. $\sum_{n=1}^{\infty} \frac{1}{\sqrt{n+1}}$

13. $\sum_{n=1}^{\infty} \frac{2^n}{n+1}$

14. $\sum_{n=1}^{\infty} \left(\frac{n}{3n+1}\right)^n$

15. $\sum_{n=1}^{\infty} -\frac{n^2}{2^n}$

16. $\sum_{n=1}^{\infty} \frac{1}{\sqrt{n}}$

17. $\sum_{n=1}^{\infty} \frac{1}{\sqrt{n^3 + 2}}$

18. $\sum_{n=1}^{\infty} \frac{1}{\sqrt[n]{2}}$

19. $\displaystyle\sum_{n=1}^{\infty} \frac{(n+1)(n+2)}{n!}$ **20.** $\displaystyle\sum_{n=1}^{\infty} \frac{\sqrt{n}}{n^2+1}$

21. $\displaystyle\sum_{n=1}^{\infty} \frac{n}{n^2+1}$ **22.** $\displaystyle\sum_{n=1}^{\infty} n^2 e^{-n}$

23. $\displaystyle\sum_{n=1}^{\infty} \left(1 + \frac{1}{n}\right)^n$ **24.** $\displaystyle\sum_{n=1}^{\infty} \frac{1}{3^{n-1}+1}$

25. $\displaystyle\sum_{n=1}^{\infty} \frac{(n+3)!}{3!\,n!\,3^n}$ **26.** $\displaystyle\sum_{n=2}^{\infty} \frac{1}{n \ln n}$

27. $\displaystyle\sum_{n=1}^{\infty} \frac{1}{(2n+1)!}$ **28.** $\displaystyle\sum_{n=1}^{\infty} \frac{1}{(\ln 2)^n}$

29. $\displaystyle\sum_{n=1}^{\infty} \frac{n!}{n^n}$ **30.** $\displaystyle\sum_{n=1}^{\infty} \frac{1-n}{n \cdot 2^n}$

31. Show that the series

$$\sum_{n=1}^{\infty} \frac{1}{2n-1} = 1 + \frac{1}{3} + \frac{1}{5} + \cdots$$

diverges. [*Hint.* Compare the series with a multiple of the harmonic series.]

In Problems 32 through 34, find all values of x for which the given series converge. Begin with the ratio test or the root test, and then apply other tests as needed.

32. $\displaystyle\sum_{n=1}^{\infty} \left(\frac{x^2+1}{3}\right)^n$ **33.** $\displaystyle\sum_{n=1}^{\infty} \frac{x^{2n+1}}{n^2}$

34. $\displaystyle\sum_{n=1}^{\infty} \left(\frac{1}{|x|}\right)^n$

35. (*Calculator*) Use Inequality (9) of this article to estimate $\sum_{n=1}^{\infty} (1/n^2)$ with an error less than 0.005. Compare your result with the value given in Problem 36.

36. (*Calculator*) Euler discovered that

$$\sum_{n=1}^{\infty} \frac{1}{n^2} = \sum_{n=1}^{\infty} \frac{3[(n-1)!]^2}{(2n)!} = \frac{\pi^2}{6}.$$

Compute s_6 for each series. To 10 decimal places, $\pi^2/6 = 1.6449340668$.

37. (*Calculator*) Use the expression in (10) of this article to find the value of $\sum_{n=1}^{\infty} (1/n^4) = (\pi^4/90)$ with an error less than 10^{-6}.

38. (*Calculator*) To estimate partial sums of the divergent harmonic series, Inequality (8) with $f(x) = 1/x$ tells us that

$$\ln n < 1 + \frac{1}{2} + \cdots + \frac{1}{n} < 1 + \ln n.$$

Suppose that the summation started with $s_1 = 1$ thirteen billion years ago (one estimate of the age of the universe) and that a new term has been added every *second* since then. How large would you expect s_n to be today?

39. There are no values of x for which $\sum_{n=1}^{\infty} (1/nx)$ converges. Why?

40. Show that if $\sum_{n=1}^{\infty} a_n$ is a convergent series of nonnegative numbers then the series $\sum_{n=1}^{\infty} (a_n/n)$ converges.

41. Show that if $\sum a_n$ and $\sum b_n$ are convergent series with $a_n \geq 0$ and $b_n \geq 0$, then $\sum a_n b_n$ converges. [*Hint.* From some index on, $a_n b_n < a_n + b_n$.]

42. A sequence of numbers

$$s_1 \geq s_2 \geq \cdots \geq s_n \geq s_{n+1} \geq \cdots,$$

in which $s_n \geq s_{n+1}$ for every n, is called a *decreasing sequence*. A sequence $\{s_n\}$ is *bounded from below* if there is a finite constant M with $M \leq s_n$ for every n. Such a number M is called a *lower bound* for the sequence. Deduce from Theorem 1 that a decreasing sequence that is bounded from below converges, and that a decreasing sequence that is not bounded from below diverges.

43. The *Cauchy condensation test* says:

Let $\{a_n\}$ be a decreasing sequence ($a_n \geq a_{n+1}$, all n) of positive terms that converges to 0. Then,

$$\sum a_n \text{ converges} \quad \text{if and only if} \quad \sum 2^n a_{2^n} \text{ converges}.$$

For example, $\sum (1/n)$ diverges because $\sum 2^n \cdot (1/2^n) = \sum 1$. Show why the test works.

44. Use the Cauchy condensation test of Problem 43 to show that

a) $\displaystyle\sum_{n=2}^{\infty} \frac{1}{n \ln n}$ diverges.

b) $\displaystyle\sum_{n=1}^{\infty} \frac{1}{n^p}$ converges if $p > 1$ and diverges if $p \leq 1$.

45. Pictures like the one in Fig. 16–10 suggest that, as n increases, there is very little change in the difference between the sum

$$1 + \frac{1}{2} + \cdots + \frac{1}{n}$$

and the integral

$$\ln n = \int_1^n \frac{1}{x}\,dx.$$

To explore this idea, carry out the following steps.

a) By taking $f(x) = (1/x)$ in inequality (8), show that

$$\ln n < 1 + \frac{1}{2} + \cdots + \frac{1}{n} < 1 + \ln n$$

or

$$0 < 1 + \frac{1}{2} + \cdots + \frac{1}{n} - \ln n < 1.$$

Thus, the sequence

$$a_n = 1 + \frac{1}{2} + \cdots + \frac{1}{n} - \ln n$$

is bounded from below.

b) Show that

$$\frac{1}{n+1} < \int_n^{n+1} \frac{1}{x}\,dx = \ln(n+1) - \ln n,$$

so that the sequence $\{a_n\}$ in part (a) is decreasing.

Since a decreasing sequence that is bounded from below converges (Problem 42) the numbers a_n defined in (a)

converge:

$$1 + \frac{1}{2} + \cdots + \frac{1}{n} - \ln n \to \gamma.$$

The number γ, whose value is $0.5772\ldots$, is called *Euler's constant*. In contrast to other special numbers like π and e, no other expression with a simple law of formulation has ever been found for γ.

16-6

ABSOLUTE CONVERGENCE

We now extend to series that have both positive and negative terms the techniques that we have developed for answering questions about the convergence of series of nonnegative numbers. The extension is made possible by a theorem that says that, if a series converges after all its negative terms have been made positive, then the unaltered series converges also.

Theorem. *If $\sum_{n=1}^{\infty} |a_n|$ converges, then $\sum_{n=1}^{\infty} a_n$ converges.*

Proof of the theorem. For each n,

$$-|a_n| \le a_n \le |a_n|,$$

so that

$$0 \le a_n + |a_n| \le 2|a_n|.$$

If $\sum_{n=1}^{\infty} |a_n|$ converges, then $\sum_{n=1}^{\infty} 2|a_n|$ converges and, by the comparison test, the nonnegative series

$$\sum_{n=1}^{\infty} (a_n + |a_n|)$$

converges. The equality $a_n = (a_n + |a_n|) - |a_n|$ now lets us express $\sum_{n=1}^{\infty} a_n$ as the difference of two convergent series:

$$\sum_{n=1}^{\infty} a_n = \sum_{n=1}^{\infty} (a_n + |a_n| - |a_n|) = \sum_{n=1}^{\infty} (a_n + |a_n|) - \sum_{n=1}^{\infty} |a_n|.$$

Therefore, $\sum_{n=1}^{\infty} a_n$ converges.

Definition. *A series $\sum_{n=1}^{\infty} a_n$ is said to **converge absolutely** if $\sum_{n=1}^{\infty} |a_n|$ converges.*

Our theorem can now be rephrased to say that *every absolutely convergent series converges*. We will see in the next article, however, that the converse of this statement is false. Many convergent series do not converge absolutely. That is, there are many series whose convergence depends on the presence of negative terms.

Here are some examples of how the theorem can and cannot be used to determine convergence.

EXAMPLE 1. For $\sum\limits_{n=1}^{\infty} (-1)^{n+1} \dfrac{1}{n^2} = 1 - \dfrac{1}{4} + \dfrac{1}{9} - \dfrac{1}{16} + \cdots,$

the corresponding series of absolute values is

$$\sum_{n=1}^{\infty} \frac{1}{n^2} = 1 + \frac{1}{4} + \frac{1}{9} + \frac{1}{16} + \cdots,$$

which converges because it is a *p*-series with $p = 2 > 1$ (Article 16–5). Therefore

$$\sum_{n=1}^{\infty} (-1)^{n+1} \frac{1}{n^2}$$

converges absolutely. Therefore

$$\sum_{n=1}^{\infty} (-1)^{n+1} \frac{1}{n^2}$$

converges.

EXAMPLE 2. For $\sum\limits_{n=1}^{\infty} \dfrac{\sin n}{n^2} = \dfrac{\sin 1}{1} + \dfrac{\sin 2}{4} + \dfrac{\sin 3}{9} + \cdots,$

the corresponding series of absolute values is

$$\sum_{n=1}^{\infty} \left| \frac{\sin n}{n^2} \right| = \frac{|\sin 1|}{1} + \frac{|\sin 2|}{4} + \cdots,$$

which converges by comparison with $\sum_{n=1}^{\infty} (1/n^2)$, because $|\sin n| \leq 1$ for every *n*. The original series converges absolutely; therefore it converges.

EXAMPLE 3. For $\sum\limits_{n=1}^{\infty} (-1)^{n+1} \dfrac{1}{n} = 1 - \dfrac{1}{2} + \dfrac{1}{3} - \dfrac{1}{4} + \cdots,$

the corresponding series of absolute values is

$$\sum_{n=1}^{\infty} \frac{1}{n} = 1 + \frac{1}{2} + \frac{1}{3} + \frac{1}{4} + \cdots,$$

which diverges. *We can draw no conclusion from this about the convergence or divergence of the original series.* Some other test must be found. In fact, the original series converges, but we will have to wait until the next article to see why.

EXAMPLE 4. The series

$$\sum_{n=1}^{\infty} (-1)^{n} \frac{n}{5n+1} = -\frac{1}{6} + \frac{2}{11} - \frac{3}{16} + \frac{4}{21} - \cdots$$

does not converge, by the *n*th term test. Therefore, the series does not converge absolutely.

REMARK.   We know that $\sum a_n$ converges if $\sum |a_n|$ converges, but the two series will generally not converge to the same sum. For example,

$$\sum_{n=0}^{\infty} \left| \frac{(-1)^n}{2^n} \right| = \sum_{n=0}^{\infty} \frac{1}{2^n} = \frac{1}{1 - \frac{1}{2}} = 2,$$

while

$$\sum_{n=0}^{\infty} \frac{(-1)^n}{2^n} = \frac{1}{1+\frac{1}{2}} = \frac{2}{3}.$$

In fact, when a series $\sum a_n$ converges absolutely, we can expect $\sum a_n$ to equal $\sum |a_n|$ only if none of the numbers a_n is negative.

PROBLEMS

Determine whether the following series converge absolutely. In each case give a reason for the convergence or divergence of the corresponding series of absolute values.

1. $\displaystyle\sum_{n=1}^{\infty} \frac{1}{n^2}$

2. $\displaystyle\sum_{n=1}^{\infty} \frac{1}{(-n)^3}$

3. $\displaystyle\sum_{n=1}^{\infty} \frac{1-n}{n^2}$

4. $\displaystyle\sum_{n=1}^{\infty} \left(-\frac{1}{5}\right)^n$

5. $\displaystyle\sum_{n=1}^{\infty} \frac{-1}{n^2+2n+1}$

6. $\displaystyle\sum_{n=1}^{\infty} \frac{(-1)^n}{2n}$

7. $\displaystyle\sum_{n=1}^{\infty} \frac{\cos n\pi}{n\sqrt{n}}$

8. $\displaystyle\sum_{n=1}^{\infty} \frac{-10}{n}$

9. $\displaystyle\sum_{n=0}^{\infty} \frac{(-1)^n}{(2n)!}$

10. $\displaystyle\sum_{n=0}^{\infty} \frac{(-1)^n}{(2n+1)!}$

11. $\displaystyle\sum_{n=2}^{\infty} (-1)^n \frac{n}{n+1}$

12. $\displaystyle\sum_{n=1}^{\infty} \frac{-n}{2^n}$

13. $\displaystyle\sum_{n=1}^{\infty} (5)^{-n}$

14. $\displaystyle\sum_{n=1}^{\infty} \left(\frac{1}{2^n}-1\right)$

15. $\displaystyle\sum_{n=1}^{\infty} \frac{(-100)^n}{n!}$

16. $\displaystyle\sum_{n=2}^{\infty} (-1)^n \frac{\ln n}{\ln n^2}$

17. $\displaystyle\sum_{n=1}^{\infty} \frac{2-n}{n^3}$

18. $\displaystyle\sum_{n=1}^{\infty} \left(\frac{1}{2^n}-\frac{1}{3^n}\right)$

19. Show that if $\sum_{n=1}^{\infty} a_n$ diverges, then $\sum_{n=1}^{\infty} |a_n|$ diverges.

20. Show that if $\sum_{n=1}^{\infty} a_n$ converges absolutely, then

$$\left|\sum_{n=1}^{\infty} a_n\right| \le \sum_{n=1}^{\infty} |a_n|.$$

21. Show that if $\sum_{n=1}^{\infty} a_n$ and $\sum_{n=1}^{\infty} b_n$ both converge absolutely, then so does

a) $\sum (a_n + b_n)$ b) $\sum (a_n - b_n)$

c) $\sum k a_n$ (k any number)

16–7

ALTERNATING SERIES. CONDITIONAL CONVERGENCE

When some of the terms of a series $\sum a_n$ are positive and others are negative, the series converges if $\sum |a_n|$ converges. Thus we may apply any of our tests for convergence of nonnegative series, provided we apply them to the series of absolute values. But we do not know, when the series of absolute values *diverges*, whether the *original* series diverges or converges. If it converges, but not absolutely, we say that it *converges conditionally*.

We shall discuss one simple case of series with mixed signs, namely, series that take the form

$$a_1 - a_2 + a_3 - a_4 + \cdots (-1)^{n+1} a_n + \cdots, \tag{1}$$

with all a's > 0. Such series are called *alternating series* because successive terms have alternate signs. Examples of alternating series are:

$$1 - \tfrac{1}{2} + \tfrac{1}{3} - \tfrac{1}{4} + \tfrac{1}{5} - \tfrac{1}{6} + \cdots, \tag{2}$$

$$\frac{1}{\ln 2} - \frac{1}{\ln 3} + \frac{1}{\ln 4} - \frac{1}{\ln 5} + \cdots \tag{3}$$

$$1 - \sqrt{2} + \sqrt{3} - \sqrt{4} + \cdots. \tag{4}$$

The series

$$1 - \frac{1}{2} - \frac{1}{4} + \frac{1}{6} - \frac{1}{8} - \frac{1}{10} + \frac{1}{12} \cdots \tag{5}$$

is *not* an alternating series. The signs of its terms do not alternate.

Definition. *A sequence $\{a_n\}$ is called a **decreasing sequence** if $a_n \geq a_{n+1}$ for every n.*

Examples of decreasing sequences are

$$1, \quad \frac{1}{2}, \quad \frac{1}{3}, \quad \frac{1}{4}, \quad \cdots,$$

$$1, \quad 1, \quad 1, \quad 1, \quad \cdots.$$

The sequence

$$\frac{1}{3}, \quad \frac{1}{2}, \quad \frac{1}{6}, \quad \frac{1}{4}, \quad \cdots, \quad \frac{1}{3n}, \quad \frac{1}{2n}, \quad \cdots$$

is *not* a decreasing sequence even though it converges to 0 from above.

One reason for selecting alternating series for study is that every alternating series whose numbers a_n form a decreasing sequence with limit 0 converges. Another reason is that whenever an alternating series converges, it is easy to estimate its sum. This fortunate combination of assured convergence and easy estimation gives us an opportunity to see how a wide variety of series behave. We look first at the convergence.

Theorem 1. Leibniz's Theorem. $\sum_{n=1}^{\infty} (-1)^{n+1} a_n$ *converges if all three of the following conditions are satisfied:*

1. *The a_n's are all positive;*
2. $a_n \geq a_{n+1}$ *for every n;*
3. $a_n \to 0.$

Proof. If n is an even integer, say $n = 2m$, then the sum of the first n terms is

$$s_{2m} = (a_1 - a_2) + (a_3 - a_4) + \cdots + (a_{2m-1} - a_{2m})$$
$$= a_1 - (a_2 - a_3) - (a_4 - a_5) - \cdots - (a_{2m-2} - a_{2m-1}) - a_{2m}.$$

The first equality exhibits s_{2m} as the sum of m nonnegative terms, since each expression in parentheses is positive or zero. Hence $s_{2m+2} \geq s_{2m}$, and the sequence $\{s_{2m}\}$ is increasing. The second equality shows that $s_{2m} \leq a_1$. Since $\{s_{2m}\}$ is increasing and bounded from above it has a limit, say

$$\lim_{n \to \infty} s_{2m} = L. \tag{6}$$

If n is an odd integer, say $n = 2m + 1$, then the sum of the first n terms is

$$s_{2m+1} = s_{2m} + a_{2m+1}.$$

Since $a_n \to 0$,

$$\lim_{m \to \infty} a_{2m+1} = 0.$$

Hence, as $m \to \infty$,

$$s_{2m+1} = s_{2m} + a_{2m+1} \to L + 0 = L. \tag{7}$$

Finally, we may combine (6) and (7) and say simply

$$\lim_{n \to \infty} s_n = L. \qquad\qquad \text{Q.E.D.}$$

Here are some examples of what Theorem 1 can do.

EXAMPLE 1.   The *alternating harmonic* series

$$\sum_{n=1}^{\infty} (-1)^{n+1} \frac{1}{n} = 1 - \frac{1}{2} + \frac{1}{3} - \frac{1}{4} + \cdots$$

satisfies the three requirements of the theorem; therefore it converges. It converges conditionally because the corresponding series of absolute values is the harmonic series, which diverges.

EXAMPLE 2

$$\sum_{n=1}^{\infty} (-1)^{n+1} \sqrt{n} = 1 - \sqrt{2} + \sqrt{3} - \sqrt{4} + \cdots$$

diverges by the nth-term test.

EXAMPLE 3.   Theorem 1 gives no information about

$$\frac{2}{1} - \frac{1}{1} + \frac{2}{2} - \frac{1}{2} + \frac{2}{3} - \frac{1}{3} + \cdots + \frac{2}{n} - \frac{1}{n} + \cdots.$$

The sequence $\frac{2}{1}, \frac{1}{1}, \frac{2}{2}, \frac{1}{2}, \frac{2}{3}, \frac{1}{3}, \ldots$ is not a decreasing sequence. Some other test must be found. When we group the terms of the series in consecutive pairs

$$\left(\frac{2}{1} - \frac{1}{1}\right) + \left(\frac{2}{2} - \frac{1}{2}\right) + \left(\frac{2}{3} - \frac{1}{3}\right) + \cdots + \left(\frac{2}{n} - \frac{1}{n}\right) + \cdots,$$

we see that the $2n$th partial sum of the given series is the same number as the nth partial sum of the harmonic series. Thus the sequence of partial sums, and hence the series, diverges.

We use the following graphical interpretation of the partial sums to gain added insight into the way in which an alternating series converges to its limit L when the three conditions of the theorem are satisfied. Starting from the origin O on a scale of real numbers (Fig. 16–13), we lay off the positive distance

$$s_1 = a_1.$$

To find the point corresponding to

$$s_2 = a_1 - a_2$$

we must back up a distance equal to a_2. Since $a_2 \le a_1$, we do not back up any farther than O at most. Next we go forward a distance a_3 and mark the point corresponding to

$$s_3 = a_1 - a_2 + a_3.$$

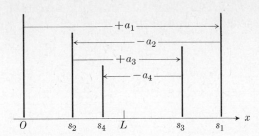

16–13 The partial sums of an alternating series that satisfies the hypotheses of Leibniz's theorem straddle their limit.

Since $a_3 \leq a_2$, we go forward by an amount that is no greater than the previous backward step; that is, s_3 is less than or equal to s_1. We continue in this seesaw fashion, backing up or going forward as the signs in the series demand. But each forward or backward step is shorter than (or at most the same size as) the preceding step, because $a_{n+1} \leq a_n$. And since the nth term approaches zero as n increases, the size of step we take forward or backward gets smaller and smaller. We thus oscillate across the limit L, but the amplitude of oscillation continually decreases and approaches zero as its limit. The even-numbered partial sums s_2, s_4, s_6, ..., s_{2m} continually increase toward L, while the odd-numbered sums s_1, s_3, s_5, ..., s_{2m+1} continually decrease toward L. The limit L is between any two successive sums s_n and s_{n+1} and hence differs from s_n by an amount less than a_{n+1}.

It is because

$$|L - s_n| < a_{n+1} \qquad \text{for every } n \qquad (8)$$

that we can make useful estimates of the sums of convergent alternating series.

Theorem 2.   The Alternating Series Estimation Theorem. *If*

$$\sum_{n=1}^{\infty} (-1)^{n+1} a_n$$

is an alternating series that satisfies the three conditions of Theorem 1, then

$$s_n = a_1 - a_2 + \cdots + (-1)^{n+1} a_n$$

approximates the sum L of the series with an error whose absolute value is less than a_{n+1}, the numerical value of the first unused term. Furthermore, the remainder, $L - s_n$, has the same sign as the first unused term.

We will leave the determination of the sign of the remainder as an exercise.

EXAMPLE 4.   Let us first try the estimation theorem on an alternating series whose sum we already know, namely, the geometric series:

$$\sum_{n=0}^{\infty} (-1)^n \frac{1}{2^n} = 1 - \frac{1}{2} + \frac{1}{4} - \frac{1}{8} + \frac{1}{16} - \frac{1}{32} + \frac{1}{64} - \frac{1}{128} + \frac{1}{256} - \cdots$$

Theorem 2 says that, when we truncate the series after the eighth term, we throw away a total that is positive and less than $\frac{1}{256}$. A rapid calculation shows that the sum of the first eight terms is

$$0.6640625.$$

The sum of the series is

$$\frac{1}{1 - (-\frac{1}{2})} = \frac{1}{3/2} = \frac{2}{3}. \tag{9}$$

The difference,

$$\frac{2}{3} - 0.6640625 = 0.0026041666\ldots,$$

is positive and less than

$$\tfrac{1}{256} = 0.00390625.$$

A series for computing $\ln (1 + x)$ when $|x| < 1$ is

$$\ln (1 + x) = x - \frac{x^2}{2} + \frac{x^3}{3} - \cdots + (-1)^{n+1} \frac{x^n}{n} \cdots. \tag{10}$$

For $0 < x < 1$, this series satisfies all three conditions of Theorem 1, and we may use the estimation theorem to see how good an approximation of $\ln (1 + x)$ we get from the first few terms of the series.

EXAMPLE 5.   Calculate ln 1.1 with the approximation

$$\ln (1 + x) \approx x - \frac{x^2}{2}, \tag{11}$$

and estimate the error involved. Is $x - (x^2/2)$ too large, or too small in this case?

Solution

$$\ln (1.1) \approx (0.1) - \frac{(0.1)^2}{2} = 0.095.$$

This approximation differs from the exact value of ln 1.1 by less than

$$\frac{(0.1)^3}{3} = 0.000333\ldots.$$

Since the sign of this, the first unused term, is positive, the remainder is positive. That is, 0.095 underestimates ln 1.1.

EXAMPLE 6.   How many terms of the series (10) do we need to use in order to be sure of calculating ln (1.2) with an error of less than 10^{-6}?

Solution

$$\ln (1.2) = (0.2) - \frac{(0.2)^2}{2} + \frac{(0.2)^3}{3} - \cdots$$

We find by trial that the eighth term

$$-\frac{(0.2)^8}{8} = -3.2 \times 10^{-7}$$

is the first term in the series whose absolute value is less than 10^{-6}. Therefore the sum of the first *seven* terms will give ln 1.2 with an error of less than 10^{-6}. The use of more terms would give an approximation that is even better, but seven terms are enough to guarantee the accuracy we wanted. Note also that we have not shown that six terms would *not* provide that accuracy.

PROBLEMS

In Problems 1 through 10, determine which of the following alternating series converge and which diverge.

1. $\displaystyle\sum_{n=1}^{\infty} (-1)^{n+1}\frac{1}{n^2}$ **2.** $\displaystyle\sum_{n=2}^{\infty} (-1)^{n+1}\frac{1}{\ln n}$

3. $\displaystyle\sum_{n=1}^{\infty} (-1)^{n+1}$ **4.** $\displaystyle\sum_{n=1}^{\infty} (-1)^{n+1}\frac{10^n}{n^{10}}$

5. $\displaystyle\sum_{n=1}^{\infty} (-1)^{n+1}\frac{\sqrt{n+1}}{n+1}$ **6.** $\displaystyle\sum_{n=1}^{\infty} (-1)^{n+1}\frac{\ln n}{n}$

7. $\displaystyle\sum_{n=1}^{\infty} (-1)^{n+1}\frac{1}{n^{3/2}}$ **8.** $\displaystyle\sum_{n=1}^{\infty} (-1)^{n+1}\frac{\ln n}{\ln n^2}$

9. $\displaystyle\sum_{n=1}^{\infty} (-1)^{n} \ln\left(1+\frac{1}{n}\right)$ **10.** $\displaystyle\sum_{n=1}^{\infty} (-1)^{n+1}\frac{3\sqrt{n+1}}{\sqrt{n+1}}$

In Problems 11 through 28, determine whether the following series are absolutely convergent, conditionally convergent, or divergent.

11. $\displaystyle\sum_{n=1}^{\infty} (-1)^{n+1}(0.1)^n$ **12.** $\displaystyle\sum_{n=1}^{\infty} (-1)^{n+1}\frac{1}{\sqrt{n}}$

13. $\displaystyle\sum_{n=1}^{\infty} (-1)^{n+1}\frac{n}{n^3+1}$ **14.** $\displaystyle\sum_{n=1}^{\infty} \frac{n!}{2^n}$

15. $\displaystyle\sum_{n=1}^{\infty} (-1)^{n}\frac{1}{n+3}$ **16.** $\displaystyle\sum_{n=1}^{\infty} (-1)^{n}\frac{\sin n}{n^2}$

17. $\displaystyle\sum_{n=1}^{\infty} (-1)^{n+1}\frac{3+n}{5+n}$ **18.** $\displaystyle\sum_{n=2}^{\infty} (-1)^{n}\frac{1}{\ln n^3}$

19. $\displaystyle\sum_{n=1}^{\infty} (-1)^{n+1}\frac{1+n}{n^2}$ **20.** $\displaystyle\sum_{n=1}^{\infty} \frac{(-2)^{n+1}}{n+5^n}$

21. $\displaystyle\sum_{n=1}^{\infty} n^2(\tfrac{2}{3})^n$ **22.** $\displaystyle\sum_{n=1}^{\infty} (-1)^{n+1}(\sqrt[n]{10})$

23. $\displaystyle\sum_{n=1}^{\infty} (-1)^{n}\frac{\tan^{-1} n}{n^2+1}$ **24.** $\displaystyle\sum_{n=2}^{\infty} (-1)^{n+1}\frac{1}{n\ln n}$

25. $\displaystyle\sum_{n=1}^{\infty} \left(\frac{1}{n}-\frac{1}{2n}\right)$ **26.** $\displaystyle\sum_{n=1}^{\infty} (-1)^{n+1}\frac{(0.1)^n}{n}$

27. $\displaystyle\sum_{n=1}^{\infty} (-1)^{n+1}(\sqrt{n+1}-\sqrt{n})$ **28.** $\displaystyle\sum_{n=1}^{\infty} \frac{(-1)^{n+1}(n!)^2}{(2n)!}$

In Problems 29 through 32, estimate the magnitude of the error if the first four terms are used to approximate the series.

29. $\displaystyle\sum_{n=1}^{\infty} (-1)^{n+1}\frac{1}{n}$ **30.** $\displaystyle\sum_{n=1}^{\infty} (-1)^{n+1}\frac{1}{10^n}$

31. $\displaystyle\ln(1.01) = \sum_{n=1}^{\infty} (-1)^{n+1}\frac{(0.01)^n}{n}$

32. $\displaystyle\frac{1}{1+t} = \sum_{n=0}^{\infty} (-1)^{n}t^{n}, \qquad 0 < t < 1$

Approximate the following two sums to five decimal places (magnitude of the error less than 5×10^{-6}).

33. $\displaystyle\sum_{n=0}^{\infty} (-1)^{n}\frac{1}{(2n)!}$

(This is cos 1, the cosine of one radian.)

34. $\displaystyle\sum_{n=0}^{\infty} (-1)^{n}\frac{1}{n!}$ (This is $1/e$.)

35. a) The series

$$\frac{1}{3}-\frac{1}{2}+\frac{1}{9}-\frac{1}{4}+\frac{1}{27}-\frac{1}{8}+\cdots+\frac{1}{3^n}-\frac{1}{2^n}+\cdots$$

does not meet one of the conditions of Theorem 1. Which one?

b) Find the sum of the series in (a).

36. The limit L of an alternating series that satisfies the conditions of Theorem 1 lies between the values of any two consecutive partial sums. This suggests using the average

$$\frac{s_n + s_{n+1}}{2} = s_n + \frac{1}{2}a_{n+1}$$

to estimate L. Compute

$$s_{20} + \tfrac{1}{2}\cdot\tfrac{1}{21}$$

as an approximation to the sum of the alternating harmonic series. The exact sum is ln 2.

37. Show that whenever an alternating series is approximated by one of its partial sums, if the three conditions of Leibniz's theorem are satisfied, then the *remainder* (sum of the unused terms) has the same sign as the first unused term. [*Hint*. Group the terms of the remainder in consecutive pairs.]

38. Prove the "zipper" theorem for sequences: If $\{a_n\}$ and $\{b_n\}$ both converge to L, then the sequence

$$a_1, \quad b_1, \quad a_2, \quad b_2, \quad \ldots, \quad a_n, \quad b_n, \quad \ldots$$

also converges to L.

39. Show by example that $\sum_{n=1}^{\infty} a_n b_n$ may diverge even though $\sum_{n=1}^{\infty} a_n$ and $\sum_{n=1}^{\infty} b_n$ both converge.

16–8

POWER SERIES FOR FUNCTIONS

The rational operations of arithmetic are addition, subtraction, multiplication, and division. Using only these simple operations, we can evaluate any rational function of x. But other functions, such as $\sqrt{x}$, ln x, cos x, and so on, cannot be evaluated so simply. These functions occur so frequently, however, that their values have been printed in mathematical tables, and many calculators and computers have been programmed to produce them on demand. One may wonder where the values in the tables came from, and how a calculator produces the number it displays. By and large, these numbers come from calculating partial sums of power series.

Definition. *A* **power series** *is a series of the form*

$$\sum_{n=0}^{\infty} a_n x^n = a_0 + a_1 x + a_2 x^2 + \cdots.$$

In this article we shall show how a power series can arise when we seek to approximate a function

$$y = f(x) \tag{1}$$

by a sequence of polynomials $f_n(x)$ of the form

$$f_n(x) = a_0 + a_1 x + a_2 x^2 + \cdots + a_n x^n. \tag{2}$$

We shall be interested, at least at first, in making the approximation for values of x near 0, because we want the term $a_n x^n$ to decrease as n increases. Hence we focus our attention on a portion of the curve $y = f(x)$ near the point $A(0, f(0))$, as shown in Fig. 16–14.

1. The graph of the polynomial $f_0(x) = a_0$ of degree zero will pass through $(0, f(0))$ if we take

$$a_0 = f(0).$$

2. The graph of the polynomial $f_1(x) = a_0 + a_1 x$ will pass through $(0, f(0))$ and have the same slope as the given curve at that point if we choose

$$a_0 = f(0) \qquad \text{and} \qquad a_1 = f'(0).$$

3. The graph of the polynomial $f_2(x) = a_0 + a_1 x + a_2 x^2$ will pass through $(0, f(0))$ and have the same slope and curvature as the given curve at that point if

$$a_0 = f(0), \qquad a_1 = f'(0), \qquad \text{and } a_2 = \frac{f''(0)}{2}.$$

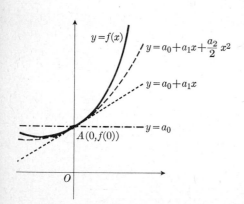

16–14 $f(x)$ is approximated near $x = 0$ by polynomials whose derivatives at $x = 0$ match the derivatives of f.

4. In general, the polynomial $f_n(x) = a_0 + a_1 x + a_2 x^2 + \cdots + a_n x^n$, which we choose to approximate $y = f(x)$ near $x = 0$, is the one whose graph passes through $(0, f(0))$ and whose first n derivatives match the derivatives of $f(x)$ at $x = 0$. To match the derivatives of f_n to those of f at $x = 0$, we merely have to choose the coefficients a_0 through a_n properly. To see how this may be done, we write down the polynomial and its derivatives as follows:

$$f_n(x) = a_0 + a_1 x + a_2 x^2 + a_3 x^3 + \cdots + a_n x^n$$

$$f_n'(x) = a_1 + 2a_2 x + 3a_3 x^2 + \cdots + na_n x^{n-1}$$

$$f_n''(x) = 2a_2 + 3 \cdot 2a_3 x + \cdots + n(n-1)a_n x^{n-2}$$

$$\vdots$$

$$f_n^{(n)}(x) = (n!)a_n.$$

When we substitute 0 for x in the array above, we find that

$$a_0 = f(0), \qquad a_1 = f'(0), \qquad a_2 = \frac{f''(0)}{2!}, \qquad \ldots, \qquad a_n = \frac{f^{(n)}(0)}{n!}.$$

Thus,

$$f_n(x) = f(0) + f'(0)x + \frac{f''(0)}{2!} x^2 + \cdots + \frac{f^{(n)}(0)}{n!} x^n \qquad \textbf{(3)}$$

is the polynomial we seek. Its graph passes through the point $(0, f(0))$, and its first n derivatives match the first n derivatives of $y = f(x)$ at $x = 0$. It is called the nth-degree *Taylor polynomial of f at $x = 0$.*

EXAMPLE 1. Find the Taylor polynomials $f_n(x)$ for the function $f(x) = e^x$.

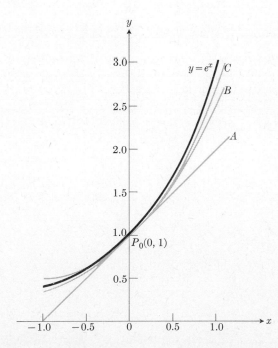

16–15 The graph of the function $y = e^x$, and graphs of three approximating polynomials, (*A*) a straight line, (*B*) a parabola, and (*C*) a cubic curve.

Solution. Expressed in terms of x, the given function and its derivatives are

$$f(x) = e^x, \qquad f'(x) = e^x, \qquad \ldots, \qquad f^{(n)}(x) = e^x,$$

so that

$$f(0) = e^0 = 1, \qquad f'(0) = 1, \qquad \ldots, \qquad f^{(n)}(0) = 1,$$

and

$$f_n(x) = 1 + x + \frac{x^2}{2!} + \frac{x^3}{3!} + \cdots + \frac{x^n}{n!}.$$

See Fig. 16–15.

EXAMPLE 2. Find the Taylor polynomials $f_n(x)$ for $f(x) = \cos x$.

Solution. The cosine and its derivatives are

$$
\begin{array}{llll}
f(x) & = & \cos x, & f'(x) & = & -\sin x, \\
f''(x) & = & -\cos x, & f^{(3)}(x) & = & \sin x, \\
\vdots & & & \vdots & & \\
f^{(2k)}(x) & = & (-1)^k \cos x, & f^{(2k+1)}(x) & = & (-1)^{k+1} \sin x.
\end{array}
$$

When $x = 0$, the cosines are 1 and the sines are 0, so that

$$f^{(2k)}(0) = (-1)^k, \qquad f^{(2k+1)}(0) = 0.$$

The Taylor polynomials have only even-powered terms, and for $n = 2k$ we have

$$f_{2k}(x) = 1 - \frac{x^2}{2!} + \frac{x^4}{4!} - \cdots + (-1)^k \frac{x^{2k}}{(2k)!}. \qquad (4)$$

Figure 16–16 shows how well these polynomials can be expected to approximate $y = \cos x$ near $x = 0$. Only the righthand portions of the graphs are shown because the graphs are symmetric about the y-axis.

16–16 The polynomials $c_n(x) = \sum_{k=0}^{n} [(-1)^k x^{2k}/(2k)!]$ converge to $\cos x$ as $n \to \infty$. (Adapted from Helen M. Kammerer, *American Mathematical Monthly*, 43(1936), 293–294.)

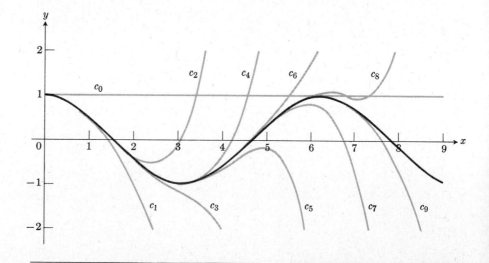

The degrees of the Taylor polynomials of a given function are limited by the degree of differentiability of the function at $x = 0$. But if $f(x)$ has derivatives of all orders at the origin, it is natural to ask whether, for a fixed value of x, the values of these approximating polynomials converge to $f(x)$ as $n \to \infty$. Now, these polynomials are precisely the partial sums of a series known as the *Maclaurin series* for f:

The Maclaurin series for f

$$f(0) + f'(0)x + \frac{f''(0)}{2!}x^2 + \cdots + \frac{f^{(n)}(0)}{n!}x^n + \cdots. \qquad (5)$$

Thus, the question just posed is equivalent to asking whether the Maclaurin series for f converges to $f(x)$ as a sum. It certainly has the correct value, $f(0)$, at $x = 0$, but how far away from $x = 0$ may we go and still have convergence? And if the series does converge away from $x = 0$, does it still converge to $f(x)$? The graphs in Figs. 16–15 and 16–16 are encouraging, and the next few articles will confirm that we can normally expect a Maclaurin series to converge to its function in an interval about the origin. For many functions, this interval is the entire x-axis.

If, instead of approximating the values of f near zero, we are concerned with values of x near some other point a, we write our approximating polynomials in powers of $(x - a)$:

$$f_n(x) = a_0 + a_1(x - a) + a_2(x - a)^2 + \cdots + a_n(x - a)^n. \qquad (6)$$

When we now determine the coefficients $a_0, a_1, \ldots, a_n$, so that the polynomial and its first n derivatives agree with the given function and its derivatives at $x = a$, we are led to a series that is called the *Taylor series expansion of f about $x = a$*, or simply the *Taylor series for f at $x = a$.*

The Taylor series for f at $x = a$

$$f(a) + f'(a)(x - a) + \frac{f''(a)}{2!}(x - a)^2 + \cdots + \frac{f^{(n)}(a)}{n!}(x - a)^n + \cdots. \qquad (7)$$

There are two things to notice here. The first is that Maclaurin series are Taylor series with $a = 0$. The second is that a function cannot have a Taylor series expansion about $x = a$ unless it has finite derivatives of all orders at $x = a$. For instance, $f(x) = \ln x$ does not have a Maclaurin series expansion, since the function itself, to say nothing of its derivatives, does not have a finite value at $x = 0$. On the other hand, it does have a Taylor series expansion in powers of $(x - 1)$, since $\ln x$ and all its derivatives are finite at $x = 1$.

Here are some examples of Taylor series.

EXAMPLE 3. From the formula derived for the Taylor polynomials of $\cos x$ in Example 2, it follows immediately that

$$\sum_{k=0}^{\infty} (-1)^k \frac{x^{2k}}{(2k)!} = 1 - \frac{x^2}{2!} + \frac{x^4}{4!} - \frac{x^6}{6!} + \cdots$$

is the Maclaurin series for $\cos x$.

EXAMPLE 4.   Find the Taylor series expansion of $\cos x$ about the point $a = 2\pi$.

Solution.   The values of $\cos x$ and its derivatives at $a = 2\pi$ are the same as their values at $a = 0$. Therefore,

$$f^{(2k)}(2\pi) = f^{(2k)}(0) = (-1)^k \qquad \text{and} \qquad f^{(2k+1)}(2\pi) = f^{(2k+1)}(0) = 0,$$

as in Example 2. The required series is

$$\sum_{k=0}^{\infty} (-1)^{2k} \frac{(x - 2\pi)^{2k}}{(2k)!} = 1 - \frac{(x - 2\pi)^2}{2!} + \frac{(x - 2\pi)^4}{4!} - \cdots .$$

REMARK.   There is a convention about how formulas like

$$\frac{x^{2k}}{(2k)!} \qquad \text{and} \qquad \frac{(x - 2\pi)^{2k}}{(2k)!},$$

which arise in the power series of Examples 3 and 4, are to be evaluated when $k = 0$. Besides the usual agreement that $0! = 1$, we also assume that

$$\frac{x^0}{0!} = \frac{1}{1} = 1 \qquad \text{and} \qquad \frac{(x - 2\pi)^0}{0!} = \frac{1}{1} = 1,$$

even when $x = 0$ or 2π.

One of the most celebrated series of all times, the *binomial series*, is the Maclaurin series for the function $f(x) = (1 + x)^m$. Newton used it to estimate integrals (we will, in Article 16–13) and it can be used to give accurate estimates of roots. To derive the series, we first list the function and its derivatives:

$$
\begin{aligned}
f(x) &= (1 + x)^m, \\
f'(x) &= m(1 + x)^{m-1}, \\
f''(x) &= m(m - 1)(1 + x)^{m-2}, \\
f'''(x) &= m(m - 1)(m - 2)(1 + x)^{m-3}, \\
&\vdots \\
f^{(k)}(x) &= m(m - 1)(m - 2) \cdots (m - k + 1)(1 + x)^{m-k}.
\end{aligned}
$$

We then substitute the values of these at $x = 0$ in the basic Maclaurin series (5) to obtain

$$1 + mx + \frac{m(m - 1)}{2!} x^2 + \cdots + \frac{m(m - 1)(m - 2) \cdots (m - k + 1)}{k!} x^k + \cdots \quad (8)$$

If m is an integer, the series terminates after $(m + 1)$ terms, because the coefficients from $k = m + 1$ on are 0. But when k is not an integer, the series is infinite. (For a proof that the series converges to $(1 + x)^m$ when $|x| < 1$, see Courant and John's *Introduction to Calculus and Analysis*, Wiley-Interscience, 1974.)

EXAMPLE 5. Use the binomial series to estimate $\sqrt{1.25}$ with an error of less than 0.001.

Solution. We take $x = \frac{1}{4}$ and $m = \frac{1}{2}$ in (8) to obtain

$$(1 + \tfrac{1}{4})^{1/2} = 1 + \tfrac{1}{2}(\tfrac{1}{4}) + \frac{(\tfrac{1}{2})(-\tfrac{1}{2})}{2!}(\tfrac{1}{4})^2 + \frac{(\tfrac{1}{2})(-\tfrac{1}{2})(-\tfrac{3}{2})}{3!}(\tfrac{1}{4})^3 + \cdots$$

$$= 1 + \tfrac{1}{8} - \tfrac{1}{128} + \tfrac{1}{1024} - \tfrac{1}{32768} + \cdots$$

The series alternates after the first term, so that the approximation

$$\sqrt{1.25} \approx 1 + \tfrac{1}{8} - \tfrac{1}{128} \approx 1.117$$

is within $\frac{1}{1024}$ of the exact value and thus has the required accuracy.

PROBLEMS

In Problems 1 through 9, use Eq. (3) to write the Taylor polynomials $f_3(x)$ and $f_4(x)$ for each of the following functions $f(x)$. In each case, your first step should be to complete a table like the one shown below.

n	$f^{(n)}(x)$	$f^{(n)}(0)$
0		
1		
2		
3		
4		

1. e^{-x} 2. $\sin x$ 3. $\cos x$

4. $\sin\left(x + \dfrac{\pi}{2}\right)$ 5. $\sinh x$ 6. $\cosh x$

7. $x^4 - 2x + 1$ 8. $x^3 - 2x + 1$ 9. $x^2 - 2x + 1$

In Problems 10 through 13, find the Maclaurin series for each function.

10. $\dfrac{1}{1 + x}$ 11. x^2

12. $(1 + x)^2$ 13. $(1 + x)^{3/2}$

14. Find the Maclaurin series for $f(x) = 1/(1 - x)$. Show that the series diverges when $|x| \geq 1$ and converges when $|x| < 1$.

In Problems 15–20, use Eq. (7) to write the Taylor series expansion of the given function about the given point a.

15. $f(x) = e^x$, $a = 10$

16. $f(x) = x^2$, $a = \frac{1}{2}$

17. $f(x) = \ln x$, $a = 1$

18. $f(x) = \sqrt{x}$, $a = 4$

19. $f(x) = \dfrac{1}{x}$, $a = -1$

20. $f(x) = \cos x$, $a = -\dfrac{\pi}{4}$

In Problems 21 and 22, write the sum of the first three terms of the Taylor series for the given function about the given point a.

21. $f(x) = \tan x$, $a = \dfrac{\pi}{4}$

22. $f(x) = \ln \cos x$, $a = \dfrac{\pi}{3}$

23. Use the binomial theorem to estimate $\sqrt{1.02}$ with an error of less than 0.001.

In the previous article, we asked when a Taylor series for a function can be expected to converge to the function. In this article, we answer the question with a theorem named after the English mathematician Brook Taylor (1685–1731). Unfortunately, although several proofs of the theorem are known, none of them seems to have an obvious point of departure.

The path we shall follow starts with the simple formula

$$\int_a^b f'(t)\, dt = f(t)\Big|_a^b = f(b) - f(a), \tag{1}$$

16-9

**TAYLOR'S THEOREM
WITH REMAINDER:
SINES, COSINES, AND e^x**

which we rewrite in the form

$$f(b) = f(a) + \int_a^b f'(t) \, dt. \tag{2}$$

We then apply the integration-by-parts formula

$$\int u \, dv = uv - \int v \, du$$

with

$$u = f'(t) \qquad \text{and} \qquad v = t - b,$$

where, in determining v from $dv = dt$, we introduce the constant of integration $-b$ for future convenience. As a result,

$$f(b) = f(a) + (t - b)f'(t)\Big|_a^b - \int_a^b (t - b)f''(t) \, dt$$

$$= f(a) + (b - a)f'(a) + \int_a^b (b - t)f''(t) \, dt.$$

A second integration by parts, with

$$u = f''(t), \qquad v = -\frac{(b - t)^2}{2},$$

leads to

$$f(b) = f(a) + (b - a)f'(a) - \frac{(b - t)^2}{2}f''(t)\Big|_a^b + \int_a^b \frac{(b - t)^2}{2}f'''(t) \, dt$$

$$= f(a) + (b - a)f'(a) + \frac{(b - a)^2}{2!}f''(a) + \int_a^b \frac{(b - t)^2}{2!}f'''(t) \, dt.$$

By continuing in this fashion, we find that

$$f(b) = f(a) + (b - a)f'(a) + \frac{(b - a)^2}{2!}f''(a) + \cdots$$

$$+ \frac{(b - a)^n}{n!}f^{(n)}(a) + \int_a^b \frac{(b - t)^n}{n!}f^{(n+1)}(t) \, dt.$$

Finally, we replace b by x, to obtain the formula of Taylor's theorem.

Theorem 1. Taylor's Theorem. *Let f be a function that is continuous together with its first $n + 1$ derivatives on an interval containing a and x. Then the value of the function at x is given by*

$$f(x) = f(a) + f'(a) \cdot (x - a) + \frac{f''(a)}{2!}(x - a)^2 + \frac{f'''(a)}{3!}(x - a)^3 + \cdots$$

$$+ \frac{f^{(n)}(a)}{n!}(x - a)^n + R_n(x, a), \tag{3}$$

where

$$R_n(x, a) = \int_a^x \frac{(x - t)^n}{n!}f^{(n+1)}(t) \, dt.$$

Equation (3) is often referred to as *Taylor's formula*.

The application of integration by parts n times in succession requires that the integral in Eq. (3) exist at each stage. This will indeed be the case provided the $(n + 1)$st derivative of the function exists and is continuous in some closed interval that includes the domain of integration from a to x.

The term $R_n(x, a)$ is called the *remainder* in the Taylor-series expansion for $f(x)$. If the remainder is omitted in Eq. (3), the right side becomes the Taylor polynomial approximation to $f(x)$. The error in this approximation is what is measured by $R_n(x, a)$. Hence, we can pursue the question of whether the series converges to $f(x)$ by investigating this remainder. The series will converge to $f(x)$ provided

$$\lim_{n \to \infty} R_n(x, a) = 0. \tag{4}$$

In other words, when this limit is 0,

$$f(x) = \sum_{k=0}^{\infty} \frac{f^{(k)}(a)}{k!} (x - a)^k.$$

EXAMPLE 1. Let $f(x) = e^x$. This function and all its derivatives are continuous at every point, so Taylor's theorem may be applied with any convenient value of a. We take $a = 0$, since the values of f and its derivatives are easy to compute there. Taylor's theorem leads to

$$e^x = 1 + x + \frac{x^2}{2!} + \frac{x^3}{3!} + \cdots + \frac{x^n}{n!} + R_n(x, 0), \tag{5}$$

with

$$R_n(x, 0) = \int_0^x \frac{(x - t)^n}{n!} e^t \, dt. \tag{6}$$

When x is positive, we may *estimate* the remainder (6) by observing that the integrand is positive for $0 < t < x$, and that $e^t < e^x < 3^x$. Therefore,

$$|R_n(x, 0)| \leq \int_0^x \frac{(x - t)^n}{n!} 3^x \, dt = 3^x \int_0^x \frac{(x - t)^n}{n!} \, dt = 3^x \frac{x^{n+1}}{(n + 1)!}, \qquad x > 0. \tag{7}$$

When x is negative, we merely replace x by $|x|$ on the right, and the inequality continues to hold. Therefore, for all real values of x, we have

$$|R_n(x, 0)| \leq 3^{|x|} \frac{|x|^{n+1}}{(n + 1)!}, \tag{8}$$

and since

$$\lim_{n \to \infty} 3^{|x|} \frac{|x|^{n+1}}{(n + 1)!} = 3^{|x|} \lim_{n \to \infty} \frac{|x|^{n+1}}{(n + 1)!} = 3^{|x|} \cdot 0 = 0, \tag{9}$$

we know that

$$R_n(x, 0) \to 0.$$

Therefore, the Taylor series for e^x converges to e^x for every x:

$$e^x = \sum_{n=0}^{\infty} \frac{x^n}{n!} = 1 + x + \frac{x^2}{2!} + \frac{x^3}{3!} + \cdots.$$

Estimating the Remainder

It is often possible to estimate $R_n(x, a)$ as we did in Example 1 without having to evaluate the integral for it. The basis for such estimates is the following theorem, although the reason may not be immediately apparent upon reading the Theorem. We first state and prove the theorem. Then we state a corollary of the theorem (we will call the corollary Theorem 3) that is formulated specifically for estimating remainders.

Theorem 2. *Let $g(t)$ and $h(t)$ be continuous for $a \leq t \leq b$, and suppose that $h(t)$ does not change sign in this interval. Then there exists a number c between a and b such that*

$$\int_a^b g(t)h(t)\, dt = g(c) \int_a^b h(t)\, dt. \tag{10}$$

Proof. Let m and M be respectively the least and greatest values of $g(t)$ for $a \leq t \leq b$. Then

$$m \leq g(t_i) \leq M \tag{11}$$

for any t_i between a and b, inclusive. We form a subdivision

$$a = t_0 < t_1 < t_2 < \cdots < t_n = b$$

of the interval $a \leq t \leq b$ with

$$t_i - t_{i-1} = \Delta t = (b - a)/n, \qquad (i = 1, \ldots, n),$$

and multiply each term in the inequalities (11) by $h(t_i)\, \Delta t$. Since the sign of $h(t)$ does not change over the interval $a \leq t \leq b$, all the terms $h(t_i)\, \Delta t$ are of the same sign, say positive. [If they are all negative, replace $h(t)$ by $-h(t)$ in the argument that follows.] Then

$$mh(t_i)\, \Delta t \leq g(t_i)h(t_i)\, \Delta t \leq Mh(t_i)\, \Delta t,$$

and the order of inequality is preserved when we sum on i from 1 to n; that is,

$$\sum_{i=1}^n mh(t_i)\, \Delta t \leq \sum_{i=1}^n g(t_i)h(t_i)\, \Delta t \leq \sum_{i=1}^n Mh(t_i)\, \Delta t. \tag{12}$$

Finally, we let n increase indefinitely and recall that, because the functions involved are continuous on $[a, b]$, the sums converge to definite integrals:

$$m \int_a^b h(t)\, dt \leq \int_a^b g(t)h(t)\, dt \leq M \int_a^b h(t)\, dt,$$

or

$$m \leq \frac{\int_a^b g(t)h(t)\, dt}{\int_a^b h(t)\, dt} \leq M. \tag{13}$$

Since

$$Q = \frac{\int_a^b g(t)h(t)\, dt}{\int_a^b h(t)\, dt} \tag{14}$$

is a number between the least and greatest values taken on by $g(t)$ for $a \leq t \leq b$ and $g(t)$ is assumed to be continuous, there is a number c between *a* and *b* such that

$$Q = g(c).$$

This leads at once to the result in Eq. (10) and completes the proof of the theorem.   Q.E.D.

We now apply this theorem to the integral in Eq. (3) with

$$h(t) = \frac{(x-t)^n}{n!}, \qquad g(t) = f^{(n+1)}(t).$$

As *t* varies from *a* to *x*, $h(t)$ is continuous and does not change sign. Hence, if $f^{(n+1)}(t)$ is continuous, Eq. (10) applies, and we have

$$R_n(x, a) = f^{(n+1)}(c) \int_a^x \frac{(x-t)^n}{n!}\, dt$$

$$= f^{(n+1)}(c) \frac{(x-a)^{n+1}}{(n+1)!}.$$

This is known as *Lagrange's* form of the remainder:

Lagrange's Form of the Remainder

$$R_n(x, a) = f^{(n+1)}(c) \frac{(x-a)^{n+1}}{(n+1)!}, \qquad c \text{ between } a \text{ and } x.* \qquad (15)$$

In applying Lagrange's form we can, in general, only estimate $f^{(n+1)}(c)$ because we do not know *c* exactly. But we do know that if the values of $|f^{(n+1)}(t)|$ are bounded above by some constant *M* for all *t* between *a* and *x*, inclusive, then

$$|R_n(x, a)| = |f^{(n+1)}(c)| \frac{|x-a|^{n+1}}{(n+1)!} \leq M \frac{|x-a|^{n+1}}{(n+1)!}. \qquad (16)$$

This was the estimate used in Example 1 when e^t in Eq. (6) was replaced by $M = 3^{|x|}$ to produce the inequality in (7), although the work was done in several steps there.

This method of estimation is so convenient that we state it as a theorem for future reference.

Theorem 3. The Remainder Estimation Theorem. *If there is a positive constant M such that $|f^{(n+1)}(t)| \leq M$ for all t between a and x, inclusive, then the remainder term $R_n(x, a)$ in Taylor's theorem satisfies the inequality*

$$|R_n(x, a)| \leq M \frac{|x-a|^{n+1}}{(n+1)!}.$$

---

* Another proof of Taylor's theorem, leading directly to the Lagrange form of the remainder, is outlined in Problem 74 (Extended Mean Value Theorem), in the miscellaneous problems at the end of Chapter 3.

We are now ready to look at some examples of how the Remainder Estimation Theorem and Taylor's Theorem can be used together to settle questions of convergence. As you will see, they can also be used to determine the accuracy with which a function is approximated by one of its Taylor polynomials.

EXAMPLE 2. The Maclaurin series for sin x converges to sin x for all x.

Expressed in terms of x, the function and its derivatives are

$$f(x) \quad = \quad \sin x, \qquad f'(x) \quad = \quad \cos x,$$

$$f''(x) \quad = \quad -\sin x, \qquad f'''(x) \quad = \quad -\cos x,$$

$$\vdots \qquad\qquad\qquad \vdots$$

$$f^{(2k)}(x) = (-1)^k \sin x, \qquad f^{(2k+1)}(x) = (-1)^k \cos x,$$

so that

$$f^{(2k)}(0) = 0 \quad \text{and} \quad f^{(2k+1)}(0) = (-1)^k.$$

The series has only odd-powered terms and, for $n = 2k + 1$, Taylor's formula gives

$$\sin x = x - \frac{x^3}{3!} + \frac{x^5}{5!} - \cdots + \frac{(-1)^k x^{2k+1}}{(2k+1)!} + R_{2k+1}(x, 0).$$

Now, since all the derivatives of sin x have absolute values less than or equal to 1, we can apply the Remainder Estimation Theorem with $M = 1$ to obtain

$$|R_{2k+1}(x, 0)| \le 1 \cdot \frac{|x|^{2k+2}}{(2k+2)!}.$$

Since $[|x|^{2k+2}/(2k+2)!] \to 0$ as $k \to \infty$, whatever the value of x,

$$R_{2k+1}(x, 0) \to 0,$$

and the Maclaurin series for sin x converges to sin x for every x:

$$\sin x = \sum_{k=0}^{\infty} \frac{(-1)^k x^{2k+1}}{(2k+1)!} = x - \frac{x^3}{3!} + \frac{x^5}{5!} - \frac{x^7}{7!} + \cdots$$

EXAMPLE 3. The Maclaurin series for cos x converges to cos x for every value of x. We begin by adding the remainder term to the Taylor polynomial for cos x in Eq. (4) of the previous article, to obtain Taylor's formula for cos x with $n = 2k$:

$$\cos x = 1 - \frac{x^2}{2!} + \frac{x^4}{4!} - \cdots + (-1)^k \frac{x^{2k}}{(2k)!} + R_{2k}(x, 0).$$

Since the derivatives of the cosine have absolute value less than or equal to 1, we apply the Remainder Estimation Theorem with $M = 1$ to obtain

$$|R_{2k}(x, 0)| \le 1 \cdot \frac{|x|^{2k+1}}{(2k+1)!}.$$

For every value of x, $R_{2k} \to 0$ as $k \to 0$. Therefore, the series converges to cos x for every value of x.

$$\cos x = \sum_{k=0}^{\infty} \frac{(-1)^k x^{2k}}{(2k)!} = 1 - \frac{x^2}{2!} + \frac{x^4}{4!} - \frac{x^6}{6!} + \cdots.$$

EXAMPLE 4. Find the Maclaurin series for cos $2x$ and show that it converges to cos $2x$ for every value of x.

Solution. The Maclaurin series for cos x converges to cos x for every value of x, and therefore converges for every value of $2x$:

$$\cos 2x = \sum_{k=0}^{\infty} \frac{(-1)^k (2x)^{2k}}{(2k)!} = 1 - \frac{(2x)^2}{2!} + \frac{(2x)^4}{4!} - \frac{(2x)^6}{6!} + \cdots$$

Taylor series can be added, subtracted, and multiplied by constants, just as other series can, and the results are once again Taylor series. The Taylor series for $f(x) + g(x)$ is the sum of the Taylor series for $f(x)$ and $g(x)$, because the nth derivative of $f(x) + g(x)$ is $f^{(n)}(x) + g^{(n)}(x)$, and so on. In the next example, we add the series for e^x and e^{-x} and divide by 2, to obtain the Taylor series for cosh x.

EXAMPLE 5. Find the Taylor series for cosh x.

Solution

$$e^x = 1 + x + \frac{x^2}{2!} + \frac{x^3}{3!} + \frac{x^4}{4!} + \frac{x^5}{5!} + \cdots,$$

$$e^{-x} = 1 - x + \frac{x^2}{2!} - \frac{x^3}{3!} + \frac{x^4}{4!} - \frac{x^5}{5!} + \cdots;$$

$$\cosh x = \frac{e^x + e^{-x}}{2} = 1 \quad + \frac{x^2}{2!} \quad + \frac{x^4}{4!} \quad + \cdots = \sum_{k=0}^{\infty} \frac{x^{2k}}{(2k)!}.$$

Here are some examples of how to use the Remainder Estimation Theorem to estimate truncation error.

EXAMPLE 6. Calculate e with an error of less than 10^{-6}.

Solution. By Taylor's Theorem,

$$e = e^1 = 1 + 1 + \frac{1}{2!} + \frac{1}{3!} + \cdots + \frac{1}{n!} + R_n(x, 0),$$

where

$$R_n(x, 0) = \int_0^1 \frac{(x - t)^n}{n!} e^t \, dt.$$

The interval of integration is $0 \leq t \leq 1$. Since $|e^t| < 3$ when $0 \leq t \leq 1$, the Remainder Estimation Theorem, with $M = 3$ and $x = 1$, gives

$$|R_n| \leq 3 \cdot \frac{|1|^{n+1}}{(n+1)!} = \frac{3}{(n+1)!}.$$

By trial we find that $3/9! > 10^{-6}$, while $3/10! < 10^{-6}$. Thus we should take $(n + 1)$ to be at least 10, or n to be at least 9. With an error of less than 10^{-6},

$$e = 1 + 1 + \frac{1}{2} + \frac{1}{3!} + \cdots + \frac{1}{9!} \approx 2.718282.$$

EXAMPLE 7. For what values of x can $\sin x$ be replaced by $x - (x^3/3!)$ with an error of magnitude no greater than 3×10^{-4}?

Solution.   Here we can take advantage of the fact that the Maclaurin series for $\sin x$ is an alternating series for every nonzero value of x. According to the Alternating Series Estimation Theorem in Article 16–7, the error in truncating

$$\sin x = x - \frac{x^3}{3!} + \frac{x^5}{5!} - \cdots$$

after $(x^3/3!)$ is no greater than

$$\left| \frac{x^5}{5!} \right| = \frac{|x|^5}{120}.$$

Therefore the error will be less than or equal to 3×10^{-4} if

$$\frac{|x|^5}{120} < 3 \times 10^{-4}$$

or

$$|x| < \sqrt[5]{360 \times 10^{-4}} \approx 0.514.$$

The Alternating Series Estimation Theorem tells us something that the Remainder Estimation Theorem does not: namely, that the estimate $x - (x^3/3!)$ for $\sin x$ is an underestimate when x is positive, because then $x^5/120$ is positive.

Figure 16–17 shows the graph of $\sin x$, along with the graphs of a number of its approximating Taylor polynomials. Note that the graph of $s_1 = x - (x^3/3!)$ is almost indistinguishable from the sine curve when $-1 \le x \le 1$. However, it crosses the x-axis at $\pm\sqrt{6} \approx \pm 2.45$, whereas the sine curve crosses the axis at $\pm\pi \approx \pm 3.14$.

One might wonder how the estimate given by the Remainder Estimation Theorem would compare with the one we just obtained from the Alternating Series Estimation Theorem. If we write

$$\sin x = x - \frac{x^3}{3!} + R_3,$$

then the Remainder Estimation Theorem gives

$$|R_3| \le 1 \cdot \frac{|x|^4}{4!} = \frac{|x|^4}{24},$$

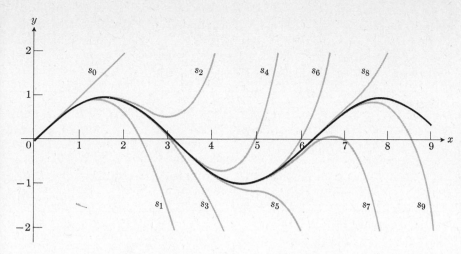

16–17 The polynomials $s_n(x) = \sum_{k=0}^{n} [(-1)^k x^{2k+1}/(2k+1)!]$ converge to $\sin x$ as $n \to \infty$. (Adapted from Helen M. Kammerer, *American Mathematical Monthly*, 43(1936), 293–294.)

which is not very good. But, if we are clever, and write

$$\sin x = x - \frac{x^3}{3!} + 0 + R_4,$$

then the Remainder Estimation Theorem gives

$$|R_4| \leq 1 \cdot \frac{|x|^5}{5!} = \frac{|x|^5}{120},$$

which is just what we had from the Alternating Series Estimation Theorem.

PROBLEMS

In Problems 1 through 6, write the Maclaurin series for each function.

1. $e^{x/2}$ **2.** $\sin 3x$

3. $5 \cos \dfrac{x}{\pi}$ **4.** $\sinh x$

5. $\dfrac{x^2}{2} - 1 + \cos x$ **6.** $\cos^2 2x = \dfrac{1 + \cos 2x}{2}$

7. Use series to verify that

a) $\cos(-x) = \cos x$ **b)** $\sin(-x) = -\sin x$

8. Show that

$$e^x = e^a \left[1 + (x - a) + \frac{(x - a)^2}{2!} + \cdots \right]$$

In Problems 9 through 11, write Taylor's formula (Eq. (3)), with $n = 2$ and $a = 0$, for the given function.

9. $\dfrac{1}{1 + x}$ **10.** $\ln(1 + x)$ **11.** $\sqrt{1 + x}$

12. Find the Taylor series for e^x at $a = 1$. Compare your series with the result in Problem 8.

13. For approximately what values of x can one replace $\sin x$ by $x - (x^3/6)$ with an error of magnitude no greater than 5×10^{-4}?

14. If $\cos x$ is replaced by $1 - (x^2/2)$ and $|x| < 0.5$, what estimate can be made of the error? Does $1 - (x^2/2)$ tend to be too large, or too small?

15. How close is the approximation $\sin x = x$ when $|x| < 10^{-3}$? For which of these values of x is $x < \sin x$?

16. The estimate $\sqrt{1 + x} = 1 + (x/2)$ is used when $|x|$ is small. Estimate the error when $|x| < 0.01$.

17. The approximation $e^x = 1 + x + (x^2/2)$ is used when x is small. Use the Remainder Estimation Theorem to estimate the error when $|x| < 0.1$.

18. When $x < 0$, the series for e^x is an alternating series. Use the Alternating Series Estimation Theorem to estimate the error that results from replacing e^x by $1 + x + (x^2/2)$ when $-0.1 < x < 0$. Compare with Problem 17.

19. Estimate the error in the approximation $\sinh x = x + (x^3/3!)$ when $|x| < 0.5$. [*Hint.* Use R_4, not R_3.]

20. When $0 \le h \le 0.01$, show that e^h may be replaced by $1 + h$ with an error of magnitude no greater than six-tenths of one percent of h. Use $e^{0.1} = 1.105$.

21. Let $f(x)$ and $g(x)$ have derivatives of all orders at $a = 0$. Show that the Maclaurin series for $f + g$ is

$$\sum_{n=0}^{\infty} \frac{f^{(n)}(0) + g^{(n)}(0)}{n!} x^n.$$

22. Each of the following sums is the value of an elementary function at some point. Find the function and the point.

a) $(0.1) - \dfrac{(0.1)^3}{3!} + \dfrac{(0.1)^5}{5!} - \cdots + \dfrac{(-1)^k(0.1)^{2k+1}}{(2k+1)!} + \cdots$

b) $1 - \dfrac{\pi^2}{4^2 \cdot 2!} + \dfrac{\pi^4}{4^4 \cdot 4!} - \cdots + \dfrac{(-1)^k(\pi)^{2k}}{4^{2k} \cdot (2k)!} + \cdots$

c) $1 + \dfrac{1}{2!} + \dfrac{1}{4!} + \cdots + \dfrac{1}{(2k)!} + \cdots$

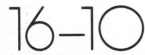

16-10

FURTHER COMPUTATIONS, LOGARITHMS, ARCTANGENTS, AND π

The Taylor-series expansion

$$f(x) = f(a) + f'(a)(x - a) + \frac{f''(a)}{2!}(x - a)^2 + \cdots$$

$$+ \frac{f^{(n)}(a)}{n!}(x - a)^n + R_n(x, a) \tag{1}$$

expresses the value of the function at x in terms of its value and the values of its derivatives at a, plus a remainder term, which we hope is so small that it may safely be omitted. In applying series to numerical computations, it is therefore *necessary* that a be chosen so that $f(a), f'(a), f''(a), \ldots$ are known. In dealing with the trigonometric functions, for example, one might take $a = 0, \pm\pi/6, \pm\pi/4, \pm\pi/3, \pm\pi/2$, and so on. It is also clear that it is *desirable* to choose the value of a near to the value of x for which the function is to be computed, in order to make $(x - a)$ small, so that the terms of the series decrease rapidly as n increases.

EXAMPLE 1. What value of a might one choose in the Taylor series (1) to compute $\sin 35°$?

Solution. We could choose $a = 0$ and use the series

$$\sin x = x - \frac{x^3}{3!} + \frac{x^5}{5!} - \cdots + (-1)^n \frac{x^{2n+1}}{(2n+1)!} + 0 \cdot x^{2n+2} + R_{2n+2}(x, 0), \tag{2}$$

or we could choose $a = \pi/6$ (which corresponds to 30°) and use the series

$$\sin x = \sin \frac{\pi}{6} + \cos \frac{\pi}{6}\left(x - \frac{\pi}{6}\right) - \sin \frac{\pi}{6} \frac{(x - \pi/6)^2}{2!} - \cos \frac{\pi}{6} \frac{(x - \pi/6)^3}{3!} + \cdots$$

$$+ \sin\left(\frac{\pi}{6} + n\frac{\pi}{2}\right) \frac{(x - \pi/6)^n}{n!} + R_n\left(x, \frac{\pi}{6}\right).$$

The remainder in the series (2) satisfies the inequality

$$|R_{2n+2}(x, 0)| \le \frac{|x|^{2n+3}}{(2n+3)!}, \tag{3}$$

which tends to zero as n becomes infinite, no matter how large $|x|$ may be.

We could therefore calculate sin 35° by placing

$$x = \frac{35\pi}{180} = 0.6108652$$

in the approximation

$$\sin x \approx x - \frac{x^3}{6} + \frac{x^5}{120} - \frac{x^7}{5040},$$

with an error of magnitude no greater than 3.3×10^{-8}, since

$$\left| R_8 \left(\frac{35\pi}{180}, 0 \right) \right| < \frac{(0.611)^9}{9!} < 3.3 \times 10^{-8}.$$

By using the series with $a = \pi/6$, we could obtain equal accuracy with a smaller exponent n, but at the expense of introducing $\cos \pi/6 = \sqrt{3}/2$ as one of the coefficients. In this series, with $a = \pi/6$, we would take

$$x = \frac{35\pi}{180},$$

but the quantity that appears raised to the various powers is

$$x - \frac{\pi}{6} = \frac{5\pi}{180} = 0.0872665,$$

which decreases rapidly when raised to high powers.

As a matter of fact, various trigonometric identities may be used, such as

$$\sin \left(\frac{\pi}{2} - x \right) = \cos x,$$

to facilitate the calculation of the sine or cosine of any angle with the Maclaurin series of the two functions. This method of finding the sine or cosine of an angle is used in computers.

Computation of Logarithms

Natural logarithms may be computed from series. The starting point is the series for $\ln (1 + x)$ in powers of x:

$$\ln (1 + x) = x - \frac{x^2}{2} + \frac{x^3}{3} - \cdots + (-1)^{n-1} \frac{x^n}{n} + \cdots$$

This series may be found directly from the Taylor-series expansion, Eq. (1), with $a = 0$. It may also be obtained by integrating the geometric series for $1/(1 + t)$ from $t = 0$ to $t = x$:

$$\int_0^x \frac{dt}{1 + t} = \int_0^x (1 - t + t^2 - t^3 + \cdots) \, dt,$$

$$\ln (1 + t) \Big]_0^x = t - \frac{t^2}{2} + \frac{t^3}{3} - \frac{t^4}{4} + \cdots \Big]_0^x,$$

$$\ln (1 + x) = x - \frac{x^2}{2} + \frac{x^3}{3} - \frac{x^4}{4} + \cdots \qquad (4)$$

The expansion (4) is valid for $|x| < 1$, since then the remainder, $R_n(x, 0)$, approaches zero as $n \to \infty$, as we shall now see. The remainder is given by the integral of the remainder in the geometric series, that is,

$$R_n(x, 0) = \int_0^x \frac{(-1)^n t^n}{1+t} \, dt. \tag{5}$$

We now suppose that $|x| < 1$. For every t between 0 and x inclusive we have

$$|1 + t| \geq 1 - |x|$$

and

$$|(-1)^n t^n| = |t|^n,$$

so that

$$\left| \frac{(-1)^n t^n}{1+t} \right| \leq \frac{|t|^n}{1 - |x|}.$$

Therefore,

$$|R_n(x, 0)| \leq \int_0^{|x|} \frac{t^n}{1 - |x|} \, dt = \frac{1}{n+1} \cdot \frac{|x|^{n+1}}{1 - |x|}. \tag{6}$$

When $n \to \infty$, the right side of the inequality (6) approaches zero, and so must the left side. Thus (4) holds for $|x| < 1$.

If we replace x by $-x$, we obtain

$$\ln(1 - x) = -x - \frac{x^2}{2} - \frac{x^3}{3} - \cdots - \frac{x^n}{n} - \cdots, \tag{7}$$

which is also valid for $|x| < 1$. When we subtract (7) from (4), we get

$$\ln \frac{1+x}{1-x} = 2 \left(x + \frac{x^3}{3} + \frac{x^5}{5} + \cdots + \frac{x^{2k-1}}{2k-1} + \cdots \right), \tag{8}$$

which is true for $|x| < 1$. Equation (8) may be used to compute the natural logarithm of any positive number y by taking

$$y = \frac{1+x}{1-x} \qquad \text{or} \qquad x = \frac{y-1}{y+1}.$$

But the series converges most rapidly for values of x near zero, or when $(1 + x)/(1 - x)$ is near one. For this reason, the logarithms of the numbers

$$\frac{2}{1}, \quad \frac{3}{2}, \quad \frac{4}{3}, \quad \frac{5}{4}, \quad \cdots, \quad \frac{N+1}{N}$$

are ordinarily computed first in forming a table of natural logarithms of the integers. Then it is a matter of simple arithmetic to compute

$$\ln 3 = \ln \tfrac{2}{1} + \ln \tfrac{3}{2},$$

$$\ln 4 = \ln 3 + \ln \tfrac{4}{3},$$

$$\ln 5 = \ln 4 + \ln \tfrac{5}{4},$$

$$\vdots$$

$$\ln(N + 1) = \ln N + \ln \frac{N+1}{N}.$$

For this purpose, one may solve the equation

$$\frac{1+x}{1-x} = \frac{N+1}{N}$$

for

$$x = \frac{1}{2N+1}.$$

This may be substituted into Eq. (8), which becomes

$$\ln\frac{N+1}{N} = 2\left(\frac{1}{2N+1} + \frac{1}{3(2N+1)^3} + \frac{1}{5(2N+1)^5} + \cdots\right). \qquad \textbf{(9)}$$

For example, to calculate ln 2, we take $N = 1$, $x = \frac{1}{3}$, and calculate

$$x = 0.33333 \quad 33,$$

$$\frac{x^3}{3} = 0.01234 \quad 57,$$

$$\frac{x^5}{5} = 0.00082 \quad 30,$$

$$\frac{x^7}{7} = 0.00006 \quad 53,$$

$$\frac{x^9}{9} = 0.00000 \quad 56,$$

$$\frac{x^{11}}{11} = 0.00000 \quad 05,$$

$$\overline{\text{Sum} = 0.34657 \quad 34,} \qquad \ln 2 \approx 0.69314 \quad 68.$$

Computation of π

Archimedes (287–212 B.C.) gave the approximation

$$3\tfrac{1}{7} > \pi > 3\tfrac{10}{71},$$

in the third century B.C. A French mathematician, Viéta (1540–1603), gave the formula

$$\frac{2}{\pi} = \sqrt{\tfrac{1}{2}} \times \sqrt{\left(\tfrac{1}{2} + \tfrac{1}{2}\sqrt{\tfrac{1}{2}}\right)} \times \sqrt{\left(\tfrac{1}{2} + \tfrac{1}{2}\sqrt{\left(\tfrac{1}{2} + \tfrac{1}{2}\sqrt{\tfrac{1}{2}}\right)}\right)} \times \cdots,$$

which Turnbull* calls "the first actual formula for the time-honoured number π." Other interesting formulas for π include†

$$\frac{\pi}{4} = \cfrac{1}{1 + \cfrac{1^2}{2 + \cfrac{3^2}{2 + \cfrac{5^2}{2 + \cdots}}}},$$

---

*   *World of Mathematics*, Vol. 1, p. 121.

†   *Ibid.*, p. 138.

which is credited to Lord Brouncker, an Irish peer;

$$\frac{\pi}{4} = \frac{2 \times 4 \times 4 \times 6 \times 6 \times 8 \times \cdots}{3 \times 3 \times 5 \times 5 \times 7 \times 7 \times \cdots},$$

discovered by the English mathematician Wallis; and

$$\frac{\pi}{4} = 1 - \frac{1}{3} + \frac{1}{5} - \frac{1}{7} + \cdots,$$

known as Leibniz's formula.

All of these formulas involve limits. To derive Viéta's formula, for example, we may begin with the trigonometric half-angle formulas:

$$\sin x = 2 \sin \frac{x}{2} \cos \frac{x}{2},$$

$$\sin \frac{x}{2} = 2 \sin \frac{x}{4} \cos \frac{x}{4}, \tag{10}$$

$$\sin \frac{x}{4} = 2 \sin \frac{x}{8} \cos \frac{x}{8},$$

$$\vdots \qquad\qquad \vdots$$

With these we write

$$\sin x = 2 \sin \frac{x}{2} \cos \frac{x}{2}$$

$$= 2^2 \sin \frac{x}{4} \cos \frac{x}{2} \cos \frac{x}{4} \tag{11}$$

$$= 2^3 \sin \frac{x}{8} \cos \frac{x}{2} \cos \frac{x}{4} \cos \frac{x}{8}$$

$$\vdots$$

Then, by induction on n,

$$\sin x = 2^n \sin \left(\frac{x}{2^n}\right) \cos \frac{x}{2} \cos \frac{x}{4} \cdots \cos \left(\frac{x}{2^n}\right).$$

Hence,

$$\frac{\sin x}{x} = \frac{\sin (x/2^n)}{(x/2^n)} \cos \frac{x}{2} \cos \frac{x}{4} \cdots \cos \left(\frac{x}{2^n}\right). \tag{12}$$

When $n \to \infty$,

$$\frac{\sin (x/2^n)}{(x/2^n)} \to 1,$$

while the left side of Eq. (12) remains unchanged. Therefore,

$$\frac{\sin x}{x} = \lim_{n \to \infty} \frac{\sin (x/2^n)}{(x/2^n)} \cos \frac{x}{2} \cos \frac{x}{4} \cdots \cos \frac{x}{2^n}$$

$$= 1 \cdot \cos \frac{x}{2} \cos \frac{x}{4} \cos \frac{x}{8} \cos \frac{x}{16} \cdots \tag{13}$$

Finally, substituting $x = \pi/2$ in Eq. (13) gives

$$\frac{2}{\pi} = \cos \frac{\pi}{4} \cos \frac{\pi}{8} \cos \frac{\pi}{16} \cos \frac{\pi}{32} \cdots \tag{14}$$

$$= \sqrt{\tfrac{1}{2}} \times \sqrt{\tfrac{1}{2}(1 + \sqrt{\tfrac{1}{2}})} \times \sqrt{\tfrac{1}{2}(1 + \sqrt{\tfrac{1}{2}(1 + \sqrt{\tfrac{1}{2}})})} \times \cdots, \tag{15}$$

which is Viéta's formula. The law of formation on the right is

$$\cos \frac{\pi}{4} = \sqrt{\tfrac{1}{2}}, \qquad \cos \frac{\theta}{2} = \sqrt{\tfrac{1}{2}(1 + \cos \theta)}.$$

Similarly, we could interpret the other formulas as expressing certain limits in terms of π. However, we now turn our attention to the series for $\tan^{-1} x$, since it leads to the Leibniz formula and others from which π has been computed to a great many decimal places.

Since

$$\tan^{-1} x = \int_0^x \frac{dt}{1 + t^2},$$

we integrate the geometric series, with remainder,

$$\frac{1}{1 + t^2} = 1 - t^2 + t^4 - t^6 + \cdots + (-1)^n t^{2n} + \frac{(-1)^{n+1} t^{2n+2}}{1 + t^2}. \tag{16}$$

Thus

$$\tan^{-1} x = x - \frac{x^3}{3} + \frac{x^5}{5} - \frac{x^7}{7} + \cdots + (-1)^n \frac{x^{2n+1}}{2n+1} + R,$$

where

$$R = \int_0^x \frac{(-1)^{n+1} t^{2n+2}}{1 + t^2} dt.$$

The denominator of the integrand is greater than or equal to 1; hence

$$|R| \le \int_0^{|x|} t^{2n+2} \, dt = \frac{|x|^{2n+3}}{2n+3}.$$

If $|x| \le 1$, the right side of this inequality approaches zero as $n \to \infty$. Therefore R also approaches zero and we have:

$$\tan^{-1} x = \sum_{n=0}^{\infty} \frac{(-1)^n x^{2n+1}}{2n+1},$$

or

$$\tan^{-1} x = x - \frac{x^3}{3} + \frac{x^5}{5} - \frac{x^7}{7} + \cdots, \quad |x| \le 1. \tag{17}$$

Various trigonometric identities are useful if one wishes to use Eq. (17) to calculate π. For example, if

$$\alpha = \tan^{-1} \tfrac{1}{2} \qquad \text{and} \qquad \beta = \tan^{-1} \tfrac{1}{3},$$

then

$$\tan (\alpha + \beta) = \frac{\tan \alpha + \tan \beta}{1 - \tan \alpha \tan \beta} = \frac{\tfrac{1}{2} + \tfrac{1}{3}}{1 - \tfrac{1}{6}} = 1 = \tan \frac{\pi}{4}$$

and

$$\frac{\pi}{4} = \alpha + \beta = \tan^{-1}\tfrac{1}{2} + \tan^{-1}\tfrac{1}{3}. \tag{18}$$

Now Eq. (17) may be used with $x = \tfrac{1}{2}$ to evaluate $\tan^{-1}\tfrac{1}{2}$ and with $x = \tfrac{1}{3}$ to give $\tan^{-1}\tfrac{1}{3}$. The sum of these results, multiplied by 4, gives π.

In 1961, π was computed to more than 100,000 decimal places on an IBM 7090 computer. More recently, in 1973, Jean Guilloud and Martine Bouyer computed π to 1,000,000 decimal places on a CDC 7600 computer, by applying the arctangent series (17) to the formula

$$\pi = 48 \tan^{-1}\tfrac{1}{18} + 32 \tan^{-1}\tfrac{1}{57} - 20 \tan^{-1}\tfrac{1}{239}. \tag{19}$$

They checked their work with the formula

$$\pi = 24 \tan^{-1}\tfrac{1}{8} + 8 \tan^{-1}\tfrac{1}{57} + 4 \tan^{-1}\tfrac{1}{239}. \tag{20}$$

A number of current computations of π are being carried out with an algorithm discovered by Eugene Salamin (Problem 17). The algorithm produces sequences that converge to π even more rapidly than the sequence of partial sums of the arctangent series in Eqs. (19) and (20). [For a delightful account of attempts to compute, and even to *legislate*(!) the value of π, see Chapter 12 of David A. Smith's *Interface: Calculus and the Computer*, Houghton Mifflin Company, Boston, MA, 1976.]

REMARK.   Two types of numerical error tend to occur in computing with series. One is the *truncation error*, which is the remainder $R_n(x, a)$ and consists of the sum of the infinite number of terms in the series that follow the term $(x - a)^n f^{(n)}(a)/n!$. This is the only error we have discussed so far.

The other is the *round-off error* that enters in calculating the sum of the finite number of terms

$$f(a) + f'(a)(x - a) + \cdots + \frac{f^{(n)}(a)(x - a)^n}{n!}$$

when we approximate each of these terms by a decimal number with only a finite number of decimal places. For example, taking 0.3333 in place of $\tfrac{1}{3}$ introduces a round-off error equal to $10^{-4}/3$. There are likely to be round-off errors associated with each term, some of these being positive and some negative. When the need for accuracy is paramount, it is important to control both the truncation error and the round-off errors. *Truncation* errors can be reduced by taking more terms of the series; *round-off* errors can be reduced by taking more decimal places.

PROBLEMS

In each of Problems 1 through 6, use a suitable series to calculate the indicated quantity to three decimal places. In each case, show that the remainder term does not exceed 5×10^{-4}.

1. $\cos 31°$

2. $\tan 46°$

3. $\sin 6.3$

4. $\cos 69$

5. $\ln 1.25$

6. $\tan^{-1} 1.02$

7. Find the Maclaurin series for $\ln(1 + 2x)$. For what values of x does the series converge?

8. For what values of x can one replace $\ln(1 + x)$ by x with an error of magnitude no greater than one percent of the absolute value of x?

Use series to evaluate the integrals in Problems 9 and 10 to three decimals.

9. $\int_0^{0.1} \dfrac{\sin x}{x}\, dx$ **10.** $\int_0^{0.1} e^{-x^2}\, dx$

11. Show that the ordinate of the catenary $y = a \cosh x/a$ deviates from the ordinate of the parabola $x^2 = 2a(y - a)$ by less than $0.003\,|a|$ over the range $|x/a| \le \frac{1}{3}$.

12. Construct a table of natural logarithms $\ln N$ for $N = 1, 2, 3, \ldots, 10$ by the method discussed in connection with Eq. (9), but taking advantage of the relationships

$$\ln 4 = 2 \ln 2, \qquad \ln 6 = \ln 2 + \ln 3, \qquad \ln 8 = 3 \ln 2,$$

$$\ln 9 = 2 \ln 3, \qquad \ln 10 = \ln 2 + \ln 5$$

to reduce the job to the calculation of relatively few logarithms by series. In fact, you may use $\ln 2$ as given in the text and calculate $\ln \frac{3}{2}$, $\ln \frac{5}{4}$, and $\ln \frac{7}{6}$ by series, and then combine these in suitable ways to get the logarithms of numbers N from 1 to 10.

13. Find the sum of the series

$$\tfrac{1}{2} - \tfrac{1}{2}(\tfrac{1}{2})^2 + \tfrac{1}{3}(\tfrac{1}{2})^3 - \tfrac{1}{4}(\tfrac{1}{2})^4 + \cdots$$

14. How many terms of the series for $\tan^{-1} 1$ would you have to add for the Alternating Series Estimation Theorem to guarantee a calculation of $\pi/4$ to two decimals?

15. (*Calculator*) Equations (17) and (19) yield a series that converges to $\pi/4$ fairly rapidly. Estimate π to three decimal places with this series. In contrast, the convergence of $\sum_{n=1}^{\infty} (1/n^2)$ to $\pi^2/6$ is so slow that even fifty terms will not yield two-place accuracy.

16. (*Calculator*) (a) Find π to two decimals with the formulas of Lord Brouncker and Wallis. (b) If your calculator is programmable, use Viéta's formula, Eqs. (14) or (15), to calculate π to five decimal places.

17. (*Calculator*) A special case of Salamin's algorithm for estimating π begins with defining sequences $\{a_n\}$ and $\{b_n\}$ by the rules

$$a_0 = 1, \qquad\qquad b_0 = \frac{1}{\sqrt{2}},$$

$$a_{n+1} = \frac{(a_n + b_n)}{2}, \qquad b_{n+1} = \sqrt{a_n b_n}.$$

Then the sequence $\{c_n\}$ defined by

$$c_n = \frac{4 a_n b_n}{1 - \sum_{j=1}^{n} 2^{j+1}(a_j^2 - b_j^2)}$$

converges to π. Calculate c_3. (E. Salamin, "Computation of

π using arithmetic–geometric mean," *Mathematics of Computation*, **30**, July, 1976, pp. 565–570.)

18. Show that the series in Eq. (17) for $\tan^{-1} x$ diverges for $|x| > 1$.

19. Show that

$$\int_0^x \frac{dt}{1 - t^2} = \int_0^x \left(1 + t^2 + t^4 + \cdots + t^{2n} + \frac{t^{2n+2}}{1 - t^2}\right) dt$$

or, in other words, that

$$\tanh^{-1} x = x + \frac{x^3}{3} + \frac{x^5}{5} + \cdots + \frac{x^{2n+1}}{2n+1} + R,$$

where

$$R = \int_0^x \frac{t^{2n+2}}{1 - t^2}\, dt.$$

20. Show that R in Problem 19 is no greater than

$$\frac{1}{1 - x^2} \cdot \frac{|x|^{2n+3}}{2n+3}, \qquad \text{if} \quad x^2 < 1.$$

21. a) Differentiate the identity

$$\frac{1}{1 - x} = 1 + x + x^2 + \cdots + x^n + \frac{x^{n+1}}{1 - x}.$$

to obtain the expansion

$$\frac{1}{(1 - x)^2} = 1 + 2x + 3x^2 + \cdots + nx^{n-1} + R.$$

b) Prove that, if $|x| < 1$, then $R \to 0$ as $n \to \infty$.

c) In one throw of two dice, the probability of getting a score of 7 is $p = \frac{1}{6}$. If the dice are thrown repeatedly, the probability that a 7 will appear for the first time at the nth throw is $q^{n-1}p$, where $q = 1 - p = \frac{5}{6}$. The expected number of throws until a 7 first appears is $\sum_{n=1}^{\infty} nq^{n-1}p$. Evaluate this series numerically.

d) In applying statistical quality control to an industrial operation, an engineer inspects items taken at random from the assembly line. Each item sampled is classified as "good" or "bad." If the probability of a good item is p and of a bad item is $q = 1 - p$, the probability that the first bad item found is the nth inspected is $p^{n-1}q$. The average number inspected up to and including the first bad item found is $\sum_{n=1}^{\infty} np^{n-1}q$. Evaluate this series, assuming $0 < p < 1$.

22. In probability theory, a random variable X may assume the values $1, 2, 3, \ldots$, with probabilities $p_1, p_2, p_3, \ldots$, where p_k is the probability that X is equal to k ($k = 1, 2, \ldots$). It is customary to assume $p_k \ge 0$ and $\sum_{k=1}^{\infty} p_k = 1$. The *expected value* of X denoted by $E(X)$ is defined as $\sum_{k=1}^{\infty} kp_k$, provided this series converges. In each of the following cases, show that $\sum p_k = 1$ and find $E(X)$, if it exists. [*Hint.* See Problem 21.]

a) $p_k = 2^{-k}$ **b)** $p_k = \dfrac{5^{k-1}}{6^k}$

c) $p_k = \dfrac{1}{k(k+1)} = \dfrac{1}{k} - \dfrac{1}{k+1}$

*16–11

A SECOND DERIVATIVE TEST FOR MAXIMA AND MINIMA OF FUNCTIONS OF TWO INDEPENDENT VARIABLES

In this article we apply Taylor's theorem to study the behavior of a function

$$w = f(x, y)$$

when the point (x, y) is close to a point (a, b) where the first-order partial derivatives vanish,

$$f_x(a, b) = f_y(a, b) = 0. \qquad (1)$$

We shall assume that w and its first- and second-order partial derivatives are continuous throughout some neighborhood G of the point $P(a, b)$, Fig. 16–18. In the discussion that follows, a, b, h, and k are held fixed. In addition, h and k are to be small, so that the point $Q(a + h, b + k)$ together with all points

$$x = a + ht, \qquad y = b + kt, \qquad 0 \le t \le 1, \qquad (2)$$

on the line PQ also lie in G. We consider the values of $w = f(x, y)$ along the line PQ of Eq. (2) as t varies from 0 to 1. Thus, if we let

$$F(t) = f(a + ht, b + kt), \qquad (3)$$

we have

$$F(0) = f(a, b) \qquad \text{when} \quad t = 0,$$

$$F(1) = f(a + h, b + k) \qquad \text{when} \quad t = 1.$$

Now, by Taylor's theorem, we have

$$F(t) = F(0) + tF'(0) + \frac{t^2}{2!} F''(t_1),$$

where t_1 is between 0 and t. In particular, taking $t = 1$,

$$F(1) = F(0) + F'(0) + \tfrac{1}{2}F''(t_1), \qquad (4)$$

with $0 < t_1 < 1$.

The derivatives in Eq. (4) may be calculated from (3) by the chain rule for partial derivatives. First of all,

$$F'(t) = \frac{\partial f}{\partial x} \frac{dx}{dt} + \frac{\partial f}{\partial y} \frac{dy}{dt}.$$

Then, since

$$\frac{dx}{dt} = h, \qquad \frac{dy}{dt} = k,$$

from Eq. (2), we have

$$F'(t) = h \frac{\partial f}{\partial x} + k \frac{\partial f}{\partial y}. \qquad (5)$$

The chain rule may be applied again to calculate

$$F''(t) = h \frac{\partial F'(t)}{\partial x} + k \frac{\partial F'(t)}{\partial y}, \qquad (6)$$

16–18 A neighborhood G of the point $P(a, b)$.

where we have used the brackets to indicate the expression on the right side of Eq. (5); that is,

$$\frac{\partial F'(t)}{\partial x} = h\frac{\partial^2 f}{\partial x^2} + k\frac{\partial^2 f}{\partial x\,\partial y}, \tag{7}$$

$$\frac{\partial F'(t)}{\partial y} = h\frac{\partial^2 f}{\partial y\,\partial x} + k\frac{\partial^2 f}{\partial y^2}.$$

When we substitute from (7) into (6), and collect terms, we have

$$F''(t) = h^2\frac{\partial^2 f}{\partial x^2} + 2hk\frac{\partial^2 f}{\partial x\,\partial y} + k^2\frac{\partial^2 f}{\partial y^2}. \tag{8}$$

Equation (5) may be interpreted as saying that applying d/dt to $F(t)$ gives the same result as applying

$$\left(h\frac{\partial}{\partial x} + k\frac{\partial}{\partial y}\right)$$

to $f(x, y)$. Similarly, Eq. (8) says that applying d^2/dt^2 to $F(t)$ gives the same result as applying

$$\left(h\frac{\partial}{\partial x} + k\frac{\partial}{\partial y}\right)^2 = h^2\frac{\partial^2}{\partial x^2} + 2hk\frac{\partial^2}{\partial x\,\partial y} + k^2\frac{\partial^2}{\partial y^2}$$

to $f(x, y)$. These are the first two instances of a more general formula that says that

$$F^{(n)}(t) = \frac{d^n}{dt^n}F(t) = \left(h\frac{\partial}{\partial x} + k\frac{\partial}{\partial y}\right)^n f(x, y), \tag{9}$$

where the term in parentheses on the right is to be expanded by the binomial theorem and then applied term by term to $f(x, y)$.

If we now take $t = 0$ in Eq. (5) and $t = t_1$ in Eq. (8) and substitute the results into Eq. (4), we obtain

$$\begin{aligned}
f(a + h, b + k) = &\, f(a, b) + (hf_x + kf_y)_{(a,b)} \\
&+ \tfrac{1}{2}(h^2 f_{xx} + 2hk f_{xy} + k^2 f_{yy})_{(a+t_1 h,\, b+t_1 k)}.
\end{aligned} \tag{10}$$

If we extend the Maclaurin series for $F(t)$ to more terms,

$$F(t) = F(0) + F'(0)\cdot t + \frac{F''(0)}{2!}t^2 + \cdots + \frac{F^{(n)}(0)}{n!}t^n + \cdots,$$

and then take $t = 1$, we obtain

$$F(1) = F(0) + F'(0) + \frac{F''(0)}{2!} + \cdots + \frac{F^{(n)}(0)}{n!} + \cdots.$$

Finally, when we replace each derivative on the right of this last series by its equivalent expression from Eq. (9) evaluated at $t = 0$, and expand each term by the binomial theorem, we arrive at the following formula:

$$f(a + h, b + k) = f(a, b) + (hf_x + kf_y)_{(a,b)}$$

$$+ \frac{1}{2!}(h^2 f_{xx} + 2hk f_{xy} + k^2 f_{yy})_{(a,b)}$$

$$+ \frac{1}{3!}(h^3 f_{xxx} + 3h^2 k f_{xxx} + 3hk^2 f_{xyy} + k^3 f_{yyy})_{(a,b)} \qquad \textbf{(11)}$$

$$+ \cdots$$

$$+ \frac{1}{n!}\left[\left(h\frac{\partial}{\partial x} + k\frac{\partial}{\partial y}\right)^n f\right]_{(a,b)} + \cdots$$

This expresses the value of the function $f(x, y)$ at $x = a + h$, $y = b + k$, in terms of the values of the function and its partial derivatives at (a, b), and powers of $h = x - a$ and $k = y - b$. This is the Taylor series expansion, about the point (a, b), of the function $f(x, y)$. Analogous formulas hold for functions of more independent variables.

Suppose, now, that we have found a point (a, b) where the first-order derivatives f_x and f_y are both zero, and we wish to determine whether the function $w = f(x, y)$ has a maximum or a minimum at (a, b). We may then rewrite Eq. (10) in the form

$$f(a + h, b + k) - f(a, b) = \tfrac{1}{2}(h^2 f_{xx} + 2hk f_{xy} + k^2 f_{yy})_{(a + t_1 h, b + t_1 k)}$$

$$= \phi(t_1).$$

Since a maximum or minimum value of w at (a, b) is reflected in the sign of $\phi(t_1)$, we are led to a consideration of the sign of $\phi(t)$. The second-order derivatives that enter this expression are to be evaluated at a point on the line segment PQ (Fig. 16–18). This is not convenient for our purposes, since we do not know precisely where to take this point; that is, we do not know anything more about t_1 than that $0 \le t_1 \le 1$. However, since we are assuming that f_{xx}, f_{xy}, and f_{yy} are *continuous* throughout the region G, and since both h and k are assumed to be *small*, the values of these derivatives at $(a + t_1 h, b + t_1 k)$ are nearly the same as their values at (a, b). In particular, the *sign* of $\phi(t_1)$ is the same, for sufficiently small values of h and k, as the sign of

$$\phi(0) = h^2 f_{xx}(a, b) + 2hk f_{xy}(a, b) + k^2 f_{yy}(a, b). \qquad \textbf{(12)}$$

We therefore have the following criteria:

Sufficient Conditions for Maxima, Minima, and Saddle Points

Let

$$\phi(0) = h^2 f_{xx}(a, b) + 2hk f_{xy}(a, b) + k^2 f_{yy}(a, b).$$

Then,

1. $f(x, y)$ has a relative *minimum* at (a, b) provided $f_x(a, b) = f_y(a, b) = 0$, and $\phi(0)$ is *positive* for all sufficiently small values of h and k (excluding, of course, the case where $h = k = 0$).

2. $f(x, y)$ has a relative *maximum* at (a, b) provided $f_x(a, b) = f_y(a, b) = 0$ and $\phi(0)$ is *negative* for all sufficiently small values of h and k (again excluding $h = k = 0$).

3. $f(x, y)$ has a *saddle point* at (a, b) provided $f_x(a, b) = f_y(a, b) = 0$, and every neighborhood of (a, b) contains points $(a + h, b + k)$ at which $\phi(0)$ is positive and points $(a + h, b + k)$ at which $\phi(0)$ is negative.

See Problems 1 and 9.

EXAMPLE. The function

$$f(x, y) = x^2 + xy + y^2 + x - 4y + 5$$

has partial derivatives

$$f_x = 2x + y + 1,$$
$$f_y = x + 2y - 4,$$

which vanish at $(-2, 3)$. The second partial derivatives are all constant:

$$f_{xx} = 2, \qquad f_{xy} = 1, \qquad f_{yy} = 2,$$

and the expression whose sign determines whether f has a maximum, a minimum, or a saddle point at $(-2, 3)$ is

$$2h^2 + 2hk + 2k^2.$$

If we multiply this by 2, we have

$$4h^2 + 4hk + 4k^2 = (2h + k)^2 + 3k^2,$$

which is the sum of two nonnegative terms and is zero only when $h = k = 0$. Hence, the function has a relative *minimum* at $(-2, 3)$. In fact, this is its absolute minimum, since

$$f(-2 + h, 3 + k) \geq f(-2, 3)$$

for *all* h and k.

PROBLEMS

1. a) Let $A = f_{xx}(a, b)$, $B = f_{xy}(a, b)$, $C = f_{yy}(a, b)$ and show that the expression for $\phi(0)$ in Eq. (12), when multiplied by A, becomes the same as

$$A\phi(0) = (Ah + Bk)^2 + (AC - B^2)k^2.$$

b) Suppose $f_x(a, b) = f_y(a, b) = 0$ and $A \neq 0$. Use the result of part (a), and the three conditions that follow Eq. (12), to show that $f(x, y)$ has at (a, b):

i) a relative minimum if $AC - B^2 > 0$ and $A > 0$,
ii) a relative maximum if $AC - B^2 > 0$ and $A < 0$,
iii) a saddle point if $AC - B^2 < 0$.

Test the following surfaces for maxima, minima, and saddle points.

2. $z = x^2 + y^2 - 2x + 4y + 6$
3. $z = x^2 - y^2 - 2x + 4y + 6$

4. $z = x^2 - 2xy + 2y^2 - 2x + 2y + 1$
5. $z = x^2 + 2xy$
6. $z = 3 + 2x + 2y - 2x^2 - 2xy - y^2$
7. $z = x^3 - y^3 - 2xy + 6$
8. $z = x^3 + y^3 + 3x^2 - 3y^2 - 8$
9. In Eq. (12), let

$$h = c \cos \alpha, \qquad k = c \sin \alpha, \qquad c > 0,$$

and show that $\phi(0) = c^2(d^2f/ds^2)$, where d^2f/ds^2 is the second-order directional derivative of f at (a, b) in the direction of the unit vector $\mathbf{u} = \mathbf{i} \cos \alpha + \mathbf{j} \sin \alpha$. Express the three criteria for maxima, minima, and saddle points at the end of Article 16–11 in terms of d^2f/ds^2. [Similar criteria also apply in higher-dimensional problems.]

10. (a) Taking $a + h = x$, $b + k = y$, and $a = b = 0$ in Eq. (11), obtain the series through the terms of second degree in x and y, for the function $f(x, y) = e^x \cos y$. (b) Obtain the series for part (a) more simply by multiplication of the series for e^x by the series for $\cos y$.

11. Write out explicitly, through the terms of second degree, the Taylor series for a function $f(x, y, z)$, in powers of

$$(x - a), \qquad (y - b), \qquad (z - c),$$

and the values of f and its partial derivatives at (a, b, c).

16–12
INDETERMINATE FORMS

In considering the ratio of two functions $f(x)$ and $g(x)$, we sometimes wish to know the value

$$\lim_{x \to a} \frac{f(x)}{g(x)} \tag{1}$$

at a point a where $f(x)$ and $g(x)$ are both zero. L'Hôpital's rule is often a help, but the differentiation involved can be time-consuming, especially if the rule has to be applied several times to reach a determinate form. In many instances, the limit in (1) can be calculated more quickly if the functions involved have power series expansions about $x = a$. In fact, the ease and reliability of the kind of calculation we are about to illustrate contributed to the early popularity of power series. The theoretical justification of the technique is too long to discuss here, but the formal manipulations are worth learning by themselves.

Suppose, then, that the functions f and g both have series expansions in powers of $x - a$,

$$f(x) = f(a) + f'(a) \cdot (x - a) + \frac{f''(a)}{2!}(x - a)^2 + \cdots, \tag{2a}$$

$$g(x) = g(a) + g'(a) \cdot (x - a) + \frac{g''(a)}{2!}(x - a)^2 + \cdots, \tag{2b}$$

that are known to us and that converge in some interval $|x - a| < \delta$. We then proceed to calculate the limit (1), provided the limit exists, in the manner shown by the following examples.

EXAMPLE 1. Evaluate $\lim_{x \to 1} [(\ln x)/(x - 1)]$.

Solution. Let $f(x) = \ln x$, $g(x) = x - 1$. The Taylor series for $f(x)$, with $a = 1$, is found as follows:

$$\begin{aligned}
f(x) &= \ln x, & f(1) &= \ln 1 = 0, \\
f'(x) &= 1/x, & f'(1) &= 1, \\
f''(x) &= -1/x^2, & f''(1) &= -1,
\end{aligned}$$

so that

$$\ln x = 0 + (x - 1) - \tfrac{1}{2}(x - 1)^2 + \cdots$$

Hence

$$\frac{\ln x}{x - 1} = 1 - \tfrac{1}{2}(x - 1) + \cdots$$

and

$$\lim_{x \to 1} \frac{\ln x}{x - 1} = \lim_{x \to 1} [1 - \tfrac{1}{2}(x - 1) + \cdots] = 1.$$

EXAMPLE 2. Evaluate $\lim_{x \to 0} [(\sin x - \tan x)/x^3]$.

Solution. The Maclaurin series for $\sin x$ and $\tan x$, to terms in x^5, are

$$\sin x = x - \frac{x^3}{3!} + \frac{x^5}{5!} - \cdots,$$

$$\tan x = x + \frac{x^3}{3} + \frac{2x^5}{15} + \cdots$$

Hence

$$\sin x - \tan x = -\frac{x^3}{2} - \frac{x^5}{8} - \cdots$$

$$= x^3 \left(-\frac{1}{2} - \frac{x^2}{8} - \cdots \right),$$

and

$$\lim_{x \to 0} \frac{\sin x - \tan x}{x^3} = \lim_{x \to 0} \left(-\frac{1}{2} - \frac{x^2}{8} - \cdots \right) = -\frac{1}{2}.$$

When we apply series to compute the limit $\lim_{x \to 0} (1/\sin x - 1/x)$ of Example 7, Article 3–9, we not only compute the limit successfully, but also discover a nice approximation formula for $\csc x$.

EXAMPLE 3. Find

$$\lim_{x \to 0} \left(\frac{1}{\sin x} - \frac{1}{x} \right).$$

Solution

$$\frac{1}{\sin x} - \frac{1}{x} = \frac{x - \sin x}{x \sin x} = \frac{x - \left[x - \dfrac{x^3}{3!} + \dfrac{x^5}{5!} - \cdots \right]}{x \cdot \left[x - \dfrac{x^3}{3!} + \dfrac{x^5}{5!} - \cdots \right]}$$

$$= \frac{x^3 \left[\dfrac{1}{3!} - \dfrac{x^2}{5!} + \cdots \right]}{x^2 \left[1 - \dfrac{x^2}{3!} + \cdots \right]} = x \frac{\dfrac{1}{3!} - \dfrac{x^2}{5!} + \cdots}{1 - \dfrac{x^2}{3!} + \cdots}.$$

Therefore,

$$\lim_{x \to 0} \left(\frac{1}{\sin x} - \frac{1}{x} \right) = \lim_{x \to 0} \left[x \frac{\dfrac{1}{3!} - \dfrac{x^2}{5!} + \cdots}{1 - \dfrac{x^2}{3!} + \cdots} \right] = 0.$$

In fact, from the series expressions above we can see that if $|x|$ is small, then

$$\frac{1}{\sin x} - \frac{1}{x} \approx x \cdot \frac{1}{3!} = \frac{x}{6}$$

or

$$\csc x \approx \frac{1}{x} + \frac{x}{6}.$$

PROBLEMS

Use series to evaluate the limits in Problems 1 through 20.

1. $\displaystyle \lim_{h \to 0} \frac{\sin h}{h}$

2. $\displaystyle \lim_{x \to 0} \frac{e^x - (1 + x)}{x^2}$

3. $\displaystyle \lim_{t \to 0} \frac{1 - \cos t - \frac{1}{2}t^2}{t^4}$

4. $\displaystyle \lim_{x \to \infty} x \sin \frac{1}{x}$

5. $\displaystyle \lim_{x \to 0} \frac{x^2}{1 - \cosh x}$

6. $\displaystyle \lim_{h \to 0} \frac{(\sin h)/h - \cos h}{h^2}$

7. $\displaystyle \lim_{x \to 0} \frac{1 - \cos x}{\sin x}$

8. $\displaystyle \lim_{x \to 0} \frac{\sin x}{e^x - 1}$

9. $\displaystyle \lim_{z \to 0} \frac{\sin (z^2) - \sinh (z^2)}{z^6}$

10. $\displaystyle \lim_{t \to 0} \frac{\cos t - \cosh t}{t^2}$

11. $\displaystyle \lim_{x \to 0} \frac{\sin x - x + \dfrac{x^3}{6}}{x^5}$

12. $\displaystyle \lim_{x \to 0} \frac{e^x - e^{-x} - 2x}{x - \sin x}$

13. $\displaystyle \lim_{x \to 0} \frac{x - \tan^{-1} x}{x^3}$

14. $\displaystyle \lim_{x \to 0} \frac{\tan x - \sin x}{x^3 \cos x}$

15. $\displaystyle \lim_{x \to \infty} x^2(e^{-1/x^2} - 1)$

16. $\displaystyle \lim_{x \to 0} \frac{\ln (1 + x^2)}{1 - \cos x}$

17. $\displaystyle \lim_{x \to 0} \frac{\tan 3x}{x}$

18. $\displaystyle \lim_{x \to 1} \frac{\ln x^2}{x - 1}$

19. $\displaystyle \lim_{x \to \infty} \frac{x^{100}}{e^x}$

20. $\displaystyle \lim_{x \to 0} \left(\frac{1}{2 - 2 \cos x} - \frac{1}{x^2} \right)$

21. **a)** Prove that $\int_0^x e^{t^2} \, dt \to +\infty$ as $x \to +\infty$.

b) Find $\lim_{x \to \infty} x \int_0^x e^{t^2 - x^2} \, dt$

22. Find values of r and s such that

$$\lim_{x \to 0} (x^{-3} \sin 3x + rx^{-2} + s) = 0.$$

23. (*Calculator*) The approximation for $\csc x$ in Example 3 leads to the approximation $\sin x \approx 6x/(6 + x^2)$. Evaluate both sides of this approximation for $x = \pm 1.0, \pm 0.1$, and ± 0.01 radians. Try these values of x in the approximation $\sin x \approx x$. Which approximation appears to give better results?

16-13

CONVERGENCE OF POWER SERIES; INTEGRATION AND DIFFERENTIATION

We now know that some power series, like the Maclaurin series for $\sin x$, $\cos x$, and e^x, converge for all values of x, while others, like the series we derived for $\ln (1 + x)$ and $\tan^{-1} x$, converge only on finite intervals. But we learned all this by analyzing remainder formulas, and we have yet to face the question of how to investigate the convergence of a power series when there is no remainder formula to analyze. Moreover, all of the power series we have worked with have been Taylor series of functions for which we already had expressions in closed forms. What about other power series? Are they Taylor series, too, of functions otherwise unknown?

The first step in answering these questions is to note that a power series $\sum_{n=0}^{\infty} a_n x^n$ defines a function whenever it converges, namely, the function f whose value at each x is the number

$$f(x) = \sum_{n=0}^{\infty} a_n x^n. \tag{1}$$

We can then ask what kind of domain f has, how f is to be differentiated and integrated (if at all), whether f has a Taylor series, and, if it has, how its Taylor series is related to the defining series $\sum_{n=0}^{\infty} a_n x^n$.

The questions of what domain f has, and for what values the series (1) may be expected to converge, are answered by Theorem 1 and the discussion that follows it. We will prove Theorem 1, and then, after looking at examples, will proceed to Theorems 2 and 3, which answer the questions of whether f *can* be differentiated and integrated and *how* to do so when it can be. Theorem 3 also solves a problem that arose many chapters ago but that has remained unsolved until now: that of finding convenient expressions for evaluating integrals like

$$\int_0^1 \sin x^2 \, dx \qquad \text{and} \qquad \int_0^{0.5} \sqrt{1 + x^4} \, dx,$$

which frequently arise in applications. Finally, we will see that, in the interior of its domain of definition, the function f does have a Maclaurin series, and that this is none other than the defining series $\sum_{n=0}^{\infty} a_n x^n$.

Theorem 1. The convergence theorem for power series. *If a power series*

$$\sum_{n=0}^{\infty} a_n x^n = a_0 + a_1 x + a_2 x^2 + \cdots \tag{2}$$

converges for $x = c$ $(c \neq 0)$, then it converges absolutely for all $|x| < |c|$. If the series diverges for $x = d$, then it diverges for all $|x| > |d|$.

Proof. Suppose the series

$$\sum_{n=0}^{\infty} a_n c^n \tag{3}$$

converges. Then

$$\lim_{n \to \infty} a_n c^n = 0.$$

Hence, there is an index N such that

$$|a_n c^n| < 1 \qquad \text{for all} \quad n \geq N.$$

That is,

$$|a_n| < \frac{1}{|c|^n} \qquad \text{for} \quad n \geq N. \tag{4}$$

Now take any x such that $|x| < |c|$ and consider

$$|a_0| + |a_1 x| + \cdots + |a_{N-1} x^{N-1}| + |a_N x^N| + |a_{N+1} x^{N+1}| + \cdots$$

There is only a finite number of terms prior to $|a_N x^N|$ and their sum is finite. Starting with $|a_N x^N|$ and beyond, the terms are less than

$$\left|\frac{x}{c}\right|^N + \left|\frac{x}{c}\right|^{N+1} + \left|\frac{x}{c}\right|^{N+2} + \cdots \tag{5}$$

by virtue of the inequality (4). But the series in (5) is a geometric series with ratio $r = |x/c|$, which is less than one, since $|x| < |c|$. Hence the series (5) converges, so that the original series (3) converges absolutely. This proves the first half of the theorem.

The second half of the theorem involves nothing new. For if the series diverges at $x = d$ and converges at a value x_0 with $|x_0| > |d|$, we may take $c = x_0$ in the first half of the theorem and conclude that the series converges absolutely at d. But the series cannot both converge absolutely and diverge at one and the same time. Hence, if it diverges at d, it diverges for all $|x| > |d|$.   Q.E.D.

The significance of Theorem 1 is that a power series always behaves in exactly *one* of the following ways.

1. It converges at $x = 0$ and diverges everywhere else.

2. There is a positive number c such that the series diverges for $|x| > c$ but converges absolutely for $|x| < c$. It may or may not converge at either of the endpoints $x = c$ and $x = -c$.

3. It converges absolutely for every x.

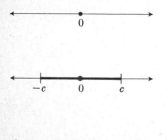

Figure 16–19

In Case 2, the set of points at which the series converges is a finite interval. We know from past examples that this interval may be open, half open, or closed, depending on the series in question. But no matter which kind of interval it is, c is called the *radius of convergence* of the series, and the convergence is absolute at every point in the interior of the interval. The interval is called the *interval of convergence*. If a power series converges absolutely for all values of x, we say that its radius of convergence is infinite. If it converges only at $x = 0$, we say that the radius of convergence is 0.

As examples of power series whose radii of convergence are infinite, we have the Taylor series of $\sin x$, $\cos x$, and e^x. These series converge for every value of $c = 2x$, and therefore converge absolutely for every value of x.

As examples of series whose radii of convergence are finite we have:

Series	Interval of convergence
$\dfrac{1}{1-x} = 1 + x + x^2 + \cdots$	$-1 < x < 1$
$\ln(1+x) = x - \dfrac{x^2}{2} + \dfrac{x^3}{3} - \dfrac{x^4}{4} + \cdots$	$-1 < x \le 1$
$\tan^{-1} x = x - \dfrac{x^3}{3} + \dfrac{x^5}{5} - \cdots$	$-1 \le x \le 1$

The interval of convergence of a power series

$$\sum_{n=0}^{\infty} a_n x^n$$

can often be found by applying the ratio test or the root test to the series of absolute values,

$$\sum_{n=0}^{\infty} |a_n x^n|.$$

Thus, if

$$\rho = \lim_{n \to \infty} \left| \frac{a_{n+1} x^{n+1}}{a_n x^n} \right|$$

or if

$$\rho = \lim_{n \to \infty} \sqrt[n]{|a_n x^n|},$$

then,

a) $\sum |a_n x^n|$ converges at all values of x for which $\rho < 1$;

b) $\sum |a_n x^n|$ diverges at all values of x for which $\rho > 1$;

c) $\sum |a_n x^n|$ may either converge or diverge at a value of x for which $\rho = 1$.

How do these three alternatives translate into statements about the series $\sum a_n x^n$? Case (a) says that $\sum a_n x^n$ converges absolutely at all values of x for which $\rho < 1$. Case (c) does not tell us anything more about the series $\sum a_n x^n$ than it does about the series $\sum |a_n x^n|$. Either series might converge or diverge at a value of x for which $\rho = 1$. In Case (b), we can actually conclude that $\sum a_n x^n$ diverges at all values of x for which $\rho > 1$. The argument goes like this: As you may recall from the discussions in Article 16–5, the fact that ρ is greater than 1 means that either

$$0 < |a_n x^n| < |a_{n+1} x^{n+1}| < |a_{n+2} x^{n+2}| < \cdots$$

or

$$\sqrt[n]{|a_n x^n|} > 1$$

for n sufficiently large. Thus the terms of the series do not approach 0 as n becomes infinite, and the series diverges *with or without absolute values*, by the nth-term test.

Therefore, the ratio and root tests, when successfully applied to $\sum |a_n x^n|$, lead us to the following conclusions about $\sum a_n x^n$:

A) $\sum a_n x^n$ converges absolutely for all values of x for which $\rho < 1$;

B) $\sum a_n x^n$ diverges at all values of x for which $\rho > 1$;

C) $\sum a_n x^n$ may either converge or diverge at a value of x for which $\rho = 1$. Another test is needed.

EXAMPLE 1. Find the interval of convergence of

$$\sum_{n=1}^{\infty} \frac{x^n}{n}. \tag{6}$$

Solution. We apply the ratio test to the series of absolute values, and find

$$\rho = \lim_{n \to \infty} \left| \frac{x^{n+1}}{n+1} \cdot \frac{n}{x^n} \right| = |x|.$$

Therefore the original series converges absolutely if $|x| < 1$ and diverges if $|x| > 1$. When $x = +1$, the series becomes

$$1 + \tfrac{1}{2} + \tfrac{1}{3} + \tfrac{1}{4} + \cdots,$$

which diverges. When $x = -1$, the series becomes

$$-(1 - \tfrac{1}{2} + \tfrac{1}{3} - \tfrac{1}{4} + \cdots),$$

which converges, by Leibnitz's Theorem. Therefore the series (6) converges for $-1 \le x < 1$ and diverges for all other values of x.

EXAMPLE 2.   For what values of x does the series

$$\sum_{n=1}^{\infty} \frac{(2x - 5)^n}{n^2}$$

converge?

Solution.   We treat the series as a power series in the variable $2x - 5$. An application of the root test to the series of absolute values yields

$$\rho = \lim_{n \to \infty} \sqrt[n]{\left| \frac{(2x - 5)^n}{n^2} \right|} = \lim_{n \to \infty} \frac{|2x - 5|}{\sqrt[n]{n^2}} = \frac{|2x - 5|}{1} = |2x - 5|.$$

The series converges absolutely for

$$|2x - 5| < 1 \qquad \text{or} \qquad -1 < 2x - 5 < 1$$

or

$$4 < 2x < 6 \qquad \text{or} \qquad 2 < x < 3.$$

When $x = 2$, the series is $\sum_{n=1}^{\infty} [(-1)^n/n^2]$, which converges.

When $x = 3$, the series is $\sum_{n=1}^{\infty} [(1)^n/n^2]$, which converges. Therefore, the interval of convergence is $2 \le x \le 3$.

Sometimes the comparison test does as well as any.

EXAMPLE 3.   For what values of x does

$$\sum_{n=1}^{\infty} \frac{\cos^n x}{n!}$$

converge?

Solution.   For every value of x,

$$\left| \frac{\cos^n x}{n!} \right| \le \frac{1}{n!}.$$

The series converges for every value of x.

The next theorem says that a function defined by a power series has derivatives of all orders at every point in the interior of its interval of convergence. The derivatives can be obtained as power series by differentiating the terms of the original series. The first derivative is obtained by differentiating the terms of the original series once:

$$\frac{d}{dx} \sum_{n=0}^{\infty} (a_n x^n) = \sum_{n=0}^{\infty} \frac{d}{dx} (a_n x^n) = \sum_{n=0}^{\infty} n a_n x^{n-1}.$$

For the second derivative, the terms are differentiated again, and so on. We state the theorem without proof, and go directly to the examples.

Theorem 2. *The term-by-term differentiation theorem. If* $f(x) = \sum_{n=0}^{\infty} a_n x^n$ *converges on the open interval* $(-c, c)$, *then,*

1. $\displaystyle\sum_{n=0}^{\infty} n a_n x^{n-1}$ *converges on* $(-c, c)$;

2. $f(x)$ *is differentiable on* $(-c, c)$; *and*

3. $f'(x) = \displaystyle\sum_{n=0}^{\infty} n a_n x^{n-1}$ *on* $(-c, c)$.

Ostensibly, Theorem 2 mentions only f and f'. But note that f' has the same radius of convergence that f has, so that the theorem applies equally well to f', saying that it has a derivative f'' on $(-c, c)$. This in turn implies that f'' is differentiable on $(-c, c)$, and so on. Thus, if $f(x) = \sum_{n=0}^{\infty} a_n x^n$ converges on $(-c, c)$, it has derivatives of all orders at every point of $(-c, c)$.

EXAMPLE 4. The relation $(d/dx)(\sin x) = \cos x$ is easily checked by differentiating the series for $\sin x$ term by term:

$$\sin x = x - \frac{x^3}{3!} + \frac{x^5}{5!} - \frac{x^7}{7!} + \cdots$$

$$\frac{d}{dx}(\sin x) = 1 - \frac{x^2}{2!} + \frac{x^4}{4!} - \frac{x^6}{6!} + \cdots$$

$$= \cos x.$$

Convergence at one or both endpoints of the interval of convergence of a power series may be lost in the process of differentiation. That is why Theorem 2 mentions only the *open* interval $(-c, c)$.

EXAMPLE 5. The series $f(x) = \sum_{n=1}^{\infty} (x^n/n)$ of Example 1 converges for $-1 \leq x < 1$. The series of derivatives

$$f'(x) = \sum_{n=1}^{\infty} x^{n-1} = 1 + x + x^2 + x^3 + \cdots$$

is a geometric series that converges only for $-1 < x < 1$. The series diverges at the endpoint $x = -1$, as well as at the endpoint $x = 1$.

Example 5 shows, however, that when the terms of a series are integrated, the resulting series may converge at an endpoint that was not a point of convergence before. The justification for term-by-term integration of a series is the following theorem, which we also state without proof.

Theorem 3. The term-by-term integration theorem. *If $f(x) = \sum_{n=0}^{\infty} a_n x^n$ converges on the open interval $(-c, c)$, then,*

1. $\displaystyle\sum_{n=0}^{n=\infty} \frac{a_n x^{n+1}}{n+1}$ *converges on* $(-c, c)$;

2. $\displaystyle\int f(x)\, dx$ *exists for x in* $(-c, c)$;

3. $\displaystyle\int f(x)\, dx = \sum_{n=0}^{n=\infty} \frac{a_n x^{n+1}}{n+1} + C$ *on* $(-c, c)$.

EXAMPLE 6. The series

$$\frac{1}{1+t} = 1 - t + t^2 - t^3 \cdots$$

converges on the open interval $-1 < t < 1$. Therefore,

$$\ln(1+x) = \int_0^x \frac{1}{1+t}\, dt = t - \frac{t^2}{2} + \frac{t^3}{3} - \frac{t^4}{4} + \cdots \Big]_0^x, \qquad -1 < x < 1,$$

$$= x - \frac{x^2}{2} + \frac{x^3}{3} - \frac{x^4}{4} + \cdots$$

As you know, the latter series also converges at $x = 1$, but that was not guaranteed by the theorem.

EXAMPLE 7. By replacing t by t^2 in the series of Example 6, we obtain

$$\frac{1}{1+t^2} = 1 - t^2 + t^4 - t^6 + \cdots, \qquad -1 < t < 1.$$

Therefore

$$\tan^{-1} x = \int_0^x \frac{1}{1+t^2}\, dt = t - \frac{t^3}{3} + \frac{t^5}{5} - \frac{t^7}{7} + \cdots \Big]_0^x$$

$$= x - \frac{x^3}{3} + \frac{x^5}{5} - \frac{x^7}{7} + \cdots, \qquad -1 < x < 1.$$

This is not as refined a result as the one we obtained in Article 16–10, where we were able to show that the interval of convergence was $-1 \le x \le 1$ by analyzing a remainder. But the result here is obtained more quickly.

EXAMPLE 8. Express

$$\int \sin x^2\, dx$$

as a power series.

Solution. From the series for $\sin x$ we obtain

$$\sin x^2 = x^2 - \frac{x^6}{3!} + \frac{x^{10}}{5!} - \frac{x^{14}}{7!} + \cdots, \qquad -\infty < x < \infty.$$

Therefore,

$$\int \sin^2 dx = C + \frac{x^3}{3} - \frac{x^7}{7 \cdot 3!} + \frac{x^{11}}{11 \cdot 5!} - \frac{x^{15}}{15 \cdot 7!} + \cdots, \qquad -\infty < x < \infty.$$

EXAMPLE 9. Estimate $\int_0^1 \sin x^2 \, dx$ with an error of less than 0.001.

Solution. From the indefinite integral in Example 8,

$$\int_0^1 \sin x^2 \, dx = \frac{1}{3} - \frac{1}{7 \cdot 3!} + \frac{1}{11 \cdot 5!} - \frac{1}{15 \cdot 7!} + \frac{1}{19 \cdot 9!} - \cdots$$

The series alternates, and we find by trial that

$$\frac{1}{11 \cdot 5!} \approx 0.00076$$

is the first term to be numerically less than 0.001. The sum of the preceding two terms gives

$$\int_0^1 \sin x^2 \, dx \approx \frac{1}{3} - \frac{1}{42} \approx 0.310.$$

With two more terms we could estimate

$$\int_0^1 \sin x^2 \, dx \approx 0.310268$$

with an error of less than 10^{-6}; and with only one term beyond that we have

$$\int_0^1 \sin x^2 \, dx \approx \frac{1}{3} - \frac{1}{42} + \frac{1}{1320} - \frac{1}{75600} + \frac{1}{6894720} \approx 0.310268303,$$

with an error of less than 10^{-9}. To guarantee this accuracy with the error formula for the trapezoid rule would require using about 13,000 subintervals.

EXAMPLE 10. Estimate $\int_0^{0.5} \sqrt{1 + x^4} \, dx$ with an error of less than 10^{-4}.

Solution. The binomial expansion of $(1 + x^4)^{1/2}$ is

$$(1 + x^4)^{1/2} = 1 + \tfrac{1}{4}x^4 - \tfrac{1}{8}x^8 + \cdots,$$

a series whose terms alternate in sign after the second term. Therefore,

$$\int_0^{0.5} \sqrt{1 + x^4} \, dx = x + \frac{1}{2 \cdot 5} x^5 - \frac{1}{8 \cdot 9} x^9 + \cdots \Big]_0^{0.5}$$

$$= 1 + 0.0031 - 0.00003 + \cdots$$

$$\approx 1.0031,$$

with an error of magnitude less than 0.00003.

At the beginning of this article we asked whether a function

$$f(x) = \sum_{n=0}^{\infty} a_n x^n$$

defined by a convergent power series has a Taylor series. We can now answer that a function defined by a power series with a radius of convergence $c > 0$ has a Maclaurin series that converges to the function at every point of $(-c, c)$. Why? Because the Maclaurin series for the function $f(x) = \sum_{n=0}^{\infty} a_n x^n$ is the series $\sum_{n=0}^{\infty} a_n x^n$ itself. To see this, we differentiate

$$f(x) = a_0 + a_1 x + a_2 x^2 + \cdots + a_n x^n + \cdots$$

term by term and substitute $x = 0$ in each derivative $f^{(n)}(x)$. This produces

$$f^{(n)}(0) = n! \, a_n \quad \text{or} \quad a_n = \frac{f^{(n)}(0)}{n!}$$

for every n. Thus,

$$f(x) = \sum_{n=0}^{\infty} a_n x^n = \sum_{n=0}^{\infty} \frac{f^{(n)}(0)}{n!} x^n, \qquad -c < x < c. \tag{7}$$

An immediate consequence of this is that series like

$$x \sin x = x^2 - \frac{x^4}{3!} + \frac{x^6}{5!} - \frac{x^8}{7!} + \cdots,$$

and

$$x^2 e^x = x^2 + x^3 + \frac{x^4}{2!} + \frac{x^5}{3!} + \cdots,$$

which are obtained by multiplying Maclaurin series by powers of x, as well as series obtained by integration and differentiation of power series, are themselves the Maclaurin series of the functions they represent.

Another consequence of (7) is that, if two power series $\sum_{n=0}^{\infty} a_n x^n$ and $\sum_{n=0}^{\infty} b_n x^n$ are equal for all values of x in an open interval that contains the origin $x = 0$, then $a_n = b_n$ for every n. For if

$$f(x) = \sum_{n=0}^{\infty} a_n x^n = \sum_{n=0}^{\infty} b_n x^n, \qquad -c < x < c,$$

then a_n and b_n are both equal to $f^{(n)}(0)/n!$.

PROBLEMS

In Problems 1–20, find the interval of absolute convergence. If the interval is finite, determine whether the series converges at each endpoint.

1. $\displaystyle\sum_{n=0}^{\infty} x^n$

2. $\displaystyle\sum_{n=0}^{\infty} n^2 x^n$

3. $\displaystyle\sum_{n=1}^{\infty} \frac{nx^n}{2^n}$

4. $\displaystyle\sum_{n=0}^{\infty} \frac{(2x)^n}{n!}$

5. $\displaystyle\sum_{n=0}^{\infty} \frac{(-1)^n x^{2n+1}}{(2n+1)!}$

6. $\displaystyle\sum_{n=1}^{\infty} (-1)^{n-1} \frac{(x-1)^n}{n}$

7. $\displaystyle\sum_{n=0}^{\infty} \frac{n^2}{2^n} (x+2)^n$

8. $\displaystyle\sum_{n=0}^{\infty} \frac{x^{2n+1}}{2n+1}$

9. $\displaystyle\sum_{n=0}^{\infty} (-1)^n \frac{x^{2n+1}}{2n+1}$

10. $\displaystyle\sum_{n=1}^{\infty} \frac{(x-2)^n}{n^2}$

11. $\displaystyle\sum_{n=0}^{\infty} \frac{\cos nx}{2^n}$

12. $\displaystyle\sum_{n=1}^{\infty} \frac{2^n x^n}{n^5}$

13. $\displaystyle\sum_{n=0}^{\infty} \frac{x^n e^n}{n+1}$

14. $\displaystyle\sum_{n=1}^{\infty} \frac{(\cos x)^n}{n^n}$

15. $\displaystyle\sum_{n=0}^{\infty} n^n x^n$

16. $\displaystyle\sum_{n=0}^{\infty} \frac{(3x+6)^n}{n!}$

17. $\displaystyle\sum_{n=1}^{\infty} (-2)^n (n+1)(x-1)^n$

18. $\displaystyle\sum_{n=1}^{\infty} \frac{(-1)^{n+1}(x-2)^n}{n \cdot 2^n}$

19. $\displaystyle\sum_{n=0}^{\infty} \left(\frac{x^2-1}{2}\right)^n$

20. $\displaystyle\sum_{n=1}^{\infty} \frac{(x+3)^{n-1}}{n}$

21. Find the sum of the series in Problem 16.

22. When the series of Problem 19 converges, to what does it converge?

23. Use series to verify that:

a) $\dfrac{d}{dx}(\cos x) = -\sin x$ **b)** $\displaystyle\int_0^x \cos t \, dt = \sin x$

c) $y = e^x$ is a solution of the equation $y' = y$.

24. Obtain the Maclaurin series for $1/(1 + x)^2$ from the series for $-1/(1 + x)$.

25. Use the Maclaurin series $1/(1 - x^2)$ to obtain a series for $2x/(1 - x^2)^2$.

26. Use the identity $\sin^2 x = (1 - \cos 2x)/2$ to obtain a series for $\sin^2 x$. Then differentiate this series to obtain a series for $2 \sin x \cos x$. Check that this is the series for $\sin 2x$.

(*Calculator*) In Problems 27 through 34, use series and a calculator to estimate each integral with an error of magnitude less than 0.001.

27. $\displaystyle\int_0^{0.2} \sin x^2 \, dx$ **28.** $\displaystyle\int_0^{0.1} \tan^{-1} x \, dx$

29. $\displaystyle\int_0^{0.1} x^2 e^{-x^2} \, dx$ **30.** $\displaystyle\int_0^{0.1} \dfrac{\tan^{-1} x}{x} \, dx$

31. $\displaystyle\int_0^{0.4} \dfrac{1 - e^{-x}}{x} \, dx$ **32.** $\displaystyle\int_0^{0.1} \dfrac{\ln(1 + x)}{x} \, dx$

33. $\displaystyle\int_0^{0.1} \dfrac{1}{\sqrt{1 + x^4}} \, dx$ **34.** $\displaystyle\int_0^{0.25} \sqrt[3]{1 + x^2} \, dx$

35. (*Calculator*) **a)** Obtain a power series for

$$\sinh^{-1} x = \int_0^x \frac{dt}{\sqrt{1 + t^2}}.$$

b) Use the result of (a) to estimate $\sinh^{-1} 0.25$ to three decimal places.

36. (*Calculator*) Estimate $\int_0^1 \cos x^2 \, dx$ with an error of less than one millionth.

37. Show by example that there are power series that converge only at $x = 0$.

38. Show by examples that the convergence of a series at an endpoint of its interval of convergence may be either conditional or absolute.

39. Let r be any positive number. Use Theorem 1 to show that if $\sum_{n=0}^\infty a_n x^n$ converges for $-r < x < r$, then it converges absolutely for $-r < x < r$.

40. Use the ratio test to show that the binomial series converges for $|x| < 1$. (This still does not show that the series converges to $(1 + x)^m$.)

REVIEW QUESTIONS AND EXERCISES

1. Define "sequence," "series," "sequence of partial sums of a series."

2. Define "convergence" (a) of a sequence, (b) of an infinite series.

3. Which of the following statements are true, and which are false?

a) If a sequence does not converge, then it diverges.

b) If a sequence $\{n, f(n)\}$ does not converge, then $f(n)$ tends to infinity as n does.

c) If a series does not converge, then its nth term does not approach zero as n tends to infinity.

d) If the nth term of a series does not approach zero as n tends to infinity, then the series diverges.

e) If a sequence $\{n, f(n)\}$ converges, then there is a number L such that $f(n)$ lies within 1 unit of L (i) for all values of n, (ii) for all but a finite number of values of n.

f) If all partial sums of a series are less than some constant L, then the series converges.

g) If a series converges, then its partial sums s_n are bounded (that is, $m \le s_n \le M$ for some constants m and M).

4. List three tests for convergence (or divergence) of an infinite series.

5. Under what circumstances do you know that a bounded sequence converges?

6. Define "absolute convergence" and "conditional convergence." Give examples of series that are (a) absolutely convergent, (b) conditionally convergent.

7. State Taylor's theorem, with remainder, giving two different expressions for the remainder.

8. It can be shown (though not very simply) that the function f defined by

$$f(x) = \begin{cases} 0 & \text{when} \quad x = 0, \\ e^{-1/x^2} & \text{when} \quad x \ne 0 \end{cases}$$

is everywhere continuous, together with its derivatives of all orders. At 0, the derivatives are all equal to 0.

a) Write the Taylor series expansion of f in powers of x.

b) What is the remainder $R_n(x, 0)$ for this function? Does the Taylor series for f converge to $f(x)$ at some value of x different from zero? Give a reason for your answer.

9. If a Taylor series in powers of $x - a$ is to be used for the numerical evaluation of a function, what is necessary or desirable in the choice of a?

10. Write the Taylor series in powers of $x - a$ and $y - b$ for a function f of two variables x and y, about the point (a, b).

11. Describe a method that may be useful in finding $\lim_{x \to a} f(x)/g(x)$ if $f(a) = g(a) = 0$. Illustrate.

12. What tests may be used to find the interval of convergence of a power series? Do they also work at the endpoints of the interval? Illustrate with examples.

13. What test is usually used to decide whether a given alternating series converges? Give examples of convergent and divergent alternating series.

MISCELLANEOUS PROBLEMS

1. Find explicitly the nth partial sum of the series $\sum_{n=2}^{\infty} \ln (1 - 1/n^2)$, and thereby determine whether the series converges.

2. Evaluate $\sum_{k=2}^{\infty} 1/(k^2 - 1)$ by finding the nth partial sum and taking the limit as n becomes infinite.

3. Prove that the sequence $\{x_n\}$ and the series $\sum_{k=1}^{\infty} (x_{k+1} - x_k)$ both converge or both diverge.

4. In an attempt to find a root of the equation $x = f(x)$, a first approximation x_1 is estimated from the graphs of $y = x$ and $y = f(x)$. Then $x_2, x_3, \ldots, x_n, \ldots$ are computed successively from the formula $x_n = f(x_{n-1})$. If the points x_1, $x_2, \ldots, x_n, \ldots$ all lie on an interval $a \le x \le b$ on which $f(x)$ has a derivative such that $|f'(x)| < M < 1$, show that the sequence $\{x_n\}$ converges to a root of the given equation.

5. Assuming $|x| > 1$, show that

$$\frac{1}{1 - x} = -\frac{1}{x} - \frac{1}{x^2} - \frac{1}{x^3} - \cdots$$

6. (a) Find the expansion, in powers of x, of $x^2/(1 + x)$. (b) Does the series expansion of $x^2/(1 + x)$ in powers of x converge when $x = 2$? (Give a brief reason.)

7. Obtain the Maclaurin series expansion for $\sin^{-1} x$ by integrating the series for $(1 - t^2)^{-1/2}$ from 0 to x. Find the intervals of convergence of these series.

8. Obtain the Maclaurin series for $\ln (x + \sqrt{x^2 + 1}) = \sinh^{-1} x$ by integrating the series for $(1 + t^2)^{-1/2}$ from 0 to x. Find the intervals of convergence of these two series.

9. Obtain the first four terms in the Maclaurin series for $e^{\sin x}$ by substituting the series for $y = \sin x$ in the series for e^y.

10. Assuming $|x| > 1$, obtain the expansions

$$\tan^{-1} x = \frac{\pi}{2} - \frac{1}{x} + \frac{1}{3x^3} - \frac{1}{5x^5} + \cdots, \qquad x > 1,$$

$$\tan^{-1} x = -\frac{\pi}{2} - \frac{1}{x} + \frac{1}{3x^3} - \frac{1}{5x^5} + \cdots, \qquad x < -1,$$

by integrating the series

$$\frac{1}{1 + t^2} = \frac{1}{t^2} \cdot \frac{1}{1 + (1/t^2)} = \frac{1}{t^2} - \frac{1}{t^4} + \frac{1}{t^6} - \frac{1}{t^8} + \cdots$$

from x (> 1) to $+\infty$ or from $-\infty$ to x (< -1).

11. (a) Obtain the Maclaurin series, through the term in x^6, for $\ln (\cos x)$ by substituting the series for $y = 1 - \cos x$ in

the series for $\ln (1 - y)$. (b) Use the result of part (a) to estimate $\int_0^{0.1} \ln (\cos x) \, dx$ to five decimal places.

12. Compute $\int_0^1 [(\sin x)/x] \, dx$ to three decimal places.

13. Compute $\int_0^1 e^{-x^2} \, dx$ to three decimal places.

14. Expand the function $f(x) = \sqrt{1 + x^2}$ in powers of $(x - 1)$, obtaining three nonvanishing terms.

15. Expand the function $f(x) = 1/(1 - x)$ in powers of $(x - 2)$, and find the interval of convergence.

16. Find the first three nonvanishing terms of the Maclaurin series of $\tan x$.

17. Expand $f(x) = 1/(x + 1)$ in powers of $(x - 3)$.

18. Expand $\cos x$ in powers of $(x - \pi/3)$.

19. Find the first three terms of the Taylor series expansion of the function $1/x$ about the point π.

20. Let f and g be functions satisfying the following conditions: (a) $f(0) = 1$, (b) $f'(x) = g(x)$, $g'(x) = f(x)$, (c) $g(0) = 0$. Estimate $f(1)$ to three decimal places.

21. Suppose $f(x) = \sum_{n=0}^{\infty} a_n x^n$. Prove that (a) if $f(x)$ is an even function, then $a_1 = a_3 = a_5 = \cdots = 0$; (b) if $f(x)$ is an odd function, then $a_0 = a_2 = a_4 = \cdots = 0$.

22. Find the first four terms (up to x^3) of the Maclaurin series of $f(x) = e^{(e^x)}$.

23. Estimate the error involved in using $x - x^2/2$ as an approximation to $\ln (1 + x)$ for values of x between 0 and 0.2, inclusive.

24. If $(1 + x)^{1/3}$ is replaced by $1 + x/3$ and $0 \le x \le \frac{1}{10}$, what estimate can be given for the error?

25. Use series to find

$$\lim_{x \to 0} \frac{\ln (1 - x) - \sin x}{1 - \cos^2 x}.$$

26. Find $\lim_{x \to 0} [(\sin x)/x]^{1/x^2}$.

27. Does the series $\sum_{n=1}^{\infty} \operatorname{sech} n$ converge? Why?

28. Does $\sum_{n=1}^{\infty} (-1)^n \tanh n$ converge? Why?

Establish the convergence or divergence of the series whose nth terms are given in Problems 29–40.

29. $\dfrac{1}{\ln (n + 1)}$

30. $\dfrac{n}{2(n + 1)(n + 2)}$

31. $\dfrac{\sqrt{n + 1} - \sqrt{n}}{\sqrt{n}}$

32. $\dfrac{1}{n(\ln n)^2}$, $\quad n \ge 2$

33. $\dfrac{1 + (-2)^{n-1}}{2^n}$

34. $\dfrac{n}{1000n^2 + 1}$

35. $e^n/n!$

36. $\dfrac{1}{n\sqrt{n^2+1}}$

37. $\dfrac{1}{n^{1+1/n}}$

38. $\dfrac{1\cdot3\cdot5\cdots(2n-1)}{2\cdot4\cdot6\cdots(2n)}$

39. $\dfrac{n^2}{n^3+1}$

40. $\dfrac{n+1}{n!}$

41. Find the sum of the convergent series

$$\sum_{n=1}^{\infty}\frac{1}{(n+1)(n+2)}.$$

42. (a) Suppose $a_1, a_2, a_3, \ldots, a_n$ are positive numbers satisfying the following conditions:

i) $a_1 \geq a_2 \geq a_3 \geq \cdots$;
ii) the series $a_2 + a_4 + a_8 + a_{16} + \cdots$ diverges.

Show that the series

$$\frac{a_1}{1}+\frac{a_2}{2}+\frac{a_3}{3}+\cdots$$

diverges. (b) Use the result above to show that

$$\sum_{n=2}^{\infty}\frac{1}{n\ln n}$$

diverges.

43. Given $a_n \neq 1$, $a_n > 0$, $\sum a_n$ converges. (a) Show that $\sum a_n^2$ converges. (b) Does $\sum a_n/(1-a_n)$ converge? (c) Does $\sum \ln(1+a_n)$ converge? Explain.

44. Show that $\sum_{n=2}^{\infty} 1/[n(\ln n)^k]$ converges for $k > 1$.

In Problems 45–52, find the interval of convergence of each series. Test for convergence at the endpoints if the interval is finite.

45. $1 + \dfrac{x+2}{3\cdot1} + \dfrac{(x+2)^2}{3^2\cdot2} + \cdots + \dfrac{(x+2)^n}{3^n\cdot n} + \cdots$

46. $1 + \dfrac{(x-1)^2}{2!} + \dfrac{(x-1)^4}{4!} + \cdots + \dfrac{(x-1)^{2n-2}}{(2n-2)!} + \cdots$

47. $\displaystyle\sum_{n=1}^{\infty}\frac{x^n}{n^n}$

48. $\displaystyle\sum_{n=1}^{\infty}\frac{n!\,x^n}{n^n}$

49. $\displaystyle\sum_{n=0}^{\infty}\frac{n+1}{2n+1}\frac{(x-3)^n}{2^n}$

50. $\displaystyle\sum_{n=0}^{\infty}\frac{n+1}{2n+1}\frac{(x-2)^n}{3^n}$

51. $\displaystyle\sum_{n=1}^{\infty}\frac{(-1)^{n-1}(x-1)^n}{n^2}$

52. $\displaystyle\sum_{n=1}^{\infty}\frac{x^n}{n}$

Determine *all* the values of x for which the following series converge:

53. $\displaystyle\sum_{n=1}^{\infty}\frac{(x-2)^{3n}}{n!},$

54. $\displaystyle\sum_{n=1}^{\infty}\frac{2^n(\sin x)^n}{n^2},$

55. $\displaystyle\sum_{n=1}^{\infty}\frac{1}{n}\left(\frac{x-1}{x}\right)^n.$

56. A function is defined by the power series

$$y = 1 + \frac{1}{6}x^3 + \frac{1}{180}x^6 + \cdots + \frac{1\cdot4\cdot7\cdots(3n-2)}{(3n)!}x^{3n}+\cdots$$

a) Find the interval of convergence of the series.
b) Show that there exist two constants a and b such that the function so defined satisfies a differential equation of the form $y'' = x^a y + b$.

57. If $a_n > 0$ and the series $\sum_{n=1}^{\infty} a_n$ converges, prove that $\sum_{n=1}^{\infty} a_n/(1+a_n)$ converges.

58. If $1 > a_n > 0$ and $\sum_{n=1}^{\infty} a_n$ converges, prove that $\sum_{n=1}^{\infty} \ln(1-a_n)$ converges. [*Hint.* First show that $|\ln(1-a_n)| \leq a_n/(1-a_n)$; then apply the answer to Problem 43(b).]

59. An infinite product, indicated by $\prod_{n=1}^{\infty}(1+a_n)$, is said to converge if the series $\sum_{n=1}^{\infty} \ln(1+a_n)$ converges. (The series is the natural logarithm of the product.) Prove that the product converges if every $a_n > -1$ and $\sum_{n=1}^{\infty}|a_n|$ converges. [*Hint.* Show that

$$|\ln(1+a_n)| \leq \frac{|a_n|}{1-|a_n|} < 2|a_n|$$

when $|a_n| < \tfrac{1}{2}$.]

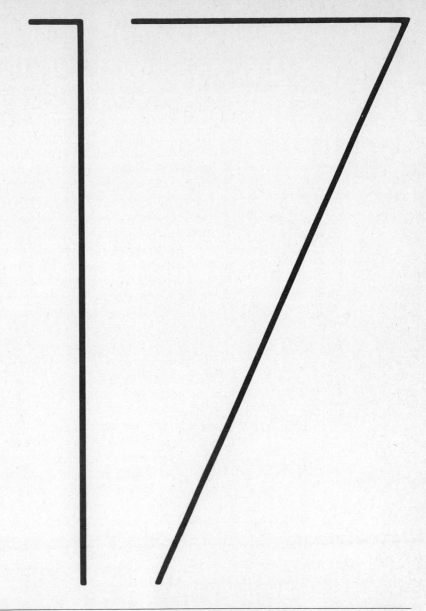

COMPLEX NUMBERS AND FUNCTIONS

17–1

INVENTED NUMBER SYSTEMS

In this chapter we shall discuss complex numbers. These are expressions of the form $a + ib$, where a and b are "real" numbers and i is a symbol for $\sqrt{-1}$. Unfortunately, the words "real" and "imaginary" have connotations that somehow place $\sqrt{-1}$ in a less favorable position than $\sqrt{2}$ in our minds. As a matter of fact, a good deal of imagination, in the sense of *inventiveness*, has been required to construct the *real* number system, which forms the basis of the calculus we have studied thus far. In this article we shall review the various stages of this invention. The further invention of a complex number system does not then seem to be so strange. It is fitting for us to study such a system, since modern engineering has found therein a convenient language for describing vibratory motion, harmonic oscillation, damped vibrations, alternating currents, and other wave phenomena.

The earliest stage of development of man's number consciousness was the recognition of the *counting numbers* 1, 2, 3, ..., which we now call the *natural numbers*, or the *positive integers*. Certain simple arithmetical operations can be performed with these numbers without getting outside the system. That is, the system of positive integers is *closed* with respect to the operations of *addition* and *multiplication*. By this we mean that, if m and n are any positive integers, then

$$m + n = p \qquad \text{and} \qquad mn = q \tag{1}$$

are also positive integers. Given the two positive integers on the *left side* of either equation in (1), we can find the corresponding positive integer on the right. More than this, we may sometimes specify the positive integers m and p and find a positive integer n such that $m + n = p$. For instance, $3 + n = 7$ can be *solved* when the only numbers we know are the positive integers. But the equation $7 + n = 3$ cannot be solved unless the number system is enlarged. Man therefore used *imagination* and invented the number concepts that we denote by zero and the *negative* integers. In a civilization that recognizes all the integers

$$\ldots, -3, -2, -1, 0, 1, 2, 3, \ldots, \tag{2}$$

an educated person may always find the missing integer that solves the equation $m + n = p$ when given the other two integers in the equation.

Suppose our educated people also know how to multiply any two integers of the set in (2). If, in Eq. (1), they are given m and q, they discover that sometimes they can find n and sometimes they can't. If their *imagination* is still in good working order, they may be inspired to invent still more numbers and introduce fractions, which are just ordered pairs m/n of integers m and n. The number zero has special properties that may bother them for a while, but they ultimately discover that it is handy to have all ratios of integers m/n, excluding only those having zero in the denominator. This system, called the set of *rational numbers*, is now rich enough for them to perform the so-called *rational operations* of:

1. **a)** addition   2. **a)** multiplication
   b) subtraction   **b)** division

on any two numbers in the system, *except that they cannot divide by zero*.

The geometry of the unit square (Fig. 17–1) and the Pythagorean Theorem showed that they could construct a geometric line segment which, in terms of some basic unit of length, has length equal to $\sqrt{2}$. Thus they could solve the equation

$$x^2 = 2$$

by a geometric construction. But then they discovered that the line segment representing $\sqrt{2}$ and the line segment representing the unit of length 1 were incommensurable quantities. This means that the ratio $\sqrt{2}/1$ cannot be expressed as the ratio of two *integral* multiples of some other, presumably more fundamental, unit of length. That is, our educated people could not find a rational number solution of the equation $x^2 = 2$.

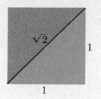

17–1 Segments of irrational length can be constructed with straightedge and compass.

There is a nice algebraic argument that there is no rational number whose square is 2. Suppose that there were such a rational number. Then we could find integers p and q with no common factor other than 1, and such that

$$p^2 = 2q^2. \tag{3}$$

Since p and q are integers, p must then be even, say $p = 2p_1$, where p_1 is an integer. This leads to $2p_1^2 = q^2$, which says that q must also be even, say $q = 2q_1$, where q_1 is also an integer. But this is contrary to our choice of p and q as integers having no common factor other than unity. Hence there is no rational number whose square is 2.

Our educated people *could*, however, get a *sequence* of rational numbers

$$\frac{1}{1}, \ \frac{7}{5}, \ \frac{41}{29}, \ \frac{239}{169}, \ \dots, \tag{4}$$

whose squares form a sequence

$$\frac{1}{1}, \ \frac{49}{25}, \ \frac{1681}{841}, \ \frac{57{,}121}{28{,}561}, \ \dots, \tag{5}$$

which converges to 2 as its *limit*. This time their *imagination* suggested that they needed the concept of a *limit of a sequence* of rational numbers. If we accept the fact that a monotone increasing sequence that is bounded always approaches a limit, and observe that the sequence in (4) has these properties, then we want it to have a limit L. This would also mean, from (5), that $L^2 = 2$, and hence L is *not* one of our rational numbers. If to the *rational* numbers we further add the *limits* of all bounded monotone increasing sequences, we arrive at the system of all "real" numbers. The word *real* is placed in quotes because there is nothing that is either "more real" or "less real" about this system than there is about any other well-defined mathematical system.

Imagination was called upon at many stages during the development of the real number system from the system of positive integers. In fact, the art of invention was needed at least three times in constructing the systems we have discussed so far:

1. The *first invented* system; the set of *all integers* as constructed from the counting numbers.

2. The *second invented* system; the set of *rational* numbers m/n as constructed from the integers.

3. The *third invented* system; the set of all "*real*" numbers x as constructed from the rational numbers.

These invented systems form a hierarchy in which each system contains the previous system. Each system is also richer than its predecessor in that it permits more operations to be performed without going outside the system. Expressed in algebraic terms, we may say that:

1. In the system of all integers, we can solve all equations of the form

$$x + a = 0, \tag{6}$$

where a may be any integer.

2. In the system of all rational numbers, we can solve all equations of the form

$$ax + b = 0 \tag{7}$$

provided a and b are rational numbers and $a \neq 0$.

3. In the system of all real numbers, we can solve all of the Eqs. (6) and (7) and, in addition, all quadratic equations

$$ax^2 + bx + c = 0 \qquad \text{having} \qquad a \neq 0 \quad \text{and} \quad b^2 - 4ac \geq 0. \tag{8}$$

Every student of algebra is familiar with the formula that gives the solutions of (8), namely,

$$x = \frac{-b \pm \sqrt{b^2 - 4ac}}{2a}, \tag{9}$$

and familiar with the further fact that when the discriminant, $d = b^2 - 4ac$, is *negative*, the solutions in (9) do *not* belong to any of the systems discussed above. In fact, the very simple quadratic equation

$$x^2 + 1 = 0 \tag{10}$$

is impossible to solve if the only number systems that can be used are the three invented systems mentioned so far.

Thus we come to the *fourth invented* system, the set of all complex numbers $a + ib$. We could, in fact, dispense entirely with the symbol i and use a notation like (a, b). We would then speak simply of a pair of real numbers a and b. Since, under algebraic operations, the numbers a and b are treated somewhat differently, it is essential to keep the *order* straight. We therefore might say that *the complex number system consists of the set of all ordered pairs of real numbers* (a, b), together with the rules by which they are to be equated, added, multiplied, and so on, listed below. We shall use both the (a, b) notation and the notation $a + ib$. We call a the "real part" and b the "imaginary part" of (a, b). We make the following definitions.

Equality

$$a + ib = c + id$$
if and only if
$$a = c \quad \text{and} \quad b = d.$$

Two complex numbers (a, b) and (c, d) are *equal* if and only if $a = c$ and $b = d$.

Addition

$(a + ib) + (c + id)$
$= (a + c) + i(b + d)$

The sum of the two complex numbers (a, b) and (c, d) is the complex number $(a + c, b + d)$.

Multiplication

$(a + ib)(c + id)$
$= (ac - bd) + i(ad + bc)$

The product of two complex numbers (a, b) and (c, d) is the complex number $(ac - bd, ad + bc)$.

$c(a + ib) = ac + i(bc)$

The product of a real number c and the complex number (a, b) is the complex number (ac, bc).

The set of all complex numbers (a, b) in which the second number is zero has all the properties of the set of ordinary "real" numbers a. For example, addition and multiplication of $(a, 0)$ and $(c, 0)$ give

$$(a, 0) + (c, 0) = (a + c, 0),$$

$$(a, 0) \cdot (c, 0) = (ac, 0),$$

which are numbers of the same type with "imaginary part" equal to zero. Also, if we multiply a "real number" $(a, 0)$ and the "complex number" (c, d), we get

$$(a, 0) \cdot (c, d) = (ac, ad) = a(c, d).$$

In particular, the complex number $(0, 0)$ plays the role of zero in the complex number system and the complex number $(1, 0)$ plays the role of unity. The number pair $(0, 1)$, which has "real part" equal to zero and "imaginary part" equal to one has the property that its square,

$$(0, 1)(0, 1) = (-1, 0),$$

has "real part" equal to minus one and "imaginary part" equal to zero. Therefore, in the system of complex numbers (a, b), there is a number $x = (0, 1)$ whose square can be added to unity $= (1, 0)$ to produce zero $= (0, 0)$; that is,

$$(0, 1)^2 + (1, 0) = (0, 0).$$

The equation

$$x^2 + 1 = 0$$

therefore has a solution $x = (0, 1)$ in this new number system.

You are probably more familiar with the $a + ib$ notation than you are with the notation (a, b). And since the laws of algebra for the ordered pairs enable us to write

$$(a, b) = (a, 0) + (0, b) = a(1, 0) + b(0, 1),$$

while $(1, 0)$ behaves like unity and $(0, 1)$ behaves like a square root of minus one, we need not hesitate to write $a + ib$ in place of (a, b). The i associated with b is like a tracer element that tags the "imaginary part" of $a + ib$. We can pass at will from the realm of ordered pairs (a, b) to the realm of expressions $a + ib$, and conversely. But there is nothing less "real" about the symbol $(0, 1) = i$ than there is about the symbol $(1, 0) = 1$, once we have learned the laws of algebra in the complex number system (a, b).

PROBLEMS

1. In the definition of multiplication of complex numbers as ordered pairs of real numbers, the product $(a, b) \cdot (c, d)$ can be found by writing a and b on one line, c and d beneath them, and then:

For the *real* part of the product, multiply the numbers a and c in the first column and from their product subtract the product of the numbers b and d in the second column.

For the *imaginary* part of the product, cross-multiply and add the products ad and bc.

Apply this method to find the following products:

a) $(2, 3) \cdot (4, -2)$ **b)** $(2, -1) \cdot (-2, 3)$
c) $(-1, -2) \cdot (2, 1)$

[*Note.* This is the way in which complex numbers are multiplied on modern computers.]

2. Solve the following equations for the real numbers x and y:

a) $(3 + 4i)^2 - 2(x - iy) = x + iy$

b) $\left(\dfrac{1 + i}{1 - i}\right)^2 + \dfrac{1}{x + iy} = 1 + i$

c) $(3 - 2i)(x + iy) = 2(x - 2iy) + 2i - 1$

17-2

THE ARGAND DIAGRAM

To reduce any rational combination of complex numbers to a single complex number, we need only apply the laws of elementary algebra, replacing i^2 wherever it appears by -1. Of course, we cannot divide by the complex number $(0, 0) = 0 + i0$. But if $a + ib \neq 0$, then we may carry out a division as follows:

$$\frac{c + id}{a + ib} = \frac{(c + id)(a - ib)}{(a + ib)(a - ib)} = \frac{(ac + bd) + i(ad - bc)}{a^2 + b^2}.$$

The result is a complex number $x + iy$ with

$$x = \frac{ac + bd}{a^2 + b^2}, \quad y = \frac{ad - bc}{a^2 + b^2},$$

and $a^2 + b^2 \neq 0$, since $a + ib = (a, b) \neq (0, 0)$. The number $a - ib$ that is used as multiplier to clear the i out of the denominator is called the *complex conjugate* of $a + ib$. It is customary to use $\bar{z}$ (read "z bar") to denote the complex conjugate of z; thus

$$z = a + ib, \quad \bar{z} = a - ib.$$

Thus, we multiplied the numerator and denominator of the complex fraction $(c + id)/(a + ib)$ by the complex conjugate of the denominator. This will always replace the denominator by a real number.

There are two geometric representations of the complex number $z = x + iy$:

a) as the point $P(x, y)$ in the xy-plane, or

b) as the vector $\overrightarrow{OP}$ from the origin to P.

In each representation, the x-axis is called the "axis of reals" and the y-axis is the "imaginary axis." Both representations are called *Argand diagrams* (Fig. 17–2).

In terms of the polar coordinates of x and y, we have

$$x = r \cos \theta, \qquad y = r \sin \theta,$$

and

$$z = x + iy = r(\cos \theta + i \sin \theta). \tag{1}$$

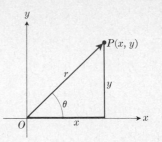

17–2 An Argand diagram representing $z = x + iy$ both as a point $P(x, y)$ and as a vector $\overrightarrow{OP}$.

We define the *absolute value* of a complex number $x + iy$ to be the length r of a vector $\overrightarrow{OP}$ from the origin to $P(x, y)$. We denote the absolute value by vertical bars, thus:

$$|x + iy| = \sqrt{x^2 + y^2}. \tag{2a}$$

Since we can always choose the polar coordinates r and θ so that $r \geq 0$, we have

$$r = |x + iy|. \tag{2b}$$

The polar angle θ is called the *argument* of z and written $\theta = \arg z$. Of course, any integral multiple of 2π may be added to θ to produce another appropriate angle. The *principal value* of the argument will, in this book, be taken to be that value of θ for which $-\pi < \theta \leq +\pi$.

The following equation gives a useful formula connecting a complex number z, its conjugate $\bar{z}$, and its absolute value $|z|$, namely,

$$z \cdot \bar{z} = |z|^2. \tag{2c}$$

We shall show in a later section how $\cos \theta + i \sin \theta$ can be expressed very conveniently as $e^{i\theta}$. But for the present, let us just introduce the abbreviation

$$\text{cis } \theta = \cos \theta + i \sin \theta. \tag{3}$$

Since cis θ is what we get from Eq. (1) by taking $r = 1$, we can say that cis θ is represented by a *unit* vector that makes an angle θ with the positive x-axis (Fig. 17–3).

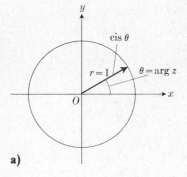

a)

EXAMPLE 1

$$\text{cis } 0 = \cos 0 + i \sin 0 = 1,$$

$$\text{cis } \frac{\pi}{4} = \cos \frac{\pi}{4} + i \sin \frac{\pi}{4} = \frac{1 + i}{\sqrt{2}},$$

$$\text{cis } \frac{3\pi}{2} = \cos \frac{3\pi}{2} + i \sin \frac{3\pi}{2} = -i.$$

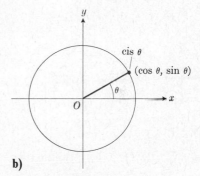

b)

17–3 Argand diagrams for $\cos \theta + i \sin \theta$: (a) as a vector; (b) as a point.

The complex-valued function cis θ has some interesting properties. For example, we shall show that

$$\text{cis } \theta_1 \cdot \text{cis } \theta_2 = \text{cis } (\theta_1 + \theta_2), \tag{4a}$$

$$(\text{cis } \theta)^{-1} = \text{cis } (-\theta), \tag{4b}$$

$$\frac{\text{cis } \theta_1}{\text{cis } \theta_2} = \text{cis } (\theta_1 - \theta_2). \tag{4c}$$

To prove the first of these, we simply multiply

$$\operatorname{cis} \theta_1 \cdot \operatorname{cis} \theta_2 = (\cos \theta_1 + i \sin \theta_1)(\cos \theta_2 + i \sin \theta_2)$$
$$= (\cos \theta_1 \cos \theta_2 - \sin \theta_1 \sin \theta_2)$$
$$+ i(\sin \theta_1 \cos \theta_2 + \cos \theta_1 \sin \theta_2).$$

From trigonometry we recognize the expressions in parentheses to be

$$\cos (\theta_1 + \theta_2) = \cos \theta_1 \cos \theta_2 - \sin \theta_1 \sin \theta_2,$$
$$\sin (\theta_1 + \theta_2) = \sin \theta_1 \cos \theta_2 + \cos \theta_1 \sin \theta_2,$$

which give us

$$\operatorname{cis} \theta_1 \cdot \operatorname{cis} \theta_2 = \cos (\theta_1 + \theta_2) + i \sin (\theta_1 + \theta_2) = \operatorname{cis} (\theta_1 + \theta_2),$$

and establish (4a). In particular,

$$\operatorname{cis} \theta \cdot \operatorname{cis} (-\theta) = \operatorname{cis} (\theta - \theta) = \operatorname{cis} 0 = 1,$$

whence

$$\operatorname{cis} (-\theta) = \frac{1}{\operatorname{cis} \theta},$$

which establishes (4b). Finally, we may combine Eqs. (4a, b) and write

$$\frac{\operatorname{cis} \theta_1}{\operatorname{cis} \theta_2} = (\operatorname{cis} \theta_1)(\operatorname{cis} \theta_2)^{-1} = \operatorname{cis} \theta_1 \cdot \operatorname{cis} (-\theta_2) = \operatorname{cis} (\theta_1 - \theta_2).$$

These properties of $\operatorname{cis} \theta$ lead to interesting geometrical interpretations of the product and quotient of two complex numbers in terms of the vectors that represent them.

Product

Let

$$z_1 = r_1 \operatorname{cis} \theta_1, \qquad z_2 = r_2 \operatorname{cis} \theta_2, \tag{5}$$

so that

$$|z_1| = r_1, \quad \arg z_1 = \theta_1; \qquad |z_2| = r_2, \quad \arg z_2 = \theta_2. \tag{6}$$

Then

$$z_1 z_2 = r_1 \operatorname{cis} \theta_1 \cdot r_2 \operatorname{cis} \theta_2 = r_1 r_2 \operatorname{cis} (\theta_1 + \theta_2)$$

and hence

$$|z_1 z_2| = r_1 r_2 = |z_1| \cdot |z_2|,$$
$$\arg (z_1 z_2) = \theta_1 + \theta_2 = \arg z_1 + \arg z_2. \tag{7}$$

Thus the product of two complex numbers is represented by a vector whose length is the product of the lengths of the two factors and whose argument is the sum of their arguments (Fig. 17–4). In particular, a vector may be rotated in the counterclockwise direction through an angle θ by simply multiplying it by $\operatorname{cis} \theta$. Multiplication by i rotates 90°, by -1 rotates 180°, by $-i$ rotates 270°, etc.

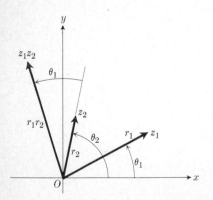

17–4 When z_1 and z_2 are multiplied, $z_1 z_2 = r_1 \cdot r_2$, and $\arg (z_1 z_2) = \theta_1 + \theta_2$.

EXAMPLE 2. Let

$$z_1 = 1 + i, \qquad z_2 = \sqrt{3} - i.$$

We plot these complex numbers in an Argand diagram (Fig. 17–5) from which we read off the polar representations

$$z_1 = \sqrt{2} \operatorname{cis} \frac{\pi}{4}, \qquad z_2 = 2 \operatorname{cis} \left(-\frac{\pi}{6} \right).$$

Then

$$z_1 z_2 = 2\sqrt{2} \operatorname{cis} \left(\frac{\pi}{4} - \frac{\pi}{6} \right)$$

$$= 2\sqrt{2} \operatorname{cis} \frac{\pi}{12}$$

$$= 2\sqrt{2} \left(\cos 15° + i \sin 15° \right)$$

$$\approx 2.73 + 0.73i.$$

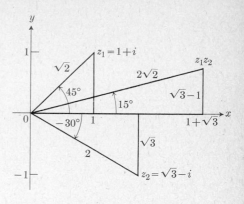

17–5 To multiply two complex numbers, one multiplies their absolute values, and adds their arguments.

Quotient

Suppose $r_2 \neq 0$ in Eq. (5). Then

$$\frac{z_1}{z_2} = \frac{r_1 \operatorname{cis} \theta_1}{r_2 \operatorname{cis} \theta_2} = \frac{r_1}{r_2} \operatorname{cis} (\theta_1 - \theta_2).$$

Hence

$$\left| \frac{z_1}{z_2} \right| = \frac{r_1}{r_2} = \frac{|z_1|}{|z_2|},$$

$$\arg (z_1/z_2) = \theta_1 - \theta_2 = \arg z_1 - \arg z_2.$$

That is, we divide lengths and subtract angles.

EXAMPLE 3. Let $z_1 = 1 + i$ and $z_2 = \sqrt{3} - i$, as in Example 2. Then,

$$\frac{1 + i}{\sqrt{3} - i} = \frac{\sqrt{2} \operatorname{cis} \pi/4}{2 \operatorname{cis} (-\pi/6)} = \frac{\sqrt{2}}{2} \operatorname{cis} (5\pi/12)$$

$$\approx 0.707 \left(\cos 75° + i \sin 75° \right)$$

$$\approx 0.183 + 0.683i.$$

Powers

If n is a positive integer, we may apply the product formulas, Eq. (7), to find

$$z^n = z \cdot z \cdot z \cdots z \qquad (n \text{ factors})$$

when

$$z = r \operatorname{cis} \theta.$$

Doing so, we obtain

$$(r \text{ cis } \theta)^n = r^n \text{ cis } (\theta + \theta + \cdots + \theta) \qquad (n \text{ summands})$$

$$= r^n \text{ cis } n\theta. \tag{8}$$

In vector language, we see that the length, $r = |z|$, is raised to the nth power and the angle, $\theta = \arg z$, is multiplied by n.

In particular, if we place $r = 1$ in Eq. (8), we obtain *De Moivre's theorem*:

$$(\cos \theta + i \sin \theta)^n = \cos n\theta + i \sin n\theta. \tag{9}$$

If we expand the left side of this equation by the binomial theorem and reduce it to the standard form $a + ib$, we obtain formulas for $\cos n\theta$ and $\sin n\theta$ as polynomials of degree n in $\cos \theta$ and $\sin \theta$.

EXAMPLE 4. If we take $n = 3$ in Eq. (9), we have

$$(\cos \theta + i \sin \theta)^3 = \cos 3\theta + i \sin 3\theta.$$

The left side of this equation is

$$\cos^3 \theta + 3i \cos^2 \theta \sin \theta - 3 \cos \theta \sin^2 \theta - i \sin^3 \theta.$$

The real part of this must equal $\cos 3\theta$ and the imaginary part must equal $\sin 3\theta$; hence

$$\cos 3\theta = \cos^3 \theta - 3 \cos \theta \sin^2 \theta,$$

$$\sin 3\theta = 3 \cos^2 \theta \sin \theta - \sin^3 \theta.$$

Roots

If $z = r \text{ cis } \theta$ is a complex number different from zero and n is a positive integer, then there are precisely n different complex numbers $w_0, w_1, \ldots, w_{n-1}$, each of which is an nth root of z. Let $w = \rho \text{ cis } \alpha$ be an nth root of $z = r \text{ cis } \theta$, so that

$$w^n = z$$

or

$$\rho^n \text{ cis } n\alpha = r \text{ cis } \theta. \tag{10}$$

Then

$$\rho = \sqrt[n]{r} \tag{11}$$

is the real, positive, nth root of r. As regards the angle, although we cannot say that $n\alpha$ and θ must be equal, we can say that they may differ only by an integral multiple of 2π. That is,

$$n\alpha = \theta + 2k\pi, \qquad k = 0, \pm 1, \pm 2, \ldots \tag{12}$$

Therefore

$$\alpha = \frac{\theta}{n} + k \frac{2\pi}{n}.$$

Hence all *n*th roots of $z = r$ cis θ are given by

$$\sqrt[n]{r \text{ cis } \theta} = \sqrt[n]{r} \text{ cis} \left(\frac{\theta}{n} + k \frac{2\pi}{n} \right), \qquad k = 0, \pm 1, \pm 2, \ldots \qquad \textbf{(13)}$$

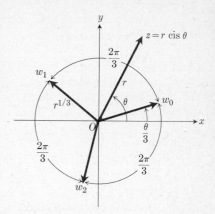

REMARK. It might appear that there are infinitely many different answers corresponding to the infinitely many possible values of k. But one readily sees that $k = n + m$ gives the same answer as $k = m$ in Eq. (13). Thus we need only take n consecutive values for k to obtain all the different nth roots of z. For convenience, we may take

$$k = 0, 1, 2, \ldots, n - 1.$$

It is worth noting that all the nth roots of r cis θ lie on a circle centered at the origin O and having radius equal to the real, positive nth root of r. One of them has argument $\alpha = \theta/n$. The others are uniformly spaced around the circumference of the circle, each being separated from its neighbors by an angle equal to $2\pi/n$. Figure 17–6 illustrates the placement of the three cube roots, w_0, w_1, w_2, of the complex number $z = r$ cis θ.

17–6 The three cube roots of $z = r$ cis θ.

EXAMPLE 5. Find the four fourth roots of -16.

Solution. As our first step, we plot the given number in an Argand diagram (Fig. 17–7) and determine its polar representation r cis θ. Here,

$$z = -16, \qquad r = +16, \qquad \theta = \pi.$$

One of the fourth roots of 16 cis π is 2 cis $(\pi/4)$. We obtain others by successive additions of $2\pi/4 = \pi/2$ to the argument of this first one. Hence

$$\sqrt[4]{16 \text{ cis } \pi} = 2 \text{ cis} \left(\frac{\pi}{4}, \frac{3\pi}{4}, \frac{5\pi}{4}, \frac{7\pi}{4} \right),$$

and the four roots are

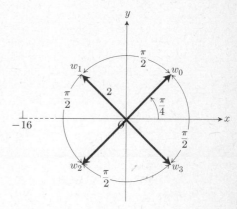

17–7 The four fourth roots of -16.

$$w_0 = 2 \left[\cos \frac{\pi}{4} + i \sin \frac{\pi}{4} \right] = \sqrt{2}(1 + i),$$

$$w_1 = 2 \left[\cos \frac{3\pi}{4} + i \sin \frac{3\pi}{4} \right] = \sqrt{2}(-1 + i),$$

$$w_2 = 2 \left[\cos \frac{5\pi}{4} + i \sin \frac{5\pi}{4} \right] = \sqrt{2}(-1 - i),$$

$$w_3 = 2 \left[\cos \frac{7\pi}{4} + i \sin \frac{7\pi}{4} \right] = \sqrt{2}(1 - i).$$

REMARK. One may well say that the invention of $\sqrt{-1}$ is all well and good and leads to a number system that is richer than the real number system alone; but where will this process end? Are we also going to invent still more systems so as to obtain $\sqrt[4]{-1}$, $\sqrt[6]{-1}$, and so on? By now it should be clear that this is not necessary. These numbers are already expressible in terms of the complex number system $a + ib$. In fact, the *Fundamental Theorem of*

Algebra (which is rather difficult to prove; we can only state it here) says that: Every polynomial equation of the form

$$a_0 z^n + a_1 z^{n-1} + a_2 z^{n-2} + \cdots + a_{n-1} z + a_n = 0,$$

in which the coefficients $a_0, a_1, \ldots, a_n$ are any complex numbers, whose degree n is greater than or equal to one, and whose leading coefficient a_0 is not zero, possesses precisely n roots in the complex number system, provided each multiple root of multiplicity m is counted as m roots.

PROBLEMS

1. Show with an Argand diagram that the law for addition of complex numbers is the same as the parallelogram law for adding vectors.

2. How may the following complex numbers be obtained from $z = x + iy$ geometrically? Sketch. (a) $\bar{z}$, (b) $(-z)$, (c) $-z$, (d) $1/z$.

3. Show that the conjugate of the sum (product, or quotient) of two complex numbers z_1 and z_2 is the same as the sum (product, or quotient) of their conjugates.

4. (a) Extend the results of Problem 3 to show that

$$f(\bar{z}) = \overline{f(z)} \text{ if } f(z) = a_0 z^n + a_1 z^{n-1} + \cdots + a_{n-1} z + a_n$$

is a polynomial with real coefficients $a_0, a_1, \ldots, a_n$. (b) If z is a root of the equation $f(z) = 0$, where $f(z)$ is a polynomial with real coefficients as in part (a) above, show that the conjugate $\bar{z}$ is also a root of the equation. [*Hint*. Let $f(z) = u + iv = 0$; then both u and v are zero. Now use the fact that $f(\bar{z}) = \overline{f(z)} = u - iv$.]

5. Show that $|\bar{z}| = |z|$.

6. If z and $\bar{z}$ are equal, what can you say about the location of the point z in the complex plane?

7. Let $R(z), I(z)$ denote respectively the real and imaginary parts of z. Show that:

a) $z + \bar{z} = 2R(z)$ **b)** $z - \bar{z} = 2iI(z)$

c) $|R(z)| \le |z|$

d) $|z_1 + z_2|^2 = |z_1|^2 + |z_2|^2 + 2R(z_1 \bar{z}_2)$

e) $|z_1 + z_2| \le |z_1| + |z_2|$

8. Show that the distance between the two points z_1 and z_2 in an Argand diagram is equal to $|z_1 - z_2|$.

In Problems 9–13, graph the points $z = x + iy$ that satisfy the given conditions:

9. a) $|z| = 2$ **b)** $|z| < 2$ **c)** $|z| > 2$

10. $|z - 1| = 2$ **11.** $|z + 1| = 1$

12. $|z + 1| = |z - 1|$ **13.** $|z + i| = |z - 1|$

Express the answer to each of the Problems 14–17 in the form $r \text{ cis } \theta$, with $r \ge 0$ and $-\pi < \theta \le \pi$. Sketch.

14. $(1 + \sqrt{-3})^2$ **15.** $\dfrac{1 + i}{1 - i}$

16. $\dfrac{1 + i\sqrt{3}}{1 - i\sqrt{3}}$ **17.** $(2 + 3i)(1 - 2i)$

18. Use De Moivre's theorem to express $\cos 4\theta$ and $\sin 4\theta$ as polynomials in $\cos \theta$ and $\sin \theta$.

19. Find the three cube roots of unity.

20. Find the two square roots of i.

21. Find the three cube roots of $-8i$.

22. Find the six sixth roots of 64.

23. Find the four roots of the equation $z^4 - 2z^2 + 4 = 0$.

24. Find the six roots of the equation $z^6 + 2z^3 + 2 = 0$.

25. Find all roots of the equation $x^4 + 4x^2 + 16 = 0$.

26. Solve: $x^4 + 1 = 0$.

17–3

COMPLEX VARIABLES

A set S of complex numbers $z = x + iy$ may be represented by points in an Argand diagram. For instance, S might be all complex z for which $|z| \le 1$. The corresponding points in the Argand diagram, or in the *z-plane* as it is called, then would be all points inside or on the circumference of a circle of radius 1 centered at O (Fig. 17–8). During a discussion, we might wish to consider the symbol z as representing any one of the complex numbers in the set S. We would then think of z as a variable whose domain is S. Or we may wish to consider a moving point that starts at time $t = 0$ from the point z_0 and moves continuously along some path in the z-plane as t increases to a second value, say $t = 1$. We would again consider the complex number z associated with this moving point (x, y) by the equation $z = x + iy$ to be a variable. This time it is a dependent variable, since its value depends upon the value of t.

The *distance* between two complex numbers $z_1 = x_1 + iy_1$ and $z_2 = x_2 + iy_2$ in the complex plane is

$$\sqrt{(x_1 - x_2)^2 + (y_1 - y_2)^2} = |z_1 - z_2|.$$

We say that the complex variable $z = x + iy$ approaches the *limit* $\alpha = a + ib$ if the distance between z and α approaches zero (Fig. 17–9). That is.

$$z \to \alpha \qquad \text{if and only if} \qquad |z - \alpha| \to 0. \tag{1}$$

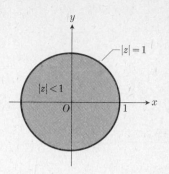

17–8 The unit circle $|z| = 1$ and its interior $|z| < 1$ in the z-plane.

If we imagine z to be a function of time, we would say, for example, that

$$\lim_{t \to 1} z = \alpha \tag{2}$$

provided it is true that

$$\lim_{t \to 1} |z - \alpha| = 0. \tag{3}$$

One way to interpret Eq. (3) is to say that if it holds, then one may prescribe as small a circle about α as center as one pleases, and the point $z = x + iy$ will be inside that circle for all values of t sufficiently close to 1. That is, $|z - \alpha|$ is small when $|t - 1|$ is small. Since

$$|z - \alpha| = |(x + iy) - (a + ib)|$$

$$= |(x - a) + i(y - b)|$$

$$= \sqrt{(x - a)^2 + (y - b)^2} \le |x - a| + |y - b|,$$

while both

$$|x - a| \qquad \text{and} \qquad |y - b| \qquad \text{are} \quad \le |z - \alpha|,$$

we see that

$$z \to \alpha \qquad \text{if and only if} \qquad x \to a \quad \text{and} \quad y \to b. \tag{4}$$

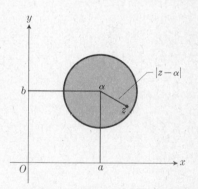

17–9 The distance between z and α in the z-plane is $|z - \alpha|$.

Both $|x - a|$ and $|y - b|$ are small when $|z - \alpha|$ is small; and conversely, if both $|x - a|$ and $|y - b|$ are small, then $|z - \alpha|$ is also small.

Function

We say that w is a function of z on a domain S and write

$$w = f(z), \qquad z \text{ in } S \tag{5}$$

if, to each z in the set S, there corresponds a complex number $w = u + iv$. For instance, S may be the set of all complex numbers and

$$w = z^2. \tag{6}$$

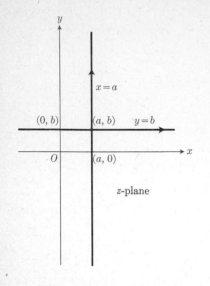

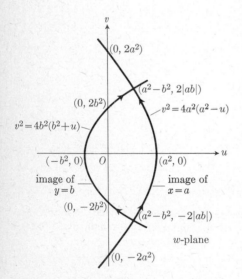

17–10 The function $w = z^2$ changes all but two of the horizontal and vertical lines of the z-plane into parabolas. The exceptions are the two axes of the z-plane, which are changed into rays instead (see Problem 1).

For each point $z = x + iy$ in the z-plane, Eq. (6) produces a complex number $w = u + iv$:

$$u + iv = (x + iy)^2 = x^2 + 2ixy + i^2 y^2 = (x^2 - y^2) + i(2xy). \qquad (7)$$

One way to represent such a function graphically is by a technique called "mapping." For example, we may use Eq. (7) to map a vertical line, $x = a$, into the w-plane. What does the image point w do as the z point traverses the line $x = a$ from $y = -\infty$ to $y = +\infty$? To find out, we separate the real and imaginary parts of Eq. (7) and obtain

$$u = x^2 - y^2 = a^2 - y^2, \qquad v = 2xy = 2ay. \qquad (8a)$$

These equations are parametric equations (in the parameter y) of the parabola

$$v^2 = 4a^2(a^2 - u). \qquad (8b)$$

When a is positive (Fig. 17–10), $v = 2ay$ has the same sign as y. Thus as the z point moves up along the line $x = a$ from $y = -\infty$ to $y = +\infty$, the w point moves upward along the parabola, (8b), in the direction indicated by the arrows in the figure.

Similarly, the image in the w-plane of the line $y = b$ has parametric equations

$$u = x^2 - b^2, \qquad v = 2bx, \qquad -\infty < x < +\infty, \qquad (9a)$$

which represent the parabola

$$v^2 = 4b^2(b^2 + u). \qquad (9b)$$

It is easily seen from (8a, b) that the line $x = -a$ maps onto the same parabola (8b) that the line $x = a$ does; but this time the parabola is traced in the opposite sense as y varies from $-\infty$ to $+\infty$. Similarly, the line $y = -b$ maps onto the same parabola as the line $y = b$. These phenomena are to be expected, since the point z and the point $-z$ both map into the same point $w = z^2 = (-z)^2$ in the w-plane.

Continuity

A function $w = f(z)$ that is defined throughout some neighborhood of the point $z = \alpha$ is said to be *continuous* at α if

$$|f(z) - f(\alpha)| \to 0 \qquad \text{as} \qquad |z - \alpha| \to 0. \qquad (10)$$

Expressed in the language of mapping, the conditions in (10) say simply that the image of z is near the image of α when z is near α. Another way to say it is that for any circle C centered at $f(\alpha)$ in the w-plane, no matter how small, there is a circle C' centered at α in the z-plane with the property that whenever z is inside C', the image point w lies inside C. (See Fig. 17–11.)

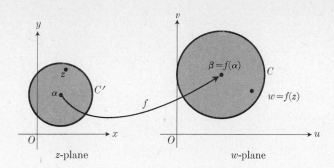

z-plane

w-plane

17–11 The continuity of $w = f(z)$ requires the image of z to be near the image of α whenever z is near α.

EXAMPLE. $f(z) = z^2$ is continuous at any point $z = \alpha$, for we have

$$|f(z) - f(\alpha)| = |z^2 - \alpha^2| = |(z - \alpha)(z + \alpha)| = |z - \alpha| \cdot |z + \alpha|.$$

Now as $z \to \alpha$, we have

$$\lim_{z \to \alpha} (z + \alpha) = 2\alpha,$$

so that

$$\lim_{z \to \alpha} |f(z) - f(\alpha)| = \lim_{z \to \alpha} |(z - \alpha)| \cdot |(z + \alpha)|$$

$$= |2\alpha| \lim_{z \to \alpha} |z - \alpha| = 0,$$

so that condition (10) is satisfied.

PROBLEMS

1. In connection with the function $w = z^2$ discussed in the text, sketch the images in the w-plane of the following figures in the z-plane. [*Hint.* Use polar coordinates.]

a) $|z| = 1$, $0 \le \arg z \le \pi$

b) $|z| = 2$, $\pi/2 \le \arg z \le \pi$

c) $\arg z = \pi/4$ **d)** $|z| < 1$, $-\pi < \arg z \le 0$

e) the x-axis   **f)** the y-axis

2. Show that the two parabolas in the w-plane in Fig. 17–10 intersect orthogonally if neither a nor b is zero.

3. Show that the function $w = z^3$ maps the wedge $0 \le \arg z \le \pi/3$ in the z-plane onto the upper half of the w-plane. Use polar coordinates and sketch.

4. Show that $f(z) = z^3$ is continuous at $z = \alpha$ for any α.

5. Show that $f(z) = 1/z$ is continuous at $z = \alpha$ if $\alpha \ne 0$.

The derivative of a function $w = f(z)$ is defined in the same way as the derivative of a real-valued function of the real variable x. Namely, the derivative at $z = \alpha$ is

$$f'(\alpha) = \lim_{z \to \alpha} \frac{f(z) - f(\alpha)}{z - \alpha}, \qquad (1)$$

17–4

DERIVATIVES

provided the limit exists. By saying that the limit in (1) exists, we mean, of course, that there is some complex number, which we have called $f'(\alpha)$, such that

$$\left| f'(\alpha) - \frac{f(z) - f(\alpha)}{z - \alpha} \right| \to 0 \quad \text{as} \quad |z - \alpha| \to 0. \tag{2}$$

Since z may approach α *along any path*, the existence of such a limit imposes a rather strong restriction on the function $w = f(z)$.

EXAMPLE 1. The function

$$w = \bar{z} = f(z), \tag{3}$$

where

$$z = x + iy, \qquad \bar{z} = x - iy$$

has no derivative at any point. For if we take $\alpha = a + ib$, then

$$\frac{f(z) - f(\alpha)}{z - \alpha} = \frac{\bar{z} - \bar{\alpha}}{z - \alpha} = \frac{(x - a) - i(y - b)}{(x - a) + i(y - b)}. \tag{4}$$

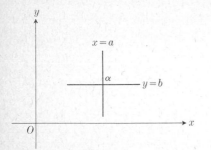

17–12 We know that the function $w = \bar{z}$ is not differentiable at any point α because the quotient $(\bar{z} - \bar{\alpha})/(z - \alpha)$ has different limits as z approaches α along the lines $x = a$ and $y = b$.

Now, from among the many different ways in which z might approach α, we shall single out for special attention the following two:

a) along the line $y = b$, and
b) along the line $x = a$. (See Fig. 17–12.)

In the first case, we therefore take $y = b$ and let $x \to a$. Then Eq. (4) becomes

$$y = b: \qquad \frac{f(z) - f(\alpha)}{z - \alpha} = \frac{x - a}{x - a} = +1,$$

so that

$$\lim_{\substack{x \to a \\ y = b}} \frac{f(z) - f(\alpha)}{z - \alpha} = +1. \tag{5a}$$

In the second case, we take $x = a$ and let $y \to b$. This time Eq. (4) becomes

$$x = a: \qquad \frac{f(z) - f(\alpha)}{z - \alpha} = \frac{-i(y - b)}{i(y - b)} = -1,$$

and hence

$$\lim_{\substack{x = a \\ y \to b}} \frac{f(z) - f(\alpha)}{z - \alpha} = -1. \tag{5b}$$

Since these two different paths along which z may approach α lead to two different limiting values of the difference quotient $(f(z) - f(\alpha))/(z - \alpha)$, there is no single complex number which we can call $f'(\alpha)$ in Eq. (1) or (2). That is, the function $w = \bar{z}$ does not have a derivative. *Question.* Is the function $w = \bar{z}$ *continuous* for some, none, or all values of z? Can you justify your answer?

In terms of the Δ-notation, we may call

$$z - \alpha = \Delta z, \qquad f(z) - f(\alpha) = \Delta w$$

and say that $w = f(z)$ has a derivative

$$\frac{dw}{dz} = \lim_{\Delta z \to 0} \frac{\Delta w}{\Delta z} \tag{6}$$

provided the limit exists and is independent of the manner in which $\Delta z \to 0$.

The formulas for differentiating sums, products, quotients, and powers are the same for complex variables as for real variables. In other words, if c is any complex constant, n is a positive integer, and if $f(z)$ and $g(z)$ are functions that have derivatives at $z = \alpha$, then at $z = \alpha$:

1. $\dfrac{dc}{dz} = 0,$

2. $\dfrac{dcf(z)}{dz} = c\,\dfrac{df(z)}{dz},$

3. $\dfrac{d[f(z) + g(z)]}{dz} = \dfrac{df(z)}{dz} + \dfrac{dg(z)}{dz},$

4. $\dfrac{d}{dz}[f(z)g(z)] = f(z)\dfrac{dg(z)}{dz} + g(z)\dfrac{df(z)}{dz},$

5. $\dfrac{d}{dz}\dfrac{f(z)}{g(z)} = \dfrac{g(z)\dfrac{df(z)}{dz} - f(z)\dfrac{dg(z)}{dz}}{[g(z)]^2},\qquad g(z) \neq 0,$

6. a) $\dfrac{d}{dz}[f(z)]^n = n[f(z)]^{n-1}\dfrac{df(z)}{dz},$ **b)** $\dfrac{d(z^n)}{dz} = nz^{n-1}.$

These formulas may all be derived rather easily in the Δ-notation, provided one first proves that the limit of a sum, product, or quotient of two complex functions is the sum, product, or quotient of their limits (always, of course, excluding division by zero), whenever the individual limits exist. We shall omit these proofs and content ourselves here with a simple example.

EXAMPLE 2. Show that

$$\frac{d(z^3)}{dz} = 3z^2.$$

Solution. Let $w = z^3$. Then

$$w + \Delta w = z^3 + 3z^2\,\Delta z + 3z\,(\Delta z)^2 + (\Delta z)^3,$$

$$\frac{\Delta w}{\Delta z} = 3z^2 + 3z\,(\Delta z) + (\Delta z)^2,$$

and

$$\left| \frac{\Delta w}{\Delta z} - 3z^2 \right| = |3z + \Delta z| \cdot |\Delta z| \to 0 \qquad \text{as} \quad \Delta z \to 0. \tag{7}$$

Therefore,

$$\lim_{\Delta z \to 0} \frac{\Delta w}{\Delta z} = 3z^2;$$

that is,

$$\frac{d(z^3)}{dz} = 3z^2.$$

Note that it makes no difference *how* Δz approaches zero in (7) above. When $|\Delta z|$ is small, the whole right side of the equation is small.

PROBLEMS

In Problems 1–3, find the derivative with respect to z of the given function at the given point z_0.

1. $\dfrac{z+1}{z-1}$, $z_0 = 1 + i$

2. $z^3 + 3z^2 + 3z + 2$, $z_0 = -1 + 2i$

3. $\sqrt{z^2 + 1}$, $z_0 = (1 + i)/\sqrt{2}$. (Here we get *two* answers, depending upon our choice of the square root.)

4. Use the definition in Eq. (1) to find $f'(\alpha)$ if $f(z) = 1/z$ and $\alpha \neq 0$.

17–5

THE CAUCHY–RIEMANN EQUATIONS

If the complex function $w = u + iv = f(z)$ is differentiable (i.e., has a derivative) at the point $\alpha = a + ib$, then by making $z \to \alpha$, once along the line $y = b$ (i.e., take $\Delta y = 0$ and make $\Delta x \to 0$) and then along the line $x = a$ (i.e., take $\Delta x = 0$ and make $\Delta y \to 0$), we quickly learn that the equations

$$\frac{\partial u}{\partial x} = \frac{\partial v}{\partial y} \quad \text{and} \quad \frac{\partial v}{\partial x} = -\frac{\partial u}{\partial y} \tag{1}$$

must be satisfied at the point (a, b).

For, assuming that dw/dz does exist at $z = \alpha$, we have

$$f'(\alpha) = \lim_{\substack{\Delta y = 0 \\ \Delta x \to 0}} \frac{\Delta u + i\,\Delta v}{\Delta x + i\,\Delta y} = \lim_{\Delta x \to 0}\left(\frac{\Delta u}{\Delta x} + i\frac{\Delta v}{\Delta x}\right)$$

$$= \left(\frac{\partial u}{\partial x} + i\frac{\partial v}{\partial x}\right)_{z = \alpha} \tag{2a}$$

and also

$$f'(\alpha) = \lim_{\substack{\Delta x = 0 \\ \Delta y \to 0}} \frac{\Delta u + i\,\Delta v}{\Delta x + i\,\Delta y} = \lim_{\Delta y \to 0}\left(\frac{\Delta u}{i\,\Delta y} + \frac{\Delta v}{\Delta y}\right)$$

$$= \left(\frac{1}{i}\frac{\partial u}{\partial y} + \frac{\partial v}{\partial y}\right)_{z = \alpha}$$

$$= \left(-i\frac{\partial u}{\partial y} + \frac{\partial v}{\partial y}\right)_{z = \alpha}. \tag{2b}$$

We have now only to equate the real and imaginary parts of these two expressions for $f'(\alpha)$, Eq. (2a, b), in order to obtain the results in Eq. (1).

These relationships, which connect the four partial derivatives of u and v with respect to x and y, are known as the *Cauchy–Riemann* differential equations. We have just shown that they must be satisfied at any point where $w = f(z)$ has a derivative. Thus we cannot, in general, specify the functions $u = u(x, y)$ and $v = v(x, y)$ independently and expect the resulting function $w = u + iv$ to be differentiable with respect to $z = x + iy$. However, if we take functions that do satisfy the Cauchy-Riemann equations and, in addition, have *continuous* partial derivatives, u_x, u_y, v_x, v_y, then it is true (but we shall not prove it here) that the resulting function $w = u + iv$ is differentiable with respect to z. In a sense, this says that if the derivatives calculated along the *two* directions $x = a$ and $y = b$ are equal, and if the partial derivatives u_x, etc., are *continuous*, then one will also get the same answer for $f'(\alpha)$ along *all* directions.*

If a function $w = f(z)$ has a derivative at every point of some region G in the z-plane, then the function is said to be *analytic* in G. If a function fails to have a derivative at one point α but does have a derivative everywhere else in a region G, we still say that it is analytic in G *except* at α and say that α is a *singular* point of the function. Thus, for example, a rational function $f(z)/g(z)$, where $f(z)$ and $g(z)$ are polynomials, is analytic everywhere except at those points where the denominator is zero. For all points where $g(z) \neq 0$, the function has a derivative

$$\frac{g(z)f'(z) - f(z)g'(z)}{[g(z)]^2}.$$

EXAMPLE. Show that the real and imaginary parts of the function $w = 1/z$ satisfy the Cauchy-Riemann equations at all points where $z \neq 0$.

Solution. Let

$$w = u + iv = \frac{1}{x + iy} = \frac{x - iy}{x^2 + y^2},$$

so that

$$u = \frac{x}{x^2 + y^2}, \qquad v = \frac{-y}{x^2 + y^2}; \qquad x^2 + y^2 \neq 0.$$

Then we find, by calculating the partial derivatives, that

$$\frac{\partial u}{\partial x} = \frac{y^2 - x^2}{(x^2 + y^2)^2} = \frac{\partial v}{\partial y},$$

$$\frac{\partial v}{\partial x} = \frac{2xy}{(x^2 + y^2)^2} = -\frac{\partial u}{\partial y},$$

so that the Cauchy-Riemann equations are satisfied at all points where

$$x^2 + y^2 \neq 0; \qquad \text{that is,} \quad z \neq 0.$$

---

*   For a discussion of conditions that, together with the Cauchy-Riemann equations, imply the differentiability of a function $w = f(z)$, see J. D. Gray and S. A. Morris, "When is a function that satisfies the Cauchy-Riemann equations analytic?" *Amer. Math. Monthly* **85** (1978), 4, pp. 246–254.

PROBLEMS

Find the real and imaginary parts of the functions $w = f(z)$, $w = u + iv$, $z = x + iy$, and show that they satisfy the Cauchy–Riemann equations

1. z^2 2. z^3 3. z^4 4. $1/z^2$, $z \neq 0$

5. If the partial derivatives of first and second order of the real and imaginary parts $u = u(x, y)$, $v = v(x, y)$ of an analytic function $w = f(z)$ are continuous, show that

$$\frac{\partial^2 u}{\partial x^2} + \frac{\partial^2 u}{\partial y^2} = 0 \quad \text{and} \quad \frac{\partial^2 v}{\partial x^2} + \frac{\partial^2 v}{\partial y^2} = 0.$$

6. Verify that the equations in Problem 5 are satisfied by the real and imaginary parts of the functions (a) z, (b) z^2, (c) z^3.

17–6

COMPLEX SERIES

The simplest functions of the complex variable $z = x + iy$ are polynomials and rational functions (ratios of polynomials) in z. These have been briefly discussed above. We might now ask whether or not it is possible to make useful definitions of other elementary functions, such as $\sin z$, $\cos z$, e^z, $\cosh z$, and so on. It is hard for us to imagine $\sin(2 + 3i)$, for example, if we try to think of $2 + 3i$ as meaning an angle. In fact, we may have had trouble thinking of the meaning of the simpler expression $\sin 2$. Of course, in the latter case, we ask "2 what?" and answer "2 radians," and look up $\sin 2$ in a table. But how was the table itself constructed? Why, by means of the series

$$\sin x = x - \frac{x^3}{3!} + \frac{x^5}{5!} - \frac{x^7}{7!} + \cdots \tag{1}$$

To use the series to calculate $\sin 2$, for example, we don't need to think of radians at all, but just take $x = 2$ as a pure number. To be sure, the trigonometric identities for $\sin(x + y)$, $\cos(x + y)$, and so on, are also used in constructing tables, but the series in Eq. (1) is the basic thing.

Now, we may ask ourselves, why can't we go ahead and define $\sin z = \sin(x + iy)$ by a series like (1) but having z in place of x? The answer is, of course, we can do this if we want to and if the series converges. We are therefore led to investigate power series in z, such as

$$\sin z = z - \frac{z^3}{3!} + \frac{z^5}{5!} - \frac{z^7}{7!} + \cdots \tag{2}$$

When y is zero, then $z = x + iy = x$ and the series in (2) is the same as the series in (1). Thus it would be consistent to use the series to extend the domain of definition of $\sin z$ from the real axis into the complex plane.

Convergence

We say that a power series

$$\sum_{n=0}^{\infty} a_n z^n = a_0 + a_1 z + a_2 z^2 + \cdots \tag{3}$$

converges at a point z if the sequence of partial sums

$$s_0 = a_0,$$

$$s_1 = a_0 + a_1 z,$$

$$\vdots$$

$$s_n = a_0 + a_1 z + \cdots + a_n z^n \tag{4}$$

tends to a limit as n becomes infinite. If we separate s_n into its real and imaginary parts,

$$s_n = u_n(x, y) + iv_n(x, y), \tag{5}$$

then

$$s_n \to u + iv \qquad \text{if and only if} \qquad u_n \to u \quad \text{and} \quad v_n \to v. \tag{6}$$

This follows from the fact that

$$|s_n - (u + iv)| = |(u_n - u) + i(v_n - v)|$$
$$= \sqrt{(u_n - u)^2 + (v_n - v)^2}$$

approaches zero if and only if $u_n - u \to 0$ and $v_n - v \to 0$.

We say that the series (3) *converges absolutely* if and only if the corresponding series of absolute values

$$\sum_{n=0}^{\infty} |a_n z^n| = |a_0| + |a_1 z| + |a_2 z^2| + \cdots \tag{7}$$

converges. Since this is a series of nonnegative real numbers, we already know tests (the comparison test, integral test, ratio test, root test) for determining whether it converges. Then, if (7) does converge, the following theorem tells us that (3) also converges.

Theorem. *If a series* $\sum_{n=0}^{\infty} a_n z^n$ *converges absolutely, then it converges.*

Proof. Separate each term of the series into its real and imaginary parts, say

$$a_k z^k = c_k + id_k, \qquad k = 0, 1, 2, \ldots, \tag{8}$$

where c_k and d_k are real. Then if the series (7) converges, we use the fact that

$$|c_k| \leq \sqrt{c_k^2 + d_k^2} = |a_k z^k|, \qquad |d_k| \leq \sqrt{c_k^2 + d_k^2} = |a_k z^k|,$$

and the comparison test for nonnegative real series, to show that

$$\sum |c_k| \qquad \text{and} \qquad \sum |d_k|$$

both converge. But from this we conclude that the series

$$\sum c_k \qquad \text{and} \qquad \sum d_k,$$

(without absolute value signs) both converge. Hence

$$\sum (c_k + id_k) = \sum c_k + i \sum d_k$$

also converges. Q.E.D.

EXAMPLE. The series for $\sin z$ in Eq. (2) converges for all complex numbers z, $|z| < \infty$.

Proof. We test (2) for *absolute convergence* by examining

$$\sum_{k=1}^{\infty} \left| \frac{(-1)^{k-1} z^{2k-1}}{(2k-1)!} \right|. \tag{9}$$

We apply the ratio test with

$$U_n = \left| \frac{(-1)^{n-1} z^{2n-1}}{(2n-1)!} \right|,$$

and calculate

$$\frac{U_{n+1}}{U_n} = \frac{|z^2|}{2n(2n+1)}.$$

For *any* fixed z such that $|z| < \infty$, we then find

$$\lim_{n \to \infty} \frac{U_{n+1}}{U_n} = \lim_{n \to \infty} \frac{|z^2|}{2n(2n+1)} = 0.$$

Since this limit is less than unity, series (9) converges. That is, series (2) converges *absolutely*. Hence, by our theorem, it also converges without the absolute value signs.

PROBLEMS

Write out the first four terms of the series in Problems 1–5, and find the region in the complex plane in which each series converges absolutely.

1. $\displaystyle\sum_{n=0}^{\infty} z^n$

2. $\displaystyle\sum_{n=1}^{\infty} (-1)^{n-1} n z^{n-1}$

3. $\displaystyle\sum_{n=1}^{\infty} (-1)^{n-1} \frac{(z-1)^n}{n}$

4. $\displaystyle\sum_{n=1}^{\infty} \frac{(z+i)^n}{n}$

5. $\displaystyle\sum_{n=0}^{\infty} (-1)^n \frac{(z+1)^n}{2^n}$

6. Show that $\sum z^k/k!$ converges absolutely for all $|z| < \infty$.

7. Show that $\sum (-1)^k z^{2k}/(2k)!$ converges absolutely for all $|z| < \infty$.

8. Show that $\sum (-1)^{k-1} z^k/k$ converges absolutely for $|z| < 1$.

17–7

ELEMENTARY FUNCTIONS

We may define other functions of a complex variable as we did the function $\sin z$, by extending formulas already developed for real valued functions. Formally, we just substitute z for x, to obtain such formulas as

$$e^z = 1 + z + \frac{z^2}{2!} + \frac{z^3}{3!} + \cdots = \sum_{k=0}^{\infty} \frac{z^k}{k!}, \tag{1}$$

$$\sin z = z - \frac{z^3}{3!} + \frac{z^5}{5!} - \frac{z^7}{7!} + \cdots = \sum_{k=1}^{\infty} \frac{(-1)^{k-1} z^{2k-1}}{(2k-1)!}, \tag{2}$$

$$\cos z = 1 - \frac{z^2}{2!} + \frac{z^4}{4!} - \frac{z^6}{6!} + \cdots = \sum_{k=0}^{\infty} \frac{(-1)^k z^{2k}}{(2k)!}, \tag{3}$$

$$\tan^{-1} z = z - \frac{z^3}{3} + \frac{z^5}{5} - \frac{z^7}{7} + \cdots = \sum_{k=1}^{\infty} \frac{(-1)^{k-1} z^{2k-1}}{2k-1}, \tag{4}$$

$$\ln(1+z) = z - \frac{z^2}{2} + \frac{z^3}{3} - \frac{z^4}{4} + \cdots = \sum_{k=1}^{\infty} (-1)^{k-1} \frac{z^k}{k}. \tag{5}$$

It is easy to show, by the ratio test, that the first three of these series converge absolutely for $|z| < \infty$. The last two converge absolutely if z is inside the unit circle $|z| < 1$, and diverge if $|z| > 1$. We realize that the inverse tangent function is multiple-valued, and the series in (4) gives the so-called *principal value* of $\tan^{-1} z$. We shall show that the logarithm of a complex number is also multiple-valued, and the series in (5) gives the principal value of $\ln(1 + z)$ when $|z| < 1$.

It is a basic theorem in the theory of functions of a complex variable that a power series $\sum a_k z^k$ either

a) converges only at $z = 0$, or
b) converges inside a circle $|z| < R$, or
c) converges for all z, $|z| < \infty$.

The second case occurs when the function represented by the power series is analytic everywhere inside the circle $|z| < R$, but has a singularity on the circle $|z| = R$. In this case, the theorem tells us that the *largest* circle inside which the series will converge has radius R equal to the distance from $z = 0$ to the nearest singular point of the function. Thus, for example,

$$\frac{1}{1 + z^2} = 1 - z^2 + z^4 - z^6 + \cdots = \sum_{k=0}^{\infty} (-1)^k z^{2k} \qquad (6)$$

converges inside a circle of radius $R = 1$, since the singularities of the function occur at $z = \pm i$, which are at distance $R = 1$ from the origin. We call the circle $|z| = 1$ the "circle of convergence," by which we mean that the series converges for all z *inside* this circle and diverges for any z *outside* it (Fig. 17–13). Behavior *on* the circle of convergence constitutes a difficult problem, which we are not prepared to discuss.

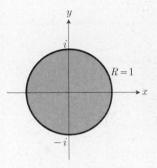

17–13   The circle of convergence of the series $\sum_{k=0}^{\infty} (-1)^k z^{2k}$.

Certain basic properties of the elementary functions can be shown to extend from the domain of real variables x to complex variables z by algebraic manipulation with series. For example, we can prove the following theorem by appealing to the series definition of e^z.

Theorem. $e^{z_1} \cdot e^{z_2} = e^{z_1 + z_2}$ \qquad (7)

Proof.   We multiply the series for e^{z_1} by the series for e^{z_2} and collect terms of like degree. By the *degree* of a term

$$z_1^p z_2^q,$$

we mean simply the sum of the exponents $p + q$. We shall focus our attention on all those terms in the product that are of a certain degree, say n. Then we may safely ignore all powers

$$z_1^{n+1}, \quad z_1^{n+2}, \quad \ldots \quad \text{and} \quad z_2^{n+1}, \quad z_2^{n+2}, \quad \ldots,$$

since these would enter only in terms of degree greater than n. Now we want all terms of the form $z_1^k z_2^{n-k}$, with $k = 0, 1, 2, \ldots, n$. When we multiply

$$e^{z_1} = 1 + z_1 + \frac{z_1^2}{2!} + \frac{z_1^3}{3!} + \cdots + \frac{z_1^n}{n!} + \cdots$$

by

$$e^{z_2} = 1 + z_2 + \frac{z_2^2}{2!} + \frac{z_2^3}{3!} + \cdots + \frac{z_2^n}{n!} + \cdots,$$

the following terms are of degree n:

$$\frac{z_1^n}{n!} \cdot 1 + \frac{z_1^{n-1}}{(n-1)!} \cdot z_2 + \frac{z_1^{n-2}}{(n-2)!} \cdot \frac{z_2^2}{2!} + \cdots$$

$$+ \frac{z_1^{n-k}}{(n-k)!} \cdot \frac{z_2^k}{k!} + \cdots + 1 \cdot \frac{z_2^n}{n!} = \sum_{k=0}^{n} \frac{z_1^{n-k} z_2^k}{(n-k)! \, k!}. \qquad (8)$$

On the other hand, the terms of degree n in the series for

$$e^{z_1 + z_2} = 1 + (z_1 + z_2) + \frac{(z_1 + z_2)^2}{2!} + \cdots + \frac{(z_1 + z_2)^n}{n!} + \cdots$$

are in the one binomial expression

$$\frac{(z_1 + z_2)^n}{n!} = \frac{1}{n!} \left[z_1^n + n z_1^{n-1} z_2 + \frac{n(n-1)}{2!} z_1^{n-2} z_2^2 + \cdots \right.$$

$$\left. + \frac{n(n-1) \cdots (n-k+1)}{k!} z_1^{n-k} z_2^k + \cdots + z_2^n \right].$$

By noticing that

$$\frac{n(n-1) \cdots (n-k+1)}{k!} \cdot \frac{(n-k)!}{(n-k)!} = \frac{n!}{k! \, (n-k)!},$$

we may also write this in summation form as

$$\frac{(z_1 + z_2)^n}{n!} = \frac{1}{n!} \sum_{k=0}^{n} \frac{n!}{k! \, (n-k)!} z_1^{n-k} z_2^k = \sum_{k=0}^{n} \frac{z_1^{n-k} z_2^k}{(n-k)! \, k!}. \qquad (9)$$

A comparison of Eqs. (8) and (9) shows us that we have precisely the same terms of degree n in the product of the two series for e^{z_1} and e^{z_2} that we have in the series for $e^{z_1 + z_2}$. The argument above is valid for any positive integer n. For $n = 0$, the terms of degree zero are

$$z_1^0 \cdot z_2^0 = 1 \qquad \text{and} \qquad (z_1 + z_2)^0 = 1,$$

respectively, and these again are equal. Thus the terms of degree n ($n = 0, 1, 2, 3, \ldots$) are the same in the product of the series for e^{z_1} and e^{z_2} as they are in the series for $e^{z_1 + z_2}$; that is,

(the series for e^{z_1}) $\cdot$ (the series for e^{z_2}) = (the series for $e^{z_1 + z_2}$).

Q.E.D.

REMARK. The sum of the series we get when we multiply two series together may depend on how the terms of the product series are arranged or grouped. The way we arranged the terms of the product $e^{z_1} \cdot e^{z_2}$ in the proof of the preceding theorem, for instance, is quite different from

$$1 \cdot \left(1 + z_2 + \frac{z_2^2}{2!} + \cdots\right) + z_1 \left(1 + z_2 + \frac{z_2^2}{2!} + \cdots\right) + \cdots$$

$$+ \frac{z_1^n}{n!} \left(1 + z_2 + \frac{z_2^2}{2!} + \cdots\right) + \cdots,$$

where we agree to add all terms not containing z_1, then all terms containing only the first power of z_1, then all terms containing only the second power of z_1, and so on. This certainly isn't convenient to do if we are trying to show that the result is the same as

$$1 + (z_1 + z_2) + \frac{(z_1 + z_2)^2}{2!} + \frac{(z_1 + z_2)^3}{3!} + \cdots$$

And conceivably it might lead to a different answer. However, it is shown in more advanced courses in analysis that when both of the series in a product are *absolutely convergent*, then it is permissible to arrange the terms in any way one may wish, provided one ultimately takes all terms into account. The series for e^z does converge absolutely for all values of z. Hence the series for e^{z_1} and e^{z_2} satisfy the requirements of this theorem, and it is permissible to arrange the terms according to ascending degree, as we have done above.

By similar operations with power series, one can show that

$$\sin (z_1 + z_2) = \sin z_1 \cos z_2 + \cos z_1 \sin z_2,$$

$$\cos (z_1 + z_2) = \cos z_1 \cos z_2 - \sin z_1 \sin z_2,$$

$$\sin^2 z + \cos^2 z = 1.$$

One of the most famous results involving the elementary complex functions is the formula

$$e^{iz} = \cos z + i \sin z, \tag{10}$$

which is known as *Euler's formula*. To establish Eq. (10) we simply substitute iz in place of z in the series (1). The various powers of i that enter can all be reduced to one of the four numbers

$$i, \quad -1, \quad -i, \quad +1$$

by observing that

$$i^2 = -1, \qquad i^3 = i^2 \cdot i = -i,$$

$$i^4 = (i^2)^2 = (-1)^2 = +1, \qquad i^5 = i^4 \cdot i = i,$$

and so on. In fact, if n is any integer, then

$$i^{4n} = +1, \qquad i^{4n+1} = i, \qquad i^{4n+2} = -1, \qquad i^{4n+3} = -i.$$

Thus we have

$$e^{iz} = 1 + iz + \frac{(iz)^2}{2!} + \frac{(iz)^3}{3!} + \frac{(iz)^4}{4!} + \frac{(iz)^5}{5!} + \cdots$$

$$= \left(1 - \frac{z^2}{2!} + \frac{z^4}{4!} - \frac{z^6}{6!} + \cdots\right) + i\left(z - \frac{z^3}{3!} + \frac{z^5}{5!} - \frac{z^7}{7!} + \cdots\right)$$

$$= \cos z + i \sin z,$$

where we have recognized the series for $\sin z$ and $\cos z$, Eqs. (2) and (3).

If we use Euler's formula (10) and the companion equation

$$e^{-iz} = \cos z - i \sin z, \tag{11}$$

which results from replacing z by $-z$ in (10), we may express the trigonometric functions of z in terms of exponentials. For example, if we add Eqs. (10) and (11) and then divide by two, we obtain

$$\cos z = \tfrac{1}{2}(e^{iz} + e^{-iz}). \tag{12a}$$

On the other hand, if we subtract (11) from (10) we may express $\sin z$ in the form

$$\sin z = \frac{1}{2i}\left(e^{iz} - e^{-iz}\right). \tag{12b}$$

The other trigonometric functions of z are defined in the usual way in terms of $\sin z$ and $\cos z$.

Thus, for example,

$$\tan z = \frac{\sin z}{\cos z} = \frac{1}{i}\,\frac{e^{iz} - e^{-iz}}{e^{iz} + e^{-iz}}.$$

To establish the usual trigonometric identities, we may express the trigonometric functions as exponentials and use Eq. (7).

EXAMPLE. Show that

$$\cos^2 z + \sin^2 z = 1.$$

Solution. We square both sides of Eqs. (12a, b) and add:

$$\cos^2 z + \sin^2 z = \tfrac{1}{4}(e^{2iz} + 2e^0 + e^{-2iz}) - \tfrac{1}{4}(e^{2iz} - 2e^0 + e^{-2iz})$$

$$= \tfrac{1}{4}(4e^0) = 1.$$

Equations (12a, b) show the very intimate relationship between the circular functions and the hyperbolic functions. For if we define, as in the real case,

$$\cosh z = \tfrac{1}{2}(e^z + e^{-z}) = 1 + \frac{z^2}{2!} + \frac{z^4}{4!} + \frac{z^6}{6!} + \cdots,$$

$$\sinh z = \tfrac{1}{2}(e^z - e^{-z}) = z + \frac{z^3}{3!} + \frac{z^5}{5!} + \frac{z^7}{7!} + \cdots,$$

then Eqs. (12a, b) say that

$$\cos z = \cosh iz, \tag{13a}$$

$$i \sin z = \sinh iz. \tag{13b}$$

These relationships explain the similarity in form between the identities of circular trigonometry, such as

$$\cos^2 z + \sin^2 z = 1, \tag{14a}$$

and the corresponding identities of hyperbolic trigonometry, such as

$$\cosh^2 u - \sinh^2 u = 1. \tag{14b}$$

In fact, any identity in circular functions produces a corresponding identity in hyperbolic functions, provided $\sin^2$ is replaced by $-\sinh^2$. The minus is a consequence of the i in Eq. (13b).

PROBLEMS

1. Take $z = (1 + i)/\sqrt{2}$ in Eq. (1), and calculate an approximation to $e^{(1+i)/\sqrt{2}}$ by using the first four terms of the series.

2. Express the sines and cosines in the following identity in terms of exponentials and thereby show that

$$\sin (A + B) = \sin A \cos B + \cos A \sin B$$

is a consequence of the exponential law $e^{z_1} \cdot e^{z_2} = e^{z_1 + z_2}$.

3. By differentiating the appropriate series, Eqs. (1)–(5), term by term, show that

a) $\dfrac{de^z}{dz} = e^z$ **b)** $\dfrac{d \sin z}{dz} = \cos z$

c) $\dfrac{d \cos z}{dz} = -\sin z$ **d)** $\dfrac{d \tan^{-1} z}{dz} = \dfrac{1}{1 + z^2}$

e) $\dfrac{d \ln (1 + z)}{dz} = \dfrac{1}{1 + z}$

4. a) Show that $y = e^{i\omega x}$ and $y = e^{-i\omega x}$ are solutions of the differential equation

$$\frac{d^2 y}{dx^2} + \omega^2 y = 0.$$

b) Show that $y = e^{(a + ib)x}$ and $y = e^{(a - ib)x}$ are solutions of the differential equation

$$\frac{d^2 y}{dx^2} - 2a \frac{dy}{dx} + (a^2 + b^2)y = 0.$$

c) Assuming that a and b are real in part 4(b) above, show that both

$$e^{ax} \cos bx = R(e^{(a + ib)x}) \quad \text{and} \quad e^{ax} \sin bx = I(e^{(a + ib)x})$$

are solutions of the given differential equation.

5. Find values of m such that $y = e^{mx}$ is a solution of the differential equation:

a) $\dfrac{d^2 y}{dx^2} + 2\dfrac{dy}{dx} + 5y = 0$ **b)** $\dfrac{d^4 y}{dx^4} + 4y = 0$

c) $\dfrac{d^3 y}{dx^3} - 8y = 0.$

6. Show that the point (x, y) describes a unit circle with angular velocity ω if $z = x + iy = e^{i\omega t}$ and ω is a real constant.

7. If x and y are real, show that $|e^{x+iy}| = e^x$.

8. Show that the real and imaginary parts of $\omega = e^z$ satisfy the Cauchy–Riemann equations.

9. Show by reference to the appropriate series that (a) $\sin (iz) = i \sinh z$, (b) $\cos (iz) = \cosh z$.

10. Show, by reference to the results of Problems 2 and 9, that $\sin (x + iy) = \sin x \cosh y + i \cos x \sinh y$, and find a value of z such that $\sin z = 2$.

11. Show that the real and imaginary parts of $\omega = \sin z$, Problem 10, satisfy the Cauchy–Riemann equations.

12. Show that $|\sin (x + iy)| = \sqrt{\sin^2 x + \sinh^2 y}$ if x and y are real.

13. Let $z = x + iy$, $w = u + iv$, $w = \sin z$. Show that the line segment $y = $ constant, $-\pi < x \leq +\pi$, in the z-plane maps into the ellipse

$$\frac{u^2}{\cosh^2 y} + \frac{v^2}{\sinh^2 y} = 1$$

in the w-plane.

14. Show that the only complex roots $z = x + iy$ (x and y real) of the equation $\sin z = 0$ are at points on the real axis ($y = 0$) at which $\sin x = 0$.

15. Show that

$$\cosh (x + iy) = \cosh x \cos y + i \sinh x \sin y.$$

16. Show that

$$|\cosh (x + iy)| = \sqrt{\cos^2 y + \sinh^2 x}$$

if x and y are real.

17. If x and y are real and $\cosh (x + iy) = 0$, show that $x = 0$ and $\cos y = 0$.

18. What is the image in the w-plane of a line $x = $ constant in the z-plane if (a) $w = e^z$, (b) $w = \sin z$? Sketch.

19. Integrate: $\int e^{(a + ib)x} dx$ and, by equating real and imaginary parts, obtain formulas for $\int e^{ax} \cos bx \, dx$ and $\int e^{ax} \sin bx \, dx$.

17–8

LOGARITHMS

In the previous article, we mentioned that the logarithm (as an inverse of the exponential) is a multiple-valued function of z. The multiple-valuedness is introduced by the polar angle θ. We see this when we write

$$z = r \operatorname{cis} \theta$$

or, as we may do in view of Euler's formula,

$$z = re^{i\theta}, \tag{1}$$

and ask that

$$\log_e z = \log_e r + \log_e e^{i\theta}$$
$$= \ln r + i\theta. \tag{2}$$

Then the angle θ may be given its principal value θ_0, $-\pi < \theta_0 \le \pi$, which leads to the *principal value* of log z,

$$\ln z = \ln r + i\theta_0, \qquad -\pi < \theta_0 \le \pi. \tag{3}$$

But many other values of θ will still give the same z in Eq. (1), namely,

$$\theta = \theta_0 + 2n\pi, \qquad n = 0, \pm 1, \pm 2, \ldots, \tag{4}$$

and each of these values of θ gives rise, in turn, to a value of log z (we shall omit writing the base e henceforth), namely,

$$\log z = \ln r + i(\theta_0 + 2n\pi). \tag{5a}$$

In terms of the principal value, we have

$$\log z = \ln z + 2n\pi i, \tag{5b}$$

so that all of the infinitely many different values of log z differ from the principal value by an integral multiple of $2\pi i$.

EXAMPLE.   Find all values of log $(1 + i)$.

Solution. The complex number $1 + i$ is seen to have polar coordinates $r = \sqrt{2}$, $\theta_0 = \pi/4$ (Fig. 17–14). Hence

$$1 + i = \sqrt{2}\, e^{i(\pi/4 + 2n\pi)}$$

and

$$\log (1 + i) = \ln \sqrt{2} + i\left(\frac{\pi}{4} + 2n\pi\right),$$

$$n = 0, \pm 1, \pm 2, \ldots$$

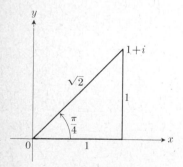

17–14   Argand diagram of $1 + i$.

PROBLEMS

1. Find the principal value of log z for each of the following complex numbers z:

a) $2 - 2i$, **b)** $\sqrt{3} + i$, **c)** -4,

d) $+4$, **e)** $2i$, **f)** $\dfrac{1 + i}{1 - i}$.

2. Find *all* values of log z for each of the following complex numbers z:

a) 2, **b)** -2, **c)** $2i$,

d) $-2i$, **e)** $i - \sqrt{3}$.

3. Express $w = \tan z$ in terms of exponentials; then solve for z in terms of w and thereby show that

$$\tan^{-1} w = \frac{1}{2i} \log \frac{1 + iw}{1 - iw}.$$

4. a) Show that

$$\sin^{-1} z = -i \log (iz + \sqrt{1 - z^2}).$$

b) Find $\sin^{-1} 3$.

5. Sketch the images in the w-plane of the following sets in the z-plane, under the mapping function $w = \ln z$:

a) $|z| = $ constant, $-\pi < \arg z \leq +\pi$,

b) $\arg z = $ constant, $0 < |z| < +\infty$.

REVIEW QUESTIONS AND EXERCISES

1. Define the system of complex numbers.

2. Define, for complex numbers, the concepts of equality, addition, multiplication, and division.

3. Is the system of complex numbers closed under the operations of addition, subtraction, multiplication, division (by numbers $\neq 0$), and raising to powers (including complex exponents; see Article 6–9, Eq. (3))? [A system is said to be *closed* under an operation $\otimes$ if $a \otimes b$ is in the system whenever a and b are.]

4. How may the complex number $a + ib$ be represented graphically in an Argand diagram?

5. Illustrate, on an Argand diagram, how the absolute values and arguments of the product and quotient of two complex numbers z_1 and z_2 are related to the absolute values and the arguments of z_1 and z_2.

6. State De Moivre's theorem, and explain how it may be used to find expressions for $\cos n\theta$ and $\sin n\theta$ as polynomials in $\cos \theta$ and $\sin \theta$.

7. Prove that, if n is an even positive integer, then $\cos n\theta$ may be expressed as a polynomial, with integral coefficients, in $\cos^2 \theta$. [*Example.* $\cos 2\theta = 2 \cos^2 \theta - 1$.]

8. Using an Argand diagram, explain how to find the n complex nth roots of any complex number $a + ib$.

9. On an Argand diagram, illustrate how the conjugate and the reciprocal of a complex number $a + ib$ are related to that number.

10. If the conjugate of a complex number is equal to the number, what else can you conclude about the number?

11. If z is a complex number such that $z = -\bar{z}$, what more can you conclude about z?

12. What is the location of the complex variable z if:

a) $|z - \alpha| = k$ **b)** $|z - \alpha| < k$ **c)** $|z - \alpha| > k$,

when $\alpha = a + ib$ is a given complex number and k is a positive real constant?

13. Define the concept of continuity of a function of a complex variable, $w = f(z)$. Define the derivative of f at $\alpha = a + ib$.

14. What are the Cauchy–Riemann equations, and when are they known to be satisfied?

15. Define convergence of a series of complex numbers.

16. How do we define e^z, $\sin z$, $\cos z$, $\log z$, and $\tan z$ for complex $z = x + iy$?

17. How would you define z^α for complex z and α? Illustrate for $z = 1 + i$, $\alpha = 2i$.

MISCELLANEOUS PROBLEMS

1. Let $z = 2 - 2i$, $i = \sqrt{-1}$. (a) Plot the points z, $\bar{z}$, and z^2. (b) Plot the three complex cube roots of z^2 (that is, $z^{2/3}$).

2. Express each of the following complex numbers in the form $re^{i\theta}$ with $r \geq 0$ and $-\pi < \theta \leq \pi$. Sketch.

a) $(1 + i)(1 - i\sqrt{3})^2$ **b)** $\sqrt[3]{2 - 2i}$ (three answers).

3. Express the following complex numbers in the form $a + bi$.

a) The four 4th roots of $-16i$

b) $\sin^{-1} (5)$.

4. (a) Solve the equation $z^4 + 16 = 0$, obtaining four distinct roots. (b) Express the five roots of the equation $z^5 + 32 = 0$ in polar form.

5. (a) Find all complex numbers z such that $z^4 + 1 + i\sqrt{3} = 0$. (b) Express the number $e^{2 + \pi i/4}$ in the form $a + bi$.

6. Plot the complex number $2 - 2\sqrt{3}\,i$ in an Argand diagram and find (a) its two square roots, (b) the principal value of its logarithm.

7. Find values of r and θ such that $3 + 4i = re^{i\theta}$.

8. If $z = 3 - 3i$, find all values of log z.

9. Find a complex number $a + ib$ that will satisfy the equation

$$e^{a + ib} = 1 - i\sqrt{3}.$$

10. Express the following in the form $a + bi$:

a) $(-1 - i)^{1/3}$ (write down all the roots),
b) $\ln (3 + i\sqrt{3})$,
c) $e^{2 + \pi i}$.

11. Let $f(z) = \bar{z} = $ the conjugate of z. (a) Study the behavior of the quotient

$$\frac{f(z) - f(z_1)}{z - z_1}$$

when $z \to z_1$ along straight lines of slope m. (b) From the results of (a) what can you conclude about the derivative of $f(z)$?

12. If $f(z) = \sum_{n=0}^{\infty} a_n z^n$ and $f(\bar{z}) = \overline{f(z)}$, for $|z| < R$, show that the a_n are real.

13. If $f(z) = \sum_{n=0}^{\infty} a_n z^n$ and $f(\bar{z}) = f(z)$, for $|z| < R$, show that $f(z)$ is a constant.

14. Show that

$$\frac{d^n}{d\theta^n} (\cos \theta + i \sin \theta) = i^n(\cos \theta + i \sin \theta).$$

15. In each of the following, indicate graphically the locus of points $z = x + iy$ that satisfy the given condition:

a) $R(z) > 0$, **b)** $I(z - i) \le 0$, **c)** $\left| \dfrac{z - i}{z + i} \right| < 1$,
d) $|e^z| \ge 1$, **e)** $|\sin z| \le 1$.

16. If $u(x, y)$, $v(x, y)$ are the real and imaginary parts of an analytic function of $z = x + iy$, show that the family of curves $u = $ constant is orthogonal to the family $v = $ constant at every point of intersection where $f'(z) \ne 0$.

17. Let $u(x, y) + iv(x, y) = (x + iy)^2$. Sketch the curves $u(x, y) = a$, $v(x, y) = b$, for the cases $a = 1, 0, -1$, and $b = 1, 0, -1$. Show that the locus $u = 0$ is not orthogonal to the locus $v = 0$.

18. Verify that the real and imaginary parts of the following functions satisfy Laplace's equation $\phi_{xx} + \phi_{yy} = 0$:

a) $\sin z$ **b)** $\ln z \; (z \ne 0)$
c) e^z **d)** $\cosh z$

19. Find all solutions of the following equations:

a) $z^5 = 32$ **b)** $e^z = -2$
c) $\cos z = 10$ **d)** $\tanh z = 2$
e) $z = i^i$ **f)** $z^3 + 3z^2 + 3z + 9 = 0$

DIFFERENTIAL EQUATIONS

18–1

INTRODUCTION

A differential equation is an equation that involves one or more derivatives, or differentials. Differential equations are classified by

a) type (namely, *ordinary* or *partial*),

b) order (that of the highest order derivative that occurs in the equation), and

c) degree (the exponent of the highest power of the highest order derivative, after the equation has been cleared of fractions and radicals in the dependent variable and its derivatives).

For example,

$$\left(\frac{d^3y}{dx^3}\right)^2 + \left(\frac{d^2y}{dx^2}\right)^5 + \frac{y}{x^2 + 1} = e^x \tag{1}$$

is an ordinary differential equation, of order three and degree two.

Only "ordinary" derivatives occur when the dependent variable y is a function of a single independent variable x. On the other hand, if the dependent variable y is a function of two or more independent variables, say

$$y = f(x, t),$$

where x and t are independent variables, then partial derivatives of y may occur. For example,

$$\frac{\partial^2 y}{\partial t^2} = a^2 \frac{\partial^2 y}{\partial x^2} \tag{2}$$

is a partial differential equation, of order two and degree one. (It is the one-dimensional "wave equation." A systematic treatment of partial differential equations lies beyond the scope of this book. For a discussion of partial differential equations, including the wave equation, and solutions of associated physical problems, see Kaplan, *Advanced Calculus*, Chapter 10.)

Many physical problems, when formulated in mathematical terms, lead to differential equations. In Article 11–2, for example, we discussed and solved the system of differential equations

$$m\frac{d^2x}{dt^2} = 0, \qquad m\frac{d^2y}{dt^2} = -mg \tag{3}$$

which described the motion of a projectile (neglecting air resistance). Indeed, one of the chief sources of differential equations in mechanics is Newton's second law:

$$\mathbf{F} = \frac{d}{dt}(m\mathbf{v}), \tag{4}$$

where $\mathbf{F}$ is the resultant of the forces acting on a body of mass m and $\mathbf{v}$ is its velocity.

In the field of radiochemistry, the following situation is a typical simplification of what may happen. Suppose that, at time t, there are x, y, and z grams, respectively, of three radioactive substances A, B, and C, which have the following properties:

i) A, through radioactive decomposition, transforms into B at a rate proportional to the amount of A present.

ii) B, in turn, transforms into C at a rate proportional to the amount of B present.

iii) Finally, C transforms back into A at a rate proportional to the amount of C present; see Fig. 18–1.

If we call the proportionality factors k_1, k_2, and k_3, respectively, we have the following system of differential equations:

$$\frac{dx}{dt} = -k_1 x + k_3 z, \qquad \frac{dy}{dt} = k_1 x - k_2 y, \qquad \frac{dz}{dt} = k_2 y - k_3 z. \qquad (5)$$

The first of these simply says that the amount of A present at time t, namely x, is decreasing at a rate $k_1 x$ through transformation into substance B, but is gaining at a rate $k_3 z$ from substance C. The other two equations have similar meanings. It is an immediate consequence of Eqs. (5) that

$$\frac{dx}{dt} + \frac{dy}{dt} + \frac{dz}{dt} = 0. \qquad (6)$$

From Eq. (6), in turn, we readily deduce that

$$x + y + z = \text{constant}.$$

In other words, in the hypothetical case under consideration, the total amount of substances A, B, and C remains constant.

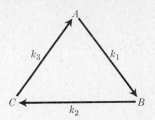

18–1 Three radioactive substances may transform in such a way that A changes into B, B into C, and C back into A.

A function

$$y = f(x)$$

is said to be a *solution* of a differential equation if the latter is satisfied when y and its derivatives are replaced throughout by $f(x)$ and its corresponding derivatives. For example, if c_1 and c_2 are any constants, then

$$y = c_1 \cos x + c_2 \sin x \qquad (1a)$$

is a solution of the differential equation

$$\frac{d^2 y}{dx^2} + y = 0. \qquad (1b)$$

A physical problem that translates into a differential equation usually involves additional conditions not expressed by the differential equation itself. In mechanics, for example, the initial position and velocity of the moving body are usually prescribed, as well as the forces. The differential equation, or equations, of motion will usually have solutions in which certain arbitrary constants occur, as in (1a) above. Specific values are then assigned to these arbitrary constants to meet the prescribed initial conditions. (See the examples worked out in Articles 6–11 and 11–2.)

18–2

SOLUTIONS

A differential equation of order n will generally have a solution involving n arbitrary constants. (There is a more precise mathematical theorem, which we shall neither state nor prove.) This solution is called the *general* solution. Once this general solution is known, it is only a matter of algebra to determine specific values of the constants if initial conditions are also prescribed. Hence we shall devote our attention to the problem of finding the general solutions of certain types of differential equations.

The subject of differential equations is complex, and there are many textbooks on differential equations and advanced calculus where you can find a more extensive treatment than we shall present here. The field is also the subject of a great deal of current research; and, with the widespread availability of computers, numerical methods for solving differential equations play an important role.

In the remainder of this chapter, the following topics will be treated. Throughout, only *ordinary* differential equations will be considered.

1. First order.
   a) Variables separable.   c) Linear.
   b) Homogeneous.   d) Exact differentials.

2. Special types of second order.

3. Linear equations with constant coefficients.
   a) Homogeneous.
   b) Nonhomogeneous.

Several new terms occur in this list, and they will be defined in the appropriate places.

PROBLEMS

Show that each function is a solution of the accompanying differential equation.

1. $xy'' - y' = 0$;

a) $y = x^2 + 3$;   b) $y = C_1 x^2 + C_2$

2. $x^3 y''' + 4x^2 y'' + xy' + y = x$; $y = \frac{1}{2}x$

3. $yy'' = 2(y')^2 - 2y'$;

a) $y = C$;   b) $C_1 y = \tan(C_1 x + C_2)$

4. $y' + \frac{1}{x} y = 1$; $y = \frac{C}{x} + \frac{x}{2}$

5. $2y' + 3y = e^{-x}$; $y = e^{-x} + Ce^{-(3/2)x}$

6. $(x \sin x)y' + (\sin x + x \cos x)y = e^x/x$;

$$y = \frac{1}{x \sin x} \int_{-1/2}^{x} \frac{e^t}{t} \, dt$$

18–3

FIRST ORDER: VARIABLES SEPARABLE

A first order differential equation can be solved by integration if it is possible to collect all y terms with dy and all x terms with dx. That is, if it is possible to write the equation in the form

$$f(y) \, dy + g(x) \, dx = 0,$$

then the general solution is

$$\int f(y) \, dy + \int g(x) \, dx = C,$$

where C is an arbitrary constant.

EXAMPLE.   Solve the equation

$$(x + 1)\frac{dy}{dx} = x(y^2 + 1).$$

Solution.   We change to differential form, separate the variables, and integrate:

$$(x + 1)\, dy = x(y^2 + 1)\, dx,$$

$$\frac{dy}{y^2 + 1} = \frac{x\, dx}{x + 1},$$

$$\tan^{-1} y = x - \ln |x + 1| + C.$$

Some models of population growth assume that the rate of change of the population at time t is proportional to the number y of individuals present at that time. This leads to the equation

$$\frac{dy}{dt} = ky, \qquad\qquad\qquad (1)$$

where k is a constant that is positive if the population is increasing and negative if it is decreasing. To solve Eq. (1), we separate variables and integrate, to obtain

$$\int \frac{dy}{y} = \int k\, dt,$$

or

$$\ln y = kt + C_1$$

(remember that y is positive). It follows that

$$y = e^{kt + C_1}$$

$$= Ce^{kt},$$

where $C = e^{C_1}$. If y_0 denotes the population when $t = 0$, then $C = y_0$ and

$$y = y_0 e^{kt}. \qquad\qquad\qquad (2)$$

This equation is called the *law of exponential growth.*

PROBLEMS

Separate the variables and solve the following differential equations.

1. $x(2y - 3)\, dx + (x^2 + 1)\, dy = 0$

2. $x^2(y^2 + 1)\, dx + y\sqrt{x^3 + 1}\, dy = 0$

3. $\dfrac{dy}{dx} = e^{x-y}$

4. $\sqrt{2xy}\,\dfrac{dy}{dx} = 1$

5. $\sin x\,\dfrac{dx}{dy} + \cosh 2y = 0$

6. $\ln x\,\dfrac{dx}{dy} = \dfrac{x}{y}$

7. $xe^y\, dy + \dfrac{x^2 + 1}{y}\, dx = 0$

8. $y\sqrt{2x^2 + 3}\, dy + x\sqrt{4 - y^2}\, dx = 0$

9. $\sqrt{1 + x^2}\, dy + \sqrt{y^2 - 1}\, dx = 0$

10. $x^2 y\,\dfrac{dy}{dx} = (1 + x)\csc y$

11. *Growth of bacteria.* Suppose that the bacteria in a colony can grow unchecked, by the law of exponential growth. The colony starts with one bacterium, and doubles every half hour. How many bacteria will the colony contain at the end of 24 hours? (Under favorable laboratory conditions, the number of cholera bacteria can double every 30 minutes. Of course, in an infected person, many of the bacteria are destroyed, but this example helps to explain why a person who feels well in the morning may be dangerously ill by evening.)

12. *Discharging capacitor.* As a result of leakage, an electrical capacitor discharges at a rate proportional to the charge. If the charge Q has the value Q_0 at the time $t = 0$, find Q as a function of t.

13. *Electric current.* Ohm's law, $E = Ri$, requires modification in a circuit containing self-inductance, as in a coil. The modified form is

$$L\frac{di}{dt} + Ri = E$$

for the series circuit shown in Fig. 18–2. Here R denotes the resistance of the circuit in ohms, L is the inductance in henries, E is the impressed electromotive force in volts, i is the current in amperes, and t is the time in seconds. (See Sears, Zemansky, Young, *University Physics* (Fifth ed., 1976), Chapter 28.) (a) Solve the differential equation under the assumption that E is constant, and that $i = 0$ when $t = 0$. (b) Find the steady-state current $i_{ss} = \lim_{t \to \infty} i$. (See Fig. 18–3.)

14. The decay of a radioactive element can be described by Eq. (2), because the rate of decay is proportional to the number of radioactive nuclei present. The *half-life* of a radioactive element is the time required for half of the radioactive nuclei originally present in any sample to decay. Show that the half-life of a radioactive element is a constant that does not depend on the number of radioactive nuclei initially present in the sample.

15. *Carbon-14 dating.* The half-lives of radioactive elements (see Problem 14) can sometimes be used to date events from the earth's past. The ages of rocks more than 2 billion years old have been measured by the extent of the radioactive decay of uranium (half-life 4.5 billion years!). In a living organism, the ratio of radioactive carbon, carbon-14, to

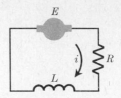

18–2 A simple series circuit.

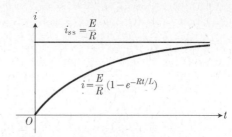

18–3 The current i in the circuit shown in Fig. 18–2 increases toward the steady state value E/R.

ordinary carbon stays fairly constant during the lifetime of the organism, being approximately equal to the ratio in the organism's surroundings at the time. After the organism's death, however, no new carbon is ingested, and the proportion of carbon-14 in the organism's remains changes as the carbon-14 decays. Since the half-life of carbon-14 is known to be about 5700 years, it is possible to estimate the age of organic remains by comparing the proportion of carbon-14 they contain with the proportion assumed to have been in the organism's environment at the time it lived. Archeologists have dated shells (which contain $CaCO_3$), seeds, and wooden artifacts this way. The estimate of 15,500 years for the age of the cave paintings at Lascaux, France, is based on carbon-14 dating.

a) Find k in Eq. (2) for carbon-14.

b) What is the age of a sample of charcoal in which 90 percent of the carbon-14 has decayed?

c) The charcoal from a tree killed in the volcanic eruption that formed Crater Lake in Oregon contained $44\frac{1}{2}$ percent of the carbon-14 found in living matter. About how old is Crater Lake?

18–4

FIRST ORDER: HOMOGENEOUS

Occasionally a differential equation whose variables cannot be separated can be transformed by a change of variable into an equation whose variables can be separated. This is the case with any equation that can be put into the form

$$\frac{dy}{dx} = F\left(\frac{y}{x}\right). \tag{1}$$

Such an equation is called *homogeneous*.

To transform Eq. (1) into an equation whose variables may be separated, we introduce the new independent variable

$$v = \frac{y}{x}. \tag{2}$$

Then

$$y = vx, \qquad \frac{dy}{dx} = v + x\frac{dv}{dx},$$

and (1) becomes

$$v + x\frac{dv}{dx} = F(v). \tag{3}$$

Equation (3) can be solved by separation of variables:

$$\frac{dx}{x} + \frac{dv}{v - F(v)} = 0. \tag{4}$$

After (4) is solved, the solution of the original equation is obtained when we replace v by y/x.

EXAMPLE. Show that the equation

$$(x^2 + y^2)\,dx + 2xy\,dy = 0$$

is homogeneous, and solve it.

Solution. From the given equation, we have

$$\frac{dy}{dx} = -\frac{x^2 + y^2}{2xy} = -\frac{1 + (y/x)^2}{2(y/x)}.$$

This has the form of Eq. (1), with

$$F(v) = -\frac{1 + v^2}{2v}, \qquad \text{where} \quad v = \frac{y}{x}.$$

Then Eq. (4) becomes

$$\frac{dx}{x} + \frac{dv}{v + \dfrac{1 + v^2}{2v}} = 0,$$

or

$$\frac{dx}{x} + \frac{2v\,dv}{1 + 3v^2} = 0.$$

The solution of this is

$$\ln|x| + \tfrac{1}{3}\ln(1 + 3v^2) = \tfrac{1}{3}\ln C,$$

so that

$$x^3(1 + 3v^2) = \pm C.$$

In terms of y and x, the solution is

$$x(x^2 + 3y^2) = C.$$

PROBLEMS

Show that the following equations are homogeneous, and solve.

1. $(x^2 + y^2)\, dx + xy\, dy = 0$

2. $x^2\, dy + (y^2 - xy)\, dx = 0$

3. $(xe^{y/x} + y)\, dx - x\, dy = 0$

4. $(x + y)\, dy + (x - y)\, dx = 0$

5. $y' = \dfrac{y}{x} + \cos \dfrac{y - x}{x}$

6. $\left(x \sin \dfrac{y}{x} - y \cos \dfrac{y}{x}\right) dx + x \cos \dfrac{y}{x}\, dy = 0$

7. Solve the equation

$$(x + y + 1)\, dx + (y - x - 3)\, dy = 0$$

by making a change of variable of the form

$$x = r + a, \qquad y = s + b,$$

and choosing the constants a and b so that the resulting equation is

$$(r + s)\, dr + (r - s)\, ds = 0.$$

Then solve this equation and express its solution in terms of x and y.

8. Use the substitution $u = x + y$ to solve the equation $y' = (x + y)^2$.

If every member of a family of curves is a solution of the differential equation

$$M(x, y)\, dx + N(x, y)\, dy = 0,$$

while every member of a second family of curves is a solution of the related equation

$$N(x, y)\, dx - M(x, y)\, dy = 0,$$

then each curve of the one family is orthogonal to every curve of the other family. Each family is said to be a family of *orthogonal trajectories* of the other. In Problems 9 and 10, find the family of solutions of the given differential equation and the family of orthogonal trajectories. Sketch both families.

9. $x\, dy - 2y\, dx = 0$

10. $2xy\, dy + (x^2 - y^2)\, dx = 0$

11. Find the orthogonal trajectories of the family of curves $xy = c$.

18-5

FIRST ORDER: LINEAR

The complexity of a differential equation depends primarily upon the way in which the *dependent* variable and its derivatives occur. Of particular importance are those equations that are linear. In a linear differential equation, each term of the equation is of degree one or zero, where, in computing the degree of a term, we add the exponents of the dependent variable and of any of its derivatives that occur. Thus, for example, (d^2y/dx^2) is of the first degree, while $y(dy/dx)$ is of the second degree because we must add 1 for the exponent of y, and 1 for the exponent of dy/dx.

A differential equation of first order, which is also linear, can always be put into the standard form

$$\frac{dy}{dx} + Py = Q, \tag{1}$$

where P and Q are functions of x.

One method for solving Eq. (1) is to find a function $\rho = \rho(x)$ such that if the equation is multiplied by ρ, the left side becomes the derivative of the product ρy. That is, we multiply (1) by ρ,

$$\rho \frac{dy}{dx} + \rho P y = \rho Q, \tag{1'}$$

and then try to impose upon ρ the condition that

$$\rho \frac{dy}{dx} + \rho Py = \frac{d}{dx}(\rho y). \tag{2}$$

When we expand the right side of (2) and cancel terms, we obtain, as the condition to be satisfied by ρ,

$$\frac{d\rho}{dx} = \rho P. \tag{3}$$

In Eq. (3), $P = P(x)$ is a known function, so we can separate the variables and solve for ρ:

$$\frac{d\rho}{\rho} = P\,dx, \quad \ln|\rho| = \int P\,dx + \ln C,$$

$$\rho = \pm Ce^{\int P\,dx}. \tag{4}$$

Since we do not require the most general function ρ, we may take $\pm C = 1$ in (4) and use

$$\rho = e^{\int P\,dx}. \tag{5}$$

This function is called an *integrating factor* for Eq. (1). With its help, (1') becomes

$$\frac{d}{dx}(\rho y) = \rho Q,$$

whose solution is

$$\rho y = \int \rho Q\,dx + C. \tag{6}$$

Since ρ is given by (5), while P and Q are known from the given differential equation (1), we have, in Eqs. (5) and (6), a summary of all that is required to solve (1).

EXAMPLE 1.   Solve the equation

$$\frac{dy}{dx} + y = e^x.$$

Solution

$$P = 1, \quad Q = e^x,$$

$$\rho = e^{\int dx} = e^x,$$

$$e^x y = \int e^{2x}\,dx + C = \tfrac{1}{2}e^{2x} + C,$$

$$y = \tfrac{1}{2}e^x + Ce^{-x}.$$

EXAMPLE 2.   Solve the equation

$$x\frac{dy}{dx} - 3y = x^2.$$

Solution. We put the equation in standard form,

$$\frac{dy}{dx} - \frac{3}{x}y = x,$$

and then read off

$$P = -\frac{3}{x}, \qquad Q = x.$$

Hence

$$\rho = e^{\int -(3/x)\,dx} = e^{-3\ln x} = \frac{1}{e^{3\ln x}} = \frac{1}{x^3},$$

and

$$\frac{1}{x^3}y = \int \frac{x}{x^3}\,dx + C = -\frac{1}{x} + C,$$

$$y = -x^2 + Cx^3.$$

REMARKS. Note that whenever $\int P\,dx$ involves logarithms, as in Example 2, it is profitable to simplify the expression for $e^{\int P\,dx}$ before substituting into Eq. (6). To simplify the expression, we use the properties of the logarithmic and exponential functions:

$$e^{\ln A} = A, \qquad e^{m\ln A} = A^m, \qquad e^{n+m\ln A} = A^m e^n.$$

A differential equation that is linear in y and dy/dx may also be separable, or homogeneous. In such cases, we have a choice of methods of solution. Observe also that an equation that is linear in x and dx/dy can be solved by the technique of this article; one need only interchange the roles of x and y in Eqs. (1), (5), and (6).

PROBLEMS

Solve:

1. $\dfrac{dy}{dx} + 2y = e^{-x}$ **2.** $2\dfrac{dy}{dx} - y = e^{x/2}$

3. $x\dfrac{dy}{dx} + 3y = \dfrac{\sin x}{x^2}$ **4.** $x\,dy + y\,dx = \sin x\,dx$

5. $x\,dy + y\,dx = y\,dy$

6. $(x-1)^3\dfrac{dy}{dx} + 4(x-1)^2 y = x + 1$

7. $\cosh x\,dy + (y\sinh x + e^x)\,dx = 0$

8. $e^{2y}\,dx + 2(xe^{2y} - y)\,dy = 0$

9. $(x - 2y)\,dy + y\,dx = 0$

10. $(y^2 + 1)\,dx + (2xy + 1)\,dy = 0$

11. If glucose is fed intravenously at a constant rate, the change in the overall concentration $c(t)$ of glucose in the blood with respect to time may be described by the differential equation

$$\frac{dc}{dt} = \frac{G}{100V} - kc.$$

In this equation, G, V, and k are positive constants, G being the rate at which glucose is admitted, in milligrams per minute, and V the volume of blood in the body, in liters (around 5 liters for an adult). The concentration $c(t)$ is measured in milligrams per centiliter. The term $-kc$ is included because the glucose is assumed to be changing continually into other molecules at a rate proportional to its concentration. (a) Solve the equation for $c(t)$, using c_0 to denote $c(0)$. (b) Find the steady state concentration, $\lim_{t\to\infty} c(t)$.

An equation that can be written in the form

$$M(x, y) \, dx + N(x, y) \, dy = 0, \tag{1}$$

and having the property that

$$\frac{\partial M}{\partial y} = \frac{\partial N}{\partial x}, \tag{2}$$

is said to be *exact*, because its left side is an exact differential. The technique of solving an exact equation consists in finding a function $f(x, y)$ such that

$$df = M \, dx + N \, dy. \tag{3}$$

Then (1) becomes

$$df = 0$$

and the solution is

$$f(x, y) = C,$$

where C is an arbitrary constant. The method of finding $f(x, y)$ to satisfy (3) is discussed and illustrated in Article 13–13.

It can be proved that every first-order differential equation

$$P(x, y) \, dx + Q(x, y) \, dy = 0$$

can be made exact by multiplication by a suitable *integrating factor* $\rho(x, y)$. Such an integrating factor has the property that

$$\frac{\partial}{\partial y} [\rho(x, y)P(x, y)] = \frac{\partial}{\partial x} [\rho(x, y)Q(x, y)].$$

Unfortunately, it is not easy to determine ρ from this equation. In fact, there is no general technique by which even a single integrating factor can be produced for an arbitrary differential equation, and the search for one can be a frustrating experience. However, one can often recognize certain combinations of differentials that can be made exact by the use of "ingenious devices."

EXAMPLE. Solve the equation

$$x \, dy - y \, dx = xy^2 \, dx.$$

Solution. The combination $x \, dy - y \, dx$ may ring a bell in our memories and cause us to recall the formula

$$d\left(\frac{u}{v}\right) = \frac{v \, du - u \, dv}{v^2} = -\left[\frac{u \, dv - v \, du}{v^2}\right].$$

Therefore we might divide the given equation by x^2, or change signs and divide by y^2. Clearly, the latter approach will be more profitable, so we proceed as follows:

$$x \, dy - y \, dx = xy^2 \, dx, \qquad \frac{y \, dx - x \, dy}{y^2} = -x \, dx,$$

$$d\left(\frac{x}{y}\right) + x \, dx = 0, \qquad \frac{x}{y} + \frac{x^2}{2} = C.$$

The same result would be obtained if we wrote our equation in the form

$$(xy^2 + y) \, dx - x \, dy = 0$$

and multiplied by the integrating factor $1/y^2$. This would give

$$\left(x + \frac{1}{y}\right) dx - \left(\frac{x}{y^2}\right) dy = 0,$$

which is exact, since

$$\frac{\partial}{\partial y}\left(x + \frac{1}{y}\right) = \frac{\partial}{\partial x}\left(-\frac{x}{y^2}\right).$$

PROBLEMS

In Problems 1–3, use the given integrating factors to make differential equations exact. Then solve the equations.

1. $(x + 2y) \, dx - x \, dy = 0; \quad 1/x^3$

2. $y \, dx + x \, dy = 0;$

a) $\dfrac{1}{xy}$ **b)** $\dfrac{1}{(xy)^2}$

3. $y \, dx - x \, dy = 0;$

a) $\dfrac{1}{y^2}$ **b)** $\dfrac{1}{x^2}$

c) $\dfrac{1}{xy}$ **d)** $\dfrac{1}{x^2 + y^2}$

4. $(x + y) \, dx + (x + y^2) \, dy = 0$

5. $(2xe^y + e^x) \, dx + (x^2 + 1)e^y \, dy = 0$

6. $(2xy + y^2) \, dx + (x^2 + 2xy - y) \, dy = 0$

7. $(x + \sqrt{y^2 + 1}) \, dx - \left(y - \dfrac{xy}{\sqrt{y^2 + 1}}\right) dy = 0$

8. $x \, dy - y \, dx + x^3 \, dx = 0$

9. $x \, dy - y \, dx = (x^2 + y^2) \, dx$

10. $(x^2 + x - y) \, dx + x \, dy = 0$

11. $\left(e^x + \ln y + \dfrac{y}{x}\right) dx + \left(\dfrac{x}{y} + \ln x + \sin y\right) dy = 0$

12. $\left(\dfrac{y^2}{1 + x^2} - 2y\right) dx + (2y \tan^{-1} x - 2x + \sinh y) \, dy = 0$

13. $dy + \dfrac{y - \sin x}{x} \, dx = 0$

18–7

SPECIAL TYPES OF SECOND ORDER EQUATIONS

Certain types of second order differential equations, of which the general form is

$$F\left(x, y, \frac{dy}{dx}, \frac{d^2y}{dx^2}\right) = 0, \tag{1}$$

can be reduced to first order equations by a suitable change of variables.

Type 1. *Equations with dependent variable missing.* When Eq. (1) has the special form

$$F\left(x, \frac{dy}{dx}, \frac{d^2y}{dx^2}\right) = 0, \tag{2}$$

we can reduce it to a first order equation by substituting

$$p = \frac{dy}{dx}, \qquad \frac{d^2y}{dx^2} = \frac{dp}{dx}.$$

Then Eq. (2) takes the form

$$F\left(x, p, \frac{dp}{dx}\right) = 0,$$

which is of the first order in p. If this can be solved for p as a function of x, say

$$p = \phi(x, C_1);$$

then we can find y by one additional integration:

$$y = \int (dy/dx)\, dx = \int p\, dx = \int \phi(x, C_1)\, dx + C_2.$$

The differential equation

$$\frac{d^2y}{dx^2} = \frac{w}{H} \sqrt{1 + \left(\frac{dy}{dx}\right)^2}$$

was solved by this technique in Article 9–6.

Type 2. *Equations with independent variable missing.* When Eq. (1) does not contain x explicitly but has the form

$$F\left(y, \frac{dy}{dx}, \frac{d^2y}{dx^2}\right) = 0, \tag{3}$$

the substitutions to use are

$$p = \frac{dy}{dx} \qquad \text{and} \qquad \frac{d^2y}{dx^2} = p\frac{dp}{dy}.$$

Then Eq. (3) takes the form

$$F\left(y, p, p\frac{dp}{dy}\right) = 0,$$

which is of the first order in p. Its solution gives p in terms of y, and then a further integration gives the solution of Eq. (3).

EXAMPLE. Solve the equation

$$\frac{d^2y}{dx^2} + y = 0.$$

Solution. Let

$$\frac{dy}{dx} = p, \qquad \frac{d^2y}{dx^2} = \frac{dp}{dx} = \frac{dp}{dy}\frac{dy}{dx} = \frac{dp}{dy}p.$$

Then we proceed as follows:

$$p \frac{dp}{dy} + y = 0, \qquad p \, dp + y \, dy = 0,$$

$$\frac{p^2}{2} + \frac{y^2}{2} = \frac{C_1^2}{2}, \qquad p = \frac{dy}{dx} = \pm \sqrt{C_1^2 - y^2},$$

$$\frac{dy}{\sqrt{C_1^2 - y^2}} = \pm dx, \qquad \sin^{-1} \frac{y}{C_1} = \pm (x + C_2),$$

$$y = C_1 \sin [\pm (x + C_2)] = \pm C_1 \sin (x + C_2).$$

Since C_1 is arbitrary, there is no need for the $\pm$ sign, and we have

$$y = C_1 \sin (x + C_2)$$

as the general solution.

PROBLEMS

Solve:

1. $\dfrac{d^2 y}{dx^2} + \dfrac{dy}{dx} = 0$

2. $\dfrac{d^2 y}{dx^2} + y \dfrac{dy}{dx} = 0$

3. $\dfrac{d^2 y}{dx^2} + x \dfrac{dy}{dx} = 0$

4. $x \dfrac{d^2 y}{dx^2} + \dfrac{dy}{dx} = 0$

5. $\dfrac{d^2 y}{dx^2} - y = 0$

6. $\dfrac{d^2 y}{dx^2} + \omega^2 y = 0 \quad (\omega = \text{constant} \neq 0)$

7. $xy''' - 2y'' = 0.$ [*Hint.* Substitute $y'' = q$.]

8. $2y'' - (y')^2 + 1 = 0$

9. A mass m is suspended from one end of a vertical spring whose other end is attached to a rigid support. The body is allowed to come to rest, and is then pulled down an additional slight amount A and released. Find its motion. [*Hint.* Assume Newton's second law of motion and Hooke's law, which says that the tension in the spring is proportional to the amount it is stretched. Let x denote the displacement of the body at time t, measured from the equilibrium position. Then $m(d^2 x/dt^2) = -kx$, where k, the "spring constant," is the proportionality factor in Hooke's law.]

10. A man suspended from a parachute falls through space under the pull of gravity. If air resistance produces a retarding force proportional to the man's velocity and he starts from rest at time $t = 0$, find the distance he falls in time t.

18-8

LINEAR EQUATIONS WITH CONSTANT COEFFICIENTS

An equation of the form

$$\frac{d^n y}{dx^n} + a_1 \frac{d^{n-1} y}{dx^{n-1}} + a_2 \frac{d^{n-2} y}{dx^{n-2}} + \cdots + a_{n-1} \frac{dy}{dx} + a_n y = F(x), \qquad (1)$$

which is linear in y and its derivatives, is called a *linear* equation of order n. If $F(x)$ is identically zero, the equation is said to be *homogeneous*; otherwise it is called nonhomogeneous. The equation is called linear even when the coefficients $a_1, a_2, \ldots, a_n$ are functions of x. However, we shall consider only the case where these coefficients are *constants*.

It is convenient to introduce the symbol D to represent the operation of differentiation with respect to x. That is, we write $Df(x)$ to mean $(d/dx)f(x)$.

Furthermore, we define powers of D to mean taking successive derivatives:

$$D^2 f(x) = D\{Df(x)\} = \frac{d^2 f(x)}{dx^2},$$

$$D^3 f(x) = D\{D^2 f(x)\} = \frac{d^3 f(x)}{dx^3},$$

and so on. A polynomial in D is to be interpreted as an operator which, when applied to $f(x)$, produces a linear combination of f and its successive derivatives. For example,

$$(D^2 + D - 2)f(x) = D^2 f(x) + Df(x) - 2f(x)$$

$$= \frac{d^2 f(x)}{dx^2} + \frac{df(x)}{dx} - 2f(x).$$

Such a polynomial in D is called a *linear differential operator* and may be denoted by the single letter L. If L_1 and L_2 are two such linear operators, their sum and product are defined by the equations

$$(L_1 + L_2)f(x) = L_1 f(x) + L_2 f(x),$$

$$L_1 L_2 f(x) = L_1(L_2 f(x)).$$

Linear differential operators that are polynomials in D with constant coefficients satisfy basic algebraic laws that make it possible to treat them like ordinary polynomials so far as addition, multiplication, and factoring are concerned. Thus,

$$(D^2 + D - 2)f(x) = (D + 2)(D - 1)f(x)$$

$$= (D - 1)(D + 2)f(x). \tag{2}$$

Since Eq. (2) holds for any twice-differentiable function f, we also write the equality between operators:

$$D^2 + D - 2 = (D + 2)(D - 1) = (D - 1)(D + 2). \tag{3}$$

Suppose, now, we wish to solve a differential equation of order two, say

$$\frac{d^2 y}{dx^2} + 2a\frac{dy}{dx} + by = 0, \tag{1}$$

where a and b are constants. In operator notation, this becomes

$$(D^2 + 2aD + b)y = 0. \tag{1'}$$

Associated with this differential equation is the algebraic equation

$$r^2 + 2ar + b = 0, \tag{1''}$$

which we get by replacing D by r and suppressing y. This is called the *characteristic equation* of the differential equation. Suppose the roots of (1″)

18–9

LINEAR, SECOND ORDER, HOMOGENEOUS EQUATIONS WITH CONSTANT COEFFICIENTS

are r_1 and r_2. Then

$$r^2 + 2ar + b = (r - r_1)(r - r_2)$$

and

$$D^2 + 2aD + b = (D - r_1)(D - r_2).$$

Hence Eq. (1') is equivalent to

$$(D - r_1)(D - r_2)y = 0. \tag{2}$$

If we now let

$$(D - r_2)y = u \tag{3a}$$

and

$$(D - r_1)u = 0, \tag{3b}$$

we can solve Eq. (1') in two steps. From Eq. (3b), which is separable, we find

$$u = C_1 e^{r_1 x}.$$

We substitute this into (3a), which becomes

$$(D - r_2)y = C_1 e^{r_1 x}$$

or

$$\frac{dy}{dx} - r_2 y = C_1 e^{r_1 x}.$$

This equation is linear. Its integrating factor is

$$\rho = e^{-r_2 x},$$

(see Article 18–5), and its solution is

$$e^{-r_2 x} y = C_1 \int e^{(r_1 - r_2)x} \, dx + C_2. \tag{4}$$

How we proceed at this point depends on whether r_1 and r_2 are equal.

CASE 1.   If $r_1 \neq r_2$, the evaluation of the integral in Eq. (4) leads to

$$e^{-r_2 x} y = \frac{C_1}{r_1 - r_2} e^{(r_1 - r_2)x} + C_2$$

or

$$y = \frac{C_1}{r_1 - r_2} e^{r_1 x} + C_2 e^{r_2 x}.$$

Since C_1 is an arbitrary constant, so is $C_1/(r_1 - r_2)$, and the solution of Eq. (2) can be written simply as

$$y = C_1 e^{r_1 x} + C_2 e^{r_2 x}, \qquad \text{if} \quad r_1 \neq r_2, \tag{5}$$

CASE 2.   If $r_1 = r_2$, then $e^{(r_1 - r_2)x} = e^0 = 1$, and Eq. (4) reduces to

$$e^{-r_2 x} y = C_1 x + C_2$$

or

$$y = (C_1 x + C_2)e^{r_2 x}, \qquad \text{if} \quad r_1 = r_2. \tag{6}$$

EXAMPLE 1.   Solve the equation

$$\frac{d^2y}{dx^2} + \frac{dy}{dx} - 2y = 0.$$

Solution. $r^2 + r - 2 = 0$ has roots $r_1 = 1$, $r_2 = -2$. Hence, by Eq. (5), the solution of the differential equation is

$$y = C_1 e^x + C_2 e^{-2x}.$$

EXAMPLE 2.   Solve the equation

$$\frac{d^2y}{dx^2} + 4\frac{dy}{dx} + 4y = 0.$$

Solution

$$r^2 + 4r + 4 = (r + 2)^2,$$
$$r_1 = r_2 = -2,$$
$$y = (C_1 x + C_2)e^{-2x}.$$

Imaginary Roots

If the coefficients a and b in Eq. (1) are real, the roots of the characteristic Eq. (1″) either will be real, or will be a pair of complex conjugate numbers:

$$r_1 = \alpha + i\beta, \qquad r_2 = \alpha - i\beta. \tag{7}$$

If $\beta \neq 0$, Eq. (5) applies, with the result

$$y = c_1 e^{(\alpha + i\beta)x} + c_2 e^{(\alpha - i\beta)x}$$
$$= e^{\alpha x}[c_1 e^{i\beta x} + c_2 e^{-i\beta x}]. \tag{8}$$

By Euler's formula, Eq. (10) of Article 17–7,

$$e^{i\beta x} = \cos \beta x + i \sin \beta x,$$
$$e^{-i\beta x} = \cos \beta x - i \sin \beta x.$$

Hence, Eq. (8) may be replaced by

$$y = e^{\alpha x}[(c_1 + c_2) \cos \beta x + i(c_1 - c_2) \sin \beta x]. \tag{9}$$

Finally, if we introduce new arbitrary constants

$$C_1 = c_1 + c_2, \qquad C_2 = i(c_1 - c_2),$$

Eq. (9) takes the form

$$y = e^{\alpha x}[C_1 \cos \beta x + C_2 \sin \beta x]. \tag{9'}$$

The arbitrary constants C_1 and C_2 in (9′) will be real provided the constants c_1 and c_2 in (9) are complex conjugates:

$$c_1 = \tfrac{1}{2}(C_1 - iC_2), \qquad c_2 = \tfrac{1}{2}(C_1 + iC_2).$$

To solve a problem where the roots of the characteristic equation are complex conjugates, we simply write down the appropriate version of Eq. (9′).

EXAMPLE 3. Solve the equation

$$\frac{d^2 y}{dx^2} + 2\frac{dy}{dx} + 2y = 0.$$

Solution. $r^2 + 2r + 2 = 0$ has roots $r_1 = -1 + i$, $r_2 = -1 - i$. Hence, in Eq. (9'), we take

$$\alpha = -1, \qquad \beta = 1,$$

and obtain

$$y = e^{-x}[C_1 \cos x + C_2 \sin x].$$

EXAMPLE 4. Solve the equation

$$\frac{d^2 y}{dx^2} + \omega^2 y = 0, \qquad \omega \neq 0,$$

Solution. $r^2 + \omega^2 = 0$ has roots $r_1 = i\omega$, $r_2 = -i\omega$. Hence we take $\alpha = 0$, $\beta = \omega$ in Eq. (9'), and

$$y = C_1 \cos \omega x + C_2 \sin \omega x.$$

PROBLEMS

Solve:

1. $\dfrac{d^2 y}{dx^2} + 2\dfrac{dy}{dx} = 0$

2. $\dfrac{d^2 y}{dx^2} + 5\dfrac{dy}{dx} + 6y = 0$

7. $\dfrac{d^2 y}{dx^2} + 6\dfrac{dy}{dx} + 9y = 0$

8. $\dfrac{d^2 y}{dx^2} - 6\dfrac{dy}{dx} + 10y = 0$

3. $\dfrac{d^2 y}{dx^2} + 6\dfrac{dy}{dx} + 5y = 0$

4. $\dfrac{d^2 y}{dx^2} - 2\dfrac{dy}{dx} - 3y = 0$

9. $\dfrac{d^2 y}{dx^2} - 2\dfrac{dy}{dx} + 4y = 0$

10. $\dfrac{d^2 y}{dx^2} - 10\dfrac{dy}{dx} + 16y = 0$

5. $\dfrac{d^2 y}{dx^2} + \dfrac{dy}{dx} + y = 0$

6. $\dfrac{d^2 y}{dx^2} - 4\dfrac{dy}{dx} + 4y = 0$

18–10

LINEAR, SECOND ORDER, NONHOMOGENEOUS EQUATIONS WITH CONSTANT COEFFICIENTS

In Article 18–9, we learned how to solve the homogeneous equation

$$\frac{d^2 y}{dx^2} + 2a\frac{dy}{dx} + by = 0. \tag{1}$$

We can now describe a method for solving the nonhomogeneous equation

$$\frac{d^2 y}{dx^2} + 2a\frac{dy}{dx} + by = F(x). \tag{2}$$

To solve Eq. (2), we first obtain the general solution of the related homogeneous Eq. (1) obtained by replacing $F(x)$ by zero. Denote this solution by

$$y_h = C_1 u_1(x) + C_2 u_2(x), \tag{3}$$

where C_1 and C_2 are arbitrary constants and $u_1(x)$, $u_2(x)$ are functions of one or more of the following forms:

$$e^{rx}, \quad xe^{rx}, \quad e^{\alpha x}\cos \beta x, \quad e^{\alpha x}\sin \beta x.$$

Now we might, by inspection or by inspired guesswork, be able to discover *one* particular function $y = y_p(x)$ that satisfies Eq. (2). In this case, we would be able to solve Eq. (2) completely, as

$$y = y_h(x) + y_p(x).$$

EXAMPLE 1. Solve the equation

$$\frac{d^2 y}{dx^2} + 2\frac{dy}{dx} - 3y = 6.$$

Solution. y_h satisfies

$$\frac{d^2 y_h}{dx^2} + 2\frac{dy_h}{dx} - 3y_h = 0.$$

The characteristic equation is

$$r^2 + 2r - 3 = 0,$$

and its roots are

$$r_1 = -3, \qquad r_2 = 1.$$

Hence

$$y_h = C_1 e^{-3x} + C_2 e^x.$$

Now, to find a particular solution of the original equation, observe that $y = $ constant would do, provided $-3y = 6$. Hence,

$$y_p = -2$$

is one particular solution. The complete solution is

$$y = y_p + y_h = -2 + C_1 e^{-3x} + C_2 e^x.$$

Variation of Parameters

Fortunately, there is a general method for finding the solution of the nonhomogeneous Eq. (2) once the general solution of the corresponding homogeneous equation is known. The method is known as the method of *variation of parameters*. It consists in replacing the constants C_1 and C_2 in Eq. (3) by functions $v_1 = v_1(x)$ and $v_2 = v_2(x)$, and requiring (in a way to be explained) that the resulting expression satisfy Eq. (2). There are two functions to be determined, and requiring that Eq. (2) be satisfied is only one condition. As a second condition, we also require that

$$v_1' u_1 + v_2' u_2 = 0. \tag{4}$$

Then we have

$$y = v_1 u_1 + v_2 u_2,$$

$$\frac{dy}{dx} = v_1 u_1' + v_2 u_2',$$

$$\frac{d^2 y}{dx^2} = v_1 u_1'' + v_2 u_2'' + v_1' u_1' + v_2' u_2'.$$

If we substitute these expressions into the left side of Eq. (2), we obtain

$$v_1 \left[\frac{d^2 u_1}{dx^2} + 2a \frac{du_1}{dx} + bu_1 \right] + v_2 \left[\frac{d^2 u_2}{dx^2} + 2a \frac{du_2}{dx} + bu_2 \right] + v_1' u_1' + v_2' u_2' = F(x).$$

The two bracketed terms are zero, since u_1 and u_2 are solutions of the homogeneous Eq. (1). Hence Eq. (2) is satisfied if, in addition to Eq. (4), we require that

$$v_1' u_1' + v_2' u_2' = F(x). \tag{5}$$

Equations (4) and (5) together may be solved for the unknown functions v_1' and v_2'. Then v_1 and v_2 can be found by integration. In applying the method, we can work directly from Eqs. (4) and (5); it is not necessary to rederive them.

EXAMPLE 2.   Solve the equation

$$\frac{d^2 y}{dx^2} + 2 \frac{dy}{dx} - 3y = 6$$

of Example 1 by variation of parameters.

Solution.   We first solve the associated homogeneous equation to find

$$u_1(x) = e^{-3x}, \qquad u_2(x) = e^x.$$

We then have

$$v_1' e^{-3x} + v_2' e^x = 0,$$

$$v_1'(-3e^{-3x}) + v_2' e^x = 6.$$

By Cramer's rule:

$$v_1' = \frac{\begin{vmatrix} 0 & e^x \\ 6 & e^x \end{vmatrix}}{\begin{vmatrix} e^{-3x} & e^x \\ -3e^{-3x} & e^x \end{vmatrix}} = -\frac{3}{2} e^{3x}, \qquad v_2' = \frac{\begin{vmatrix} e^{-3x} & 0 \\ -3e^{-3x} & 6 \end{vmatrix}}{\begin{vmatrix} e^{-3x} & e^x \\ -3e^{-3x} & e^x \end{vmatrix}} = \frac{3}{2} e^{-x},$$

Hence

$$v_1 = \int -\tfrac{3}{2} e^{3x} \, dx = -\tfrac{1}{2} e^{3x} + c_1,$$

$$v_2 = \int \tfrac{3}{2} e^{-x} \, dx = -\tfrac{3}{2} e^{-x} + c_2,$$

and

$$y = v_1 u_1 + v_2 u_2$$

$$= (-\tfrac{1}{2} e^{3x} + c_1) e^{-3x} + (-\tfrac{3}{2} e^{-x} + c_2) e^x$$

$$= -2 + c_1 e^{-3x} + c_2 e^x.$$

PROBLEMS

Solve:

1. $\dfrac{d^2y}{dx^2} + \dfrac{dy}{dx} = x$

2. $\dfrac{d^2y}{dx^2} + y = \tan x$

3. $\dfrac{d^2y}{dx^2} + y = \sin x$

4. $\dfrac{d^2y}{dx^2} + 2\dfrac{dy}{dx} + y = e^x$

5. $\dfrac{d^2y}{dx^2} + 2\dfrac{dy}{dx} + y = e^{-x}$

6. $\dfrac{d^2y}{dx^2} - y = x$

7. $\dfrac{d^2y}{dx^2} - y = e^x$

8. $\dfrac{d^2y}{dx^2} - y = \sin x$

9. $\dfrac{d^2y}{dx^2} + 4\dfrac{dy}{dx} + 5y = 10$

10. $\dfrac{d^2y}{dx^2} + 4\dfrac{dy}{dx} + 5y = x + 2$

11. Solve the integral equation

$$y(x) + \int_0^x y(t)\, dt = x.$$

[*Hint.* Differentiate.]

12. *Bernouilli's equation of order* 2. Solve the equation

$$\frac{dy}{dx} + y = (xy)^2$$

by carrying out the following steps: (1) divide both sides of the equation by y^2; (2) make the change of variable $u = y^{-1}$; (3) solve the resulting equation for u in terms of x; (4) let $y = u^{-1}$.

The methods of Articles 18–9 and 18–10 can be extended to equations of higher order. The characteristic algebraic equation associated with the differential equation

$$(D^n + a_1 D^{n-1} + \cdots + a_{n-1}D + a_n)y = F(x) \tag{1}$$

is

$$r^n + a_1 r^{n-1} + \cdots + a_{n-1}r + a_n = 0. \tag{2}$$

If its roots $r_1, r_2, \ldots, r_n$ are all distinct, the solution of the homogeneous equation obtained by replacing $F(x)$ by 0 in Eq. (1) is

$$y_h = c_1 e^{r_1 x} + c_2 e^{r_2 x} + \cdots + c_n e^{r_n x}.$$

Pairs of complex conjugate roots $\alpha \pm i\beta$ can be grouped together, and the corresponding part of y_h can be written in terms of the functions

$$e^{\alpha x} \cos \beta x \qquad \text{and} \qquad e^{\alpha x} \sin \beta x.$$

In case the roots of Eq. (2) are not all distinct, the portion of y_h which corresponds to a root r of multiplicity m is to be replaced by

$$(C_1 x^{m-1} + C_2 x^{m-2} + \cdots + C_m)e^{rx}.$$

Note that the polynomial in parentheses contains m arbitrary constants.

EXAMPLE. Solve the equation

$$\frac{d^4y}{dx^4} - 3\frac{d^3y}{dx^3} + 3\frac{d^2y}{dx^2} - \frac{dy}{dx} = 0.$$

Solution. $r^4 - 3r^3 + 3r^2 - r = r(r - 1)^3$. The roots of the characteristic equation are

$$r_1 = 0, \qquad r_2 = r_3 = r_4 = 1.$$

18–11

HIGHER ORDER LINEAR EQUATIONS WITH CONSTANT COEFFICIENTS

The solution is

$$y = C_1 + (C_2 x^2 + C_3 x + C_4)e^x.$$

Variation of Parameters

If the general solution of the homogeneous equation is

$$y_h = C_1 u_1 + C_2 u_2 + \cdots + C_n u_n,$$

then

$$y = v_1 u_1 + v_2 u_2 + \cdots + v_n u_n$$

will be a solution of the nonhomogeneous Eq. (1), provided

$$v_1' u_1 + v_2' u_2 \quad + \quad \cdots + v_n' u_n \quad = 0,$$
$$v_1' u_1' + v_2' u_2' \quad + \quad \cdots + v_n' u_n' \quad = 0,$$
$$\vdots$$
$$v_1' u_1^{(n-2)} + v_2' u_2^{(n-2)} + \cdots + v_n' u_n^{(n-2)} = 0,$$
$$v_1' u_1^{(n-1)} + v_2' u_2^{(n-1)} + \cdots + v_n' u_n^{(n-1)} = F(x).$$

These equations may be solved for $v_1', v_2', \ldots, v_n'$ by Cramer's rule, and the results integrated to give $v_1, v_2, \ldots, v_n$.

PROBLEMS

Solve:

1. $\dfrac{d^3 y}{dx^3} - 3\dfrac{d^2 y}{dx^2} + 2\dfrac{dy}{dx} = 0$ **2.** $\dfrac{d^3 y}{dx^3} - y = 0$

3. $\dfrac{d^4 y}{dx^4} - 4\dfrac{d^2 y}{dx^2} + 4y = 0$ **4.** $\dfrac{d^4 y}{dx^4} - 16y = 0$

5. $\dfrac{d^4 y}{dx^4} + 16y = 0$ **6.** $\dfrac{d^3 y}{dx^3} - 3\dfrac{dy}{dx} + 2y = e^x$

7. $\dfrac{d^4 y}{dx^4} - 4\dfrac{d^3 y}{dx^3} + 6\dfrac{d^2 y}{dx^2} - 4\dfrac{dy}{dx} + y = 7$

8. $\dfrac{d^4 y}{dx^4} + y = x + 1$

18–12

VIBRATIONS

A spring of natural length L has its upper end fastened to a rigid support at A (Fig. 18–4). A weight W, of mass m, is suspended from the spring. The weight stretches the spring to a length $L + s$ when the system is allowed to come to rest in a new equilibrium position. By Hooke's law, the tension in the spring is ks, where k is the so-called spring constant. The force of gravity pulling down on the weight is $W = mg$. Equilibrium requires

$$ks = mg. \tag{1}$$

Suppose now that the weight is pulled down an additional amount a beyond the equilibrium position, and released. We shall discuss its motion.

Let x, positive direction downward, denote the displacement of the weight away from equilibrium at any time t after the motion has started. Then the forces acting upon the weight are

$+mg$, due to gravity,

$-k(s + x)$, due to the spring tension.

The resultant of these forces is, by Newton's second law, also equal to

$$m \frac{d^2x}{dt^2}.$$

Therefore

$$m \frac{d^2x}{dt^2} = mg - ks - kx. \tag{2}$$

By Eq. (1), $mg - ks = 0$, so that (2) becomes

$$m \frac{d^2x}{dt^2} + kx = 0. \tag{3}$$

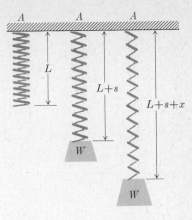

18–4 A spring stretched beyond its natural length by a weight.

In addition to the differential equation (3), the motion satisfies the initial conditions:

$$\text{At } t = 0: \quad x = a \quad \text{and} \quad \frac{dx}{dt} = 0. \tag{4}$$

Let $\omega = \sqrt{k/m}$. Then Eq. (3) becomes

$$\frac{d^2x}{dt^2} + \omega^2 x = 0$$

or

$$(D^2 + \omega^2)x = 0,$$

where

$$D = \frac{d}{dt}.$$

The roots of the characteristic equation

$$r^2 + \omega^2 = 0$$

are complex conjugates

$$r = \pm \omega i.$$

Hence

$$x = c_1 \cos \omega t + c_2 \sin \omega t \tag{5}$$

is the general solution of the differential equation. To fit the initial conditions, we also compute

$$\frac{dx}{dt} = -c_1 \omega \sin \omega t + c_2 \omega \cos \omega t,$$

and then substitute from (4). This yields

$$a = c_1, \qquad 0 = c_2 \omega.$$

Therefore

$$c_1 = a, \qquad c_2 = 0,$$

and

$$x = a \cos \omega t \tag{6}$$

describes the motion of the weight. Equation (6) represents simple harmonic motion of amplitude a and period $T = 2\pi/\omega$.

The two terms on the right side of Eq. (5) can be combined into a single term by using the trigonometric identity

$$\sin (\omega t + \phi) = \cos \omega t \sin \phi + \sin \omega t \cos \phi.$$

To apply the identity, we take

$$c_1 = C \sin \phi, \qquad c_2 = C \cos \phi, \tag{7a}$$

where

$$C = \sqrt{c_1^2 + c_2^2}, \qquad \phi = \tan^{-1} \frac{c_1}{c_2}, \tag{7b}$$

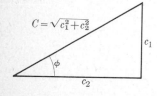

18–5 $c_1 = C \sin \phi$ and $c_2 = C \cos \phi$.

as in Fig. 18–5. Then Eq. (5) can be written in the alternative form

$$x = C \sin (\omega t + \phi). \tag{8}$$

Here C and ϕ may be taken as two new arbitrary constants, replacing the two constants c_1 and c_2 of Eq. (5). Equation (8) represents simple harmonic motion of amplitude C and period $T = 2\pi/\omega$. The angle $\omega t + \phi$ is called the *phase angle*, and ϕ may be interpreted as the initial value of the phase angle. A graph of Eq. (8) is given in Fig. 18–6.

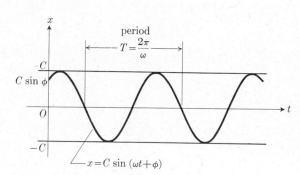

18–6 Undamped vibration.

Equation (3) assumes that there is no friction in the system. Next, consider the case where the motion of the weight is retarded by a friction force $c(dx/dt)$ proportional to the velocity, where c is a positive constant. Then the differential equation is

$$m \frac{d^2x}{dt^2} = -kx - c \frac{dx}{dt},$$

or

$$\frac{d^2x}{dt^2} + 2b \frac{dx}{dt} + \omega^2 x = 0, \tag{9}$$

where

$$2b = \frac{c}{m} \quad \text{and} \quad \omega = \sqrt{\frac{k}{m}}.$$

If we introduce the operator $D = d/dt$, Eq. (9) becomes

$$(D^2 + 2bD + \omega^2)x = 0.$$

The characteristic equation is

$$r^2 + 2br + \omega^2 = 0$$

with roots

$$r = -b \pm \sqrt{b^2 - \omega^2}. \tag{10}$$

Three cases now present themselves, depending upon the relative sizes of b and ω.

CASE 1.   If $b = \omega$, the two roots in Eq. (10) are equal, and the solution of (9) is

$$x = (c_1 + c_2 t)e^{-\omega t}. \tag{11}$$

As time goes on, x approaches zero. The motion is not oscillatory.

CASE 2.   If $b > \omega$, then the roots (10) are both real but unequal, and

$$x = c_1 e^{r_1 t} + c_2 e^{r_2 t}, \tag{12}$$

where

$$r_1 = -b + \sqrt{b^2 - \omega^2} \quad \text{and} \quad r_2 = -b - \sqrt{b^2 - \omega^2}.$$

Here again the motion is not oscillatory. Both r_1 and r_2 are negative, and x approaches zero as time goes on.

CASE 3.   If $b < \omega$, let

$$\omega^2 - b^2 = \alpha^2.$$

Then

$$r_1 = -b + \alpha i, \quad r_2 = -b - \alpha i$$

and

$$x = e^{-bt}[c_1 \cos \alpha t + c_2 \sin \alpha t]. \tag{13a}$$

If we introduce the substitutions (7), we may also write Eq. (13a) in the equivalent form

$$x = Ce^{-bt} \sin (\alpha t + \phi). \tag{13b}$$

This equation represents damped vibratory motion. It is analogous to simple harmonic motion, of period $T = 2\pi/\alpha$, except that the amplitude is not constant but is given by Ce^{-bt}. Since this tends to zero as t increases, the vibrations tend to die out as time goes on. Observe, however, that Eq. (13b) reduces to Eq. (8) in the absence of friction. The effect of friction is twofold:

1. $b = c/(2m)$ appears as a coefficient in the exponential *damping factor* e^{-bt}. The larger b is, the more quickly do the vibrations tend to become unnoticeable.

2. The period $T = 2\pi/\alpha = 2\pi/\sqrt{\omega^2 - b^2}$ is greater than the period $T_0 = 2\pi/\omega$ in the friction-free system.

Curves representing solutions of Eq. (9) in typical cases are shown in Figs. 18–6 and 18–7. The size of b, relative to ω, determines the kind of solution, and b also determines the rate of damping. It is therefore customary to say that there is

a) critical damping if $b = \omega$;
b) overcritical damping if $b > \omega$;
c) undercritical damping if $0 < b < \omega$;
d) no damping if $b = 0$.

18–7 Three kinds of damping of vibration.

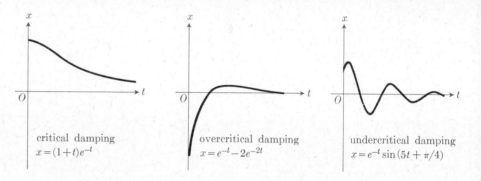

critical damping
$x = (1+t)e^{-t}$

overcritical damping
$x = e^{-t} - 2e^{-2t}$

undercritical damping
$x = e^{-t} \sin(5t + \pi/4)$

PROBLEMS

1. Suppose the motion of the weight in Fig. 18–4 is described by the differential equation (3). Find the motion if $x = x_0$ and $dx/dt = v_0$ at $t = 0$. Express the answer in two equivalent forms [Eqs. (5) and (8)].

2. A 5-lb weight is suspended from the lower end of a spring whose upper end is attached to a rigid support. The weight extends the spring by 2 in. If, after the weight has come to rest in its new equilibrium position, it is struck a sharp blow that starts it downward with a velocity of 4 ft/sec, find its subsequent motion, assuming there is no friction.

3. A simple electrical circuit shown in Fig. 18–8 contains a capacitor of capacitance C farads, a coil of inductance L henrys, a resistance of R ohms, and a generator which produces an electromotive force E volts, in series. If the current intensity at time t at some point of the circuit is I amperes, the differential equation describing the current I is

$$L\frac{d^2I}{dt^2} + R\frac{dI}{dt} + \frac{1}{C}I = \frac{dE}{dt}.$$

Find I as a function of t if

a) $R = 0$, $\quad 1/(LC) = \omega^2$, $\quad E = $ constant,
b) $R = 0$, $\quad 1/(LC) = \omega^2$, $\quad E = A \sin \alpha t$;
$\qquad \alpha = $ constant $\neq \omega$,

c) $R = 0$, $\quad 1/(LC) = \omega^2$, $\quad E = A \sin \omega t$,
d) $R = 50$, $\quad L = 5$, $\quad C = 9 \times 10^{-6}$, $\quad E = $ constant.

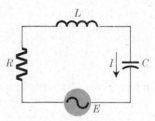

18–8 A simple electrical circuit.

4. A simple pendulum of length l makes an angle θ with the vertical. As it swings back and forth, its motion, neglecting friction, is described by the differential equation

$$\frac{d^2\theta}{dt^2} = -\frac{g}{l}\sin \theta,$$

where g (the acceleration due to gravity, $g \approx 32$ ft/sec^2) is a constant. Solve the differential equation of motion, under the assumption that θ is so small that $\sin \theta$ may be replaced by θ without appreciable error. Assume that $\theta = \theta_0$ and $d\theta/dt = 0$ when $t = 0$.

5. A circular disk of mass m and radius r is suspended by a thin wire attached to the center of one of its flat faces. If the disk is twisted through an angle θ, torsion in the wire tends to turn the disk back in the opposite direction. The differential equation for the motion is

$$\tfrac{1}{2}mr^2\frac{d^2\theta}{dt^2} = -k\theta,$$

where k is the coefficient of torsion of the wire. Find the motion if $\theta = \theta_0$ and $d\theta/dt = v_0$ at $t = 0$.

6. A cylindrical spar buoy, diameter 1 foot, weight 100 lb, floats, partially submerged, in an upright position. When it is depressed slightly from its equilibrium position and released, it bobs up and down according to the differential equation

$$\frac{100}{g}\frac{d^2x}{dt^2} = -16\pi x - c\frac{dx}{dt}.$$

Here $c\,(dx/dt)$ is the frictional resistance of the water. Find c if the period of oscillation is observed to be 1.6 sec. (Take $g = 32$ ft/sec^2.)

7. Suppose the upper end of the spring in Fig. 18–4 is attached, not to a rigid support at A, but to a member which itself undergoes up and down motion given by a function of the time t, say $y = f(t)$. If the positive direction of y is downward, the differential equation of motion is

$$m\frac{d^2x}{dt^2} + kx = kf(t).$$

Let $x = x_0$ and $dx/dt = 0$ when $t = 0$, and solve for x:

a) if $f(t) = A \sin \alpha t$ and $\alpha \neq \sqrt{k/m}$,
b) if $f(t) = A \sin \alpha t$ and $\alpha = \sqrt{k/m}$.

In the study of emission of particles from a radioactive substance, it is found that the number X of particles emitted during a fixed time interval is not precisely predictable. In fact X is a variable that can assume only the values 0, 1, 2, ... Some of these values are more likely to be observed than others. It is useful to introduce the symbol $P_n(t)$ to denote the *probability* that n particles will be emitted in a t-second interval. It is possible to arrive at a formula for $P_n(t)$ if we make the following assumptions:

1. The number of particles emitted in any time interval is independent of the number emitted in any other nonoverlapping time interval.

2. The probability that a single particle is emitted in an interval $(t, t + h)$ is $\lambda \cdot h + o(h)$, where λ is a constant (for a particular substance) and $o(h)$, read "small oh of h," denotes a function having the property

$$\lim_{h \to 0} \frac{o(h)}{h} = 0. \qquad (1)$$

3. The probability that more than one particle will be emitted in $(t, t + h)$ is $o(h)$.

A variable that satisfies these three postulates will be called a *Poisson random variable*. The significance of the postulates is as follows:

1. Independence of numbers of particles emitted in nonoverlapping time intervals means that the probability of r particles in one interval and s in another is the product of the respective probabilities:

(Probability of r particles in 1st time interval)

times

(Probability of s particles in 2nd time interval).

2. (Probability of particle in interval $t, t + h$) $= \lambda \cdot h + o(h)$ means that the probability is approximately proportional to the length h of the time inter-

18–13

POISSON PROBABILITY DISTRIBUTION

val. The approximation λh is better the smaller h is, the error $o(h)$ being composed of terms (like h^2 or $h \sin h$, for instance) which are themselves small compared to h, since $(o(h)/h) \to 0$ as $h \to 0$.

3. The probability that more than one particle is emitted in a very short time interval $(t, t + h)$ is $o(h)$, and is small compared to h.

From postulates 2 and 3 it follows that the probability of one *or more* particles in the interval $[t, t + h]$ is also $\lambda h + o(h)$, because

$$P(1 \text{ or more particles})* = P(1 \text{ particle}) + P(\text{more than 1 particle})$$

and

$$P(1 \text{ particle}) = \lambda h + o_1(h), \qquad P(\text{more than 1 particle}) = o_2(h).$$

Hence

$$P(1 \text{ or more particles}) = \lambda h + o_1(h) + o_2(h)$$
$$= \lambda h + o(h), \qquad \textbf{(2)}$$

since the sum of two functions $o_1(h)$ and $o_2(h)$, having the property that

$$\lim_{h \to 0} \frac{o_1(h)}{h} = 0, \qquad \lim_{h \to 0} \frac{o_2(h)}{h} = 0,$$

is a function having the same property:

$$\lim_{h \to 0} \frac{o_1(h) + o_2(h)}{h} = \lim_{h \to 0} \frac{o_1(h)}{h} + \lim_{h \to 0} \frac{o_2(h)}{h} = 0.$$

From the postulates for a Poisson random variable, we may deduce the following system of differential equations:

$$\frac{dP_0(t)}{dt} = -\lambda P_0(t), \qquad \textbf{(3a)}$$

$$\frac{dP_n(t)}{dt} = -\lambda P_n(t) + \lambda P_{n-1}(t), \qquad n = 1, 2, 3, \ldots \qquad \textbf{(3b)}$$

Demonstration

We first establish (3a). Consider

$$P_0(t + h) = P(0 \text{ emissions in time } t + h)$$
$$= P(0 \text{ in time } t) \times P(0 \text{ in time } [t, t + h])$$
$$= P_0(t) \cdot \{1 - P(1 \text{ or more in } [t, t + h])\}$$
$$= P_0(t) \cdot [1 - \lambda h - o(h)].$$

---

*   The notation $P(1$ or more particles) is an abbreviation for "probability that 1 or more particles are emitted."

Therefore

$$P_0(t + h) - P_0(t) = -P_0(t) \cdot [\lambda h + o(h)],$$

$$\frac{P_0(t + h) - P_0(t)}{h} = -P_0(t) \cdot \left[\lambda + \frac{o(h)}{h}\right],$$

$$\frac{dP_0(t)}{dt} = \lim_{h \to 0} \frac{P_0(t + h) - P_0(t)}{h} = -P_0(t) \cdot [\lambda + 0] = -\lambda P_0(t).$$

Thus (3a) holds.

To establish (3b), consider the probability of n emissions in a time $(0, t + h)$, where n is a positive integer. Consider the nonoverlapping intervals of time $(0, t)$ and $(t, t + h)$. The only possibilities for n particles in $(0, t + h)$ are:

a) n particles in $(0, t)$ and 0 in $(t, t + h)$,
b) $(n - 1)$ particles in $(0, t)$ and 1 in $(t, t + h)$,
c) $(n - 2)$ particles in $(0, t)$ and 2 in $(t, t + h)$,
d) $(n - 3)$ particles in $(0, t)$ and 3 in $(t, t + h)$, and so on.

Since these are mutually exclusive events, their probabilities add, and

$$P_n(t + h) = P_n(t) \cdot P_0(h) + P_{n-1}(t) \cdot P_1(h)$$
$$+ P_{n-2}(t) \cdot P_2(h) + \cdots + P_0(t) \cdot P_n(h). \tag{4}$$

Now for any $t \geq 0$,

$$P_0(t) + P_1(t) + P_2(t) + \cdots = 1, \tag{5}$$

since it is certain (that is, the probability $= 1$) that the number of particles emitted in time t is one of the integers 0, or 1, or 2, or 3, ..., and these possibilities are mutually exclusive so their probabilities add. Hence, in particular, if $t = h$ is small, we may replace t by h in (5) and use the fact, Eq. (2), that

$$P(1 \text{ or more particles}) = P_1(h) + P_2(h) + \cdots$$
$$= \lambda h + o(h)$$

to obtain

$$P_0(h) = 1 - \lambda h - o(h). \tag{6}$$

Hence Eq. (4) becomes

$$P_n(t + h) = P_n(t) \cdot [1 - \lambda h - o(h)] + P_{n-1}(t) \cdot [\lambda h + o_1(h)] + o_2(h), \tag{7}$$

since

$$P_{n-2}(t) \cdot P_2(h) + P_{n-3}(t) \cdot P_3(h) + \cdots + P_0(t) \cdot P_n(h)$$
$$\leq 1 \cdot P_2(h) + 1 \cdot P_3(h) + \cdots + 1 \cdot P_n(h) = o(h).$$

Therefore, from Eq. (7),

$$P_n(t + h) - P_n(t) = -P_n(t) \cdot [\lambda h + o(h)]$$
$$+ P_{n-1}(t) \cdot [\lambda h + o_1(h)] + o_2(h),$$

and

$$\frac{dP_n}{dt} = \lim_{h \to 0} \frac{P_n(t + h) - P_n(t)}{h}$$

$$= \lim_{h \to 0} \left[-P_n(t) \cdot \left(\lambda + \frac{o(h)}{h} \right) + P_{n-1}(t) \cdot \left(\lambda + \frac{o_1(h)}{h} \right) + \frac{o_2(h)}{h} \right]$$

$$= -\lambda P_n(t) + \lambda P_{n-1}(t). \qquad\qquad\qquad \text{Q.E.D.}$$

The probabilities $P_0(t)$, $P_1(t)$, ... satisfy the system of differential equations (3a, b) and the initial conditions:

$$P_0(0) = 1, \qquad P_1(0) = P_2(0) = \cdots P_n(0) = 0, \qquad n > 1. \qquad \textbf{(8)}$$

That is, the number of particles emitted in 0 time is 0, with probability 1. The solution of Eq. (3a), with $P_0(0) = 1$, is

$$P_0(t) = e^{-\lambda t}.$$

If we substitute this into Eq. (3b), with $n = 1$, we have

$$\frac{dP_1(t)}{dt} = -\lambda P_1(t) + e^{-\lambda t},$$

or

$$\frac{dP_1(t)}{dt} + \lambda P_1(t) = e^{-\lambda t}.$$

This equation is linear in $P_1(t)$, with integrating factor $e^{\lambda t}$. It is equivalent to

$$\frac{d}{dt} [e^{\lambda t} P_1(t)] = \lambda.$$

Hence

$$e^{\lambda t} P_1(t) = \lambda t + C_1.$$

But when $t = 0$, $P_1(0) = 0$, so

$$C_1 = 0.$$

Therefore

$$P_1(t) = \lambda t e^{-\lambda t}.$$

We can now substitute this into (3b) with $n = 2$ and have

$$\frac{dP_2(t)}{dt} + \lambda P_2(t) = \lambda(\lambda t)e^{-\lambda t}.$$

Again the equation is linear, with integrating factor $e^{\lambda t}$, and

$$\frac{d}{dt} [e^{\lambda t} P_2(t)] = e^{\lambda t} \cdot \lambda(\lambda t)e^{-\lambda t}$$

$$= \lambda^2 t.$$

Hence

$$e^{\lambda t} P_2(t) = \frac{\lambda^2 t^2}{2} + C_2,$$

but $P_2(0) = 0$, so

$$C_2 = 0.$$

Therefore

$$P_2(t) = \frac{(\lambda t)^2}{2!} e^{-\lambda t}.$$

Proceeding in this fashion, one discovers that

$$P_3(t) = \frac{(\lambda t)^3}{3!} e^{-\lambda t},$$

$$P_4(t) = \frac{(\lambda t)^4}{4!} e^{-\lambda t},$$

and so on. The general term is

$$P_n(t) = e^{-\lambda t} \frac{(\lambda t)^n}{n!}, \qquad n = 0, 1, 2, \dots \tag{9}$$

The set of numbers 0, 1, 2, 3, …, with corresponding probabilities given by Eq. (9), is called a *Poisson probability distribution*. Figure 18–9 shows the graph of a Poisson distribution with $\lambda t = 2$. The viewpoint to adopt when considering a Poisson distribution is, in most instances, to imagine λt as fixed, and then Eq. (9) gives the probability of observing n occurrences of the event in question, for all possible different values of n.

The probability of 0 emissions is $P_0(t) = e^{-\lambda t}$. Observe that this probability tends to 0 as t increases: It becomes very improbable that *no* emissions occur over a very long interval of time.

Do the probabilities found in Eq. (9) add up to 1, as Eq. (4) requires? Let's try it and see:

$$P_0(t) + P_1(t) + \cdots = e^{-\lambda t}\left[1 + \frac{\lambda t}{1!} + \frac{(\lambda t)^2}{2!} + \cdots\right]$$

$$= e^{-\lambda t} \sum_{n=0}^{\infty} \frac{(\lambda t)^n}{n!}$$

$$= e^{-\lambda t} \cdot e^{\lambda t}$$

$$= e^0 = 1. \qquad \text{Q.E.D.}$$

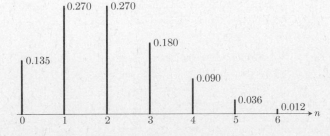

18–9 Poisson distribution with $\lambda t = 2$.

Interpretation of λ

The *mean* value of a random variable X is obtained by taking the weighted average of the possible values X may assume, each weighted according to its probability of occurring. Equations (9) give these probabilities for a Poisson random variable, shown in Table 18–1.

Table 18–1.   Probabilities for a Poisson random variable

Possible values of X	Probabilities of these possibilities	(Possible values) $\times$ (probability)
0	$e^{-\lambda t}$	$0 \cdot e^{-\lambda t}$
1	$e^{-\lambda t} \cdot (\lambda t)$	$1 \cdot e^{-\lambda t} \cdot (\lambda t)$
2	$e^{-\lambda t} \cdot (\lambda t)^2/2!$	$2 \cdot e^{-\lambda t} \cdot (\lambda t)^2/2!$
3	$e^{-\lambda t} \cdot (\lambda t)^3/3!$	$3 \cdot e^{-\lambda t} \cdot (\lambda t)^3/3!$
$\vdots$	$\vdots$	$\vdots$
n	$e^{-\lambda t} \cdot (\lambda t)^n/n!$	$n \cdot e^{-\lambda t} \cdot (\lambda t)^n/n!$
$\vdots$	$\vdots$	$\vdots$

Thus, the mean value of the Poisson random variable is

$$e^{-\lambda t}[0 + 1 \cdot (\lambda t) + 2 \cdot (\lambda t)^2/2! + 3 \cdot (\lambda t)^3/3! + \cdots + n \cdot (\lambda t)^n/n! + \cdots]$$
$$= e^{-\lambda t} \cdot (\lambda t) \cdot [1 + (\lambda t) + (\lambda t)^2/2! + \cdots + (\lambda t)^{n-1}/(n-1)! + \cdots]$$
$$= e^{-\lambda t} \cdot (\lambda t) \cdot e^{\lambda t} = \lambda t.$$

Therefore λt is the *mean* number of particles emitted in time $(0, t)$. In particular, the mean number emitted in unit time, $t = 1$, is λ. In 2 units of time, it is 2λ, and so on. The mean number in t units of time is proportional to t, and λ is the proportionality factor.

REMARKS.   Many phenomena have been found that satisfy the postulates for a Poisson random variable, or nearly do.* Among these are: the number of telephone calls coming into a central office during a particular hour of the day, the number of splices in a certain manufactured tape (per linear foot), the number of surface flaws (per square foot) in plating sheets of metal, the number of failures of electron tubes (per hour) in a given airborne instrumentation device, the number of flying bomb hits in the south of London during World War II (on regions of area $= \frac{1}{4}$ square kilometer). In some of these cases, the "t" in Eqs. (9) should be interpreted as so many units of length, or of area, rather than of time; but the formulas are correct with such interpretations and with λ equal to the mean number of occurrences of the event in question per unit of t.

EXAMPLE 1.   Suppose there are 500 misprints in a book of 750 pages. Assuming that the number of misprints per page is (approximately) a Pois-

---

*   References. W. Feller, *An Introduction to Probability Theory and Its Applications*, 3rd edition, Wiley, 1968, p. 159. B. W. Lindgren and G. W. McElrath, *Introduction to Probability and Statistics*, Macmillan, 1959, pp. 54–59.

son random variable, find:

a) the probability that a page selected at random has no misprints,

b) the probability of more than one misprint on a given page.

Solution.   Let one page be the unit, $t = 1$. The mean number of misprints, per page, is $500/750 = \frac{2}{3}$. So we apply (9) with $\lambda = \frac{2}{3}$:

$$P_n(t) = \text{probability of } n \text{ misprints on } t \text{ pages}$$

$$= e^{-(2/3)t} \frac{(\frac{2}{3}t)^n}{n!}, \qquad n = 0, 1, 2, \ldots$$

a) The probability of no misprints on a single page is $P_n(t)$ with $n = 0$, $t = 1$, or

$$P_0(1) = e^{-2/3} \approx 0.514.$$

b) The probability of more than one misprint on a single page is $\sum_{n=2}^{\infty} P_n(t)$ with $t = 1$. This is also equal to $1 - P_0(t) - P_1(t)$, or

$$1 - e^{-2/3}[1 + \tfrac{2}{3}] \approx 0.143.$$

PROBLEMS

1. Substitute $n = 3$ and $P_2(t) = e^{-\lambda t}(\lambda t)^2/2!$ into Eq. (3b) and solve for $P_3(t)$, subject to the appropriate initial condition.

2. Assuming that Eq. (9) is correct for some integer $n - 1$, so that $P_{n-1}(t) = e^{-\lambda t}(\lambda t)^{n-1}/(n-1)!$, solve Eq. (3b) for $P_n(t)$, subject to the appropriate initial condition. [In other words, show that Eq. (9) is valid for all integers $n \geq 0$ by the method of mathematical induction.]

3. Sketch the graph of $y = P_n(t)$ as a function of t, $t \geq 0$, for $n = 2$ and $\lambda = 2, 1$, and $\frac{1}{2}$. Find the maximum, minimum, and inflection points.

4. Prove directly that $e^{-\lambda t}(\lambda t)^n/n!$ is never greater than 1 if $\lambda > 0$, $t \geq 0$, and n is an integer ≥ 0. This result must be true, of course, since $P_n(t)$ is a probability and hence is never greater than 1.

5. In the example of the book of 750 pages and 500 misprints, what is the probability:

a) that a chapter of 15 pages has no misprints?

b) that a section of 6 pages has 1 or more misprints?

6. A company that makes automobile radiators found that the number of minor defects in its radiators is (approximately) a Poisson random variable with mean equal to 0.02. If 20 radiators are selected at random from the production line, what is the probability that there will be:

a) no minor defects in the entire group of 20 radiators?

b) one or more minor defects in the group of 20 radiators?

c) no minor defects in the first radiator of the 20?

7. A bakery finds that the number of raisins, per loaf, in its raisin bread is (approximately) a Poisson random variable with mean equal to 200 raisins per loaf. Suppose that each loaf is sliced into 20 slices of uniform size.

a) What is the mean number of raisins per slice?

b) What is the probability of getting 5 or fewer raisins in a slice?

8. The first term of a certain Poisson probability distribution is $P_0(t) = 0.135$. Find (a) $P_1(t)$, (b) $P_3(t)$, (c) $P_0(t/2)$, (d) $P_1(2t)$.

9. Assume that the number of α-particles registered by a Geiger counter in a certain experiment is a Poisson random variable. Suppose that the mean number registered per ten-second interval of time is eight. What is the probability that there will be exactly four registered in a given interval of five seconds?

10. Let $Q_n(t, t + h)$ be the probability that the nth particle is emitted between times t and $t + h$. Then, explain why it is true that if $t + h > t > 0$,

$$Q_n(t, t + h) = P_{n-1}(t) \cdot P_1(h) + P_{n-2}(t) \cdot P_2(h) + \cdots$$
$$+ P_0(t) \cdot P_n(h);$$

and from this show that

$$Q_n(t, t + h) = he^{-\lambda t}\lambda^n t^{n-1}/(n-1)! + o(h).$$

11. Using the result in Problem 10, show that

$$Q_n(a, b) = \int_a^b \frac{e^{-\lambda t}\lambda^n t^{n-1}}{(n-1)!} \, dt, \qquad b > a > 0.$$

[*Hint.* Let p be a positive integer, $\Delta t = h = (b-a)/p$, and

$$Q_n(a, b)$$

$$= Q_n(a, a+h) + Q_n(a+h, a+2h) + \cdots + Q_n(b-h, b)$$

$$= \sum_{i=1}^{p} f(t_i)\,\Delta t + \frac{b-a}{h}\,o(h),$$

with $f(t) = e^{-\lambda t}\lambda^n t^{n-1}/(n-1)!$ and $t_i = a + (i-1)h$. Then let $p \to \infty$.]

12. Let $F(n) = \int_0^\infty e^{-\lambda t}\lambda^n t^{n-1}\,dt = \int_0^\infty e^{-u}u^{n-1}\,du$.

a) Integrate by parts and show that $F(n) = (n-1)F(n-1)$.

b) Show directly that $F(1) = 1$.

c) From (a) and (b), show that $F(2) = 1$, $F(3) = 2F(2) = 2!$, and in general $F(n) = (n-1)!$.

d) Using the result of part (c) above, and of Problem 11, show that $Q_n(0, \infty) = 1$, for any integer $n \geq 1$. What does this mean in terms of probability?

REVIEW QUESTIONS AND EXERCISES

1. List some differential equations (having physical interpretations) that you have come across in your courses in chemistry, physics, engineering, or life and social sciences; or look for some in the articles on differential equations, dynamics, electromagnetic waves, hydromechanics, quantum mechanics, or thermodynamics, in the *Encyclopaedia Britannica*.

2. How are differential equations classified?

3. What is meant by a "solution" of a differential equation?

4. Review methods for solving ordinary, first-order, and first-degree differential equations:

a) when the variables are separable,
b) when the equation is homogeneous,
c) when the equation is linear in one variable,
d) when the equation is exact.

Illustrate each with an example.

5. Review methods of solving second order equations:

a) with dependent variable missing,
b) with independent variable missing.

Illustrate each with an example.

6. Review methods for solving linear differential equations with constant coefficients:

a) in the homogeneous case,
b) in the nonhomogeneous case.

Illustrate each with an example.

7. If an external force F acts upon a system whose mass varies with time, Newton's law of motion is

$$\frac{d(mv)}{dt} = F + (v + u)\frac{dm}{dt}.$$

In this equation, m is the mass of the system at time t, v its velocity, and $v + u$ is the velocity of the mass that is entering (or leaving) the system at the rate dm/dt. Suppose that a rocket of initial mass m_0 starts from rest, but is driven upward by firing some of its mass directly backward at the constant rate of $dm/dt = -b$ units per second and at constant speed relative to the rocket $u = -c$. The only external force acting on the rocket is $F = -mg$ due to gravity. Under these assumptions, show that the height of the rocket above the ground at the end of t seconds (t small compared to m_0/b) is

$$y = c\left[t + \frac{m_0 - bt}{b}\ln\frac{m_0 - bt}{m_0}\right] - \frac{1}{2}gt^2.$$

(See Martin and Reissner, *Elementary Differential Equations*, 2nd edition, Addison-Wesley, 1961, pp. 26 ff.)

MISCELLANEOUS PROBLEMS

Solve the following differential equations:

1. $y \ln y \, dx + (1 + x^2)\,dy = 0$

2. $\dfrac{dy}{dx} = \dfrac{y^2 - y - 2}{x^2 + x}$

3. $e^{x+2y}\,dy - e^{y-2x}\,dx = 0$

4. $\sqrt{1 + \left(\dfrac{dy}{dx}\right)^2} = ky$

5. $y\,dy = \sqrt{1 + y^4}\,dx$

6. $(2x + y)\,dx + (x - 2y)\,dy = 0$

7. $\dfrac{dy}{dx} = \dfrac{x^2 + y^2}{2xy}$

8. $x\dfrac{dy}{dx} = y + \sqrt{x^2 + y^2}$

9. $x\,dy = \left(y + x\cos^2\dfrac{y}{x}\right)dx$

10. $x(\ln y - \ln x)\, dy = y(1 + \ln y - \ln x)\, dx$

11. $x\, dy + (2y - x^2 - 1)\, dx = 0$

12. $\cos y\, dx + (x \sin y - \cos^2 y)\, dy = 0$

13. $\cosh x\, dy - (y + \cosh x) \sinh x\, dx = 0$

14. $(x + 1)\, dy + (2y - x)\, dx = 0$

15. $(1 + y^2)\, dx + (2xy + y^2 + 1)\, dy = 0$

16. $(x^2 + y)\, dx + (e^y + x)\, dy = 0$

17. $(x^2 + y^2)\, dx + (2xy + \cosh y)\, dy = 0$

18. $(e^x + \ln y)\, dx + \dfrac{x + y}{y}\, dy = 0$

19. $x(1 + e^y)\, dx + \tfrac{1}{2}(x^2 + y^2)e^y\, dy = 0$

20. $\left(\sin x + \tan^{-1} \dfrac{y}{x}\right) dx - (y - \ln \sqrt{x^2 + y^2})\, dy = 0$

21. $\dfrac{d^2 y}{dx^2} - 2y\dfrac{dy}{dx} = 0$

22. $\dfrac{d^2 x}{dy^2} + 4x = 0$

23. $\dfrac{d^2 y}{dx^2} = 1 + \left(\dfrac{dy}{dx}\right)^2$

24. $\dfrac{d^2 x}{dy^2} = 1 - \left(\dfrac{dx}{dy}\right)^2$

25. $x^2 \dfrac{d^2 y}{dx^2} + x\dfrac{dy}{dx} = 1$

26. $\dfrac{d^2 y}{dx^2} - 4\dfrac{dy}{dx} + 3y = 0$

27. $\dfrac{d^3 y}{dx^3} - 2\dfrac{d^2 y}{dx^2} + \dfrac{dy}{dx} = 0$

28. $\dfrac{d^2 y}{dx^2} + 4y = \sec 2x$

29. $\dfrac{d^2 y}{dx^2} - \dfrac{dy}{dx} - 2y = e^{2x}$

30. $\dfrac{d^2 y}{dx^2} - 2\dfrac{dy}{dx} + 5y = e^{-x}$

31. Find the *general solution* of the differential equation $4x^2 y'' + 4xy' - y = 0$, given that there is a particular solution of the form $y = x^c$ for some constant c.

32. Show that the only plane curves that have constant curvature are circles and straight lines. (Assume that the appropriate derivatives exist and are continuous.)

33. Find the orthogonal trajectories of the family of curves $x^2 = Cy^3$. [*Caution.* The differential equation should not contain the arbitrary constant C.]

34. Find the orthogonal trajectories of the family of circles $(x - C)^2 + y^2 = C^2$.

35. Find the orthogonal trajectories of the family of parabolas $y^2 = 4C(C - x)$.

36. The equation $d^2 y/dt^2 + 100y = 0$ represents a simple harmonic motion. Find the general solution of the equation and determine the constants of integration if $y = 10$, $dy/dt = 50$, when $t = 0$. Find the period and the amplitude of the motion.

MATRICES

A *matrix* is a rectangular array of numbers. For example,

$$A = \begin{bmatrix} 2 & 1 & 3 \\ 1 & 0 & -2 \end{bmatrix} \tag{1}$$

is a matrix with two rows and three columns. We call A a "2 by 3" matrix. More generally, an "m by n" matrix is one that has m rows and n columns.

The element in the ith row and jth column of a matrix can be represented by a_{ij}. In the example above, we have

$$a_{11} = 2, \qquad a_{12} = 1, \qquad a_{13} = 3,$$
$$a_{21} = 1, \qquad a_{22} = 0, \qquad a_{23} = -2.$$

Two matrices A and B are *equal* if and only if they have the same elements in the same positions. That is, $A = B$ if and only if A and B have the same number of rows, say m, and the same number of columns, say n, and

$$a_{ij} = b_{ij} \qquad \text{for} \quad i = 1, 2, \ldots, m \quad \text{and} \quad j = 1, 2, \ldots, n.$$

For example, if

$$B = \begin{bmatrix} b_{11} & b_{12} & b_{13} \\ b_{21} & b_{22} & b_{23} \end{bmatrix} \tag{2}$$

and $B = A$, with A given by Eq. (1), then

$$b_{11} = 2, \qquad b_{12} = 1, \qquad b_{13} = 3,$$
$$b_{21} = 1, \qquad b_{22} = 0, \qquad b_{23} = -2.$$

Two matrices A and B can be added if and only if they have the same number of rows and the same number of columns. Their sum, $A + B$, is the matrix we get by adding corresponding elements in the two matrices. For example,

$$\begin{bmatrix} 2 & 1 & 3 \\ 1 & 0 & -2 \end{bmatrix} + \begin{bmatrix} 1 & -2 & 2 \\ 2 & 3 & -1 \end{bmatrix} = \begin{bmatrix} 3 & -1 & 5 \\ 3 & 3 & -3 \end{bmatrix}.$$

To multiply a matrix by a number c, we multiply each element by c. For example,

$$7 \begin{bmatrix} 2 & 1 & 3 \\ 1 & 0 & -2 \end{bmatrix} = \begin{bmatrix} 14 & 7 & 21 \\ 7 & 0 & -14 \end{bmatrix}. \tag{3}$$

A system of simultaneous linear equations

$$a_{11}x + a_{12}y + a_{13}z = b_1,$$
$$a_{21}x + a_{22}y + a_{23}z = b_2, \tag{4a}$$

can be written in matrix form as

$$\begin{bmatrix} a_{11} & a_{12} & a_{13} \\ a_{21} & a_{22} & a_{23} \end{bmatrix} \begin{bmatrix} x \\ y \\ z \end{bmatrix} = \begin{bmatrix} b_1 \\ b_2 \end{bmatrix}, \tag{4b}$$

or, more compactly, as

$$AX = B, \tag{4c}$$

where

$$A = \begin{bmatrix} a_{11} & a_{12} & a_{13} \\ a_{21} & a_{22} & a_{23} \end{bmatrix}, \qquad X = \begin{bmatrix} x \\ y \\ z \end{bmatrix}, \qquad B = \begin{bmatrix} b_1 \\ b_2 \end{bmatrix}. \tag{4d}$$

To form the product indicated by AX in Eq. (4c), we take the elements of the first row of A in order from left to right and multiply by the corresponding elements of X from the top down, and add these products. The result is the left side of the first equation in Eqs. (4a) and we set it equal to b_1, the element in the first row of B. Then we repeat the process using the second row of A: Multiply its individual elements by the corresponding elements in X, add the products, and set the result equal to b_2, the element in the second row of B.

More generally, a matrix A that has m rows and n columns can multiply a matrix B that has n rows and p columns to give a matrix $C = AB$ that has m rows and p columns. The element in the ith row and jth column of AB is the sum

$$c_{ij} = a_{i1}b_{1j} + a_{i2}b_{2j} + \cdots + a_{in}b_{nj} = \sum_{k=1}^{n} a_{ik}b_{kj}, \tag{5}$$

$$i = 1, 2, \ldots, m \quad \text{and} \quad j = 1, 2, \ldots, p.$$

For example:

$$\begin{bmatrix} 2 & -1 & 3 \\ 3 & 2 & 2 \end{bmatrix} \begin{bmatrix} a & b & c \\ d & e & f \\ u & v & w \end{bmatrix}$$

$$= \begin{bmatrix} 2a - d + 3u & 2b - e + 3v & 2c - f + 3w \\ 3a + 2d + 2u & 3b + 2e + 2v & 3c + 2f + 2w \end{bmatrix}.$$

There are two rows in the answer on the right, one for each row in the first factor on the left. There are three columns in the product AB, one for each column in B. In words, Eq. (5) is saying "to get the element in the ith row and jth column of AB, multiply the individual entries in the ith row of A, one after the other from left to right, by the corresponding entries in the jth column of B from top to bottom, and add these products: their sum is a single number c_{ij}."

PROBLEMS

1. Write the following system of linear equations in matrix form $AX = B$:

$$2x - 3y + 4z = -19,$$
$$6x + 4y - 2z = 8,$$
$$x + 5y + 4z = 23.$$

2. Let A be an arbitrary matrix with 3 rows and 3 columns and let I be the 3 by 3 matrix that has 1's on the main diagonal and zeros elsewhere:

$$I = \begin{bmatrix} 1 & 0 & 0 \\ 0 & 1 & 0 \\ 0 & 0 & 1 \end{bmatrix}.$$

Show that $IA = A$ and also that $AI = A$. For this reason, I is called the 3 by 3 identity matrix: It is the multiplicative identity matrix for all 3 by 3 matrices.

3. Let A be an arbitrary 3 by 3 matrix and let R_{12} be the matrix that is obtained from the 3-by-3 identity matrix by interchanging rows 1 and 2:

$$R_{12} = \begin{bmatrix} 0 & 1 & 0 \\ 1 & 0 & 0 \\ 0 & 0 & 1 \end{bmatrix}$$

Compute $R_{12}A$ and show that you would get the same result by interchanging rows 1 and 2 of A.

4. Let A and R_{12} be as in Problem 3 above. Compute AR_{12} and show that the result is what you would get by interchanging columns 1 and 2 of A. (Note that R_{12} is also the result of interchanging columns 1 and 2 of the 3 by 3 identity matrix I.)

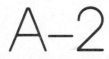

ELEMENTARY ROW OPERATIONS AND ROW REDUCTION

Two systems of linear equations are called *equivalent* if they have the same set of solutions. To solve a system of linear equations it is often possible to transform it step by step into an equivalent system of equations that is so simple it can be solved by inspection. We shall illustrate such a sequence of steps by transforming the system of equations

$$\begin{aligned} 2x + 3y - 4z &= -3, \\ x + 2y + 3z &= 3, \\ 3x - y - z &= 6, \end{aligned} \tag{1}$$

into the equivalent system of equations

$$\begin{aligned} x &= 2, \\ y &= -1, \\ z &= 1. \end{aligned} \tag{2}$$

EXAMPLE. Solve the system of equations (1).

Solution. The system (1) is the same as

$$AX = B, \qquad A = \begin{bmatrix} 2 & 3 & -4 \\ 1 & 2 & 3 \\ 3 & -1 & -1 \end{bmatrix}, \qquad B = \begin{bmatrix} -3 \\ 3 \\ 6 \end{bmatrix}. \tag{3}$$

We start with the 3 by 4 matrix $[A \mathbin{\vdots} B]$ whose first three columns are the columns of A, and whose fourth column is B. That is,

$$[A \mathbin{\vdots} B] = \begin{bmatrix} 2 & 3 & -4 & \vdots & -3 \\ 1 & 2 & 3 & \vdots & 3 \\ 3 & -1 & -1 & \vdots & 6 \end{bmatrix}. \tag{4}$$

We are going to transform this augmented matrix with a sequence of so-called *elementary row operations*. These operations, which are to be performed on the rows of the matrix, are of three kinds:

1. Multiply any row by a constant different from 0.
2. Add a constant multiple of any row to another row.
3. Interchange two rows.

Our goal is to replace the matrix $[A \mathbin{\vdots} B]$ by the matrix $[I \mathbin{\vdots} S]$, where

$$I = \begin{bmatrix} 1 & 0 & 0 \\ 0 & 1 & 0 \\ 0 & 0 & 1 \end{bmatrix} \quad \text{and} \quad S = \begin{bmatrix} s_1 \\ s_2 \\ s_3 \end{bmatrix}. \tag{5}$$

If we succeed, the matrix $[I \mathbin{\vdots} S]$ will be the matrix of the system

$$\begin{aligned} x & & & = s_1, \\ & y & & = s_2, \\ & & z & = s_3. \end{aligned} \tag{6}$$

The virtue of this system is that its solution, $x = s_1$, $y = s_2$, $z = s_3$, is the same as the solution of (1).

Our systematic approach will be to get a 1 in the upper left corner and use Type 2 operations to get zeros elsewhere in the first column. That will make the first column the same as the first column of I. Then we will use Type 1 or Type 3 operations to get a 1 in the second position in the second row, and follow that by Type 2 operations to get the second column to be what we want: namely, like the second column of I. Then we will work on the third column.

STEP 1.　Interchange rows 1 and 2 and get

$$\begin{bmatrix} 1 & 2 & 3 & \vdots & 3 \\ 2 & 3 & -4 & \vdots & -3 \\ 3 & -1 & -1 & \vdots & 6 \end{bmatrix}. \tag{7}$$

STEP 2.　Add -2 times row 1 to row 2.

STEP 3.　Add -3 times row 1 to row 3.

The result of steps 2 and 3 is

$$\begin{bmatrix} 1 & 2 & 3 & \vdots & 3 \\ 0 & -1 & -10 & \vdots & -9 \\ 0 & -7 & -10 & \vdots & -3 \end{bmatrix}. \tag{8}$$

STEP 4.　Multiply row 2 by -1; then

STEP 5.　Add -2 times row 2 to row 1, and

STEP 6.　Add 7 times row 2 to row 3.

The combined result of these steps is

$$\begin{bmatrix} 1 & 0 & -17 & \vdots & -15 \\ 0 & 1 & 10 & \vdots & 9 \\ 0 & 0 & 60 & \vdots & 60 \end{bmatrix}. \tag{9}$$

STEP 7.　Multiply row 3 by $1/60$.

STEP 8.　Add 17 times row 3 to row 1.

STEP 9.　Add -10 times row 3 to row 2.

The final result is

$$[I \vdots S] = \begin{bmatrix} 1 & 0 & 0 & \vdots & 2 \\ 0 & 1 & 0 & \vdots & -1 \\ 0 & 0 & 1 & \vdots & 1 \end{bmatrix}. \tag{10}$$

This represents the system (2). The solution of this system, and therefore of the system (1), is $x = 2$, $y = -1$, $z = 1$. To check the solution, we substitute these values in (1) and find that

$$2(2) + 3(-1) - 4(1) = -3,$$
$$(2) + 2(-1) + 3(1) = 3, \tag{11}$$
$$3(2) - (-1) - (1) = 6.$$

The method of using elementary row operations to reduce the augmented matrix of a system of linear equations to a simpler form is sometimes called the *method of row reduction*. It works because at each step the system of equations represented by the transformed matrix is equivalent to the original system. Thus, in the Example, when we finally arrived at the matrix (10), which represented the system (2) whose solution could be found by inspection, we knew that this solution was also the solution of (1). Note that we checked the solution anyhow. It is always a good idea to do that.

The matrix I in Eq. (5) is the multiplicative identity for all 3 by 3 matrices. That is, if M is any 3 by 3 matrix, then

$$IM = MI = M. \tag{12}$$

If P is a matrix with the property that

$$PM = I,$$

then we call P the *inverse* of M, and use the alternative notation

$$P = M^{-1},$$

pronounced "M inverse."

The sequence of row operations that we used in the Example to find the solution of the system $AX = B$ can be used to find the inverse of the matrix A. We start with the 3 by 6 matrix $[A \vdots I]$ whose first three columns are the columns of A and whose last three columns are the columns of I, namely

$$[A \vdots I] = \begin{bmatrix} 2 & 3 & -4 & \vdots & 1 & 0 & 0 \\ 1 & 2 & 3 & \vdots & 0 & 1 & 0 \\ 3 & -1 & -1 & \vdots & 0 & 0 & 1 \end{bmatrix}. \tag{13}$$

We then carry out Steps 1 through 9 of the Example on the augmented matrix $[A \vdots I]$. The final result is

$$[A \vdots A^{-1}] = \begin{bmatrix} 1 & 0 & 0 & \vdots & \frac{1}{60} & \frac{7}{60} & \frac{17}{60} \\ 0 & 1 & 0 & \vdots & \frac{10}{60} & \frac{10}{60} & -\frac{10}{60} \\ 0 & 0 & 1 & \vdots & -\frac{7}{60} & \frac{11}{60} & \frac{1}{60} \end{bmatrix}. \tag{14}$$

The 3-by-3 matrix in the last 3 columns is

$$A^{-1} = \frac{1}{60} \begin{bmatrix} 1 & 7 & 17 \\ 10 & 10 & -10 \\ -7 & 11 & 1 \end{bmatrix}. \tag{15}$$

By direct matrix multiplication, we verify our answer:

$$A = \frac{1}{60} \begin{bmatrix} 1 & 7 & 17 \\ 10 & 10 & -10 \\ -7 & 11 & 1 \end{bmatrix} \begin{bmatrix} 2 & 3 & -4 \\ 1 & 2 & 3 \\ 3 & -1 & -1 \end{bmatrix}$$

$$= \frac{1}{60} \begin{bmatrix} 2 + 7 + 51 & 3 + 14 - 17 & -4 + 21 - 17 \\ 20 + 10 - 30 & 30 + 20 + 10 & -40 + 30 + 10 \\ -14 + 11 + 3 & -21 + 22 - 1 & 28 + 33 - 1 \end{bmatrix} \tag{16}$$

$$= \frac{1}{60} \begin{bmatrix} 60 & 0 & 0 \\ 0 & 60 & 0 \\ 0 & 0 & 60 \end{bmatrix} = \begin{bmatrix} 1 & 0 & 0 \\ 0 & 1 & 0 \\ 0 & 0 & 1 \end{bmatrix}.$$

Knowing A^{-1} provides a second way to solve the system of equations with which this article began. We write the system in the form given in (3), and then multiply B on the left by A^{-1} to find the solution matrix X. Thus,

$$X = IX = (A^{-1}A)X = A^{-1}(AX) = A^{-1}B = \frac{1}{60} \begin{bmatrix} 1 & 7 & 17 \\ 10 & 10 & -10 \\ -7 & 11 & 1 \end{bmatrix} \begin{bmatrix} -3 \\ 3 \\ 6 \end{bmatrix}$$

$$= \frac{1}{60} \begin{bmatrix} 120 \\ -60 \\ 60 \end{bmatrix} = \begin{bmatrix} 2 \\ -1 \\ 1 \end{bmatrix}. \tag{17}$$

REMARK 1.　Only square matrices can have inverses. If an n by n matrix A has an inverse, the method shown above for $n = 3$ will give it: Put the n by n identity matrix alongside A and use the row operations to get an n by n identity matrix in place of A. The n by n matrix that is now beside that is A^{-1}.

REMARK 2.　Not every n by n matrix has an inverse. For example, the 2 by 2 matrix

$$\begin{bmatrix} 1 & 1 \\ a & a \end{bmatrix}$$

has no inverse. The method we outlined above would reduce this to

$$\begin{bmatrix} 1 & 1 \\ 0 & 0 \end{bmatrix},$$

which cannot be further changed by elementary row operations into the 2 by 2 identity matrix. We shall have more to say about inverses in the next article.

REMARK 3.   A system of m equations in n unknowns may have no solutions, only one solution, or infinitely many solutions. If there are any solutions, they can be found by the method of successive elimination, which is like the elementary row operations we used above.

PROBLEMS

1. Use the method of row operations to find the inverse of each of the following matrices:

a) $A = \begin{bmatrix} 1 & 2 \\ 2 & 3 \end{bmatrix}$ **b)** $A = \begin{bmatrix} 1 & 2 & 3 \\ 0 & 2 & 4 \\ 0 & 0 & 3 \end{bmatrix}$

2. Define the determinant of the 2 by 2 matrix

$$A = \begin{bmatrix} a & b \\ c & d \end{bmatrix} \quad \text{by} \quad \det A = ad - bc.$$

If $ad - bc \neq 0$, verify that the matrix

$$P = \frac{1}{ad - bc} \begin{bmatrix} d & -b \\ -c & a \end{bmatrix}$$

is the inverse of A; that is, show that

$$AP = PA = I_2 = \begin{bmatrix} 1 & 0 \\ 0 & 1 \end{bmatrix}.$$

3. Use the result of Problem 2 to write down by inspection the inverses of the following matrices:

a) $A = \begin{bmatrix} 2 & -1 \\ 3 & 1 \end{bmatrix}$ **b)** $B = \begin{bmatrix} 2 & 3 \\ -1 & 1 \end{bmatrix}$

(In this example, B is the transpose of A. Is B^{-1} also the transpose of A^{-1}? *Note.* "Transpose" means to write the rows of a matrix as columns.)

4. Solve the system of equations in Problem 1, Article A–1.

5. Solve the equations for x and y in terms of z:

$$\begin{array}{l} 2x - y + 2z = 5 \\ 3x + y - 3z = 7 \end{array} \quad \text{or} \quad \begin{bmatrix} 2 & -1 \\ 3 & 1 \end{bmatrix} \begin{bmatrix} x \\ y \end{bmatrix} = \begin{bmatrix} 5 - 2z \\ 7 + 3z \end{bmatrix}.$$

You can use the result of Problem 3(a) above if you want to. (Each equation represents a plane. In how many points do the planes intersect?)

6. Apply the nine steps of the Example to the matrix in (13), to obtain the matrix in (14).

A–3
DETERMINANTS

An n by n square matrix is called a *matrix of order n*, for short. With such a matrix we associate a number called the *determinant* of A and written sometimes det A and sometimes $|a_{ij}|$ with vertical bars (which do not mean absolute value). For $n = 1$ and $n = 2$ we have these definitions:

$$\det [a] = a, \qquad \det \begin{bmatrix} a & b \\ c & d \end{bmatrix} = ad - bc. \tag{1}$$

For a matrix of order 3, we define

$$\det \begin{bmatrix} a_{11} & a_{12} & a_{13} \\ a_{21} & a_{22} & a_{23} \\ a_{31} & a_{32} & a_{33} \end{bmatrix} = \begin{array}{l} \text{Sum of all signed products} \\ \text{of the form } \pm a_{1i} a_{2j} a_{3k}, \end{array}$$

where i, j, k is a permutation of 1, 2, 3 in some order. There are $3! = 6$ such permutations, so there are six terms in the sum. Half of these have plus signs and the other half have minus signs, according to the index of the permutation, where the index is a number we next define.

Index of a permutation.   *Given any permutation of the numbers 1, 2, 3, ..., n, denote the permutation by $i_1, i_2, i_3, ..., i_n$. In this arrangement, some of the* numbers following i_1 may be less than i_1, and however many of these there are is called the **number of inversions** in the arrangement pertaining to i_1. Likewise, there is a number of inversions pertaining to each of the other i's; it is the number of indices that come after that particular one in the arrangement and are less than it. The **index** of the permutation is the sum of all of the numbers of inversions pertaining to the separate indices.

EXAMPLE 1. For $n = 5$, the permutation

$$5\ 3\ 1\ 2\ 4$$

has

4 inversions pertaining to the first element, 5,

2 inversions pertaining to the second element, 3,

and no further inversions, so the index is $4 + 2 = 6$.

The following table shows the permutations of 1, 2, 3 and the index of each permutation. The signed product in the determinant of Eq. (2) is also shown.

Permutation	Index	Signed product
1 2 3	0	$+a_{11}a_{22}a_{33}$
1 3 2	1	$-a_{11}a_{23}a_{32}$
2 1 3	1	$-a_{12}a_{21}a_{33}$
2 3 1	2	$+a_{12}a_{23}a_{31}$
3 1 2	2	$+a_{13}a_{21}a_{32}$
3 2 1	3	$-a_{13}a_{22}a_{31}$

The sum of the six signed products is:

$$a_{11}(a_{22}a_{33} - a_{23}a_{32}) - a_{12}(a_{21}a_{33} - a_{23}a_{31}) + a_{13}(a_{21}a_{32} - a_{22}a_{31})$$

$$= a_{11}\begin{vmatrix} a_{22} & a_{23} \\ a_{32} & a_{33} \end{vmatrix} - a_{12}\begin{vmatrix} a_{21} & a_{23} \\ a_{31} & a_{33} \end{vmatrix} + a_{13}\begin{vmatrix} a_{21} & a_{22} \\ a_{31} & a_{32} \end{vmatrix}$$

$$= \begin{vmatrix} a_{11} & a_{12} & a_{13} \\ a_{21} & a_{22} & a_{23} \\ a_{31} & a_{32} & a_{33} \end{vmatrix}. \tag{2}$$

Minors and Cofactors

In Eq. (2) there are some second order determinants. There are other ways in which the six terms in the expansion of the third order determinant could be written. We have chosen to write it as the sum of the products of the elements of the first row of the matrix A, each multiplied by its *cofactor*. In order to define the cofactor of an element in a matrix, we first define the *minor* of that element, which is the determinant of the matrix that remains when the row and column that contain the given element are deleted. Thus the *minor* of the element in the ith row and jth column is the determinant of the $(n - 1)$ by $(n - 1)$ matrix that remains when row i and column j are deleted. The *cofactor* of a_{ij} is denoted by A_{ij} and it is $(-1)^{i+j}$ times the minor of a_{ij}.

EXAMPLE 2. Find the cofactors of the matrix

$$A = \begin{bmatrix} 2 & 1 & 3 \\ 3 & -1 & -2 \\ 2 & 3 & 1 \end{bmatrix},$$

and evaluate det (A).

Solution. The cofactors are

$$A_{11} = (-1)^{1+1} \begin{vmatrix} -1 & -2 \\ 3 & 1 \end{vmatrix}, \qquad A_{12} = (-1)^{1+2} \begin{vmatrix} 3 & -2 \\ 2 & 1 \end{vmatrix},$$

$$A_{13} = (-1)^{1+3} \begin{vmatrix} 3 & -1 \\ 2 & 3 \end{vmatrix}.$$

To find det (A), we multiply each element of the first row of A by its cofactor and add:

$$\det (A) = 2 \begin{vmatrix} -1 & -2 \\ 3 & 1 \end{vmatrix} + (-1) \begin{vmatrix} 3 & -2 \\ 2 & 1 \end{vmatrix} + 3 \begin{vmatrix} 3 & -1 \\ 2 & 3 \end{vmatrix}$$

$$= 2(-1 + 6) - 1(3 + 4) + 3(9 + 2) = 10 - 7 + 33 = 36.$$

Note. There is a simple checkerboard pattern for remembering the signs that correspond to $(-1)^{i+j}$ and that can be applied to convert the *minor* of an element in a matrix to the *cofactor* of the element. For a third order determinant the sign pattern is

$$\begin{matrix} + & - & + \\ - & + & - \\ + & - & + \end{matrix}$$

In the upper left corner, $i = 1, j = 1$ and $(-1)^{1+1} = +1$. In going from any cell to an adjacent cell in the same row or column, we change i by 1 or j by 1, but not both, so we change the exponent from even to odd or from odd to even, which changes the sign from $+$ to $-$ or from $-$ to $+$.

If we were to expand the determinant in Example 2 by cofactors according to elements of its third column, say, we would get

$$+3 \begin{vmatrix} 3 & -1 \\ 2 & 3 \end{vmatrix} - (-2) \begin{vmatrix} 2 & 1 \\ 2 & 3 \end{vmatrix} + 1 \begin{vmatrix} 2 & 1 \\ 3 & -1 \end{vmatrix}$$

$$= 3(9 + 2) + 2(6 - 2) + 1(-2 - 3) = 33 + 8 - 5 = 36.$$

It is no accident that the answer is the same. If we were to multiply the elements of any row (or column) by the cofactors of the corresponding elements and add the products, we would get the same answer: the value of the determinant.

PROBLEM

Evaluate the following third order determinant by expanding according to cofactors of (a) the first row, and (b) the second column:

$$\begin{vmatrix} 2 & -1 & 2 \\ 1 & 0 & 3 \\ 0 & 2 & 1 \end{vmatrix}.$$

We now state some facts about determinants. You should know and be able to use these facts, but we omit the proofs.

FACT 1.　If two rows of a matrix are identical, the determinant is zero.

FACT 2.　If two rows of a matrix are interchanged, the determinant just changes its sign.

FACT 3.　The determinant of a matrix is the sum of the products of the elements of the ith row (or column) by their cofactors, for any i.

FACT 4.　The determinant of the transpose of a matrix is equal to the original determinant.

FACT 5.　If each element of some row (or column) of a matrix is multiplied by a constant c, the determinant is multiplied by c.

FACT 6.　If all elements of a matrix above the principal diagonal (or all below it) are zero, the determinant of the matrix is the product of the elements on the main diagonal.

A–4

PROPERTIES OF DETERMINANTS

EXAMPLE 1

$$\begin{vmatrix} 3 & 4 & 7 \\ 0 & -2 & 5 \\ 0 & 0 & 5 \end{vmatrix} = (3)(-2)(5) = -30.$$

FACT 7.　If the elements of any row of a matrix are multiplied by the cofactors of the corresponding elements of a different row and these products are summed, the sum is zero.

EXAMPLE 2. If A_{11}, A_{12}, A_{13} are the cofactors of the elements of the first row of $A = a_{ij}$, then the sums

$$a_{21}A_{11} + a_{22}A_{12} + a_{23}A_{13}$$

(elements of second row times cofactors of elements of first row)

and

$$a_{31}A_{11} + a_{32}A_{12} + a_{33}A_{13}$$

are both zero. A similar result holds for columns.

FACT 8.   If the elements of any column of a matrix are multiplied by the cofactors of the corresponding elements of a different column and these products are summed, the sum is zero.

FACT 9.   If each element of a row of a matrix is multiplied by a constant c and the results are added to a different row, the determinant is not changed.

EXAMPLE 3.   Evaluate the fourth order determinant

$$\begin{vmatrix} 1 & -2 & 3 & 1 \\ 2 & 1 & 0 & 2 \\ -1 & 2 & 1 & -2 \\ 0 & 1 & 2 & 1 \end{vmatrix}.$$

Solution.   By adding appropriate multiples of row 1 to rows 2 and 3, we can get the equal determinant

$$\begin{vmatrix} 1 & -2 & 3 & 1 \\ 0 & 5 & -6 & 0 \\ 0 & 0 & 4 & -1 \\ 0 & 1 & 2 & 1 \end{vmatrix}.$$

We could further reduce this to a triangular matrix (one with zeros below the main diagonal), or expand it by cofactors of its first column. By multiplying the elements of the first column by their respective cofactors, we get the third order determinant

$$\begin{vmatrix} 5 & -6 & 0 \\ 0 & 4 & -1 \\ 1 & 2 & 1 \end{vmatrix} = 5(4 + 2) - (-6)(0 + 1) + 0 = 36.$$

PROBLEMS

Evaluate the following determinants.

1. $\begin{vmatrix} 2 & 3 & 1 \\ 4 & 5 & 2 \\ 1 & 2 & 3 \end{vmatrix}$

2. $\begin{vmatrix} 2 & -1 & -2 \\ -1 & 2 & 1 \\ 3 & 0 & -3 \end{vmatrix}$

3. $\begin{vmatrix} 1 & 2 & 3 & 4 \\ 0 & 1 & 2 & 3 \\ 0 & 0 & 2 & 1 \\ 0 & 0 & 3 & 2 \end{vmatrix}$

4. $\begin{vmatrix} 1 & -1 & 2 & 3 \\ 2 & 1 & 2 & 6 \\ 1 & 0 & 2 & 3 \\ -2 & 2 & 0 & -5 \end{vmatrix}$

Here is another way to find the inverse of a square matrix A (assuming that A has one). It depends on the fact that square matrix A has an inverse if and only if det $(A) \neq 0$. First we describe the method. Then we do an example. Finally, we indicate why the method works.

THE METHOD. Given the matrix A, construct, in order,

i) the matrix of minors of elements of A;
ii) by appropriate sign changes, the matrix of cofactors of the elements of A;
iii) The transposed matrix of cofactors. This matrix is called the *adjoint* of A:

$$\text{adj } A = \text{transposed matrix of cofactors.}$$

iv) Then,

$$A^{-1} = \frac{1}{\det A} \text{adj } A.$$

A–5
DETERMINANTS AND THE INVERSE OF A MATRIX

EXAMPLE. Let us take the same matrix A that we used in illustrating the method of elementary row operations:

$$A = \begin{bmatrix} 2 & 3 & -4 \\ 1 & 2 & 3 \\ 3 & -1 & -1 \end{bmatrix}.$$

You can verify that the matrix of minors is

$$\begin{bmatrix} 1 & -10 & -7 \\ -7 & 10 & -11 \\ 17 & 10 & 1 \end{bmatrix}.$$

We next apply the sign corrections according to the checkerboard pattern $(-1)^{i+j}$ to get the matrix of cofactors

$$\begin{bmatrix} 1 & 10 & -7 \\ 7 & 10 & 11 \\ 17 & -10 & 1 \end{bmatrix}.$$

The adjoint of A is the transposed cofactor matrix

$$\text{adj } A = \begin{bmatrix} 1 & 7 & 17 \\ 10 & 10 & -10 \\ -7 & 11 & 1 \end{bmatrix}.$$

We get the determinant of A by multiplying the first row of A and the first column of adj A (which is the first row of the matrix of cofactors, so we are multiplying the elements of the first row of A by their own cofactors):

$$\det A = 2(1) + 3(10) + (-4)(-7) = 2 + 30 + 28 = 60.$$

Therefore, when we divide adj A by det A, we get

$$A^{-1} = \frac{1}{60}\begin{bmatrix} 1 & 7 & 17 \\ 10 & 10 & -10 \\ -7 & 11 & 1 \end{bmatrix},$$

which agrees with our previous work.

Why does the method work? Let us take a closer look at the products A adj A and (adj A) A for $n = 3$. Because adj A is the transposed cofactor matrix, we get:

A (adj A)

$$= \begin{bmatrix} a_{11} & a_{12} & a_{13} \\ a_{21} & a_{22} & a_{23} \\ a_{31} & a_{32} & a_{33} \end{bmatrix} \begin{bmatrix} A_{11} & A_{21} & A_{31} \\ A_{12} & A_{22} & A_{32} \\ A_{13} & A_{23} & A_{33} \end{bmatrix} = \begin{bmatrix} \det A & 0 & 0 \\ 0 & \det A & 0 \\ 0 & 0 & \det A \end{bmatrix};$$

(here A_{ij} = cofactor of a_{ij}).

An element on the main diagonal in the final product is the product of a row of A and the corresponding column of adj A. This is the same as the sum of the products of the elements of a row of A and the cofactors of the same row, which is just det A. For those elements not on the main diagonal in the product, we are adding products of elements of some row of A by the cofactors of the corresponding elements of a different row of A, and that sum is zero.

If we were to multiply in the other order, (adj A) A, we would again get

$$(\text{adj } A)\, A = \begin{bmatrix} \det A & 0 & 0 \\ 0 & \det A & 0 \\ 0 & 0 & \det A \end{bmatrix},$$

because we are multiplying the elements of the jth column of A, say, by the cofactors of the corresponding elements of the ith column, in order to get the entry in the ith row and jth column in the product. The result is det A when $i = j$ and is 0 when $i \neq j$.

PROBLEMS

Use the method of cofactors and adjoint matrices to find A^{-1} in each case where det $A \neq 0$. Check your work by computing A (adj A).

1. $A = \begin{bmatrix} 1 & 2 \\ 2 & 3 \end{bmatrix}$

2. $A = \begin{bmatrix} -1 & 2 & 1 \\ 2 & 2 & 1 \\ 1 & 0 & 2 \end{bmatrix}$

3. $A = \begin{bmatrix} 2 & 1 & 1 & 1 \\ 0 & 2 & 1 & 1 \\ 0 & 0 & 2 & 1 \\ 0 & 0 & 0 & 2 \end{bmatrix}$

APPENDIX

FORMULAS FROM ELEMENTARY MATHEMATICS

ALGEBRA

1. Laws of Exponents

$$a^m a^n = a^{m+n}, \quad (ab)^m = a^m b^m, \quad (a^m)^n = a^{mn}, \quad a^{m/n} = \sqrt[n]{a^m}.$$

If $a \neq 0$,

$$\frac{a^m}{a^n} = a^{m-n}, \quad a^0 = 1, \quad a^{-m} = \frac{1}{a^m}.$$

2. Zero

$$a \cdot 0 = 0 \cdot a = 0 \text{ for any finite number } a.$$

If $a \neq 0$,

$$\frac{0}{a} = 0, \quad 0^a = 0, \quad a^0 = 1.$$

Division by zero is not defined.

3. Fractions

$$\frac{a}{b} + \frac{c}{d} = \frac{ad + bc}{bd}, \quad \frac{a}{b} \cdot \frac{c}{d} = \frac{ac}{bd}, \quad \frac{a/b}{c/d} = \frac{a}{b} \cdot \frac{d}{c}, \quad \frac{-a}{b} = -\frac{a}{b} = \frac{a}{-b}.$$

$$\frac{(a/b) + (c/d)}{(e/f) + (g/h)} = \frac{(a/b) + (c/d)}{(e/f) + (g/h)} \cdot \frac{bdfh}{bdfh} = \frac{(ad + bc)fh}{(eh + fg)bd}.$$

4. Binomial Theorem, for n = positive integer

$$(a + b)^n = a^n + na^{n-1}b + \frac{n(n-1)}{1 \cdot 2} a^{n-2}b^2$$

$$+ \frac{n(n-1)(n-2)}{1 \cdot 2 \cdot 3} a^{n-3}b^3 + \cdots + nab^{n-1} + b^n.$$

5. Proportionality Factor

If y is proportional to x, or y varies directly as x, then $y = kx$ for some constant k, called the *proportionality factor*. If $y = k/x$, we say that y is *inversely proportional* to x, or that y *varies inversely* as x.

6. Remainder Theorem and Factor Theorem

If the polynomial $f(x)$ is divided by $x - r$ until a remainder R independent of x is obtained, then $R = f(r)$. In particular, $x - r$ is a *factor* of $f(x)$ if and only if r is a *root* of the equation $f(x) = 0$.

7. Quadratic Formula

If $a \neq 0$, the roots of the equation $ax^2 + bx + c = 0$ are given by the formula

$$x = \frac{-b \pm \sqrt{b^2 - 4ac}}{2a}.$$

(A = area, B = area of base, C = circumference, S = lateral area or surface area, V = volume.)

B

GEOMETRY

1. Triangle

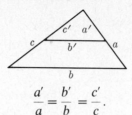

$A = \frac{1}{2}bh.$

2. Similar Triangles

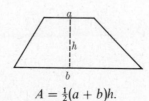

$$\frac{a'}{a} = \frac{b'}{b} = \frac{c'}{c}.$$

3. Theorem of Pythagoras

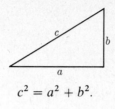

$c^2 = a^2 + b^2.$

4. Parallelogram

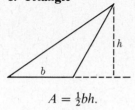

$A = bh.$

5. Trapezoid

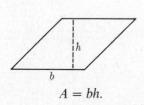

$A = \frac{1}{2}(a + b)h.$

6. Circle

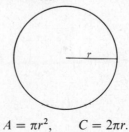

$A = \pi r^2, \qquad C = 2\pi r.$

7. Any Cylinder or Prism with Parallel Bases

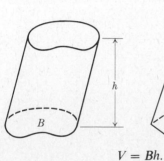

$V = Bh.$

8. Right Circular Cylinder

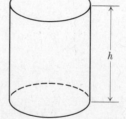

$V = \pi r^2 h, \qquad S = 2\pi rh.$

9. Any Cone or Pyramid

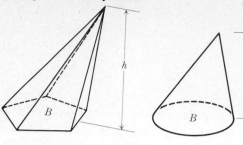

$$V = \tfrac{1}{3}Bh.$$

10. Right Circular Cone

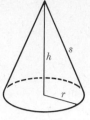

$$V = \tfrac{1}{3}\pi r^2 h, \qquad S = \pi rs.$$

11. Sphere

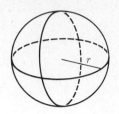

$$V = \tfrac{4}{3}\pi r^3, \qquad A = 4\pi r^2.$$

C

TRIGONOMETRY

1. Definitions and Fundamental Identities

$$\sin \theta = \frac{y}{r} = \frac{1}{\csc \theta}.$$

$$\cos \theta = \frac{x}{r} = \frac{1}{\sec \theta}.$$

$$\tan \theta = \frac{y}{x} = \frac{1}{\cot \theta}.$$

$$\sin (-\theta) = -\sin \theta, \qquad \cos (-\theta) = \cos \theta.$$

$$\sin^2 \theta + \cos^2 \theta = 1.$$

$$\sin 2\theta = 2 \sin \theta \cos \theta, \qquad \cos 2\theta = \cos^2 \theta - \sin^2 \theta.$$

$$\sin^2 \frac{\theta}{2} = \frac{1 - \cos \theta}{2}, \qquad \cos^2 \frac{\theta}{2} = \frac{1 + \cos \theta}{2}.$$

$$\sin (\alpha + \beta) = \sin \alpha \cos \beta + \cos \alpha \sin \beta.$$

$$\cos (\alpha + \beta) = \cos \alpha \cos \beta - \sin \alpha \sin \beta.$$

$$\tan (\alpha + \beta) = \frac{\tan \alpha + \tan \beta}{1 - \tan \alpha \tan \beta}.$$

2. Angles and Sides of a Triangle

Law of cosines: $a^2 = b^2 + c^2 - 2bc \cos A.$

Law of sines: $\dfrac{\sin A}{a} = \dfrac{\sin B}{b} = \dfrac{\sin C}{c}.$

Area $= \tfrac{1}{2}bc \sin A = \tfrac{1}{2}ac \sin B = \tfrac{1}{2}ab \sin C.$

APPENDIX

TABLES

Table 1. Natural trigonometric functions

Angle					Angle				
De-gree	Ra-dian	Sine	Co-sine	Tan-gent	De-gree	Ra-dian	Sine	Co-sine	Tan-gent
0°	0.000	0.000	1.000	0.000					
1°	0.017	0.017	1.000	0.017	46°	0.803	0.719	0.695	1.036
2°	0.035	0.035	0.999	0.035	47°	0.820	0.731	0.682	1.072
3°	0.052	0.052	0.999	0.052	48°	0.838	0.743	0.669	1.111
4°	0.070	0.070	0.998	0.070	49°	0.855	0.755	0.656	1.150
5°	0.087	0.087	0.996	0.087	50°	0.873	0.766	0.643	1.192
6°	0.105	0.105	0.995	0.105	51°	0.890	0.777	0.629	1.235
7°	0.122	0.122	0.993	0.123	52°	0.908	0.788	0.616	1.280
8°	0.140	0.139	0.990	0.141	53°	0.925	0.799	0.602	1.327
9°	0.157	0.156	0.988	0.158	54°	0.942	0.809	0.588	1.376
10°	0.175	0.174	0.985	0.176	55°	0.960	0.819	0.574	1.428
11°	0.192	0.191	0.982	0.194	56°	0.977	0.829	0.559	1.483
12°	0.209	0.208	0.978	0.213	57°	0.995	0.839	0.545	1.540
13°	0.227	0.225	0.974	0.231	58°	1.012	0.848	0.530	1.600
14°	0.244	0.242	0.970	0.249	59°	1.030	0.857	0.515	1.664
15°	0.262	0.259	0.966	0.268	60°	1.047	0.866	0.500	1.732
16°	0.279	0.276	0.961	0.287	61°	1.065	0.875	0.485	1.804
17°	0.297	0.292	0.956	0.306	62°	1.082	0.883	0.469	1.881
18°	0.314	0.309	0.951	0.325	63°	1.100	0.891	0.454	1.963
19°	0.332	0.326	0.946	0.344	64°	1.117	0.899	0.438	2.050
20°	0.349	0.342	0.940	0.364	65°	1.134	0.906	0.423	2.145
21°	0.367	0.358	0.934	0.384	66°	1.152	0.914	0.407	2.246
22°	0.384	0.375	0.927	0.404	67°	1.169	0.921	0.391	2.356
23°	0.401	0.391	0.921	0.424	68°	1.187	0.927	0.375	2.475
24°	0.419	0.407	0.914	0.445	69°	1.204	0.934	0.358	2.605
25°	0.436	0.423	0.906	0.466	70°	1.222	0.940	0.342	2.748
26°	0.454	0.438	0.899	0.488	71°	1.239	0.946	0.326	2.904
27°	0.471	0.454	0.891	0.510	72°	1.257	0.951	0.309	3.078
28°	0.489	0.469	0.883	0.532	73°	1.274	0.956	0.292	3.271
29°	0.506	0.485	0.875	0.554	74°	1.292	0.961	0.276	3.487
30°	0.524	0.500	0.866	0.577	75°	1.309	0.966	0.259	3.732
31°	0.541	0.515	0.857	0.601	76°	1.326	0.970	0.242	4.011
32°	0.559	0.530	0.848	0.625	77°	1.344	0.974	0.225	4.332
33°	0.576	0.545	0.839	0.649	78°	1.361	0.978	0.208	4.705
34°	0.593	0.559	0.829	0.675	79°	1.379	0.982	0.191	5.145
35°	0.611	0.574	0.819	0.700	80°	1.396	0.985	0.174	5.671
36°	0.628	0.588	0.809	0.727	81°	1.414	0.988	0.156	6.314
37°	0.646	0.602	0.799	0.754	82°	1.431	0.990	0.139	7.115
38°	0.663	0.616	0.788	0.781	83°	1.449	0.993	0.122	8.144
39°	0.681	0.629	0.777	0.810	84°	1.466	0.995	0.105	9.514
40°	0.698	0.643	0.766	0.839	85°	1.484	0.996	0.087	11.43
41°	0.716	0.656	0.755	0.869	86°	1.501	0.998	0.070	14.30
42°	0.733	0.669	0.743	0.900	87°	1.518	0.999	0.052	19.08
43°	0.750	0.682	0.731	0.933	88°	1.536	0.999	0.035	28.64
44°	0.768	0.695	0.719	0.966	89°	1.553	1.000	0.017	57.29
45°	0.785	0.707	0.707	1.000	90°	1.571	1.000	0.000	

Table 2.   Exponential functions

x	e^x	e^{-x}	x	e^x	e^{-x}
0.00	1.0000	1.0000	2.5	12.182	0.0821
0.05	1.0513	0.9512	2.6	13.464	0.0743
0.10	1.1052	0.9048	2.7	14.880	0.0672
0.15	1.1618	0.8607	2.8	16.445	0.0608
0.20	1.2214	0.8187	2.9	18.174	0.0550
0.25	1.2840	0.7788	3.0	20.086	0.0498
0.30	1.3499	0.7408	3.1	22.198	0.0450
0.35	1.4191	0.7047	3.2	24.533	0.0408
0.40	1.4918	0.6703	3.3	27.113	0.0369
0.45	1.5683	0.6376	3.4	29.964	0.0334
0.50	1.6487	0.6065	3.5	33.115	0.0302
0.55	1.7333	0.5769	3.6	36.598	0.0273
0.60	1.8221	0.5488	3.7	40.447	0.0247
0.65	1.9155	0.5220	3.8	44.701	0.0224
0.70	2.0138	0.4966	3.9	49.402	0.0202
0.75	2.1170	0.4724	4.0	54.598	0.0183
0.80	2.2255	0.4493	4.1	60.340	0.0166
0.85	2.3396	0.4274	4.2	66.686	0.0150
0.90	2.4596	0.4066	4.3	73.700	0.0136
0.95	2.5857	0.3867	4.4	81.451	0.0123
1.0	2.7183	0.3679	4.5	90.017	0.0111
1.1	3.0042	0.3329	4.6	99.484	0.0101
1.2	3.3201	0.3012	4.7	109.95	0.0091
1.3	3.6693	0.2725	4.8	121.51	0.0082
1.4	4.0552	0.2466	4.9	134.29	0.0074
1.5	4.4817	0.2231	5	148.41	0.0067
1.6	4.9530	0.2019	6	403.43	0.0025
1.7	5.4739	0.1827	7	1096.6	0.0009
1.8	6.0496	0.1653	8	2981.0	0.0003
1.9	6.6859	0.1496	9	8103.1	0.0001
2.0	7.3891	0.1353	10	22026	0.00005
2.1	8.1662	0.1225			
2.2	9.0250	0.1108			
2.3	9.9742	0.1003			
2.4	11.023	0.0907			

Table 3. Natural logarithms of numbers

n	$\log_e n$	n	$\log_e n$	n	$\log_e n$
0.0	*	4.5	1.5041	9.0	2.1972
0.1	7.6974	4.6	1.5261	9.1	2.2083
0.2	8.3906	4.7	1.5476	9.2	2.2192
0.3	8.7960	4.8	1.5686	9.3	2.2300
0.4	9.0837	4.9	1.5892	9.4	2.2407
0.5	9.3069	5.0	1.6094	9.5	2.2513
0.6	9.4892	5.1	1.6292	9.6	2.2618
0.7	9.6433	5.2	1.6487	9.7	2.2721
0.8	9.7769	5.3	1.6677	9.8	2.2824
0.9	9.8946	5.4	1.6864	9.9	2.2925
1.0	0.0000	5.5	1.7047	10	2.3026
1.1	0.0953	5.6	1.7228	11	2.3979
1.2	0.1823	5.7	1.7405	12	2.4849
1.3	0.2624	5.8	1.7579	13	2.5649
1.4	0.3365	5.9	1.7750	14	2.6391
1.5	0.4055	6.0	1.7918	15	2.7081
1.6	0.4700	6.1	1.8083	16	2.7726
1.7	0.5306	6.2	1.8245	17	2.8332
1.8	0.5878	6.3	1.8405	18	2.8904
1.9	0.6419	6.4	1.8563	19	2.9444
2.0	0.6931	6.5	1.8718	20	2.9957
2.1	0.7419	6.6	1.8871	25	3.2189
2.2	0.7885	6.7	1.9021	30	3.4012
2.3	0.8329	6.8	1.9169	35	3.5553
2.4	0.8755	6.9	1.9315	40	3.6889
2.5	0.9163	7.0	1.9459	45	3.8067
2.6	0.9555	7.1	1.9601	50	3.9120
2.7	0.9933	7.2	1.9741	55	4.0073
2.8	1.0296	7.3	1.9879	60	4.0943
2.9	1.0647	7.4	2.0015	65	4.1744
3.0	1.0986	7.5	2.0149	70	4.2485
3.1	1.1314	7.6	2.0281	75	4.3175
3.2	1.1632	7.7	2.0412	80	4.3820
3.3	1.1939	7.8	2.0541	85	4.4427
3.4	1.2238	7.9	2.0669	90	4.4998
3.5	1.2528	8.0	2.0794	95	4.5539
3.6	1.2809	8.1	2.0919	100	4.6052
3.7	1.3083	8.2	2.1041		
3.8	1.3350	8.3	2.1163		
3.9	1.3610	8.4	2.1282		
4.0	1.3863	8.5	2.1401		
4.1	1.4110	8.6	2.1518		
4.2	1.4351	8.7	2.1633		
4.3	1.4586	8.8	2.1748		
4.4	1.4816	8.9	2.1861		

* Subtract 10 from $\log_e n$ entries for $n < 1.0$.

ANSWERS

CHAPTER 11

Article 11–1, p. 487

1. $\mathbf{i} - 4\mathbf{j}$ **2.** $-\mathbf{i} + \mathbf{j}$ **3.** $-2\mathbf{i} - 3\mathbf{j}$ **4.** 0 **5.** $\frac{1}{2}\sqrt{3}\,\mathbf{i} + \frac{1}{2}\mathbf{j}$ **6.** $\frac{1}{2}\sqrt{3}\,\mathbf{i} - \frac{1}{2}\mathbf{j}$ **7.** $\frac{3}{5}\mathbf{i} - \frac{4}{5}\mathbf{j}$ **8.** $(\mathbf{i} + 4\mathbf{j})/\sqrt{17}$ **9.** $(-4\mathbf{i} + \mathbf{j})/\sqrt{17}$
10. $-y\mathbf{i} + x\mathbf{j}$ or $y\mathbf{i} - x\mathbf{j}$ **11.** $\sqrt{2}$, $45°$ **12.** $\sqrt{13}$, $\tan^{-1}(-1.5) = -56.3°$ **13.** 2, $30°$
14. $\sqrt{13}$, $180° - \tan^{-1}(1.5) = 123.7°$ **15.** 13, $\tan^{-1}\frac{12}{5} = 67.4°$ **16.** 13, $180° + \tan^{-1}\frac{12}{5} = 247.4°$

Article 11–2, pp. 490–491

1. $\alpha_1 = \frac{1}{2}\sin^{-1}0.8 = 26°34'$, $\alpha_2 = 90° - \alpha_1 = 63°26'$ **5.** $x = e^t$, $y = -(7 + e^{2t})/2$ **6.** $y = (1 - t)^{-1}$, $x = -\ln|1 - t|$
7. $x = \sin t$, $y = 1 + (t - \sin t \cos t)/2$, for $0 \le t \le \pi/2$; $x = 1$, $y = t + 1 - \pi/4$, for $t > \pi/2$

Article 11–3, pp. 496–497

1. $x^2 + y^2 = 1$ **2.** $x = 1 - 2y^2$; $|y| \le 1$ **3.** $x^2 - y^2 = 1$; $x > 0$ **4.** $[(x - 2)^2/16] + [(y - 3)^2/4] = 1$ **5.** $y = x^2 - 6x$
6. $4x^2 - y^2 = 4$; $x \ge 1$, $y \ge 0$ **7.** $(x - 2)(y - 2) + 1 = 0$; $x > 2$, $y < 2$ **8.** $y = x^2 - 2x + 5$; $x \ge 1$ **9.** $2(x + y) = (x - y)^2$
10. $[(x - 3)^2/4] + [(y - 4)^2/9] = 1$; $x > 3$ **11.** $x = -at/\sqrt{t^2 + 1}$, $y = a/\sqrt{t^2 + 1}$ **12.** $x = a \tanh \theta$, $y = a \operatorname{sech} \theta$
13. $x = a \cos(s/a)$, $y = a \sin(s/a)$ **14.** $x = a \sinh^{-1}(s/a)$, $y = \sqrt{a^2 + s^2}$ **15.** $x = a \cos \phi + a\phi \sin \phi$, $y = a \sin \phi - a\phi \cos \phi$
16. $x = (a + b) \cos \theta - b \cos([(a + b)/b]\theta)$, $y = (a + b) \sin \theta - b \sin([(a + b)/b]\theta)$ **17.** $x = (a - b) \cos \theta + b \cos$
$([(a - b)/b]\theta)$, $y = (a - b) \sin \theta - b \sin([(a - b)/b]\theta)$ **18.** $8a$ **21. a)** $x = 2a \cot \theta$, $y = 2a \sin^2 \theta$ **b)** $y = 8a^3/(x^2 + 4a^2)$
22. 6723 ft

Article 11–4, p. 500

1. Straight line parallel to z-axis. **2.** Straight line, 5 units above and parallel to the line $y = x$ in the xy-plane. **3.** Circle in the plane $z = -2$, center $(0, 0, -2)$, radius 2. **4.** Ellipse in the yz-plane, center $(0, 0, 0)$, semi-axes a and b. **5.** Circle in the plane $z = 3$, radius 2, center $(0, 0, 3)$. **6.** Straight line in the plane $\theta = \pi/6$, making an angle of $45°$ with the plane $z = 0$. **7.** A right circular helix wound on a cylinder of radius 3. **8.** A right conical helix wound on a right circular cone. **9.** A semicircle of radius 5, center at the origin, lying in the plane $\theta = \pi/4$. **10.** The intersection of the sphere $\rho = 5$ and the cone $\phi = \pi/4$ is a circle of radius $\rho \sin \phi = 5/\sqrt{2}$. **11.** The plane $\theta = \pi/4$ and the cone $\phi = \pi/4$ intersect in a straight line through the origin. **12.** A semicircle in the yz-plane, center at $(0, 0, 2)$ on the z-axis, radius 2. **13.** $\rho = 2$; $r^2 + z^2 = 4$. **14.** $\rho = 4 \cos \phi$; $r^2 + z^2 = 4z$. **15.** $z^2 = x^2 + y^2$; $\phi = \pi/4$, $\phi = 3\pi/4$. **16.** $x^2 + y^2 + z^2 = 6z$; $r^2 + z^2 = 6z$ **17.** Plane $x = 0$ and half-space where $x > 0$. **18.** Spheres $\rho = 3$, $\rho = 5$, and shell between them. **19.** On or inside sphere $\rho = 5$ but outside or on cylinder $r = 2$. **20.** Wedge with two intersecting plane boundaries $\theta = 0$, $\theta = \pi/4$, and curved boundary part of cone $\phi = \pi/4$. **21.** Interior and boundary of elliptic cylinder $4x^2 + 9y^2 = 36$.

Article 11–5, p. 502

1. $(-2, 0, 2)$, $\sqrt{8}$ **2.** $(-\frac{1}{4}, -\frac{1}{4}, -\frac{1}{4})$, $\sqrt{75}/4$ **3.** $(0, 0, a)$, $|a|$ **4.** $(0, -\frac{1}{3}, \frac{1}{3})$, $\sqrt{29}/3$ **5. a)** $\sqrt{y^2 + z^2}$ **b)** $\sqrt{z^2 + x^2}$
c) $\sqrt{x^2 + y^2}$ **d)** $|z|$ **6. a)** $x^2 + y^2 + (z - 4)^2 = 4$ **b)** $4x^2 + 4y^2 + 3(z - \frac{3}{2})^2 = 27$ **c)** $5(z - \frac{3}{2})^2 - 4x^2 - 4y^2 = 5$ **7.** 3
8. 7 **9.** 9 **10.** 11 **11.** $(4\mathbf{i} + 3\mathbf{j} + 12\mathbf{k})/13$ **12.** $(2\mathbf{i} + 2\mathbf{j} + 4\mathbf{k})/3$

Article 11–6, p. 507

1. No; we cannot conclude that $\mathbf{B}_1 = \mathbf{B}_2$. All we can say is that $\mathbf{B}_1$ and $\mathbf{B}_2$ have the same projection on $\mathbf{A}$ when all three vectors start from the same initial point. **2. a)** $(\mathbf{A} \cdot \mathbf{B}/\mathbf{A} \cdot \mathbf{A})\mathbf{A}$ **b)** $\frac{7}{45}\mathbf{A}$ **3.** $\angle A = \angle C = 71.1°$, $\angle B = 37.8°$ **4.** $(3, 3, 0)$
5. $\frac{13}{15}$ **6.** $\cos^{-1}(1/\sqrt{3}) = 54.7°$ **7.** $\cos^{-1}(\sqrt{6}/3) = 35.3°$ **8.** $\cos^{-1}(\frac{13}{45}) = 73.2°$ **9.** Two: $45°$, $135°$ **12.** $z = \sqrt{x^2 + y^2}$
13. $w(z_1 - z_2)$ **18.** If $|\mathbf{v}_1| = |\mathbf{v}_2|$, then $(\mathbf{v}_1 + \mathbf{v}_2)$ and $(\mathbf{v}_1 - \mathbf{v}_2)$ are orthogonal.

Article 11–7, p. 512

1. $-\mathbf{i} - 3\mathbf{j} + 4\mathbf{k}$ **2.** $c(2\mathbf{i} + \mathbf{j} + \mathbf{k})$, $c = $ scalar **3.** $2\sqrt{6}$ **4.** $\sqrt{6}/2$ **5.** $c(\mathbf{i} - \mathbf{j})$, $c = $ scalar **6.** $\pm[4/(3\sqrt{2}), 1/(3\sqrt{2}), 1/(3\sqrt{2})]$
7. $11/\sqrt{107}$ **8. a)** $60.6°$ **b)** Yes, because the angle between the two planes is equal to the angle between their normals and this angle is neither $0°$ nor $180°$. **c)** $\mathbf{j} + \mathbf{k}$

Article 11–8, pp. 517–518

1. $(9, -5, 12)$ **2.** $x = 1 + t$, $y = 2 + t$, $z = -1 - t$; $x - 1 = y - 2 = -(z + 1)$ **4. a)** The complement of the angle between the line and a normal to the plane. **b)** $22.4°$ **5.** $3x + y + z = 5$ **6.** $|D_2 - D_1|/7$ **8.** $7x - 5y - 4z = 6$

9. Plane through the three points.   **10.** $x - 2y + z = 6$ **11.** $x - y + z = 0$ **12.** $x + 6y + z = 16$ **13.** 3   **14. b)** Yes
16. $17x - 26y + 11z = -40$ **17.** $2x - y + z = 5$ **18.** $1/\sqrt{75},\ 5/\sqrt{75},\ 7/\sqrt{75}$ **19.** The set of points in the half-space that lies on the side of the plane toward which **N** points.   **20.** $(\cos \alpha)(x - x_0) + (\cos \beta)(y - y_0) + (\cos \gamma)(z - z_0) = 0$

Article 11–9, p. 523

1. $-2\mathbf{C} = -6\mathbf{i} + 8\mathbf{j} - 24\mathbf{k};\ -22\mathbf{A} = -88\mathbf{i} + 176\mathbf{j} - 22\mathbf{k}$ **2.** 245   **3. a)** $\mathbf{A} \times \mathbf{B} = 15\mathbf{i} + 10\mathbf{j} + 20\mathbf{k};\ (\mathbf{A} \times \mathbf{B}) \times \mathbf{C} = 200\mathbf{i} - 120\mathbf{j} - 90\mathbf{k}$ **b)** $(\mathbf{A} \cdot \mathbf{C})\mathbf{B} - (\mathbf{B} \cdot \mathbf{C})\mathbf{A} = 56\mathbf{B} + 22\mathbf{A} = 200\mathbf{i} - 120\mathbf{j} - 90\mathbf{k}$ **5.** $a = (\mathbf{A} \times \mathbf{B}) \cdot \mathbf{D},\ b = -(\mathbf{A} \times \mathbf{B}) \cdot \mathbf{C}$
6. $\frac{2}{3}$ **10.** $7 - x = (3y - 19)/12 = (4 - 3z)/30$ **11. a)** $S(0, 9, -3)$ **b)** Area $PQRS = |-29\mathbf{i} - \mathbf{j} + 11\mathbf{k}| = \sqrt{963} \approx 31.03$
c) 11; 29; 1

Article 11–10, p. 526

1. Right circular cylinder of radius 1, elements parallel to y-axis, axis along y-axis.   **2.** Parabolic cylinder, with one element being the y-axis.   **3.** Parabolic cylinder, one element being the z-axis.   **4.** Elliptic cylinder, axis along the z-axis.   **5.** Plane, with one element being the x-axis.   **6.** Hyperbolic cylinder, axis along the z-axis.   **7.** Hyperbolic cylinder, axis along the y-axis.   **8.** Hyperbolic cylinder, axis along the x-axis.   **9.** Right circular cylinder of radius 4, axis along the z-axis.   **10.** Right circular cylinder of radius $\frac{1}{2}$; axis is the line $x = 0,\ y = \frac{1}{2}$.   **11.** Right circular cylinder, radius $\frac{1}{2}$; axis is the line $x = \frac{1}{2}$, $y = 0$.   **12.** Cylinder with elements parallel to z-axis. Cross sections are cardioids.   **13.** Right circular cylinder, radius a, axis along z-axis.   **14.** Right circular cylinder, radius 2; axis is the line $y = 0,\ z = 2$. The x-axis is one element.   **15.** Elliptic cylinder; axis is the line $x = 0,\ z = \frac{1}{2}$. The y-axis is one element.

Article 11–11, pp. 531–532

1. Paraboloid of revolution, vertex $(0, 0, 1)$, opening upward.   **2.** Sphere of radius 4, center $(-2, 3, 0)$.   **3.** Ellipsoid, center $(0, 0, 0)$, semiaxes $a = 2,\ b = 1,\ c = 2$.   **4.** Ellipsoid, center $(0, 1, 0)$, semiaxes $a = 2,\ b = 1,\ c = 2$.   **5.** Sphere, center $(0, 1, 0)$, radius 1.   **6.** One-sheeted hyperboloid of revolution, axis of symmetry parallel to Oy, center $(-2, -3, 0)$.   **7.** Two-sheeted hyperboloid of revolution, axis parallel to Ox, center $(-2, -3, 0)$.   **8.** Parabolic cylinder, one element being Oy.   **9.** Rotate the xy-axes through $45°$ and have $z^2 + 2y'^2 = 2x'^2$; elliptic cone with vertex O, axis along Ox'.   **10.** Rotate xy-axes $45°$; $z = 2(x'^2 - y'^2)$, hyperbolic paraboloid ("saddle").   **11.** Paraboloid of revolution obtained by rotating the parabola $z = x^2$ about the z-axis.   **12.** Rotate the line $z = x$ about the z-axis; right circular cone.   **13.** Rotate $z^2 = x$ about the z-axis.   **14.** Elliptic cone, vertex O, axis Oz.   **15.** Elliptic cone, vertex O, axis Ox.   **16.** Right circular cone, vertex O, axis Oy.   **17.** $(x - 1)^2 + 4(y + 1)^2 - (z - 2)^2 = 1$. One-sheeted hyperboloid, center $(1, -1, 2)$, axis $x - 1 = y + 1 = 0$.
18. $(z - 2)^2 = (x - 1)^2 + 4(y + 1)^2$. Elliptic cone, vertex $(1, -1, 2)$, axis $x - 1 = y + 1 = 0$.   **19.** Elliptic cylinder, axis along Oy.   **20.** Elliptic paraboloid, vertex $(1, 0, 0)$, axis along Ox.   **21.** Plane, $z = x$.   **22.** Plane, $z = y$.   **23.** Ruled surface generated by rotating about Oz a line parallel to the xy-plane and passing through Oz, whose distance above the xy-plane is $z = \sin \theta$.   **24.** Ruled surface generated by rotating about Oz a line, parallel to the xy-plane and passing through Oz, whose distance above the xy-plane is $z = \cosh \theta$.   **25. a)** $A(z_1) = \pi ab(1 - (z_1^2/c^2))$ **b)** $V = \frac{4}{3}\pi abc$ **27. a)** $\pi abh(1 + (h^2/3c^2))$
b) $A_0 = \pi ab,\ A_h = \pi ab(1 + (h^2/c^2)),\ V = (h/3)(2A_0 + A_h)$ **28.** Vertex $(0, y_1, (cy_1^2/b^2))$, focus $(0, y_1, (cy_1^2/b^2) - (a^2/4c))$
29. In any plane $\theta = $ constant, the equation $\rho = F(\phi)$ may be considered as the polar equation of a plane curve C having polar coordinates ρ and ϕ. Since the space equation is independent of θ, the surface is generated by rotating the curve C around the z-axis.   **30.** A sphere, center $\rho = (a/2),\ \phi = 0,\ \theta = 0$ and radius $(a/2)$.   **31.** A cardioid of revolution.

Miscellaneous Problems Chapter 11, pp. 532–535

1. $x = (1 - t)^{-1},\ y = 1 - \ln(1 - t),\ t < 1$ **2.** $x = \tan^{-1}(t + 1),\ \ y = (t + 1)\tan^{-1}(t + 1) - \frac{1}{4}\pi - \frac{1}{2}\ln(1 + t + \frac{1}{2}t^2)$
3. $x = e^t,\ y = e^{e^t} - e$ **4.** $x = 3 - 3\cos 2t,\ \ y = 4 + 2\sin 2t$ **5.** $x = t - \sin t,\ \ y = 1 - \cos t$
6. $y = e^t,\ \ x = 2\sqrt{1 + e^t} - 2\sqrt{2} - 2\coth^{-1}\sqrt{1 + e^t} + 2\coth^{-1}\sqrt{2}$ **7.** $x = \sinh^{-1} t,\ \ y = t\sinh^{-1} t - \sqrt{1 + t^2} + 1$
8. $x = 2 + 2\sinh(t/2),\ \ y = 2t - 4 + 4\cosh(t/2)$ **9.** $x = 4\sin t,\ \ y = 4\cos t$ **10.** $x = 2 - e^{-t},\ \ y = 2t + e^{-t}$
12. $x = 8t - 2\sin 2t,\ \ y = 4 - 2\cos 2t$ **13.** $x = 2a\sin^2\theta\tan\theta,\ \ y = 2a\sin^2\theta$ **14.** $x = \cot\theta + a\cos\theta,\ \ y = \pm a\sin\theta$
15. a) $3\pi a^2$ **b)** $8a$ **c)** $64\pi a^2/3$ **d)** $(\pi a, 5a/6)$ **17.** 0   **24.** $\frac{3}{11}(3\mathbf{i} - \mathbf{j} + \mathbf{k})$ **25.** $-\frac{1}{10}$ **26.** $\mathbf{C} = [(\mathbf{A} \cdot \mathbf{B})/(\mathbf{B} \cdot \mathbf{B})]\mathbf{B}$,
$\mathbf{D} = [(\mathbf{B} \cdot \mathbf{B})\mathbf{A} - (\mathbf{A} \cdot \mathbf{B})\mathbf{B}]/(\mathbf{B} \cdot \mathbf{B})$ **27.** $7\sqrt{2}/10$ **29.** $\mathbf{j} - \mathbf{k}$ **30.** $5\mathbf{i} + 7\mathbf{j} + \mathbf{k}$ **31.** $(\mathbf{j} + \mathbf{k})/\sqrt{2}$
33. $(10\mathbf{i} - 2\mathbf{j} - 6\mathbf{k})/\sqrt{35}$ **35.** $\cos^{-1}(3/\sqrt{35})$ **36.** $\mathbf{B} = (1/|\mathbf{A}|^2)(d\mathbf{A} + \mathbf{C} \times \mathbf{A})$ **38.** $z = 3,\ \ x - \sqrt{3}y + 2\sqrt{3} - 1 = 0$
39. $(1, -2, -1),\ \ (x - 1)/-5 = (y + 2)/3 = (z + 1)/4$ **40.** $25/\sqrt{38}$ **42.** $(\frac{11}{9}, \frac{26}{9}, -\frac{7}{9})$ **43.** $\frac{1}{3}\sqrt{78}$ **44.** $2x - y + 2z - 8 = 0$

45. a) $2x + 7y + 2z + 10 = 0$ **b)** $9/(5\sqrt{57})$ **46.** $2x + 2y + z = 5$ **49. a)** 1 **b)** $-10\mathbf{i} - 2\mathbf{j} - 12\mathbf{k}$ **50.** $\frac{1}{3}$, $\cos\theta = -\sqrt{2}/3$
56. Hyperboloid of two sheets, center $(2, -1, -1)$ **57.** $(x-1)^2 + (y-2)^2 + (z-3)^2 = 3$ **58.** $z^6 - y = 0$, $y = (x^2 + z^2)^3$

CHAPTER 12

Article 12–1, p. 542

1. $\mathbf{i}2e^{2t} + \mathbf{j}(1 - t)e^{-t}$, $-\infty < t < \infty$ **2.** $\mathbf{i}[1/(2(1 + t))] - \mathbf{j}[t/\sqrt{t^2 - 1}]$, $-1 < t < 1$
3. $\mathbf{i}(2/\sqrt{1 - 4t^2}) + \mathbf{j}(3\sec^2 3t) - \mathbf{k}(1/t^2)$, $-\frac{1}{2} < t < \frac{1}{2}$, $t \neq 0$.
4. $\mathbf{i}(1/(|x|\sqrt{9x^2 - 1})) + \mathbf{j}(2\sinh 2x) + \mathbf{k}(4\operatorname{sech}^2 4x)$, $|x| > \frac{1}{3}$ **5.** $\mathbf{i}[4/(2t + 1)^2] - \mathbf{j}(8t/(1 - 4t^2))$, $-\frac{1}{2} < t < \frac{1}{2}$

Article 12–2, p. 546

1. $\mathbf{v} = -(a\omega \sin \omega t)\mathbf{i} + (a\omega \cos \omega t)\mathbf{j}$, $\mathbf{a} = -(a\omega^2 \cos \omega t)\mathbf{i} - (a\omega^2 \sin \omega t)\mathbf{j} = -\omega^2 \mathbf{R}$;
    when $\omega t = \pi/3$, $\mathbf{v} = a\omega(-\frac{1}{2}\sqrt{3}\,\mathbf{i} + \frac{1}{2}\mathbf{j})$,   speed $= a\omega$, $\mathbf{a} = -a\omega^2(\frac{1}{2}\mathbf{i} + \frac{1}{2}\sqrt{3}\,\mathbf{j})$.
2. $\mathbf{v} = -(2 \sin t)\mathbf{i} + (3 \cos t)\mathbf{j}$, $\mathbf{a} = -(2 \cos t)\mathbf{i} - (3 \sin t)\mathbf{j}$;
    at $t = \pi/4$, $\mathbf{v} = -\sqrt{2}\,\mathbf{i} + \frac{3}{2}\sqrt{2}\,\mathbf{j}$,   speed $= \sqrt{6.5}$, $\mathbf{a} = -\sqrt{2}\,\mathbf{i} - \frac{3}{2}\sqrt{2}\,\mathbf{j}$.
3. $\mathbf{v} = \mathbf{i} + 2t\mathbf{j}$, $\mathbf{a} = 2\mathbf{j}$;   at $t = 2$, $\mathbf{v} = \mathbf{i} + 4\mathbf{j}$, $\mathbf{a} = 2\mathbf{j}$,   speed $= \sqrt{17}$.
4. $\mathbf{v} = -(2 \sin 2t)\mathbf{i} + (2 \cos t)\mathbf{j}$, $\mathbf{a} = -(4 \cos 2t)\mathbf{i} - (2 \sin t)\mathbf{j}$;   at $t = 0$, $\mathbf{v} = 2\mathbf{j}$, $a = -4\mathbf{i}$,   speed $= 2$.
5. $\mathbf{v} = e^t\mathbf{i} - 2e^{-2t}\mathbf{j}$, $\mathbf{a} = e^t\mathbf{i} + 4e^{-2t}\mathbf{j}$;   at $t = \ln 3$, $\mathbf{v} = 3\mathbf{i} - \frac{2}{9}\mathbf{j}$, $\mathbf{a} = 3\mathbf{i} + \frac{4}{9}\mathbf{j}$,   speed $= \frac{1}{9}\sqrt{733}$.
6. $\mathbf{v} = (\sec t \tan t)\mathbf{i} + (\sec^2 t)\mathbf{j}$, $\mathbf{a} = (\sec^3 t + \sec t \tan^2 t)\mathbf{i} + (2 \sec^2 t \tan t)\mathbf{j}$;
    at $t = \pi/6$, $\mathbf{v} = \frac{2}{3}\mathbf{i} + \frac{4}{3}\mathbf{j}$, $\mathbf{a} = (10\mathbf{i} + 8\mathbf{j})/(3\sqrt{3})$, speed $= \frac{1}{3}\sqrt{20}$.
7. $\mathbf{v} = (3 \sinh 3t)\mathbf{i} + (2 \cosh t)\mathbf{j}$, $\mathbf{a} = (9 \cosh 3t)\mathbf{i} + (2 \sinh t)\mathbf{j}$;   at $t = 0$, $\mathbf{v} = 2\mathbf{j}$, $\mathbf{a} = 9\mathbf{i}$,   speed $= 2$.
8. $\mathbf{v} = [\mathbf{i}/(t + 1)] + 2t\mathbf{j}$, $\mathbf{a} = [-\mathbf{i}/(t + 1)^2] + 2\mathbf{j}$;   at $t = 1$, $\mathbf{v} = \frac{1}{2}\mathbf{i} + 2\mathbf{j}$, $\mathbf{a} = -\frac{1}{4}\mathbf{i} + 2\mathbf{j}$,   speed $= \frac{1}{2}\sqrt{17}$.
9. $\mathbf{R} = -\frac{1}{2}gt^2\mathbf{j} + \mathbf{v}_0 t = (tv_0 \cos \alpha)\mathbf{i} + (tv_0 \sin \alpha - \frac{1}{2}gt^2)\mathbf{j}$.
11. $\mathbf{v} = e^t[\mathbf{i} + \mathbf{j}(\cos t + \sin t) + \mathbf{k}(\cos t - \sin t)]$, $\mathbf{a} = e^t[\mathbf{i} + 2\mathbf{j}\cos t - 2\mathbf{k}\sin t]$, $\theta = \cos^{-1}(\sqrt{15}/5) = 39.2°$.
12. $\mathbf{v} = \mathbf{i}\sec^2 t + 2\mathbf{j}\cosh 2t - 3\mathbf{k}\operatorname{sech} 3t \tanh 3t$, $\mathbf{a} = 2\mathbf{i}\sec^2 t \tan t + 4\mathbf{j}\sinh 2t + 9\mathbf{k}\operatorname{sech} 3t(\tanh^2 3t - \operatorname{sech}^2 3t)$, $\theta = 90°$.
13. $\mathbf{v} = [2t/(t^2 + 1)]\mathbf{i} + [1/(t^2 + 1)]\mathbf{j} + (t/\sqrt{t^2 + 1})\mathbf{k}$, $\mathbf{a} = [2(1 - t^2)/(1 + t^2)^2]\mathbf{i} - [2t/(1 + t^2)^2]\mathbf{j} + [\mathbf{k}/(t^2 + 1)^{3/2}]$, $\theta = 90°$.
14. $\mathbf{R} = (3 \cos \theta)\mathbf{i} + (3 \sin \theta)\mathbf{j} + (6 \cos \theta + 9 \sin \theta)\mathbf{k}$, $\mathbf{v} = -3\omega(\sin \theta)\mathbf{i} + 3\omega(\cos \theta)\mathbf{j} + 3\omega(3 \cos \theta - 2 \sin \theta)\mathbf{k}$, $\mathbf{a} = -\omega^2\mathbf{R}$.

Article 12–3, p. 551

1. $-\mathbf{i} \sin t + \mathbf{j} \cos t$ **2.** $(e^t\mathbf{i} + 2t\mathbf{j})/\sqrt{e^{2t} + 4t^2}$ **3.** $-\mathbf{i} \cos t + \mathbf{j} \sin t$ **4.** $(\mathbf{i} + 2x\mathbf{j})/\sqrt{1 + 4x^2}$ **5.** $-(2\mathbf{i} \cos t + \mathbf{j})/\sqrt{1 + 4 \cos^2 t}$
6. $(\mathbf{i}t + \mathbf{j})/\sqrt{1 + t^2}$ **7.** $[(\cos t - \sin t)/\sqrt{2}]\mathbf{i} + [(\cos t + \sin t)/\sqrt{2}]\mathbf{j}$ **8.** $(\tanh t)\mathbf{i} + (\operatorname{sech} t)\mathbf{j}$.
9. $\frac{1}{13}((12 \cos 2t)\mathbf{i} - (12 \sin 2t)\mathbf{j} + 5\mathbf{k})$ **10.** $\sqrt{\frac{1}{3}}[(\cos t - \sin t)\mathbf{i} + (\cos t + \sin t)\mathbf{j} + \mathbf{k}]$ **11.** $(\mathbf{i} \tanh 2t + \mathbf{j} + \mathbf{k} \operatorname{sech} 2t)/\sqrt{2}$
12. $(9t^2 + 25)^{-(1/2)}[3(\cos t - t \sin t)\mathbf{i} + 3(\sin t + t \cos t)\mathbf{j} + 4\mathbf{k}]$ **13.** 13π **14.** $\sqrt{3}(e^\pi - 1)$ **15.** $3\sqrt{2} \sinh 2\pi$
16. $\pi\sqrt{9\pi^2 + 25}/2 + (25/6) \sinh^{-1}(3\pi/5)$

Article 12–4, p. 557

1. $(1/a) \operatorname{sech}^2(x/a)$ **2.** $|\cos x|$ **3.** $4e^{2x}/(1 + 4e^{4x})^{3/2}$ **4.** $1/(3a|\sin t \cos t|)$ **5.** $1/|a\theta|$ **6.** $(1/4a)|\csc(\theta/2)|$ **7.** $|\cos y|$
8. $2/[\sqrt{y^2 + 2}(y^2 + 1)^2]$ **9.** $48y^5/[(4y^6 + 1)^2]$ **10.** $1/[2(1 + t^2)^{3/2}]$ **11.** $1/[|t|(1 + t^2)^{3/2}]$ **12.** $e^{-t}/\sqrt{2}$
13. $(x + 2)^2 + (y - 3)^2 = 8$.   For the circle: $y' = -(x + 2)/(y - 3)$, $y'' = -8/(y - 3)^3$.   Both of these $= +1$ at $(0, 1)$.
15. $\mathbf{N} = -\mathbf{i} \sin 2t - \mathbf{j} \cos 2t$, $\kappa = \frac{24}{169}$, $\mathbf{B} = \frac{1}{13}((5 \cos 2t)\mathbf{i} - (5 \sin 2t)\mathbf{j} - 12\mathbf{k})$.
16. $\mathbf{N} = -(\mathbf{i}/\sqrt{2})(\sin t + \cos t) + (\mathbf{j}/\sqrt{2})(\cos t - \sin t)$, $\kappa = \sqrt{2}\,e^{-t}/3$, $\mathbf{B} = [\mathbf{i}(\sin t - \cos t) - \mathbf{j}(\sin t + \cos t) + 2\mathbf{k}]/\sqrt{6}$
17. $\mathbf{N} = \mathbf{i} \operatorname{sech} 2t - \mathbf{k} \tanh 2t$, $\kappa = \frac{1}{6} \operatorname{sech}^2 2t$, $\mathbf{B} = (-\mathbf{i} \tanh 2t + \mathbf{j} - \mathbf{k} \operatorname{sech} 2t)/\sqrt{2}$
18. $d\mathbf{R}/dt = \mathbf{T}(ds/dt)$, $d^2\mathbf{R}/dt^2 = \mathbf{T}(d^2s/dt^2) + \mathbf{N}\kappa(ds/dt)^2$

Article 12–5, pp. 563–564

5. $\mathbf{v} = 2\mathbf{i} \sinh 2t + 2\mathbf{j} \cosh 2t$, $\mathbf{a} = 4\mathbf{i} \cosh 2t + 4\mathbf{j} \sinh 2t$, $ds/dt = |\mathbf{v}| = 2\sqrt{\cosh 4t}$; $a_\mathbf{T} = d^2s/dt^2 = (4 \sinh 4t)/\sqrt{\cosh 4t}$,
    $a_\mathbf{N} = \sqrt{|\mathbf{a}|^2 - a_\mathbf{T}^2} = 4\sqrt{\operatorname{sech} 4t}$ **6.** $a_\mathbf{T} = 2t/\sqrt{1 + t^2}$, $a_\mathbf{N} = 2/\sqrt{1 + t^2}$ **7.** $a_\mathbf{T} = 0$, $a_\mathbf{N} = \omega^2 a$ **8.** $a_\mathbf{T} = 0$, $a_\mathbf{N} = 2/(t^2 + 1)$
9. $a_\mathbf{T} = \sqrt{2}\,e^t$, $a_\mathbf{N} = \sqrt{2}\,e^t$ **14.** $\frac{1}{2}$

Article 12–6, p. 566

2. $\mathbf{v} = 3a \sin \theta \mathbf{u}_r + 3a(1 - \cos \theta)\mathbf{u}_\theta$, $\quad \mathbf{a} = 9a(2 \cos \theta - 1)\mathbf{u}_r + 18a \sin \theta \mathbf{u}_\theta$. **3.** $\mathbf{v} = 4at \cos 2\theta \mathbf{u}_r + 2at \sin 2\theta \mathbf{u}_\theta$,
$\mathbf{a} = (4a \cos 2\theta - 20at^2 \sin 2\theta)\mathbf{u}_r + (2a \sin 2\theta + 16at^2 \cos 2\theta)\mathbf{u}_\theta$. **4.** $\mathbf{v} = 2ae^{a\theta}\mathbf{u}_r + 2e^{a\theta}\mathbf{u}_\theta$, $\quad \mathbf{a} = 4e^{a\theta}(a^2 - 1)\mathbf{u}_r + 8ae^{a\theta}\mathbf{u}_\theta$.
5. $\mathbf{v} = (a \cos t)\mathbf{u}_r + ae^{-t}(1 + \sin t)\mathbf{u}_\theta$, $\quad \mathbf{a} = -a[\sin t + e^{-2t}(1 + \sin t)]\mathbf{u}_r + ae^{-t}[2 \cos t - 1 - \sin t]\mathbf{u}_\theta$.
6. $\mathbf{v} = -(8 \sin 4t)\mathbf{u}_r + (4 \cos 4t)\mathbf{u}_\theta$, $\quad \mathbf{a} = -(40 \cos 4t)\mathbf{u}_r - (32 \sin 4t)\mathbf{u}_\theta$

Miscellaneous Problems Chapter 12, pp. 567–569

1. a) $\mathbf{v} = 2^{-(3/2)}(-\mathbf{i} + \mathbf{j})$, $\quad \mathbf{a} = 2^{-(5/2)}(\mathbf{i} - 3\mathbf{j})$ **b)** $t = 0$ **2. a)** $\mathbf{v} = \pi(\mathbf{i}(1 - \cos \pi t) + \mathbf{j} \sin \pi t)$, $\quad \mathbf{a} = \pi^2(\mathbf{i} \sin \pi t + \mathbf{j} \cos \pi t)$
b) Slope of $PC = \cot \pi t$, slope of $PQ = \csc \pi t + \cot \pi t$ **c)** Slope of $\mathbf{v} = $ slope of PQ, slope of $\mathbf{a} = $ slope of PC
3. Speed $= a\sqrt{1 + t^2}$, $a_T = at/\sqrt{1 + t^2}$, $a_N = a(t^2 + 2)/\sqrt{1 + t^2}$ **5. b)** $\pi/2$ **6.** $|ad - bc|(a^2 + b^2)^{-(3/2)}$, provided
$a^2 + b^2 \neq 0$ **7.** $x = a\theta + a \sin \theta$, $\quad y = -a(1 - \cos \theta)$ **8.** $(-\frac{1}{2} \ln 2, 1/\sqrt{2})$ **9. b)** πab, πa^2 **10.** $\kappa = \pi s$
11. $y = \pm\sqrt{1 - x^2} \pm \ln ((1 - \sqrt{1 - x^2})/x) + C$. Set $C = 0$. Then $x = e^{-s}$ $[s = -\ln x$, measured from $(1, 0)]$;
$y = \pm\sqrt{1 - e^{-2s}} \pm \ln (e^s - \sqrt{e^{2s} - 1})$. **12.** $s = s_0 + 2\pi p$, $\quad A = A_0 + s_0 p + \pi p^2$, $\quad R = R_0 + p$, where s_0, A_0, R_0 are the
length of arc, area, and radius of curvature of the original curve. **13. a)** $320\sqrt{10}$ **b)** $16[\sqrt{2} + \ln (\sqrt{2} + 1)]$
14. $\mathbf{v} = (3 \cos t)\mathbf{i} - (2 \sin t)\mathbf{j}$, $\quad \mathbf{a} = -(3 \sin t)\mathbf{i} - (2 \cos t)\mathbf{j}$, speed $= (4 + 5 \cos^2 t)^{1/2}$, $a_T = -5 \sin t \cos t(4 + 5 \cos^2 t)^{-(1/2)}$,
$a_N = 6(4 + 5 \cos^2 t)^{-(1/2)}$ **15. a)** $a_T = 0, a_N = 4$ **b)** 1 **c)** $r = 2 \cos \theta$
16. $\mathbf{v} = (\cos t - t \sin t)\mathbf{i} + (\sin t + t \cos t)\mathbf{j}$, $\quad \mathbf{a} = -(t \cos t + 2 \sin t)\mathbf{i} - (t \sin t - 2 \cos t)\mathbf{j}$, $\quad \kappa = (t^2 + 2)/(t^2 + 1)^{3/2}$
17. $\kappa = |f^2 + 2f'^2 - ff''|/(f^2 + f'^2)^{3/2}$ **18. a)** $r = e^{2\theta}$ **b)** $\frac{1}{2}\sqrt{5}(e^{4\pi} - 1)$ **19.** $\sqrt{2}\mathbf{u}_r$ **20.** $2(\omega^2 - 1)\mathbf{i}$
21. a) $\mathbf{v} = -\mathbf{u}_r + 3\mathbf{u}_\theta$, $\quad \mathbf{a} = -9\mathbf{u}_r - 6\mathbf{u}_\theta$ **b)** $\sqrt{37} + \frac{1}{6} \ln (6 + \sqrt{37})$ **22.** $r = a \cosh \omega t$ **23.** $\mathbf{R} = r\mathbf{u}_r + z\mathbf{k}$
24. $\mathbf{v} = \mathbf{u}_r(dr/dt) + \mathbf{u}_\theta(r \, d\theta/dt) + \mathbf{k}(dz/dt)$, $\quad \mathbf{a} = \mathbf{u}_r[(d_r^2/dt^2) - r(d\theta/dt)^2] + \mathbf{u}_\theta[r(d^2\theta/dt^2) + 2(dr/dt)(d\theta/dt)] + \mathbf{k}(d^2z/dt^2)$
25. a) $2\sqrt{\pi bg/(a^2 + b^2)}$ **b)** $\theta = [b/(a^2 + b^2)](\frac{1}{2}gt^2)$, $z = [b^2/(a^2 + b^2)](\frac{1}{2}gt^2)$
c) $d\mathbf{R}/dt = gt[b/\sqrt{a^2 + b^2}]\mathbf{T}$, $\quad d^2\mathbf{R}/dt^2 = g[b/\sqrt{a^2 + b^2}]\mathbf{T} + (gt)^2[ab^2/(a^2 + b^2)^2]\mathbf{N}$.
There is never any component of acceleration in the direction of the binormal.
26. a) $d\theta/dt = \sqrt{2gb\theta/(a^2 + b^2 + a^2\theta^2)}$ **b)** $\frac{1}{2}\{\theta\sqrt{a^2 + b^2 + a^2\theta^2} + [(a^2 + b^2)/a] \sinh^{-1} (a\theta)/\sqrt{a^2 + b^2}\}$
27. a) $\mathbf{u}_\rho = \mathbf{i} \sin \phi \cos \theta + \mathbf{j} \sin \phi \sin \theta + \mathbf{k} \cos \phi$, $\quad \mathbf{u}_\phi = \mathbf{i} \cos \phi \cos \theta + \mathbf{j} \cos \phi \sin \theta - \mathbf{k} \sin \phi$, $\quad \mathbf{u}_\theta = -\mathbf{i} \sin \theta + \mathbf{j} \cos \theta$.
d) Yes, they form a right-handed system of mutually orthogonal vectors because of (b) and (c).
28. $\mathbf{R} = \rho\mathbf{u}_\rho$, $\quad (d\mathbf{R}/dt) = \mathbf{u}_\rho(d\rho/dt) + \mathbf{u}_\phi \rho(d\phi/dt) + \mathbf{u}_\theta \rho \sin \phi(d\theta/dt)$
29. a) $ds^2 = dr^2 + r^2 \, d\theta^2 + dz^2$ **b)** $ds^2 = d\rho^2 + \rho^2 \, d\phi^2 + \rho^2 \sin^2 \phi \, d\theta^2$
30. a) $7\sqrt{3}\,a$ **b)** $7\sqrt{5}$ **31.** $x = (a \cos \theta)/\sqrt{1 + \sin^2 \theta}$, $\quad y = (a \sin \theta)/\sqrt{1 + \sin^2 \theta}$, $\quad z = -(a \sin \theta)/\sqrt{1 + \sin^2 \theta}$; $\quad L = 2\pi a$
32. a) $dx/dt = \cos \theta(dr/dt) - \sin \theta(r \, d\theta/dt)$, $\quad dy/dt = \sin \theta(dr/dt) + \cos \theta(r \, d\theta/dt)$
b) $dr/dt = \cos \theta(dx/dt) + \sin \theta(dy/dt)$, $\quad r \, d\theta/dt = -\sin \theta(dx/dt) + \cos \theta(dy/dt)$ **33.** $2\sqrt{3}(\mathbf{i} + \mathbf{j} - 2\mathbf{k})$
34. $3x + 3y + 3z - 8 = 0$ **35. a)** $\mathbf{T}(\frac{2}{3}, \frac{1}{3}, \frac{2}{3})$, $\mathbf{N}(1/\sqrt{5}, -2/\sqrt{5}, 0)$, $\mathbf{B}(4/3\sqrt{5}, 2/3\sqrt{5}, -5/3\sqrt{5})$ **b)** $2\sqrt{5}/9$
36. a) $x + 2y + 3z = 6$ **b)** $3x - 3y + z = 1$ **37.** $\frac{1}{3}(t^2 + 1)^{-2}$ **39.** $x^2/4 + y^2/9 + z^2/1 = 1$, an ellipsoid
40. $1/r = \gamma M/v_0^2 r_0^2 + ((1/r_0) - (\gamma M/v_0^2 r_0^2)) \cos \theta$.

CHAPTER 13

Article 13–1, p. 573

1. Let $r = \sqrt{x^2 + y^2}$. **a)** $r < 0.1$ **b)** $r < 0.001$ **2. a)** Let $\rho = \sqrt{x^2 + y^2 + z^2}$; $\rho < 0.1$, $\rho < 0.2\sqrt{3}$ **b)** Yes, because
$|f(x, y, z) - f(0, 0, 0)| = x^2 + y^2 + z^2 = \rho^2$ is less than any positive ϵ if $\rho < \sqrt{\epsilon}$.
3. a) Along line $x = 1$, $f(x, y) = f(1, y) \to 1$; along line $y = -1$, $f(x, y) = f(x, -1) \to \frac{1}{2}$. **b)** No, because different limits are
approached as $(x, y) \to (1, -1)$ in different ways. [See answer to part (a) above.]
4. $g = r \cos^2 \theta \sin \theta$, $\lim_{(x,y) \to (0,0)} g(x, y) = 0$.
5. $h = \cos^2 \theta$. No limit as $(x, y) \to (0, 0)$. Takes on all values between 0 and 1, arbitrarily close to $(0, 0)$.
6. $w = \cos 2\theta$. No limit as $(x, y) \to (0, 0)$. Takes on values between -1 and 1, arbitrarily close to $(0, 0)$.
7. $z = \frac{1}{2}r \sin 2\theta$, $\lim_{(x,y) \to (0,0)} z(x, y) = 0$. **8.** 5 **9.** 1 **10.** The xy-plane $(-\infty < x, y < \infty)$
11. The xy-plane with the point $(0, 0)$ excluded $((x, y) \neq (0, 0))$. **12.** The xy-plane with the axes excluded; $x \neq 0, y \neq 0$. **13.** The
open upper half-plane $(-\infty < x < \infty; y > 0)$.

Article 13–2, pp. 580–581

6. $\partial w/\partial x = e^x \cos y$, $\quad \partial w/\partial y = -e^x \sin y$ **7.** $\partial w/\partial x = e^x \sin y$; $\quad \partial w/\partial y = e^x \cos y$
8. $\partial w/\partial x = -y/(x^2 + y^2)$; $\quad \partial w/\partial y = x/(x^2 + y^2)$ **9.** $\partial w/\partial x = x/(x^2 + y^2)$; $\quad \partial w/\partial y = y/(x^2 + y^2)$

10. $\partial w/\partial x = -(y/x^2)\sinh(y/x)$; $\partial w/\partial y = (1/x)\sinh(y/x)$

11. $f_x = 2xe^{2y+3z}\cos(4w)$; $f_y = 2f$; $f_z = 3f$; $f_w = -4x^2e^{2y+3z}\sin(4w)$

12. $f_x = -yz/\sqrt{x^4 - x^2y^2}$; $f_y = |x|z/(x\sqrt{x^2 - y^2})$; $f_z = \sin^{-1}(y/x)$

13. $f_u = 2u/(v^2 + w^2)$; $f_v = -2v(u^2 + w^2)/(v^2 + w^2)^2$; $f_w = -2w(u^2 - v^2)/(v^2 + w^2)^2$

14. $f_r = (z^2 - r^2)(2 - \cos 2\theta)/(r^2 + z^2)^2$; $f_\theta = 2r\sin 2\theta/(r^2 + z^2)$; $f_z = -2rz(2 - \cos 2\theta)/(r^2 + z^2)^2$

15. $f_x = 2x/(u^2 + v^2)$; $f_y = 2y/(u^2 + v^2)$; $f_u = -2u(x^2 + y^2)/(u^2 + v^2)^2$; $f_v = -2v(x^2 + y^2)/(u^2 + v^2)^2$

16. $f_x = 2\cos 2x\cosh 3r$, $f_y = 3\cosh 3y\cos 4s$, $f_r = 3\sin 2x\sinh 3r$, $f_s = -4\sinh 3y\sin 4s$

17. By the law of cosines, $\cos A = (b^2 + c^2 - a^2)/(2bc)$. $\partial A/\partial a = a/(bc\sin A)$, $\partial A/\partial b = (c^2 - a^2 - b^2)/(2b^2c\sin A)$

18. By the law of sines, $a = b\sin A\csc B$. $\partial a/\partial A = b\cos A\csc B$, $\partial a/\partial B = -b\sin A\csc B\cot B$

19. $x/\rho = x/\sqrt{x^2 + y^2 + z^2}$ 20. $-(x^2 + y^2)/(\rho^3\sin\phi) = -\sqrt{x^2 + y^2}/(x^2 + y^2 + z^2)$ 21. $x/(x^2 + y^2)$ 22. 0

23. $xz/(\rho^3\sin\phi) = xz/[(x^2 + y^2 + z^2)\sqrt{x^2 + y^2}]$ 24. $-y/(x^2 + y^2)$ 25. $\mathbf{i}\sin\phi\cos\theta + \mathbf{j}\sin\phi\sin\theta + \mathbf{k}\cos\phi$

26. $\rho\cos\phi(\mathbf{i}\cos\theta + \mathbf{j}\sin\theta) - \mathbf{k}\rho\sin\phi$ 27. $\rho\sin\phi(-\mathbf{i}\sin\theta + \mathbf{j}\cos\theta)$ 28. $\partial\mathbf{R}/\partial\rho = \mathbf{u}_\rho$; $\partial\mathbf{R}/\partial\phi = \rho\mathbf{u}_\phi$; $\partial\mathbf{R}/\partial\theta = \rho\sin\phi\mathbf{u}_\theta$

29. a) $\partial\mathbf{R}/\partial x$ is tangent to the curve in which the surface $w = f(x, y)$ and the plane $y = y_0$ intersect.   b) $\partial\mathbf{R}/\partial y$ is tangent to the curve in which the surface $w = f(x, y)$ and the plane $x = x_0$ intersect.   c) $\mathbf{v} = -\mathbf{i}f_x(x_0, y_0) - \mathbf{j}f_y(x_0, y_0) + \mathbf{k}$ is normal to the surface at (x_0, y_0, w_0).

Article 13–3, p. 583

1. $6x + 8y = z + 25$, $(x - 3)/6 = (y - 4)/8 = (z - 25)/-1$ 2. $x - 2y + 2z = 9$, $2x = -y = z$

3. $x - 3y = z - 1$, $x - 1 = (1 - y)/3 = -z - 1$ 4. $x - y + 2z = \pi/2$, $x - 1 = 1 - y = \frac{1}{2}(z - (\pi/4))$

5. $16x + 12y = 125z - 75$, $(x - 3)/16 = (y + 4)/12 = (3 - 5z)/625$

6. a) $\mathbf{N} = C(-\mathbf{i} + \mathbf{j}f_y + \mathbf{k}f_z)$, $C = $ scalar   b) $x - 2y + z = 1$, $2x = 3 - y = 2(z - 1)$

7. Line: $z = -11x/6 = -22y/7$;   plane: $12x + 14y + 11z = 0$ 8. Vertex: $(0, 0, z_0 + \frac{1}{2})$ 9. $\begin{vmatrix} \mathbf{i} & \mathbf{j} & \mathbf{k} \\ f_x & f_y & -1 \\ g_x & g_y & -1 \end{vmatrix}$

10. $\pm\sqrt{3/1105}[3\mathbf{i} + 14\mathbf{j} - 30\mathbf{k}]$

Article 13–4, p. 592

1. $\Delta w_{\tan} = 0.14$, $\Delta w = 0.1407$ 2. $\Delta w = (2x + y)\Delta x + x\Delta y + (\Delta x)^2 + \Delta x\,\Delta y$; $\Delta w_{\tan} = (2x + y)\Delta x + x\Delta y$; $\epsilon_1 = \Delta x$, $\epsilon_2 = \Delta x$ 3. $|x - y| < 0.0224$ 4. a) $\frac{1}{2}, \frac{1}{2}$ b) $0.45\overline{45}, 0.45$ 5. a) x b) y c) $(x + y)/\sqrt{2}$ 6. a) $z - y$ b) x

7. a) $x + 1$ b) $-y + \pi/2$ 8. $r = 2h$ 9. a) $S_0[(\Delta p/100) + \Delta\ell - 5\Delta w - 30\Delta h]$ b) 1 cm increase in height decreases sag 6 times as much as 1 cm increase in width.   10. 6%   11. a) $\Delta Q \approx 10\Delta K + \Delta M - 400\Delta h$ b) Most sensitive to change in h; least sensitive to change in M.   12. (13 ± 0.03) in.

Article 13–5, p. 596

1. $\frac{2}{3}$ 2. $\frac{9}{1183}$ 3. $4\sqrt{3}$ 4. $\frac{43}{15}$ 5. In the direction of $3\mathbf{i} - \mathbf{j}$ 6. $-7/\sqrt{5}$ 8. $(\pi - 3)/(2\sqrt{5}) \approx 0.032$ 9. $\pm(\mathbf{i} + \mathbf{j})$

Article 13–6, pp. 599–600

1. $-2\mathbf{i} - 2\mathbf{j} + 4\mathbf{k}$ 2. $6\mathbf{i} + 6\mathbf{j}$ 3. $2\mathbf{i}$ 4. $(-3\mathbf{i} - 4\mathbf{j})/25$ 5. $(\mathbf{i} + 2\mathbf{j} - 2\mathbf{k})/27$ 6. $(3\sqrt{3}\mathbf{i} + 4\sqrt{3}\mathbf{j} + 5\mathbf{k})/2$ 7. $5\mathbf{k}$

8. $(x - 3)/3 = (y - 4)/4 = (z + 5)/5$

9. a) $x = y = z$; $-x = -y = z$; $x = y = 0$ b) $(1, 1, 1)$ and $(-2, -2, -2)$; $(2, 2, -2)$ and $(-1, -1, 1)$; $(0, 0, 2)$

10. Two lines; $x = z = -y \pm 4$ 11. Tangent plane: $3x + 5y + 4z = 18$; normal line: $(x - 3)/3 = (y - 5)/5 = (z + 4)/4$

12. In the direction of grad $f = 10\mathbf{i} + 4\mathbf{j} + 10\mathbf{k}$. Max $(df/ds) = |\text{grad } f| = \sqrt{216} = 6\sqrt{6}$

14. grad $w = \mathbf{u}_\rho(\partial w/\partial\rho) + \mathbf{u}_\phi(1/\rho)(\partial w/\partial\phi) + \mathbf{u}_\theta[1/(\rho\sin\phi)](\partial w/\partial\theta)$

15. a) $\mathbf{i}(\partial f/\partial x) + \mathbf{j}(\partial f/\partial y)$ b) In the direction given by the vector grad $f = -\mathbf{i} + \mathbf{j}$; $|dw/ds| = \sqrt{2}$ in this direction.

23. $h = f_0/(f_x^2 + f_y^2 + f_z^2)_0$ (Smaller values of h should probably be used in calculations.) For the three equations given, we might use $h = 0.001$. One approximate solution is $(x, y, z) = (1.059, 1.944, 3.886)$. For any solution (x, y, z), there are five other solutions: (z, y, x), $(-y, -x, z)$, $(z, -x, -y)$, $(x, -z, -y)$, and $(-y, -z, x)$.

Article 13–7, pp. 604–605

1. $2e^t[x(\cos t - \sin t) + y(\sin t + \cos t) + z] = 4e^{2t}$ 2. $(y(y^2 - x^2)\sinh t + x(x^2 - y^2)\cosh t)/(x^2 + y^2)^2 = \text{sech}^2 2t$

3. $e^{2x+3y}((8t^2 + 2)\cos 4z/(t(t^2 + 1)) - 4\sin 4z) = 2t(t^2 + 1)^2[(4t^2 + 1)\cos 4t - 2t(t^2 + 1)\sin 4t]$

4. $\partial w/\partial r = e^{2r}/\sqrt{e^{2r} + e^{2s}}$; $\partial w/\partial s = e^{2s}/\sqrt{e^{2r} + e^{2s}}$ 5. $\partial w/\partial r = \partial w/\partial s = 2/(r + s)$

13. $f_x = (\partial w/\partial r)\cos\theta - (1/r)(\partial w/\partial\theta)\sin\theta$; $f_y = (\partial w/\partial r)\sin\theta + (1/r)(\partial w/\partial\theta)\cos\theta$

Article 13–8, p. 609

2. $\frac{47}{24}$ ft^3 **3.** Approx. 340 ft^2 **4. a)** $dx = \cos\theta\,dr - r\sin\theta\,d\theta$, $dy = \sin\theta\,dr + r\cos\theta\,d\theta$ **b)** $dr = \cos\theta\,dx + \sin\theta\,dy$, $d\theta = -(\sin\theta/r)\,dx + (\cos\theta/r)\,dy$ **c)** $\partial r/\partial x = \cos\theta = x/r$, $\partial r/\partial y = \sin\theta = y/r$

5. a) $dx = f_u\,du + f_v\,dv$, $dy = g_u\,du + g_v\,dv$

b) $du = \begin{vmatrix} dx & f_v \\ dy & g_v \end{vmatrix} \Big/ \begin{vmatrix} f_u & f_v \\ g_u & g_v \end{vmatrix}$, $dv = \begin{vmatrix} f_u & dx \\ g_u & dy \end{vmatrix} \Big/ \begin{vmatrix} f_u & f_v \\ g_u & g_v \end{vmatrix}$

6. a) $dx = \sin\phi\cos\theta\,d\rho + \rho\cos\phi\cos\theta\,d\phi - \rho\sin\phi\sin\theta\,d\theta$
$dy = \sin\phi\sin\theta\,d\rho + \rho\cos\phi\sin\theta\,d\phi + \rho\sin\phi\cos\theta\,d\theta$
$dz = \cos\phi\,d\rho - \rho\sin\phi\,d\phi$

b) $d\rho = \begin{vmatrix} dx & \rho\cos\phi\cos\theta & -\rho\sin\phi\sin\theta \\ dy & \rho\cos\phi\sin\theta & \rho\sin\phi\cos\theta \\ dz & -\rho\sin\phi & 0 \end{vmatrix} \Big/ \begin{vmatrix} \sin\phi\cos\theta & \rho\cos\phi\cos\theta & -\rho\sin\phi\sin\theta \\ \sin\phi\sin\theta & \rho\cos\phi\sin\theta & \rho\sin\phi\cos\theta \\ \cos\phi & -\rho\sin\phi & 0 \end{vmatrix}$

c) $\partial\rho/\partial x = \sin\phi\cos\theta = x/\rho$

7. $df = -u_0$ and $dg = -v_0$ provided $dx = ((vf_y - ug_y)/(f_x g_y - g_x f_y))_0$ and $dy = ((ug_x - vf_x)/(f_x g_y - g_x f_y))_0$

8. $dx = -\begin{vmatrix} u_0 & f_y & f_z \\ v_0 & g_y & g_z \\ w_0 & h_y & h_z \end{vmatrix} \Big/ \begin{vmatrix} f_x & f_y & f_z \\ g_x & g_y & g_z \\ h_x & h_y & h_z \end{vmatrix}$, with similar expressions for dy and dx

Article 13–9, p. 612

1. Low: $(-3, 3, -5)$ **2.** Low: $(15, -8, -63)$ **3.** High: $(-8, -23, 59)$ **4.** High: $(\frac{2}{3}, \frac{4}{3}, 0)$ **5.** $(-2, 1, 3)$ is a saddle point
6. $(-2, 2, 2)$ is a saddle point   **7.** Low: $(0, 0, 0)$; high: $(\pm 1, \pm 1, \sqrt{2})$. The partial derivatives do not exist at $(0, 0)$. They exist but are not zero at $(\pm 1, \pm 1)$.

Article 13–10, pp. 615–616

1. b) $m = \begin{vmatrix} \sum y_i & n \\ \sum x_i y_i & \sum x_i \end{vmatrix} \Big/ D$, $b = \begin{vmatrix} \sum x_i & \sum y_i \\ \sum x_i^2 & \sum x_i y_i \end{vmatrix} \Big/ D$, where $D = \begin{vmatrix} \sum x_i & n \\ \sum x_i^2 & \sum x_i \end{vmatrix}$
2. $26y + 19x = 30$ **3.** $12y = 9x + 20$ **4.** $6y = 9x + 1$ **5. a)** $y = -0.369x$ **b)** $I/I_0 = e^{-0.369x}$
6. $y = 0.123x + 3.580$ **7.** $H \approx 17$ **8.** $F = 55{,}096(1/D^2) - 2.826$

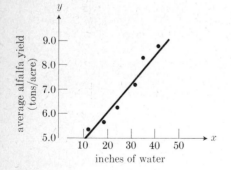

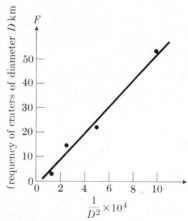

Article 13–11, pp. 627–628

1. Max is 5 at $(\sqrt{5}, \sqrt{5})$, $(-\sqrt{5}, -\sqrt{5})$;   min is -5 at $(-\sqrt{5}, \sqrt{5})$, $(\sqrt{5}, -\sqrt{5})$
2. a) No point at which minimum occurs; decreases without bound. Local minimum at $(4, 4)$.   **b)** Max is 64 at $(8, 8)$.
3. 5.4   **4.** $(0, 0, 1)$ **5.** Square bottom 8 in. by 8 in., 4 in. deep
6. Square bottom $\sqrt[3]{V/2}$ by $\sqrt[3]{V/2}$, depth $\sqrt[3]{4V}$, where V is the given volume.   **7.** $x + 2y + 2z = 6$
8. $h = $ altitude of triangle $= \sqrt{A/(6 + 3\sqrt{3})}$; $2x = $ width of rectangle $= (2\sqrt{3})h$; $y = $ altitude of rectangle $= (1 + \sqrt{3})h$
9. $z = -\frac{1}{2}x + \frac{3}{2}y - \frac{1}{4}$ **10. a)** Spheres, center at origin   **b)** No   **c)** Circle or point of tangency. Yes. In a circle.   **d)** Yes

11. $(-3.621, 1.5)$ and $(3.621, -1.5)$ for maximum, $(0.621, 1.5)$ and $(-0.621, -1.5)$ for minimum

12. a) $(-5/\sqrt{14}, -10/\sqrt{14}, -15/\sqrt{14})$, $f = -5\sqrt{14}$ **b)** $(5/\sqrt{14}, 10/\sqrt{14}, 15/\sqrt{14})$, $f = 5\sqrt{14}$.
Geometric interpretation: Planes $f = $ constant are tangent to the sphere for $f = \pm 5\sqrt{14}$.

13. Cone $|z| = r$, plane $z = 1 + r(\cos\theta + \sin\theta) = 1 + r\sqrt{2}\sin(\theta + \pi/4)$; curve of intersection lies on the hyperbolic cylinder $r = g(\theta) = 1/[\pm 1 - \sqrt{2}\sin(\theta + \pi/4)]$, $|\overrightarrow{OP}| = \sqrt{2}\,r$ with $r = g(\theta)$. The minimum value of $|g(\theta)|$ is $1/(1 + \sqrt{2}) = \sqrt{2} - 1$, and $|\overrightarrow{OB}| = \sqrt{2}(\sqrt{2} - 1) = 2 - \sqrt{2} = \sqrt{(6 - 4\sqrt{2})}$. B is the point on the cone nearest the origin; A is the point nearest the origin on the other branch of the hyperbola; there is no point farthest from the origin. **14.** If $y = x$, $z = 1 + 2x$, and $z^2 = x^2 + y^2$, then $(1 + 2x)^2 = 2x^2$ and $x = -1 \pm \sqrt{\frac{1}{2}}$, so x is not an *independent variable*. (We have no right to differentiate with respect to x if x is restricted to the set $\{-1 + \sqrt{\frac{1}{2}}, -1 - \sqrt{\frac{1}{2}}\}$.)

15. a) $2xy + 2x + 2y + 1 = 0$ is the hyperbola $2(x + 1)(y + 1) = 1$ in the xy-plane.   **b)** In space, $\{(x, y, z): 2xy + 2x + 2y + 1 = 0\}$ is a hyperbolic cylinder. Minimum for $y = x = -1 + \sqrt{\frac{1}{2}}$; no maximum.

Article 13–12, p. 632

14. $e^x \cosh y + 6\cos(2x - 3y)$ **15.** $-6/(2x + 3y)^2$ **16.** $(y^2 - x^2)(x^2 + y^2)^{-2}$ **17.** $2y + 6xy^2 + 12x^2y^3$

18. a) $F(x) = (2bk + k^2)x^3$ **b)** $c_1 = \pm\sqrt{a^2 + ah + \frac{1}{3}h^2}$ ($\pm$ sign to be chosen depending upon the signs of a and $(a + h)$)
  c) $g(y) = 3c_1^2 y^2 = (3a^2 + 3ah + h^2)y^2$ **d)** $d_1 = b + (k/2)$

19. $d_2 = b + (k/2)$, $c_2 = \pm\sqrt{a^2 + ah + \frac{1}{3}h^2}$ (with the $\pm$ sign depending upon the signs of a and $(a + h)$)

Article 13–13, p. 637

1. Exact, $f = (2x^5 + 5x^2y^3 + 3y^5)/5 + C$ **2.** Not exact   **3.** Exact, $f = x^2 + xy + y^2 + C$
4. Exact, $f = x\cosh y + y\sinh x + C$ **5.** Not exact   **6.** Exact, $f = e^x(y - x + 1) + y + C$ **7.** Not exact

Article 13–14, p. 639

1. $1/x$ **2.** $-1/(2x^2)$ **3.** $(4 - x)/(2x^3)$ **4.** $x/(\sqrt{1 - x^2}\sin^{-1}x)$ **5.** $(4x - 1)\ln x$ **7.** $2xe^{x^2}$ **8.** $y(x^2\tanh x + 2x\ln\cosh x)$
9. $y(2/(x^2 + 1) - [\ln(x^2 + 1)]/x^2)$ **10.** $y([(8x + 4)/(4x^2 + 4x + 3)]\int_x^{x^2}\ln t\,dt + (4x - 1)\ln x\ln(4x^2 + 4x + 3))$

Miscellaneous Problems Chapter 13, pp. 640–645

1. No, $\lim_{x\to 0} f(x, 0) = 1$, $\lim_{x\to 0} f(x, x) = 0$ **2.** Yes

4. If f is constant, then f has the same value for all points and there is nothing more to prove. Next, suppose f is not constant. Then there are points Q_1 and Q_2 such that $f(Q_1) \neq f(Q_2)$. Let m be any number between $f(Q_1)$ and $f(Q_2)$. Let C be a circular arc joining Q_1 and Q_2. Since f is continuous along this arc it takes all values between $f(Q_1)$ and $f(Q_2)$. Hence there is a point P_1 on C such that $f(P_1) = m$. Repeat the argument with a different circular arc; there is a point P_2 on it such that $f(P_2) = f(P_1) = m$. There are infinitely many circular arcs joining Q_1 and Q_2, and on each of them is a point P such that $f(P) = m$.

5. $\partial/\partial x\,(\sin xy)^2 = y\sin 2xy$, $\partial/\partial y\,(\sin xy)^2 = x\sin 2xy$ $\partial/\partial x\sin(xy)^2 = 2xy^2\cos(xy)^2$, $\partial/\partial y\sin(xy)^2 = 2x^2y\cos(xy)^2$

6. $-2/\sqrt{3}$ **8.** $54(x - 3) + 2y - 27(z + 2) = 0$; $(x - 3)/54 = y/2 = -(z + 2)/27$; $(54/\sqrt{3649}, 2/\sqrt{3649}, -27/\sqrt{3649})$

9. a) Hyperboloid of one sheet   **b)** $2\mathbf{i} + 3\mathbf{j} + 3\mathbf{k}$ **c)** $2(x - 2) + 3(y + 3) + 3(z - 3) = 0$, $(x - 2)/2 = (y + 3)/3 = (z - 3)/3$

10. a) $13(x + 2) - (y - 1) + 12(z - 2) = 0$, **b)** $(x + 2)/13 = 1 - y = (z - 2)/12$

11. $\partial f/\partial x = 1$, $\partial f/\partial y = 3$, $dw/ds = 3$ **14. a)** $D_u f = f_x u_1 + f_y u_2 + f_z u_3$
  b) $D_v(D_u f) = f_{xx}u_1v_1 + f_{yy}u_2v_2 + f_{zz}u_3v_3 + f_{xy}(u_1v_2 + u_2v_1) + f_{xz}(u_1v_3 + u_3v_1) + f_{yz}(u_2v_3 + u_3v_2)$

15. $dw/ds = \sqrt{3}$, maximum $= \sqrt{3}$ **16.** $(f_x = f_y = 2)$ $df/ds = \frac{14}{5}$ **17.** 7   **18.** $-14/\sqrt{6}$ **19.** $-\sqrt{\frac{2}{3}}$

21. a) $\mathbf{N}(x, y, z) = (x^2 + y^2)^{-(1/2)}[x(1 + 3x^2 + 3y^2)\mathbf{i} + y(1 + 3x^2 + 3y^2)\mathbf{j} - \sqrt{x^2 + y^2}\,\mathbf{k}]$
  b) $[(1 + 3x^2 + 3y^2)^2 + 1]^{-(1/2)}, 1/\sqrt{2}$

22. $a^2 + b^2 + c^2 = 2$ **23. a)** $4\mathbf{j} + 6\mathbf{k}$ **b)** $4(y + 1) + 6(z - 3) = 0$ **24.** $(2\mathbf{i} + 6\mathbf{j} - 3\mathbf{k})/7$ **26.** $\pm\sqrt{3}$

28. $\nabla f = \mathbf{u}_r(\partial f/\partial r) + \mathbf{u}_\theta(1/r)(\partial f/\partial\theta)$ **30. c)** $(x^2 + y^2 + z^2)/2$ **31.** $\theta + (\pi/2), 1/r$

34. a) $f = \phi(bx - ay)$ **b)** $f = \phi(x^2 + y^2)$, ϕ arbitrary in each case   **35.** $h'(x) = f_x(x, y) + f_y(x, y)[-g_x(x, y)/g_y(x, y)]$

36. $\partial g/\partial z = 1/(\partial f/\partial x)$ **37.** $dx/dz = (\sin y + \sin z - 2y^2\cos z)(\sin y + \sin z)^{-1}(\sin x + x\cos x)^{-1}$

39. $\partial F/\partial x = \frac{1}{2}(\partial f/\partial u + \partial f/\partial v)$, $\partial F/\partial y = \frac{1}{2}(\partial f/\partial v - \partial f/\partial u)$ **42.** $\partial^2 f/\partial u^2 + (y^2 + 2xy)(\partial^2 f/\partial u\,\partial v) + 2xy^3(\partial^2 f/\partial v^2) + 2y(\partial f/\partial v)$

43. $a = b = 1$ **44.** 2   **47.** $d^2y/dx^2 = -(1/f_y^3)(f_{xx}f_y^2 - 2f_{xy}f_xf_y + f_{yy}f_x^2)$ **49.** $dz/dx = (f_y - f_x)/(f_y + f_z)$

50. $x_t = x - v + ax_{vv}/x_v^2$, $0 \leq v \leq 1$, $t \geq 0$, $x(0, t) = 0$, $x(1, t) = 1$ **55.** 60.44   **56.** Minimum $(\frac{1}{2}, 0)$, $T = -\frac{1}{4}$. Maximum $(-\frac{1}{2}, \pm\sqrt{3}/2)$, $T = 2\frac{1}{4}$.   **57.** 50   **58. a)** Max $z = \sqrt{3}$ at $(0, 0)$, min $z = -\sqrt{3}$ at $(0, 0)$ **b)** Min $z = 0$ at $(0, 0)$ **c)** None

59. $(1, 1, 1); (1, -1, -1); (-1, 1, -1); (-1, -1, 1)$ **60.** Length $= (c^2V/ab)^{1/3}$, depth $= (b^2V/ca)^{1/3}$, height $= (a^2V/bc)^{1/3}$
61. $e^{-2}/6$ **62.** Minimum **63.** $(\sum_{i=1}^{n} a_i^2)^{1/2}$ **64.** $(\sqrt{3}/2)abc$
66. $\partial^2 z/\partial x\ \partial y = \cos^{-3}(y + z)[\cos^2(y + z)\sin(x + y) + \sin(y + z)\cos^2(x + y)]$ **67.** y^2 **68.** $2xyz(x^2 + y^2)^{-2}$
70. $f_{yx}(0, 0) = -1, f_{xy}(0, 0) = 1$ **71.** $f(x, y) = \frac{1}{5}(2x^5 + 5x^2y^3 + 3y^5) + C$ **72.** $f(x, y) = y\ln x + xe^y + y^2 + C$
73. $w = f(x, y) = x + e^x\cos y + y^2 + C$ **75. a)** 1 **b)** 0 **c)** 0

CHAPTER 14

Article 14–1, p. 652

1. $(4 + \pi^2)/2$

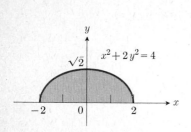

2. $8\ln 8 - 16 + e$

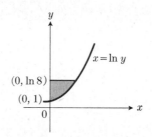

3. $\pi/4$

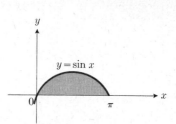

4. $\frac{5}{6}$

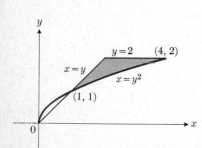

5. $\int_1^{e^2} \int_{\ln y}^2 dx\ dy = e^2 - 3$

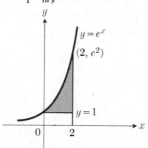

6. $\int_0^1 \int_0^{x^2} dy\ dx = \frac{1}{3}$

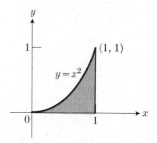

7. $\int_{-2}^2 \int_0^{\sqrt{(4-x^2)/2}} y\ dy\ dx = \frac{8}{3}$

8. $\int_{-4}^5 \int_{(y-2)/3}^{-2+\sqrt{y+4}} dx\ dy = \frac{9}{2}$

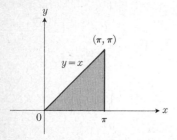

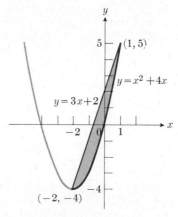

9. $\int_{-4}^1 \int_{3x}^{4-x^2} (x + 4)\ dy\ dx = \frac{625}{12}$ **10.** $4\int_0^a \int_0^{\sqrt{a^2-x^2}} [(x^2 + y^2)/a]\ dy\ dx = \pi a^3/2$

Article 14–2, p. 654

1. $a^2/2$ 2. $e - 1$ 3. 4 4. $\frac{9}{2}$ 5. $\frac{1}{3}$ 6. $a^2(\pi + 4)/2$ 7. $\frac{4}{3}$

8.

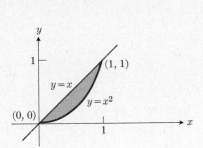

9.

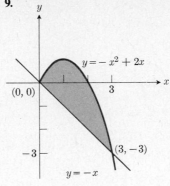

10.

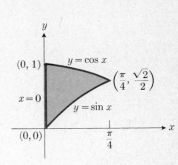

11.

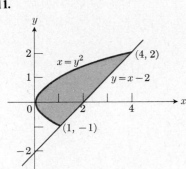

12.

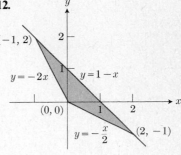

Article 14–3, p. 658

1. $(a/3, a/3)$ 2. $I_x = (e^3 - 1)/9$ 3. $\frac{104}{3}$ 4. $(-\frac{8}{5}, -\frac{1}{2})$ 5. $\frac{1}{6}$ 6. $(0, a(8 + 3\pi)/(40 + 12\pi))$ 7. $\frac{64}{105}$

Article 14–4, p. 663

1. $\int_0^{2\pi} \int_0^a r \, dr \, d\theta = \pi a^2$ 2. $\int_0^{\pi/2} \int_0^a r^3 \, dr \, d\theta = \pi a^4/8$ 3. $\int_0^{\pi/4} \int_0^a r^2 \cos \theta \, dr \, d\theta = a^3 \sqrt{2}/6$ 4. $\int_0^{\pi/2} \int_0^\infty e^{-r^2} r \, dr \, d\theta = \pi/4$
5. $\int_0^{\pi/4} \int_0^{2 \sec \theta} r^2 \sin \theta \, dr \, d\theta = 4/3$ 6. $\int_0^{\pi/2} \int_0^{2a \cos \theta} r^3 \cos^2 \theta \, dr \, d\theta = 5\pi a^4/8$ 7. $a^2(8 + \pi)/4$ 8. $\bar{x} = (32 + 15\pi)/(48 + 6\pi)a$,
$\bar{y} = 0$ 9. $I_0 = a^4(320 + 81\pi)/96$ 10. $a^3(15\pi + 32)/24$ 11. $2a^2$ 12. $(3\pi + 20 - 16\sqrt{2})2\sqrt{2} a^3/9$

Article 14–5, p. 666

1. $\frac{1}{6}|abc|$ 2. $\frac{2}{3}$ 3. $\frac{1}{3}$ 4. 4 5. $\frac{20}{3}$ 6. 32π 7. 4π 8. $16a^3/3$ 9. 27π 10. $\frac{4}{3}\pi abc$

Article 14–6, p. 667

1. $5\pi/2$ 2. 32π 3. $4\pi a^3(8 - 3\sqrt{3})/3$ 4. $\pi/2$ 5. $(8\sqrt{2} - 7)\pi a^3/6$ 6. $a^3/3$

Article 14–7, p. 669

1. $64\pi a^5(\frac{4}{15} - (17\sqrt{3}/160)) \approx 16.7a^5$ 2. $2\pi/3$ 3. $\bar{x} = \frac{1}{2}$ 4. $\bar{x} = \bar{y} = 0, \bar{z} = 7a/(2(8\sqrt{2} - 7))$ 5. $\frac{2}{5}Ma^2$ 6. $8\pi a^3/3$
7. $64\pi a^5/35$ 8. $\frac{3}{20}(a^2 + 4h^2)M$ 9. $\frac{7}{5}Ma^2$ 10. $\bar{y} = \bar{z} = 0, \bar{x} = (3\sqrt{2}/8)a$ 11. $M(3a^2 + 4b^2)/4$

Article 14–8, p. 670

1. $(16 - 10\sqrt{2})\pi/3$ 2. $\bar{x} = \bar{y} = 0, \bar{z} = 3a/[16(2 - \sqrt{3})] \approx 0.7a$ 3. $8\pi a^3/3$ 4. $a\sqrt{1270/651} \approx 1.4a$

5.

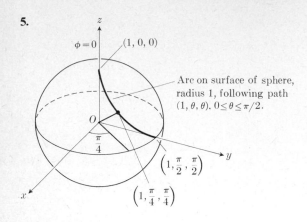

$\phi = 0$ (1, 0, 0)

Arc on surface of sphere, radius 1, following path $(1, \theta, \theta)$, $0 \le \theta \le \pi/2$.

$\left(1, \frac{\pi}{2}, \frac{\pi}{2}\right)$

$\left(1, \frac{\pi}{4}, \frac{\pi}{4}\right)$

Article 14–9, p. 675

2. $\frac{1}{2}\sqrt{b^2 c^2 + a^2 c^2 + a^2 b^2}$ **3.** $\pi a^2 / 2$ **4.** $8a^2(\pi - 2)$ **5.** $(\pi/6)(37\sqrt{37} - 5\sqrt{5})$ **6.** $2\pi a^2(2 - \sqrt{2})$ **7.** $\pi a^2 \sqrt{1 + c^2}$
8. $2\pi a^2 / 3$ **9.** $(5\sqrt{5} - 1)\pi a^2 / 6$ **10.** $16a^2$

Miscellaneous Problems Chapter 14, pp. 675–678

1. $\int_{-2}^{0} \int_{2x+4}^{4-x^2} dy \, dx = \frac{4}{3}$ **2.** $\frac{1}{5}$ **3.** $\int_{0}^{1} \int_{-y}^{y} dx \, dy$ **4.** 31.25   **5.** $\int_{0}^{1} \int_{x}^{2-x} (x^2 + y^2) \, dy \, dx = \frac{4}{3}$
6. a) $(a^2 + m^2)^{-2}\{(m^2 - a^2) \cos ax - 2am \sin ax + [(a^2 - m^2) + mx(a^2 + m^2)]e^{mx}\}$
  b) $(a^2 + m^2)^{-3}\{m(3a^2 - m^2) \cos ax + a(3m^2 - a^2) \sin ax + [(m/2)(a^2 + m^2)^2 x^2 + (a^4 - m^4)x + m(m^2 - 3a^2)]e^{mx}\}$
8. $\ln(b/a)$ **9.** $(4a/3\pi, 4a/3\pi)$ **10.** $(2a \sin \alpha / 3\alpha, 0)$
11. $(28\sqrt{2}/9\pi, 28\sqrt{2}(\sqrt{2} - 1)/9\pi)$ (cartesian coordinates)   **12.** $(-\frac{12}{5}, 2)$ **14. a)** $\frac{1}{3}(a^3 t + at^3 - t^4)$ **b)** 0
16. $A = a^2 \cos^{-1}(b/a) - b\sqrt{a^2 - b^2}$; $I_0 = (a^4/2) \cos^{-1}(b/a) - b\sqrt{a^2 - b^2}(a^2 + 2b^2)/6$
17. $b\sqrt{2/5}$ **18. a)** $(a/2)\sqrt{\pi/4 - \frac{2}{3}}$ **b)** $(a/2)\sqrt{\pi/4 + \frac{2}{3}}$
21. $\int_{-\pi/2}^{\pi/2} \int_{0}^{a} r^2 \cos \theta \, dr \, d\theta$ **24.** $a > 0, c > 0, ac - b^2 = \pi^2$
25. $A = 2a^2$, $I_y = (3\pi + 8)a^4/12$ **26. a)** $(\pi - 2)/4$ **b)** $(\sqrt{3}/4) \tan^{-1} \frac{4}{3}$
27. $K(a) = \int_{0}^{\cos \beta} dx \int_{0}^{x \tan \beta} \ln(x^2 + y^2) \, dy + \int_{a \cos \beta}^{a} dx \int_{0}^{\sqrt{a^2 - x^2}} \ln(x^2 + y^2) \, dy$
28. $\pi/8$ **29.** $(0, 0, \frac{1}{4})$ **30.** $(4\pi a^3/3)(\sqrt{2} - \frac{7}{8})$ **31.** $\pi/4$ **32.** $\pi/\sqrt{2}$ **33.** $49\pi a^5/15$ **34.** $\frac{4}{3}\pi abc$ **35.** $a^2 b^2 c^2/6$ **36.** $16a^3/3$
37. $x^2 + y^2 + z^2 = 4$; $x^2 + y^2 = 2x$; $y = 0$; $\int_{0}^{\pi/2} \int_{0}^{2 \cos \theta} \int_{-\sqrt{4-r^2}}^{\sqrt{4-r^2}} dz \, r \, dr \, d\theta$
38. $4\pi a^3/3 + (16/3)[(b/2)(3a^2 - b^2) \sin^{-1}(b/\sqrt{a^2 - b^2}) + (b^2/2)\sqrt{a^2 - 2b^2} - a^3 \tan^{-1}(a/\sqrt{a^2 - 2b^2})]$
39. a) Radius of sphere = 2, of hole = 1   **b)** $4\pi\sqrt{3}$
40. $\int_{0}^{1} \int_{\sqrt{1-x^2}}^{\sqrt{3-x^2}} \int_{1}^{\sqrt{4-x^2-y^2}} xyz^2 \, dz \, dy \, dx + \int_{1}^{\sqrt{3}} \int_{0}^{\sqrt{3-x^2}} \int_{1}^{\sqrt{4-x^2-y^2}} xyz^2 \, dz \, dy \, dx$
41. $3\pi a^3/4$ **42.** $2a^3(3\pi - 4)/9$ **43.** $\pi a^5/12$ **44.** $\pi^2 a^3/4$ **45.** $8\pi\delta(b^5 - a^5)/15$ **47.** $\rho_0(1 - \frac{1}{2}\epsilon^2)$ **48.** $2\pi(\sqrt{3} - 1)$
49. $\pi\sqrt{3}$ **50.** $\pi\sqrt{2} a^2$ **51.** $2a^2(\pi - 2)$ **52.** $\pi\sqrt{2}$ **53. a)** 144π **b)** -16π **c)** 128π
54. $4 \int_{0}^{a} \sqrt{a^2 - y^2} \sqrt{4y^2 + 1} \, dy$ **55.** $16\pi(\sqrt{2} - 1)$ **56.** $8\pi^2$ **57.** $\pi^2/2$
58. $8r^2$ **60.** $(6M/a^2)(1 - h/\sqrt{a^2 + h^2})$ **62.** $z = 1$ **63.** $4a/3$

CHAPTER 15

Article 15–1, p. 684

1. a) $x = 0, y = 0$ **b)** $x^2 + y^2 = a^2$ **2.** $\delta\pi a^4/2$ **4.** Helix
5. Replace x, y, z by $x - x_0, y - y_0, z - z_0$.   **6.** $\mathbf{F}(x, y, z) = \exp(2y + 3z)[2x\mathbf{i} + 2x^2\mathbf{j} + 3x^2\mathbf{k}]$
7. $\mathbf{F}(x, y, z) = 2(x^2 + y^2 + z^2)^{-1}[x\mathbf{i} + y\mathbf{j} + z\mathbf{k}]$ **8.** $\mathbf{F}(x, y, z) = (z^2 + x^2 y^2)^{-1}[yz\mathbf{i} + xz\mathbf{j} - xy\mathbf{k}]$
9. $\mathbf{F}(x, y, z) = 2\mathbf{i} - 3\mathbf{j} + 5\mathbf{k}$ **10.** $\mathbf{F}(x, y, z) = n(x^2 + y^2 + z^2)^{(n-2)/2}[x\mathbf{i} + y\mathbf{j} + z\mathbf{k}]$

Article 15–2, p. 690

4. πa^3 **5.** $\frac{28}{3}\sqrt{14}$ **6.** $\frac{28}{3}\sqrt{14}$ **7.** $\pi a^2/2$ **8.** 0   **9.** $\pi a^3/6$ **10.** $\pi a^4/3$

Article 15–3, pp. 701–703

1. $\frac{5}{6}\sqrt{2}$ **3.** π **4.** 0 **5. a)** 0 **b)** $-\frac{1}{3}$ **8.** $n = -1$ **9. a)** $\frac{9}{2}$ **b)** $\frac{9}{2}$ **c)** $\frac{9}{2}$ **10. a)** 2.143 **b)** 2.538 **c)** $2 + \sin 1$
11. a) 3 **b)** 3 **c)** 3 **12. a)** e^3 **b)** e^3 **c)** e^3 **13. a)** $\sin 1 = 0.8415$ **b)** 0.8415 **c)** 0.8415
14. $f(x, y, z) = x^2 + \frac{3}{2}y^2 + 2z^2 + C$ **15.** $f(x, y, z) = xy + yz + zx + C$ **16.** $f(x, y, z) = xe^{y+2z} + C$
17. $f(x, y, z) = xy \sin z + C$ **19.** 8 **20.** 24 **21.** $-e^{-2\pi} + 1$ **25. b)** $\nabla \times \mathbf{F} = 0$

Article 15–4, p. 709

2. $\pi/2$ **3.** $2\pi\delta/a$ **5. a)** 0 **b)** 4π **6. a)** 0 **b)** 4π

Article 15–5, p. 718

3. 0 **4.** 0 **5.** $\pi a^4/2$ **6.** 0 **7.** $-\pi a^2$ **11.** 0 **12.** -2 **13.** $\int_C M(x, y)\, dy - N(x, y)\, dx = \iint_R (\partial M/\partial x + \partial N/\partial y)\, dx\, dy$

Article 15–6, pp. 725–726

1. 0 **2.** 24 **3.** 0 **4.** 16 **5.** 0 **6.** 24π **7.** 48π **8.** 135π **9.** $4\pi a^3$ **10.** 24

Article 15–7, p. 734

1. 0 **2.** 0 **3.** $-\pi/4$ **4.** 0 **5.** Zero, because curl grad $\phi = 0$.

Miscellaneous Problems Chapter 15, pp. 735–737

5. 0 **6.** $\sqrt{3}\,\pi$ **7.** $(\pi/60)(17^{5/2} - 41)$ **8.** $4\pi a^4/3$ **9.** $8\pi a^3$ **10.** $-8\pi a$ **11.** $-\frac{25}{3}$ **12.** $\pi a/2$ **13.** 0 **14.** 2π **15.** 2π **16.** 0
17. 0 **18.** 0 **19.** 0 **20.** -3 **31. a)** $C_1 = -100, C_2 = 200$ **b)** $C_1 = 100, C_2 = 0$

CHAPTER 16

Article 16–2, pp. 748–749

1. $0, -\frac{1}{4}, -\frac{2}{9}, -\frac{3}{16}$; converges to 0 **2.** $\frac{1}{2}, \frac{1}{2}, \frac{3}{8}, \frac{1}{4}$; converges to 0 **3.** $\frac{1}{3}, \frac{1}{9}, \frac{1}{27}, \frac{1}{81}$; converges to 0 **4.** $1, \frac{1}{2}, \frac{1}{6}, \frac{1}{24}$; converges to 0
5. $1, -\frac{1}{3}, \frac{1}{5}, -\frac{1}{7}$; converges to 0 **6.** 1, 3, 1, 3; diverges **7.** $0, -1, 0, 1$; diverges
8. $8, 8^{1/2}, 8^{1/3}, 8^{1/4}$; converges to 1 **9.** $1, -1/\sqrt{2}, 1/\sqrt{3}, -\frac{1}{2}$; converges to 0
10. 1, 1, 1, 1; converges to 1 **11.** Converges to 0 **12.** Diverges **13.** Converges to 1 **14.** Converges to 0 **15.** Diverges
16. Diverges **17.** Converges to $-\frac{2}{3}$ **18.** Converges to $\frac{1}{2}$ **19.** Converges to $\sqrt{2}$ **20.** Converges to 0
21. Diverges **22.** Converges to 1 **23.** Diverges **24.** Converges to 0 **25.** Converges to 1
26. Converges to 1 **27.** Converges to -5 **28.** Converges to 9 **29.** Converges to 1 **30.** Converges to 0
31. Converges to 1 **32.** Diverges **33.** Converges to 5 **34.** Diverges **35.** Converges to 0
36. Converges to 10 **37.** Converges to 0 **38.** Converges to 1 **39.** Converges to $\sqrt{2}$ **40.** Converges to 2
41. Diverges **42.** Converges to 0 **43.** Converges to 0 **44.** Converges to -1 **45.** Diverges
46. Converges to 1 **47.** Converges to 0 **48.** Converges to 1 **49.** Converges to $\pi/2$ **50.** Diverges
51. Converges to 1 **52.** Converges to 2 **53.** Converges to $\frac{1}{2}$ **54.** Converges to 0 **55.** Use $0 < n!/n^n \le 1/n$
56. $x_7 = 1.732050808 = x_6$ **57.** Yes. No; the limit is 1 for any $x > 0$.
58. a) $x_1 = 1, x_2 = 1.54 \ldots, x_3 = 1.57 \ldots, x_4 = 1.570796327$ **b)** $x_1 = 5, \ldots, x_8 = x_9 = 7.853981634 \; (\approx 5\pi/2)$ **60.** 1 **61.** 1

Article 16–3, pp. 752–753

1. Converges; $L = 0$ **2.** Converges; $L = 0$ **3.** Converges; $L = 0$ **4.** Converges; $L = 1$ **5.** Converges; $L = 0$
6. Diverges **7.** Converges; $L = e^7$ **8.** Converges; $L = e^5$ **9.** Converges; $L = 0$ **10.** Converges; $L = 1$
11. Diverges **12.** Converges; $L = 0$ **13.** Converges; $L = 1$ **14.** Converges; $L = 1$ **15.** Converges; $L = 0$
16. Converges; $L = 1$ **17.** Converges; $L = 1/e$ **18.** Converges; $L = 1/e$ **19.** Converges; $L = 0$ **20.** Converges; $L = 1$
21. Converges; $L = x$ **22.** Converges; $L = 1$ **23.** Converges; $L = 1$ **24.** Converges; $L = 0$ **25.** Converges; $L = 1$
26. Converges; $L = 4$ **27.** Converges; $L = 1/e$ **28.** Converges; $L = 1$ **29.** Converges; $L = 0$ **30.** Converges; $L = 1/(p - 1)$
31. $N \ge 693$ **32.** $N \ge 9124$ **33.** $N \ge 17$

Article 16–4, pp. 761–763

1. $s_n = \frac{1}{2} - (1/n + 2)$, $\lim_{n \to \infty} s_n = \frac{1}{2}$ **2.** $s_n = -\ln (n + 1)$, diverges **3.** $s_n = (1 - (1/e)^n)/(1 - (1/e))$, $\lim_{n \to \infty} s_n = e/(e - 1)$
4. $s_n = \frac{2}{3}(1 - (-1/2)^n)$, $\lim_{n \to \infty} s_n = \frac{2}{3}$ **5.** $s_n = \frac{1}{3}(1 - (-2)^n)$, diverges **6.** $s_n = 3(1 - (\frac{1}{3})^n)$, $\lim_{n \to \infty} s_n = 3$
7. $s_n = \frac{1}{11}(1 - (\frac{1}{100})^n)$, $\lim_{n \to \infty} s_n = \frac{1}{11}$ **8.** $s_n = n(n + 1)/2$, diverges
9. a) $\sum_{n=-2}^{\infty} 1/[(n + 4)(n + 5)]$ **b)** $\sum_{n=0}^{\infty} 1/[(n + 2)(n + 3)]$ **c)** $\sum_{n=5}^{\infty} 1/[(n - 3)(n - 2)]$ **10.** $28m$
11. $1 + \frac{1}{4} + \frac{1}{16} + \frac{1}{64}; \frac{4}{3}$ **12.** $\frac{1}{16} + \frac{1}{64} + \frac{1}{256} + \frac{1}{1024}; \frac{1}{12}$ **13.** $\frac{7}{4} + \frac{7}{16} + \frac{7}{64} + \frac{7}{256}; \frac{7}{3}$
14. $5 - \frac{5}{4} + \frac{5}{16} - \frac{5}{64}; 4$ **15.** 11.5 **16.** 8.5 **17.** 5/3 **18.** 10/3 **19.** 1 **20.** $\frac{1}{4}$ **21.** $\frac{1}{9}$ **22.** 1
23. a) 234/999 **b)** Yes; if $x = 0.a_1 a_2 \cdots a_n \overline{a_1 a_2 \cdots a_n}$, then $(10^n - 1)x = a_1 a_2 \cdots a_n = p$ is an integer and $x = p/q$ with $q = 10^n - 1$. **24.** 123999/99900 **25.** $2 + \sqrt{2}$ **26.** Diverges **27.** 1 **28.** Diverges **29.** Diverges **30.** 5/6 **31.** $e^2/(e^2 - 1)$
32. Diverges **33.** Diverges **34.** 2/9 **35.** 3/2 **36.** Diverges **37.** Diverges **38.** $x/(x - 1)$ **39.** $a = 1, r = -x$
40. $a = 1, r = -x^2$ **41.** 8 **42.** $s_n = (1 + (-1)^{n+1})/2$ **48. d)** $n \geq 6$ **e)** $n \geq 999$
49. a) $R_n = C_0 e^{-kt_0}(1 - e^{-nkt_0})/(1 - e^{-kt_0})$, $R = C_0(e^{-kt_0})/(1 - e^{-kt_0}) = C_0/(e^{kt_0} - 1)$
  b) $R_1 = 1/e \approx 0.368$, $R_{10} = R(1 - e^{-10}) \approx R(0.9999546) \approx 0.58195$; $R \approx 0.58198$; $0 < (R - R_{10})/R < 0.0001$.
  c) 7 **e)** 20 hr **f)** Give initial dose that produces a concentration of 2 mg/ml, followed every $100 \ln 2 \approx 69.31$ hr by dose that raises concentration by 1.5 mg/ml **g)** $5 \ln (10/3) \approx 6$ (hr)

Article 16–5, pp. 776–778

[*Note.* The tests mentioned in Problems 1–30 may not be the only ones that apply.]
1. Converges; ratio test; geometric series, $r < 1$. **2.** Diverges; $\lim_{n \to \infty} a_n = 1$ **3.** Converges; compare with $\sum (1/2^n)$
4. Diverges; multiple of $\sum (1/n)$ **5.** Converges; ratio test **6.** Converges; ratio test **7.** Diverges; compare with $\sum (1/n)$
8. Converges; p-series, $p > 1$ **9.** Converges; ratio test **10.** Diverges; integral test; multiple of $\sum_{n=1}^{\infty} (1/n)$
11. Diverges; compare with $\sum (1/n)$ **12.** Diverges; p-series, $p < 1$; integral test **13.** Diverges; ratio test
14. Converges; compare with $\sum (\frac{1}{3})^n$; root test **15.** Converges; ratio test (or root test) **16.** Diverges; p-series, $p < 1$
17. Converges; comparison with $\sum (1/n^{3/2})$ **18.** Diverges; nth-term test **19.** Converges; ratio test **20.** Converges; compare with $\sum (1/n^{3/2})$ **21.** Diverges; integral test **22.** Converges; ratio test (or root test) **23.** Diverges; nth-term test, $a_n \to e$
24. Converges; compare with $\sum (1/3^n)$ **25.** Converges; ratio test **26.** Diverges; integral test **27.** Converges; ratio test or comparison with $\sum (1/n!)$ **28.** Diverges; root test
29. Converges; ratio test **30.** Converges; ratio test; comparison to $\sum (1/2^n)$ **32.** $x^2 < 2$ **33.** $x^2 \leq 1$
34. $|x| > 1$ **35.** 1.649767731 **36.** $\sum_{n=1}^{6} (1/n^2) = 1.49138$, $\sum_{n=1}^{6} [3[(n - 1)!]^2/(2n)!] = 1.644911616$
37. $n = 27$, $s_n + n^{-3}/3 = 1.082324151$; $\pi^4/90 = 1.082323234$; difference $\approx 0.9 \times 10^{-6}$
38. $40.5548555 < s_n < 41.5548555$ **39.** $\sum (1/n)$ is divergent, as is any nonzero multiple of this series.

Article 16–6, p. 780

[*Note.* In the answers provided for this article, "Yes" means that the series converges absolutely. "No" means that the series does *not* converge absolutely. The reasons given for the convergence or divergence of the series of absolute values may not be the only appropriate ones.]
1. Yes; p-series, $p = 2$ **2.** Yes; p-series, $p = 3$ **3.** No; harmonic series divergence **4.** Yes; geometric series; $r < 1$
5. Yes; comparison to p-series, $p = 2$ **6.** No; multiple of harmonic series **7.** Yes: comparison to p-series, $p = \frac{3}{2}$ **8.** No; multiple of harmonic series **9.** Yes; comparison test **10.** Yes; comparison test **11.** No; nth-term test
12. Yes; root test or ratio test **13.** Yes; geometric series, $r < 1$ **14.** No; nth-term test **15.** Yes; ratio test
16. No; nth-term test **17.** Yes; compare with $(2 + n)/n^3$ **18.** Yes; compare with $(1/2^n) + (1/3^n)$

Article 16–7, pp. 785–786

1. Converges **2.** Converges **3.** Diverges **4.** Diverges **5.** Converges **6.** Converges **7.** Converges **8.** Diverges
9. Converges **10.** Diverges **11.** Absolutely convergent **12.** Conditionally convergent **13.** Absolutely convergent
14. Divergent **15.** Conditionally convergent **16.** Absolutely convergent **17.** Divergent **18.** Conditionally convergent
19. Conditionally convergent **20.** Absolutely convergent **21.** Absolutely convergent **22.** Divergent
23. Absolutely convergent **24.** Conditionally convergent **25.** Divergent **26.** Absolutely convergent **27.** Conditionally convergent **28.** Absolutely convergent **29.** $\frac{1}{5} = 0.2$ **30.** 10^{-5} **31.** $(0.01)^5/5 = 2 \times 10^{-11}$ **32.** t^4
33. 0.54030 (actual: $\cos 1 = 0.540302306$) **34.** 0.36788 (actual: $1/e = 0.367879441$)
35. a) It is not decreasing (condition 2) **b)** $-\frac{1}{2}$ **36.** $s_{20} + \frac{1}{2} \cdot \frac{1}{21} = 0.692580927$, $\ln 2 = 0.693147181$
39. $\sum_{n=1}^{\infty} a_n = \sum_{n=1}^{\infty} (-1)^n(1/\sqrt{n})$, $\sum_{n=1}^{\infty} b_n = \sum_{n=1}^{\infty} (-1)^n(1/\sqrt{n})$, $\sum_{n=1}^{\infty} a_n b_n = \sum_{n=1}^{\infty} (1/n)$

Article 16–8, p. 791

1. $1 - x + (x^2/2!) - (x^3/3!)$; $1 - x + (x^2/2!) - (x^3/3!) + (x^4/4!)$ **2.** $x - (x^3/3!)$; $x - (x^3/3!)$
3. $1 - (x^2/2!)$; $1 - (x^2/2!) + (x^4/4!)$ **4.** $1 - (x^2/2!)$; $1 - (x^2/2!) + (x^4/4!)$
5. $x + (x^3/3!)$; $x + (x^3/3!)$ **6.** $1 + (x^2/2!)$; $1 + (x^2/2!) + (x^4/4!)$ **7.** $-2x + 1$; $x^4 - 2x + 1$
8. $x^3 - 2x + 1$; $x^3 - 2x + 1$ **9.** $x^2 - 2x + 1$; $x^2 - 2x + 1$ **10.** $\sum_{n=0}^{\infty}(-1)^n x^n = 1 - x + x^2 - \cdots$ **11.** x^2 **12.** $x^2 + 2x + 1$
13. $1 + (3x/2) + (3/2 \cdot 4)x^2 - [3/(8 \cdot 3!)]x^3 + [9/(16 \cdot 4!)]x^4 - [45/(32 \cdot 5!)]x^5 + \cdots = \sum_{n=0}^{\infty}(3/n^2)x^n$
14. $1 + x + x^2 + x^3 + \cdots$; geometric series with $r = x$
15. $e^{10} + e^{10}(x - 10) + (e^{10}/2!)(x - 10)^2 + (e^{10}/3!)(x - 10)^3 + \cdots$ **16.** $\frac{1}{4} + (x - \frac{1}{2}) + (x - \frac{1}{2})^2$
17. $(x - 1) - [(x - 1)^2/2] + [(x - 1)^3/3] - [(x - 1)^4/4] + \cdots$
18. $2 + \frac{1}{2}(x - 4)/2 - [1/(2 \cdot 4)][(x - 4)^2/2^3] + [(1 \cdot 3)/(2 \cdot 4 \cdot 6)][(x - 4)^3/2^5] - [(1 \cdot 3 \cdot 5)/(2 \cdot 4 \cdot 6 \cdot 8)][(x - 4)^4/2^7]$
19. $-1 - (x + 1) - (x + 1)^2 - (x + 1)^3 - \cdots$ **20.** $(\sqrt{2}/2)[1 + (x + (\pi/4)) - [(x + (\pi/4))^2/2!] - [(x + (\pi/4))^3/3!] + \cdots]$
21. $1 + 2(x - (\pi/4)) + 2(x - (\pi/4))^2$ **22.** $\ln(0.5) - \sqrt{3}(x - (\pi/3)) - 2(x - (\pi/3))^2$
23. 1.0100 with error less than 0.0001 (use 2 terms)

Article 16–9, pp. 799–800

1. $1 + \frac{1}{2}x + \frac{1}{4}(x^2/2!) + \frac{1}{8}(x^3/3!) + \frac{1}{16}(x^4/4!) + \cdots$ **2.** $3x - 3^3(x^3/3!) + 3^5(x^5/5!) - 3^7(x^7/7!) + \cdots$
3. $5 - (5/\pi^2)(x^2/2!) + (5/\pi^4)(x^4/4!) - (5/\pi^6)(x^6/6!) + \cdots$ **4.** $x + (x^3/3!) + (x^5/5!) + (x^7/7!) + \cdots$
5. $(x^4/4!) - (x^6/6!) + (x^8/8!) - (x^{10}/10!) + \cdots$ **6.** $1 - x^2 + (8x^4/4!) - (32x^6/6!) + (128x^8/8!) - \cdots$
9. $1 - x + x^2 - 3\int_0^x (x - t)^2(1 + t)^{-11} dt$ **10.** $x - (x^2/2) + \int_0^x (x - t)^2(1 + t)^{-3} dt$
11. $1 + (x/2) - \frac{1}{8}x^2 + \frac{3}{16}\int_0^x (x - t)^2(1 + t)^{-(5/2)} dt$ **12.** $e[1 + (x - 1) + [(x - 1)^2/2!] + [(x - 1)^3/3!] + \cdots]$
13. $|x| < \sqrt[5]{0.06} \approx 0.57$ **14.** $|R| < 0.00261$. Too small.   **15.** $|R| < (10^{-9}/6)$; $x < \sin x$ for $x < 0$.
16. $|R| < 1.3 \times 10^{-5}$ **17.** $|R| < e^{0.1}/6{,}000 \approx 1.84 \times 10^{-4}$ **18.** $1.\overline{6} \times 10^{-4}$
19. $R_4(x, 0) < 0.0003$ **22. a)** $\sin 0.1$ **b)** $\cos(\pi/4)$ **c)** $\cosh 1$

Article 16–10, pp. 806–807

1. Use $\cos x \approx (\sqrt{3}/2) - \frac{1}{2}(x - (\pi/6))$. $\cos 31° \approx 0.857\,299$.   Actual: $\cos 31° = 0.857\,167$.
2. Use $\tan x \approx 1 + 2(x - (\pi/4)) + 4[(x - (\pi/4))^2/2!]$. $\tan 46° \approx 1.035\,516$.   Actual: $\tan 46° = 1.035\,530$.
3. Use $\sin x \approx (x - 2\pi)$. $\sin(6.3) \approx 0.0168\,147$.   Actual: $\sin(6.3) = 0.0168\,139$.
4. Use $\cos x \approx 1 - [(x - 22\pi)^2/2!]$. $\cos 69 \approx 0.993\,383$.   Actual: $\cos 69 = 0.993\,390$.
5. Use $\ln x \approx (x - 1) - [(x - 1)^2/2] + [(x - 1)^3/3] - [(x - 1)^4/4]$. $\ln 1.25 \approx 0.222\,982$.   Actual: $\ln 1.25 = 0.223\,144$.
6. Use $\tan^{-1} x \approx (\pi/4) + \frac{1}{2}(x - 1)$. $\tan^{-1} 1.02 \approx 0.795\,398$.   Actual: $\tan^{-1} 1.02 = 0.795\,299$.
7. $\ln(1 + 2x) = 2x - [(2x)^2/2] + [(2x)^3/3] - [(2x)^4/4] + \cdots = \sum_{n=1}^{\infty}(-1)^{n+1}[(2x)^n/n]$; converges for $|x| < \frac{1}{2}$.
8. $|x| < 0.0197$ **9.** $\int_0^{0.1}[(\sin x)/x]\,dx \approx x - (x^3/18)]_0^{0.1} \approx 0.09994$
10. $\int_0^{0.1} e^{-x^2}\,dx \approx x - (x^3/3)]_0^{0.1} = 0.09967$ **13.** $\ln 1.5 \approx 0.405\,465$ **14.** 50 terms (through $\frac{1}{99}$)
17. $c_3 = 3.141592665$ **21. c)** 6   **d)** $1/q$ **22. a)** $E(x) = 2$ **b)** $E(x) = 6$ **c)** The series for $E(x)$ diverges.

Article 16–11, pp. 811–812

2. Minimum at $x = 1$, $y = -2$ **3.** Saddle point at $x = 1$, $y = 2$ **4.** Minimum at $x = 1$, $y = 0$
5. Saddle point at $x = 0$, $y = 0$ **6.** Maximum at $x = 0$, $y = 1$ **7.** Saddle point $(0, 0, 6)$; relative max $(-\frac{2}{3}, \frac{2}{3}, 6 + \frac{8}{27})$
8. Saddle points $(0, 0, -8)$, $(-2, 2, -8)$; relative max $(-2, 0, -4)$; relative min $(0, 2, -12)$
9. If $f_x(a, b) = f_y(a, b) = 0$, then $f(x, y)$ has, at the point $x = a$, $y = b$,   **a)** a relative minimum if d^2f/ds^2 is positive in all directions emanating from (a, b);   **b)** a relative maximum if d^2f/ds^2 is negative in all directions emanating from (a, b); and   **c)** a saddle point if d^2f/ds^2 is positive in some directions and negative in other directions emanating from (a, b).   **10.** $1 + x + [(x^2 - y^2)/2!] + \cdots$
11. $f(x, y, z) = f(a, b, c) + f_x(a, b, c) \cdot (x - a) + f_y(a, b, c) \cdot (y - b) + f_z(a, b, c) \cdot (z - c) + (1/2!)[f_{xx}(a, b, c) \cdot (x - a)^2$
$+ f_{yy}(a, b, c) \cdot (y - b)^2 + f_{zz}(a, b, c) \cdot (z - c)^2$
$+ 2f_{xy}(a, b, c) \cdot (x - a)(y - b) + 2f_{xz}(a, b, c) \cdot (x - a)(z - c) + 2f_{yz}(a, b, c) \cdot (y - b)(z - c)] + \cdots$

Article 16–12, p. 814

1. 1   **2.** $\frac{1}{2}$ **3.** $-\frac{1}{24}$ **4.** 1   **5.** -2 **6.** $\frac{1}{3}$ **7.** 0   **8.** 1   **9.** $-\frac{1}{3}$ **10.** -1 **11.** $\frac{1}{120}$ **12.** 2   **13.** $\frac{1}{3}$
14. $\frac{1}{2}$ **15.** -1 **16.** 2   **17.** 3   **18.** 2   **19.** 0   **20.** $\frac{1}{12}$ **21. b)** $\frac{1}{2}$ **22.** $r = -3$, $s = \frac{9}{2}$

23. This approximation gives better results than the approximation $\sin x \approx x$. See table.

x	± 1.0	± 0.1	± 0.01
$6x/(6 + x^2)$	± 0.857142857	± 0.099833611	± 0.009999833
$\sin x$	± 0.841470985	± 0.099833417	± 0.009999833

Article 16–13, pp. 822–823

1. $|x| < 1$. Diverges at $x = \pm 1$ 2. $|x| < 1$. Diverges at $x = \pm 1$ 3. $|x| < 2$. Diverges at $x = \pm 2$
4. $-\infty < x < \infty$ 5. $-\infty < x < \infty$ 6. $0 < x < 2$. Converges at $x = 2$; diverges at 0
7. $-4 < x < 0$. Diverges at $x = 0, -4$ 8. $|x| < 1$. Diverges at $x = \pm 1$ 9. $|x| < 1$. Converges at $x = \pm 1$
10. $1 \le x \le 3$ 11. $|x| < \infty$ 12. $|x| \le \frac{1}{2}$ 13. $|x| < (1/e)$. Converges at $x = -(1/e)$; diverges at $(1/e)$
14. $|x| < \infty$ 15. $x = 0$ 16. $|x| < \infty$ 17. $\frac{1}{2} < x < \frac{3}{2}$. Diverges at $x = \frac{1}{2}, \frac{3}{2}$
18. $0 < x < 4$. Converges at $x = 4$; diverges at 0 19. $|x| < \sqrt{3}$. Diverges at $x = \pm \sqrt{3}$
20. $-4 < x < -2$. Converges at $x = -4$; diverges at -2 21. e^{3x+6} 22. $2/(3 - x^2)$
24. $1 - 2x + 3x^2 - 4x^3 + \cdots = \sum_{n=0}^{\infty} (-1)^n(n + 1)x^n$ 25. $\sum_{n=1}^{\infty} 2nx^{2n-1}$
26. $\sin^2 x = \frac{1}{2}([(2x)^2/2!] - [(2x)^4/4!] + \cdots)$, $(d/dx)(\sin^2 x) = 2 \sin x \cos x = (2x/1!) - [(2x)^3/3!] + \cdots = \sin 2x$
27. 0.002666 28. 0.004992 29. 0.000331 30. 0.099889 31. 0.363305 32. 0.097605 33. 0.099999 34. 0.251715
35. a) $\sinh^{-1} x = x - \frac{1}{2}(x^3/3) + [(1 \cdot 3)/(2 \cdot 4)](x^5/5) - [(1 \cdot 3 \cdot 5)/(2 \cdot 4 \cdot 6)](x^7/7) + \cdots$
   b) $\sinh^{-1} 0.25 \approx 0.247$ (Actual: $\sinh^{-1} 0.25 = \ln(0.25 + \sqrt{(0.25)^2 + 1}) \approx 0.24746646$)
36. 0.904531532 37. $\sum_{n=1}^{\infty} n^n x^n$ 38. $\sum_{n=1}^{\infty} (x^n/n)$; conditional at $x = -1$; $\sum_{n=1}^{\infty} (x^n/n^2)$; absolute at $x = \pm 1$
39. By the theorem, the series converges absolutely for $|x| < d$, for all positive $d < r$. This means it converges absolutely for all $|x| < r$. [Take $d = \frac{1}{2}(r + |x|)$.]
40. $|a_{n+1}/a_n| = |x_{m-n}/n|$; $\lim_{n \to \infty} |a_{n+1}/a_n| = |x|$. So the series converges for $|x| < 1$.

Miscellaneous Problems Chapter 16, pp. 824–825

1. $s_n = \ln[(n + 1)/(2n)]$; series converges to $-\ln 2$ 2. $s_n = \frac{1}{2}[\frac{3}{2} - 1/(n + 1)]$; limit $= \frac{3}{4}$
6. a) $\sum_{n=2}^{\infty} (-1)^n x^n$ b) No, because it will converge in an interval symmetric about $x = 0$, and it cannot converge when $x = -1$.
7. $(1 - t^2)^{-(1/2)} = \sum_{k=0}^{\infty} 2^{-2k}(k!)^{-2}(2k)! \, t^{2k}$, $-1 < t < 1$, $\sin^{-1} x = \sum_{k=0}^{\infty} 2^{-2k}(k!)^{-2}(2k)! \, x^{2k+1}/(2k + 1)$, $-1 \le x \le 1$
8. $(1 + t^2)^{-(1/2)} = \sum_{k=0}^{\infty} (-1)^k 2^{-2k}(k!)^{-2}(2k)! \, t^{2k}$, $-1 \le t \le 1$,
   $\sinh^{-1} x = \sum_{k=0}^{\infty} (-1)^k 2^{-2k}(k!)^{-2}(2k)! \, x^{2k+1}/(2k + 1)$, $-1 \le x \le 1$
9. $e^{\sin x} = 1 + x + x^2/2! - 3x^4/4! - \cdots$ 11. a) $\ln \cos x = -(x^2/2) - (x^4/12) - (x^6/45) - \cdots$ b) -0.00017 12. 0.946
13. 0.747 14. $\sqrt{2}[1 + (x - 1)/2 + (x - 1)^2/8 + \cdots]$ 15. $\sum_{n=0}^{\infty} (-1)^{n+1}(x - 2)^n$, $1 < x < 3$
16. $\tan x = x + x^3/3 + 2x^5/15 + \cdots$ 17. $\sum_{n=0}^{\infty} [(-1)^n(x - 3)^n/4^{n+1}]$
18. $\cos x = \frac{1}{2} \sum_{n=0}^{\infty} (-1)^n[1/(2n)! \, (x - (\pi/3))^{2n} + \sqrt{3}/(2n + 1)! \, (x - (\pi/3))^{2n+1}]$ 19. $\sum_{n=0}^{\infty} (-1)^n(x - \pi)^n/\pi^{n+1}$ 20. 1.543
22. $e^{e^x} = e(1 + x + 2x^2/2! + 5x^3/3! + \cdots$ 23. 0.0027 24. -0.0011 25. $-\infty$ 26. $e^{-(1/6)}$
27. Converges; by integral test 28. Diverges, since nth term doesn't approach zero
29. Converges 30. Diverges 31. Diverges 32. Converges 33. Diverges 34. Diverges 35. Converges 36. Converges
37. Diverges 38. Diverges 39. Diverges 40. Converges 41. $\frac{1}{2}$
43. b) Converges c) Converges, by comparison test 45. $-5 \le x < 1$ 46. $-\infty < x < \infty$ 47. $-\infty < x < \infty$
48. $-e < x < e$ 49. $1 < x < 5$ 50. $-1 < x < 5$ 51. $0 \le x \le 2$ 52. $-1 \le x < 1$ 53. $-\infty < x < \infty$
54. $(6n - 1)\pi/6 \le x \le (6n + 1)\pi/6$ $(n = 0, \pm 1, \pm 2, \ldots)$ 55. $x \ge \frac{1}{2}$ 56. a) $-\infty < x < \infty$ b) $y'' = xy$ $(a = 1, b = 0)$

CHAPTER 17

Article 17–1, p. 832

1. a) $(14, 8)$ b) $(-1, 8)$ c) $(0, -5)$ 2. a) $(-\frac{7}{3}, -24)$ b) $(\frac{2}{5}, -\frac{1}{5})$ c) $(-1, 0)$

Article 17–2, p. 838

2. a) By reflecting z across the real axis b) By reflecting z across the imaginary axis c) By reflecting z in the origin
   d) By reflecting z in the real axis and then multiplying the length of the vector by $1/|z|^2$ 6. On the real axis

9. a) Points on the circle $x^2 + y^2 = 4$ **b)** Points inside the circle $x^2 + y^2 = 4$ **c)** Points outside the circle $x^2 + y^2 = 4$
10. Points on a circle of radius 2, center $(1, 0)$ **11.** Points on a circle of radius 1, center $(-1, 0)$
12. Points on the y-axis   **13.** Points on the line $y = -x$ **14.** 4 cis $(2\pi/3)$ **15.** 1 cis $(\pi/2)$ **16.** 1 cis $(2\pi/3)$
17. $\sqrt{65}$ cis $(-\tan^{-1} 0.125) = \sqrt{65}$ cis $(-7°7.5')$
18. $\cos 4\theta = \cos^4 \theta - 6 \cos^2 \theta \sin^2 \theta + \sin^4 \theta,$ $\sin 4\theta = 4 \sin \theta \cos \theta(\cos^2 \theta - \sin^2 \theta)$
19. 1, cis $(2\pi/3) = (-1 + i\sqrt{3})/2$, cis $(-2\pi/3) = (-1 - i\sqrt{3})/2$ **20.** cis $(\pi/4, 5\pi/4) = \pm$cis $(\pi/4) = \pm(1 + i)/\sqrt{2}$
21. $2i$, 2 cis $(-5\pi/6) = -\sqrt{3} - i$, 2 cis $(-\pi/6) = \sqrt{3} - i$
22. 2 cis $(0°, 60°, 120°, 180°, 240°, 300°)$; that is, 2, $1 + i\sqrt{3}$, $-1 + i\sqrt{3}$, -2, $-1 - i\sqrt{3}$, $1 - i\sqrt{3}$
23. $\pm\sqrt{2}$ cis $(\pm 30°)$; that is, $(\sqrt{3} + i)/\sqrt{2}$, $-(\sqrt{3} + i)/\sqrt{2}$, $(\sqrt{3} - i)/\sqrt{2}$, $(-\sqrt{3} + i)/\sqrt{2}$
24. $\sqrt[6]{2}$ cis $(45°, 165°, 285°, 75°, 195°, 315°)$ **25.** 2 cis $(60°, 120°, 240°, 300°)$; or $1 \pm i\sqrt{3}$, $-1 \pm i\sqrt{3}$
26. cis $(45°, 135°, 225°, 315°)$; or $(1 \pm i)/\sqrt{2}$, $(-1 \pm i)/\sqrt{2}$

Article 17–3, p. 841

1. a) $|w| = 1$, $0 \le \arg w \le 2\pi$ **b)** $|w| = 4$, $\pi \le \arg w \le 2\pi$ **c)** $\arg w = \pi/2$ **d)** $|w| < 1$, $-2\pi < \arg w \le 0$
    e) The u-axis, $u \ge 0$ **f)** The u-axis, $u \le 0$

Article 17–4, p. 844

1. $-2/(z_0 - 1)^2 = +2$ **2.** $3(z_0 + 1)^2 = -12$ **3.** $z_0/\sqrt{z_0^2 + 1} = 2^{-(1/4)}$ cis $(\pi/8, 9\pi/8)$ **4.** $-1/\alpha^2$

Article 17–5, p. 846

1. $u = x^2 - y^2$, $v = 2xy$ **2.** $u = x^3 - 3xy^2$, $v = 3x^2y - y^3$ **3.** $u = x^4 - 6x^2y^2 + y^4$, $v = 4x^3y - 4xy^3$
4. $u = (x^2 - y^2)/(x^2 + y^2)^2$, $v = -2xy/(x^2 + y^2)^2$

Article 17–6, p. 848

1. $1 + z + z^2 + z^3 + \cdots$, $|z| < 1$ **2.** $1 - 2z + 3z^2 - 4z^3 + \cdots$, $|z| < 1$
3. $(z - 1) - [(z - 1)^2/2] + [(z - 1)^3/3] - [(z - 1)^4/4] + \cdots$, $|z - 1| < 1$
4. $(z + i) + [(z + i)^2/2] + [(z + i)^3/3] + [(z + i)^4/4] + \cdots$, $|z + i| < 1$
5. $1 - [(z + 1)/2] + [(z + 1)^2/4] - [(z + 1)^3/8] + [(z + 1)^4/16] - \cdots$, $|z + 1| < 2$

Article 17–7, p. 853

1. $1.59 + 1.32i$ **5. a)** $-1 \pm 2i$ **b)** $1 \pm i$, $-1 \pm i$ **c)** 2, $-1 \pm i\sqrt{3}$
18. a) The circle $u^2 + v^2 = e^{2x}$, described once in the counterclockwise direction each time y increases through a 2π interval of
    values; for instance, $-\pi < y \le \pi$, etc.   **b)** The branch of the hyperbola $[u^2/(\sin^2 x)] - [v^2/(\cos^2 x)] = 1$ (x not an integer
    multiple of $\pi/2$) on which u and $\sin x$ have the same sign. The lines $x = n\pi(n = 0, \pm 1, \ldots)$ map into the v-axis. The lines
    $x = \pi/2 + 2n\pi(n = 0, \pm 1, \ldots)$ map into the u-axis, $u \ge 1$. The lines $x = -\pi/2 + 2n\pi(n = 0, \pm 1, \ldots)$ map into the u-axis,
    $u \le -1$.
19. $\int e^{ax} \cos bx \, dx = [e^{ax}/(a^2 + b^2)](a \cos bx + b \sin bx) + C,$ $\int e^{ax} \sin bx \, dx = [e^{ax}/(a^2 + b^2)](a \sin bx - b \cos bx) + C$

Article 17–8, p. 855

1. a) $\ln (2^{3/2}) - i(\pi/4)$ **b)** $\ln 2 + i(\pi/6)$ **c)** $\ln 4 + i\pi$ **d)** $\ln 4$ **e)** $\ln 2 + i(\pi/2)$ **f)** $i(\pi/2)$
2. a) $\ln 2 + 2n\pi i$ **b)** $\ln 2 + (2n + 1)\pi i$ **c)** $\ln 2 + (2n + \frac{1}{2})\pi i$ **d)** $\ln 2 + (2n - \frac{1}{2})\pi i$ **e)** $\ln 2 + (2n + \frac{5}{6})\pi i$ $(n = 0, \pm 1, \pm 2, \ldots)$
4. b) $((\pi/2) + 2n\pi) - i \ln (3 + 2\sqrt{2})$
5. a) The image is a straight line segment joining the points $(\ln |z|, -\pi)$ and $(\ln |z|, +\pi)$.   **b)** The image is the line $v = \arg z$,
    parallel to the real axis.

Miscellaneous Problems Chapter 17, pp. 855–856

1. $z = 2 - 2i$, $\bar{z} = 2 + 2i$, $z^2 = -8i$; 2 cis $(-\pi/6)$, 2 cis $(\pi/2)$, 2 cis $(7\pi/6)$
2. a) $r = 4\sqrt{2}$, $\theta = -\tan^{-1} (2 + \sqrt{3})$ **b)** $r = \sqrt{2}$, $\theta = -\pi/12$, $7\pi/12$, $15\pi/12$
3. a) $\pm(\sqrt{2 + \sqrt{2}} - i\sqrt{2 - \sqrt{2}})$, $\pm(\sqrt{2 - \sqrt{2}} + i\sqrt{2 + \sqrt{2}})$ **b)** $\sin^{-1} 5 = 2n\pi + \pi/2 - i \ln (5 + \sqrt{24})$, $(n = 0, \pm 1, \pm 2, \ldots)$
4. a) $\pm\sqrt{2}(1 + i)$, $\pm\sqrt{2}(1 - i)$ **b)** $2e^{i(2n\pi + \pi)/5}$ $(n = 0, 1, 2, 3, 4)$
5. a) $2^{1/4}e^{i\pi(2 + 3n)/6}$ $(n = 0, 1, 2, 3)$ **b)** $e^2/\sqrt{2} + i(e^2/\sqrt{2})$ **6. a)** $\pm(\sqrt{3} - i)$ **b)** $\ln 4 - i\pi/3$ **7.** $r = 5$, $\theta = \tan^{-1} \frac{4}{3}$
8. $\ln (3\sqrt{2}) + i(2n\pi - \pi/4)$ (n any integer)   **9.** $\ln 2 - i\pi/3$

10. a) $2^{1/3}(-1-i)$, $2^{5/6}(\sqrt{2+\sqrt{3}} - i\sqrt{2-\sqrt{3}})$, $2^{-(5/6)}(-\sqrt{2-\sqrt{3}} + i\sqrt{2+\sqrt{3}})$
b) $\ln(3\sqrt{2}) + i(2n\pi + \pi/4)$ (n any integer) **c)** $-e^2$ **11. b)** Derivative doesn't exist.
19. a) $2e^{i2n\pi/5}$ ($n = 0, 1, 2, 3, 4$) **b)** $\ln 2 + (2n+1)\pi i$ (n any integer)
c) $2n\pi \pm i \cosh^{-1}(10)$, or $2n\pi + i \ln(10 \pm 3\sqrt{11})$ (n any integer) **d)** $\ln\sqrt{3} + (2n+1)\pi i/2$ (n any integer)
e) $e^{-(4n+1)\pi/2}$ (n any integer) **f)** -3, $\pm i\sqrt{3}$

CHAPTER 18

Article 18–3, pp. 861–862

1. $(x^2+1)(2y-3) = C$ **2.** $2/3\sqrt{x^3+1} + \frac{1}{2}\ln(y^2+1) = C$ **3.** $e^y = e^x + C$ **4.** $y^{3/2} = 3\sqrt{x/2} + C$
5. $\sinh 2y - 2\cos x = C$ **6.** $\frac{1}{2}(\ln|x|)^2 = \ln|y| + C$ **7.** $(y-1)e^y + (x^2/2) + \ln|x| = C$ **8.** $\sqrt{2x^2+3} - 2\sqrt{4-y^2} = C$
9. $\cosh^{-1} y + \sinh^{-1} x = C$ **10.** $-y\cos y + \sin y = -x^{-1} + \ln|x| + C$ **11.** $2^{48} \approx 2.815 \times 10^{14}$ **12.** $Q = Q_0 e^{kt}$
13. $i = (E/R)(1 - e^{-Rt/L})$, E/R **15. a)** $(\ln 2)/5700 \approx 1.216 \times 10^{-4}$ **b)** 18,935 years **c)** 6,658 years

Article 18–4, p. 864

1. $x^2(x^2+2y^2) = C$ **2.** $x/y = \ln|x| + C$ **3.** $\ln|x| + e^{-(y/x)} = C$ **4.** $2\tan^{-1}(y/x) + \ln(x^2+y^2) = C$
5. $\ln|x| - \ln|\sec((y/x)-1) + \tan((y/x)-1)| = C$ **6.** $x \sin(y/x) = C$
7. $\ln((x+2)^2 + (y-1)^2) + 2\tan^{-1}((x+2)/(y-1)) = C$, $a = -2$, $b = 1$ **8.** $\tan^{-1}(x+y) = x + C$
9. a) $x^2 = yC$ **b)** $x^2 + 2y^2 = C$ **10. a)** $x^2 + y^2 = Cx$ **b)** $x^2 + y^2 = Cy$ **11.** $x^2 - y^2 = C$

Article 18–5, p. 866

1. $y = e^{-x} + Ce^{-2x}$ **2.** $y = \frac{1}{2}(x+C)e^{x/2}$ **3.** $x^3y = C - \cos x$ **4.** $xy = C - \cos x$ **5.** $x = (y/2) + (C/y)$
6. $(x-1)^4 y = (x^3/3) - x + C$ **7.** $y\cosh x = C - e^x$ **8.** $xe^{2y} = y^2 + C$ **9.** $xy = y^2 + C$ **10.** $x = (C-y)/(1+y^2)$
11. a) $C = G/100kV + (C_0 - G/100kV)e^{-kt}$ **b)** $G/100kV$

Article 18–6, p. 868

1. $y = Cx^2 - x$ **2.** $xy = C$ **3.** $y = Cx$ **4.** $(x^2/2) + xy + (y^3/3) = C$ **5.** $e^x + e^y(x^2+1) = C$ **6.** $x^2y + xy^2 - (y^2/2) = C$
7. $x^2 + 2x\sqrt{y^2+1} - y^2 = C$ **8.** $2y + x^3 = Cx$ **9.** $y = x\tan(x+C)$ **10.** $y = x(C - x - \ln|x|)$
11. $e^x + x\ln y + y\ln x - \cos y = C$ **12.** $y^2\tan^{-1} x - 2xy + \cosh y = C$ **13.** $xy + \cos x = C$

Article 18–7, p. 870

1. $y = C_1 e^{-x} + C_2$ **2.** $y = C$, or $y = -2a\tan(ax+C)$, or $y = 2a\tanh(ax+C)$, or $y = 2/(x+C)$
3. $y = C_1\int e^{-x^2/2}\,dx + C_2$. Note that the integral appearing here could be evaluated as an infinite series, giving
$y = C_1[x - [x^3/(2 \cdot 3)] + [x^5/(2 \cdot 4 \cdot 5)] - [x^7/(2 \cdot 4 \cdot 6 \cdot 7)] + \cdots] + C_2$
4. $y = C_1\ln|x| + C_2$ **5.** $y = C_1\sinh(x+C_2)$ **6.** $y = C_1\sin(\omega x + C_2)$ **7.** $y = C_1 x^4 + C_2 x + C_3$
8. $y = -2\ln|e^{-x/2} - C_1 e^{x/2}| + C_2$; or $x = \pm\ln|(u-1)/(u+1)| + C_2$, where $u = (1 + C_1 e^y)^{1/2}$
9. $x = A\sin(\sqrt{k/m}\,t + (\pi/2)) = A\cos(\sqrt{k/m}\,t)$
10. $s = (m^2g/k^2)[(kt/m) + e^{-kt/m} - 1]$, where m is the man's mass, g is the acceleration due to gravity, and k is the factor of proportionality in the air resistance $-kv$ (v being velocity).

Article 18–9, p. 874

1. $y = C_1 + C_2 e^{-2x}$ **2.** $y = C_1 e^{-2x} + C_2 e^{-3x}$ **3.** $y = C_1 e^{-x} + C_2 e^{-5x}$ **4.** $y = C_1 e^{3x} + C_2 e^{-x}$
5. $v = e^{-x/2}[C_1\cos(x\sqrt{3}/2) + C_2\sin(x\sqrt{3}/2)]$ **6.** $y = (C_1 + C_2 x)e^{2x}$ **7.** $y = (C_1 + C_2 x)e^{-3x}$
8. $y = e^{3x}(C_1\cos x + C_2\sin x)$ **9.** $y = e^x(C_1\cos\sqrt{3}x + C_2\sin\sqrt{3}x)$ **10.** $y = C_1 e^{2x} + C_2 e^{8x}$

Article 18–10, p. 877

1. $y = (x^2/2) - x + C_1 + C_2 e^{-x}$ **2.** $y = \cos x \sinh^{-1}(\tan x) + C_1\cos x + C_2\sin x$
3. $y = -\frac{1}{2}x\cos x + C_1\cos x + C_2\sin x$
4. $y = \frac{1}{4}e^x + e^{-x}(C_1 + C_2 x)$ **5.** $y = e^{-x}(C_1 + C_2 x + \frac{1}{2}x^2)$ **6.** $y = C_1 e^x + C_2 e^{-x} - x$ **7.** $y = C_1 e^x + C_2 e^{-x} + (x/2)e^x$
8. $y = C_1 e^x + C_2 e^{-x} - \frac{1}{2}\sin x$ **9.** $y = e^{-2x}(C_1\cos x + C_2\sin x) + 2$ **10.** $y = e^{-2x}(C_1\cos x + C_2\sin x) + \frac{1}{5}x + \frac{6}{25}$
11. $y = 1 - e^{-x}$ **12.** $y = [x^2 + 2x + 2 + Ce^x]^{-1}$

Article 18–11, p. 878

1. $y = C_1 + C_2 e^x + C_3 e^{2x}$ **2.** $y = C_1 e^x + e^{-x/2}[C_2 \cos (x\sqrt{3}/2) + C_3 \sin (x\sqrt{3}/2)]$

3. $y = (C_1 + C_2 x)e^{\sqrt{2}x} + (C_3 + C_4 x)e^{-\sqrt{2}x}$ **4.** $y = C_1 e^{2x} + C_2 e^{-2x} + C_3 \cos 2x + C_4 \sin 2x$

5. $y = e^{\sqrt{2}x}(C_1 \cos \sqrt{2}x + C_2 \sin \sqrt{2}x) + e^{-\sqrt{2}x}(C_3 \cos \sqrt{2}x + C_4 \sin \sqrt{2}x)$

6. $y = e^x((x^2/6) + C_1 x + C_2) + C_3 e^{-2x}$ **7.** $y = (C_1 + C_2 x + C_3 x^2 + C_4 x^3)e^x + 7$

8. $y = e^{x/\sqrt{2}}(C_1 \cos (x/\sqrt{2}) + C_2 \sin (x/\sqrt{2})) + e^{-x/\sqrt{2}}(C_3 \cos (x/\sqrt{2}) + C_4 \sin (x/\sqrt{2})) + x + 1$

Article 18–12, pp. 882–883

1. $x = x_0 \cos \omega t + (v_0/\omega) \sin \omega t = \sqrt{x_0^2 + (v_0^2/\omega^2)} \sin (\omega t + \phi)$, where $\omega = \sqrt{k/m}$, $\phi = \tan^{-1} (\omega x_0/v_0)$

2. $x = 0.288 \sin (13.9t)$; x in feet, t in sec

3. a) $I = C_1 \cos \omega t + C_2 \sin \omega t$ **b)** $I = C_1 \cos \omega t + C_2 \sin \omega t + (A\alpha/L(\omega^2 - \alpha^2)) \cos \alpha t$

   c) $I = C_1 \cos \omega t + C_2 \sin \omega t + (A/2L)t \sin \omega t$ **d)** $I = e^{-5t}(C_1 \cos 149t + C_2 \sin 149t)$

4. $\theta = \theta_0 \cos (\sqrt{g/\ell}\, t)$ **5.** $\theta = \theta_0 \cos \omega t + (v_0/\omega) \sin \omega t$, where $\omega = \sqrt{2k/mr^2}$ **6.** $C = 5.1$ lb sec/ft.

7. a) $x = C_1 \cos \omega t + C_2 \sin \omega t + (\omega^2 A/(\omega^2 - \alpha^2)) \sin \alpha t$, where $\omega = \sqrt{k/m}$

   b) $x = C_1 \cos \omega t + C_2 \sin \omega t - (\omega A/2)t \cos \omega t$, with $\omega = \sqrt{k/m}$

Article 18–13, pp. 889–890

3. Min at $t = 0$; max at $\lambda t = 2$; inflection points at $\lambda t = 2 - \sqrt{2}, 2 + \sqrt{2}$.   **5. a)** $e^{-10} = 0.000045$ **b)** $1 - e^{-4} = 0.9817$

6. a) 0.67 **b)** 0.33 **c)** 0.98 **7. a)** 10 **b)** $e^{-10} \sum_{n=0}^{5} [(10)^n/n!] \approx 0.067$

8. a) 0.270 **b)** 0.180 **c)** 0.368 **d)** 0.073 **9.** 0.195

Miscellaneous Problems Chapter 18, pp. 890–891

1. $\ln (C \ln y) = -\tan^{-1} x$ **2.** $y = [Cx^3 + 2(x + 1)^3][(x + 1)^3 - Cx^3]^{-1}$ **3.** $y = \ln (C - \tfrac{1}{3}e^{-3x})$ **4.** $ky + \sqrt{k^2y^2 - 1} = Ce^{kx}$

5. $y^2 + \sqrt{y^4 + 1} = Ce^{2x}$ **6.** $x^2 + xy - y^2 = C$ **7.** $y^2 = x^2 + Cx$ **8.** $y + \sqrt{x^2 + y^2} = Cx^2$ **9.** $y = x \tan^{-1} (\ln Cx)$

10. $y = xe^{\sqrt{2 \ln Cx}}$ **11.** $y = (x^2 + 2)/4 + Cx^{-2}$ **12.** $y - x \sec y = C$ **13.** $y = \cosh x \ln (C \cosh x)$

14. $y = \tfrac{1}{6}(2x^3 + 3x^2 + C)(x + 1)^{-2}$ **15.** $y^3 + 3xy^2 + 3(x + y) = C$ **16.** $x^3 + 3xy + 3e^y = C$ **17.** $x^3 + 3xy^2 + 3 \sinh y = C$

18. $e^x + x \ln y + y = C$ **19.** $x^2 + e^y(x^2 + y^2 - 2y + 2) = C$ **20.** $2x \tan^{-1} (y/x) + y \ln (x^2 + y^2) - 2 \cos x - (y + 1)^2 = C$

21. $y = C$, or $y = a \tan (ax + C)$, or $y = -a \tanh (ax + C)$, or $y = -1/(x + C)$ **22.** $x = C_1 \cos 2y + C_2 \sin 2y$

23. $y = -\ln |\cos (x + C)| + D$ **24.** $x = \pm(y + C)$, or $x + C_2 = \ln \cosh (y + C_1)$, or $x + C_2 = \ln \sinh (y + C_1)$

25. $y = \tfrac{1}{2}(\ln Cx)^2 + D$ **26.** $y = C_1 e^x + C_2 e^{3x}$ **27.** $y = C_1 + (C_2 x + C_3)e^x$ **28.** $y = C_1 \sin 2x + C_2 \cos 2x + (x/2) \sin 2x + \tfrac{1}{4} \cos 2x \ln \cos 2x$ **29.** $y = C_1 e^{-x} + (C_2 + x/3)e^{2x}$ **30.** $y = e^x(C_1 \cos 2x + C_2 \sin 2x) + \tfrac{1}{8}e^{-x}$ **31.** $y = C_1\sqrt{x} + C_2/\sqrt{x}$

33. $\tfrac{3}{2}x^2 + y^2 = D$ **34.** $x^2 + (y - D)^2 = D^2$ **35.** $y^2 = D^2 + 2Dx$ **36.** $y = 10 \cos 10t + 5 \sin 10t$

APPENDIX

Article A–1, pp. A–3 to A–4

1. $\begin{bmatrix} 2 & -3 & 4 \\ 6 & 4 & -2 \\ 1 & 5 & 4 \end{bmatrix} \begin{bmatrix} x \\ y \\ z \end{bmatrix} = \begin{bmatrix} -19 \\ 8 \\ 23 \end{bmatrix}$ **3.** $\begin{bmatrix} a_{21} & a_{22} & a_{23} \\ a_{11} & a_{12} & a_{13} \\ a_{31} & a_{32} & a_{33} \end{bmatrix}$ **4.** $\begin{bmatrix} a_{12} & a_{11} & a_{13} \\ a_{22} & a_{21} & a_{23} \\ a_{32} & a_{31} & a_{33} \end{bmatrix}$

Article A–2, p. A–8

1. a) $\begin{bmatrix} -3 & 2 \\ 2 & -1 \end{bmatrix}$ **b)** $\begin{bmatrix} 1 & -1 & \tfrac{1}{3} \\ 0 & \tfrac{1}{2} & -\tfrac{2}{3} \\ 0 & 0 & \tfrac{1}{3} \end{bmatrix}$ **3. a)** $\begin{bmatrix} \tfrac{1}{5} & \tfrac{1}{5} \\ -\tfrac{3}{5} & \tfrac{2}{5} \end{bmatrix}$ **b)** $\begin{bmatrix} \tfrac{1}{5} & -\tfrac{3}{5} \\ \tfrac{1}{5} & \tfrac{2}{5} \end{bmatrix}$.   Yes.

4. $x = -2, y = 5, z = 0$ **5.** $x = \tfrac{12}{5} + \tfrac{1}{5}z, y = -\tfrac{1}{5} + \tfrac{12}{5}z$

Article A–3, p. A–11

1. a) $2 \cdot \begin{vmatrix} 0 & 3 \\ 2 & 1 \end{vmatrix} + 1 \cdot \begin{vmatrix} 1 & 3 \\ 0 & 1 \end{vmatrix} + 2 \cdot \begin{vmatrix} 1 & 0 \\ 0 & 2 \end{vmatrix} = -7$ **b)** $1 \cdot \begin{vmatrix} 1 & 3 \\ 0 & 1 \end{vmatrix} + 0 \cdot \begin{vmatrix} 2 & 2 \\ 0 & 1 \end{vmatrix} - 2 \cdot \begin{vmatrix} 2 & 2 \\ 1 & 3 \end{vmatrix} = -7$

Article A–4, p. A–12

1. -5 **2.** 0 **3.** 1 **4.** 2

Article A–5, p. A–14

1. $\begin{bmatrix} -3 & 2 \\ 2 & -1 \end{bmatrix}$ **2.** $\begin{bmatrix} -\frac{1}{3} & \frac{1}{3} & 0 \\ \frac{1}{4} & \frac{1}{4} & -\frac{1}{4} \\ \frac{1}{6} & -\frac{1}{6} & \frac{1}{2} \end{bmatrix}$ **3.** $\begin{bmatrix} \frac{1}{2} & -\frac{1}{4} & -\frac{1}{8} & -\frac{1}{16} \\ 0 & \frac{1}{2} & -\frac{1}{4} & -\frac{1}{8} \\ 0 & 0 & \frac{1}{2} & -\frac{1}{4} \\ 0 & 0 & 0 & \frac{1}{2} \end{bmatrix}$

INDEX

INDEX

65. $\displaystyle\int \frac{\cos ax}{\sin ax}\, dx = \frac{1}{a}\ln|\sin ax| + C$

66. $\displaystyle\int \cos^n ax \sin ax\, dx = -\frac{\cos^{n+1} ax}{(n+1)a} + C, \qquad n \neq -1$

67. $\displaystyle\int \frac{\sin ax}{\cos ax}\, dx = -\frac{1}{a}\ln|\cos ax| + C$

68. $\displaystyle\int \sin^n ax \cos^m ax\, dx = -\frac{\sin^{n-1} ax \cos^{m+1} ax}{a(m+n)} + \frac{n-1}{m+n}\int \sin^{n-2} ax \cos^m ax\, dx,$

$\qquad\qquad\qquad\qquad n \neq -m \qquad \text{(If } n = -m \text{, use No. 86.)}$

69. $\displaystyle\int \sin^n ax \cos^m ax\, dx = \frac{\sin^{n+1} ax \cos^{m-1} ax}{a(m+n)} + \frac{m-1}{m+n}\int \sin^n ax \cos^{m-2} ax\, dx,$

$\qquad\qquad\qquad\qquad m \neq -n \qquad \text{(If } m = -n \text{, use No. 87.)}$

70. $\displaystyle\int \frac{dx}{b+c\sin ax} = \frac{-2}{a\sqrt{b^2-c^2}}\tan^{-1}\left[\sqrt{\frac{b-c}{b+c}}\tan\left(\frac{\pi}{4}-\frac{ax}{2}\right)\right] + C, \qquad b^2 > c^2$

71. $\displaystyle\int \frac{dx}{b+c\sin ax} = \frac{-1}{a\sqrt{c^2-b^2}}\ln\left|\frac{c+b\sin ax + \sqrt{c^2-b^2}\cos ax}{b+c\sin ax}\right| + C, \qquad b^2 < c^2$

72. $\displaystyle\int \frac{dx}{1+\sin ax} = -\frac{1}{a}\tan\left(\frac{\pi}{4}-\frac{ax}{2}\right) + C$

73. $\displaystyle\int \frac{dx}{1-\sin ax} = \frac{1}{a}\tan\left(\frac{\pi}{4}+\frac{ax}{2}\right) + C$

74. $\displaystyle\int \frac{dx}{b+c\cos ax} = \frac{2}{a\sqrt{b^2-c^2}}\tan^{-1}\left[\sqrt{\frac{b-c}{b+c}}\tan\frac{ax}{2}\right] + C, \qquad b^2 > c^2$

75. $\displaystyle\int \frac{dx}{b+c\cos ax} = \frac{1}{a\sqrt{c^2-b^2}}\ln\left|\frac{c+b\cos ax + \sqrt{c^2-b^2}\sin ax}{b+c\cos ax}\right| + C, \qquad b^2 < c^2$

76. $\displaystyle\int \frac{dx}{1+\cos ax} = \frac{1}{a}\tan\frac{ax}{2} + C$ 	77. $\displaystyle\int \frac{dx}{1-\cos ax} = -\frac{1}{a}\cot\frac{ax}{2} + C$

78. $\displaystyle\int x\sin ax\, dx = \frac{1}{a^2}\sin ax - \frac{x}{a}\cos ax + C$ 	79. $\displaystyle\int x\cos ax\, dx = \frac{1}{a^2}\cos ax + \frac{x}{a}\sin ax + C$

80. $\displaystyle\int x^n \sin ax\, dx = -\frac{x^n}{a}\cos ax + \frac{n}{a}\int x^{n-1}\cos ax\, dx$

81. $\displaystyle\int x^n \cos ax\, dx = \frac{x^n}{a}\sin ax - \frac{n}{a}\int x^{n-1}\sin ax\, dx$

82. $\displaystyle\int \tan ax\, dx = -\frac{1}{a}\ln|\cos ax| + C$ 	83. $\displaystyle\int \cot ax\, dx = \frac{1}{a}\ln|\sin ax| + C$

84. $\displaystyle\int \tan^2 ax\, dx = \frac{1}{a}\tan ax - x + C$ 	85. $\displaystyle\int \cot^2 ax\, dx = -\frac{1}{a}\cot ax - x + C$

86. $\displaystyle\int \tan^n ax\, dx = \frac{\tan^{n-1} ax}{a(n-1)} - \int \tan^{n-2} ax\, dx, \qquad n \neq 1$

87. $\displaystyle\int \cot^n ax\, dx = -\frac{\cot^{n-1} ax}{a(n-1)} - \int \cot^{n-2} ax\, dx, \qquad n \neq 1$

88. $\displaystyle\int \sec ax\, dx = \frac{1}{a}\ln|\sec ax + \tan ax| + C$ 	89. $\displaystyle\int \csc ax\, dx = -\frac{1}{a}\ln|\csc ax + \cot ax| + C$

Continued overleaf.

90. $\int \sec^2 ax\,dx = \dfrac{1}{a}\tan ax + C$ 91. $\int \csc^2 ax\,dx = -\dfrac{1}{a}\cot ax + C$

92. $\int \sec^n ax\,dx = \dfrac{\sec^{n-2} ax \tan ax}{a(n-1)} + \dfrac{n-2}{n-1}\int \sec^{n-2} ax\,dx, \quad n \neq 1$

93. $\int \csc^n ax\,dx = -\dfrac{\csc^{n-2} ax \cot ax}{a(n-1)} + \dfrac{n-2}{n-1}\int \csc^{n-2} ax\,dx, \quad n \neq 1$

94. $\int \sec^n ax \tan ax\,dx = \dfrac{\sec^n ax}{na} + C, \quad n \neq 0$

95. $\int \csc^n ax \cot ax\,dx = -\dfrac{\csc^n ax}{na} + C, \quad n \neq 0$

96. $\int \sin^{-1} ax\,dx = x \sin^{-1} ax + \dfrac{1}{a}\sqrt{1 - a^2x^2} + C$

97. $\int \cos^{-1} ax\,dx = x \cos^{-1} ax - \dfrac{1}{a}\sqrt{1 - a^2x^2} + C$

98. $\int \tan^{-1} ax\,dx = x \tan^{-1} ax - \dfrac{1}{2a}\ln(1 + a^2x^2) + C$

99. $\int x^n \sin^{-1} ax\,dx = \dfrac{x^{n+1}}{n+1}\sin^{-1} ax - \dfrac{a}{n+1}\int \dfrac{x^{n+1}\,dx}{\sqrt{1 - a^2x^2}}, \quad n \neq -1$

100. $\int x^n \cos^{-1} ax\,dx = \dfrac{x^{n+1}}{n+1}\cos^{-1} ax + \dfrac{a}{n+1}\int \dfrac{x^{n+1}\,dx}{\sqrt{1 - a^2x^2}}, \quad n \neq -1$

101. $\int x^n \tan^{-1} ax\,dx = \dfrac{x^{n+1}}{n+1}\tan^{-1} ax - \dfrac{a}{n+1}\int \dfrac{x^{n+1}\,dx}{1 + a^2x^2}, \quad n \neq -1$

102. $\int e^{ax}\,dx = \dfrac{1}{a}e^{ax} + C$ 103. $\int b^{ax}\,dx = \dfrac{1}{a}\dfrac{b^{ax}}{\ln b} + C, \quad b > 0, \; b \neq 1$

104. $\int xe^{ax}\,dx = \dfrac{e^{ax}}{a^2}(ax - 1) + C$ 105. $\int x^n e^{ax}\,dx = \dfrac{1}{a}x^n e^{ax} - \dfrac{n}{a}\int x^{n-1}e^{ax}\,dx$

106. $\int x^n b^{ax}\,dx = \dfrac{x^n b^{ax}}{a \ln b} - \dfrac{n}{a \ln b}\int x^{n-1}b^{ax}\,dx, \quad b > 0, \; b \neq 1$

107. $\int e^{ax}\sin bx\,dx = \dfrac{e^{ax}}{a^2 + b^2}(a \sin bx - b \cos bx) + C$

108. $\int e^{ax}\cos bx\,dx = \dfrac{e^{ax}}{a^2 + b^2}(a \cos bx + b \sin bx) + C$

109. $\int \ln ax\,dx = x \ln ax - x + C$

110. $\int x^n \ln ax\,dx = \dfrac{x^{n+1}}{n+1}\ln ax - \dfrac{x^{n+1}}{(n+1)^2} + C, \quad n \neq -1$

111. $\int x^{-1} \ln ax\,dx = \dfrac{1}{2}(\ln ax)^2 + C$ 112. $\int \dfrac{dx}{x \ln ax} = \ln |\ln ax| + C$

113. $\int \sinh ax\,dx = \dfrac{1}{a}\cosh ax + C$ 114. $\int \cosh ax\,dx = \dfrac{1}{a}\sinh ax + C$

115. $\int \sinh^2 ax\,dx = \dfrac{\sinh 2ax}{4a} - \dfrac{x}{2} + C$ 116. $\int \cosh^2 ax\,dx = \dfrac{\sinh 2ax}{4a} + \dfrac{x}{2} + C$

117. $\int \sinh^n ax\,dx = \dfrac{\sinh^{n-1} ax \cosh ax}{na} - \dfrac{n-1}{n}\int \sinh^{n-2} ax\,dx, \quad n \neq 0$